HERBACEOUS
PERENNIAL PLANTS

HERBACEOUS PERENNIAL PLANTS

A Treatise on their Identification, Culture, and Garden Attributes

---

Allan M. Armitage

VARSITY PRESS, INC.
Athens, Georgia

Library of Congress Cataloging in Publication Data

Armitage, Allan M.
　Herbaceous Perennial Plants
　A Treatise on their Identification, Culture and Garden Attributes

Summary: A reference guide to the identification and culture of over 2700 herbaceous perennial plant species, varieties and cultivars. Includes bibliography, common name and scientific index.

1. Plant Identification. 2. Plant Culture. 3. Plant Propagation. 4. Encyclopedia of Specific Identification and Cultural Requirements of Herbaceous Perennial Plants.

ISBN 0-942375-00

Printing: 9 8 7 6 5 4 3 2
Disclaimer of Liabilities: Due care has been taken in the preparation of this book to insure its effectiveness. The authors and publisher make no warrant, express or implied, with respect to the propagation and cultural procedures of this book. In no event will the authors or publisher be liable for direct, indirect, incidental, or consequential damages in connection with or arising from the furnishing, performance, or use of this book.

Illustrations by Bonnie L. Dirr
Photographs by Allan M. Armitage and Michael A. Dirr
Cover by Michael A. Dirr

Cover photo: Ligularia stenocephala 'The Rocket' stands guard over *Polygonum macrophyllum* in a summer garden. Dell Garden, Blooms of Bressingham

Varsity Press, Inc.
P.O. Box 6301
Athens, GA 30604
(404) 549–1542

Dedication

This book is dedicated to my wife, Susan, and my children, Laura, Heather, and Jonathan. Thank you for putting up with early evenings, early mornings, bad temper and foul humor. Without their love and understanding, this book would never have been completed.

Acknowledgements

This book would still be a distant dream if not for the following people:

Dr. Michael Dirr, whose vast knowledge of plant materials and editing skills were invaluable. His time, enthusiasm and support are gratefully appreciated. Mike's belief in the book never faltered, and his friendship is cherished.

Judy Marriott Laushman, who proofread countless times, collected flowers, spent hours in the library doing research, and whose sense of humor kept life in perspective. Her encouragement, advice and love of the work are reflected in every page.

Bonnie Dirr, for the excellent line drawings which bring life to the endless ocean of words.

Laura Ann Segrest, for passing on so much of her knowledge of Southern plants and gardens.

Sharon Illingworth, for her insight and thoughts into gardening in Canada.

Sandi MacKenzie, for sharing her holiday with a computer.

Some Thoughts of the Author

On The Meaning of Gardening:

When gardeners are asked to describe reasons for gardening, three words emerge time and again; Therapeutic, Creative and Exciting. Such words are more often associated with sporting events than gardening, however, therapy, creativity, and excitement are an intregal part of gardening.

Therapeutic because of the feeling that all is well with the world when our hands are in Mother Earth. Therapeutic because when a seed is sown, a cutting rooted, or seedling planted, we have accomplished something important.

Creative because artistry is an inescapable part of gardening. A swath of *Astilbe* brightens the shade, a grouping of cool-leaved *Artemesia* brings calm to its neighbors and a half dozen forget-me-nots sing of spring. Each grouping creates a scene of beauty. We do not require a degree in landscape architecture to create such beauty, all we need is the simple love of gardening.

Exciting is a word seldom attributed to gardening. But is it not exciting to watch a garden change with time? To watch wild ginger bull through the soil in early spring, anticipate the popping of the buds of balloon flower, and share the magic of the reemergence of resurrection flower, is truly exciting.

On a Garden:

A garden is a melding of different plants, including trees, shrubs, and herbaceous species. A garden lacks grandeur and grace without the architecture and framework provided by trees. A single specimen, such as a Cedar-of-Lebanon, can define an entire garden. Like a snow-capped mountain in the distance, it is never out of sight or out of mind. Shrubs are indispensible for screening, massing, form and texture. From *Abelia* to *Zenobia*, they provide the glue which bonds the trees and herbaceous plants together. Broad sweeps of annuals such as geraniums, celosia and marigolds provide interest through the gardening season and, like magnets, draw the eye to their carpet of color. Herbaceous perennials add a unique charm and flavor to any garden. There are few times when perennials do not add interest and change. From dormant winter state, through frenzied activity in the spring, until flower buds are visible, perennials are always changing. Finally, when flowers can wait no longer, islands of color blaze like flares in the night. Many have foliage more colorful than flowers, fruits that compete with holly, and fall colors as dramatic as sugar maples. To the connoisseur and amateur, there is nothing more colorful and interesting than a well-conceived perennial border. However, all great borders incorporate backdrops of hedges or tree canopies and annuals to fill in occasional gaps. Perennials are an important part of the garden but are just that, a part of the garden. Perennials or a perennial border should be woven into a garden, rather than being the garden. A well-conceived garden is much more beautiful than the sum of the beauty of the individual parts.

On a Gardener:

Gardening is hard work! Low maintenance does not mean no maintenance. "No maintenance" gardening does not exist, although low maintenance is possible with proper plant selection. There are many tired gardeners but I've seldom met old gardeners. I know many elderly gardeners but the majority are young at heart. Gardening simply does not allow one to be mentally old, because too many hopes and dreams are yet to be realized. The one absolute of gardeners is faith. Regardless of how bad past gardens have been, every gardener believes that next year's will be better. It is easy to age when there is nothing to believe in, nothing to hope for; gardeners, however, simply refuse to grow up. As Thomas Jefferson stated, "Though an old man, I am but a young gardener".

On North and South:

Many of the same species are cultivated in Montreal, Canada, and Athens, Georgia, areas stereotyped as far north and deep south, respectively. I have gardened in both areas as well as East Lansing, Michigan and travelled with open eyes throughout the United States, Canada, New Zealand, and Europe. Certain species thrive in one area but perform poorly in another. Obvious climatic differences exist among areas in the United States, and even subtle differences within a garden can influence plant performance. No absolute demarcation exists where North ends and South begins, but in this book the South incorporates zones 7–10 of the United States Department of Agriculture hardiness zone map.

Zone 7 (minimum 0–10° F) ranges as far north as Rhode Island, into Virginia, and cuts across Tennessee, Arkansas, central Oklahoma, central Texas, southern New Mexico and into Arizona and California. Many climatic factors interact with the plants ability to thrive or languish in a given zone, and hardiness ratings must be treated cautiously (see thoughts on hardiness ratings).

In general, summers are hotter and more humid, winters milder (although frosts are not uncommon), and less accumulation of snow occurs in the South. Several differences are obvious between plants of the same species grown in northern and southern locales. In the South, plants flower earlier, are taller and often have weaker stems. Tall forms tend to collapse without support and dwarf selections are usually more effective in the southern garden. Fertilizer need not be applied as generously in the South as in the North, particularly on tall cultivars, as additional growth is not the goal. Lanky, leggy growth occurs at the expense of flower production if too much nitrogen is applied. This happens regardless of latitude, but is more prominent in the South. Lack of snow is a major detriment to overwintering perennials in the South. Snow provides insulation from the cold and plants tucked beneath the snowy eiderdown survive cold winters well. Where rain replaces snow (as in the South), the major survival problem is inadequate drainage. This is particularly true on heavy clay where cold winter rains result in water-logged soils and roots, crowns, and bulbs are literally immersed in free standing water. Rot organisms proliferate and plants disappear; not because of lack of cold hardiness but because they rotted in the ground. Addition of bark, peat moss or other materials which aid drainage alleviate root rot problems.

Summer temperatures and humidity in the South are also detriments to perenniality. Plants not adapted to the South often perform poorly because of high night temperatures. Plants use oxygen and release carbon dioxide (similar to humans) in the process of respiration. Heat significantly affects the rate of plant respiration. In general, for every 16°F rise in temperature, respiration more than doubles. When night temperatures remain above 70°F the process of respiration continues unabated and competes more aggressively for the carbohydrates produced during the day by photosynthesis. The result is lack of stored carbohydrates, inhibition of chlorophyll synthesis, and lack of secondary cell wall formation. The end result is reduced vigor, weak stunted plants and small foliage. Species not capable of acclimatizing cannot store the reserves necessary to survive the winter. In many cases, death is due not to lack of winter hardiness, but lack of summer tolerance. Many problems may be minimized with fall planting, thereby allowing plants time to build starch reserves, and develop an extensive root system prior to the onset of winter. Fall planting is more critical in the South than the North for most temperate plant species. One of the objectives of the research program at the Department of Horticulture, University of Georgia is to evaluate perennial species for summer hardiness. Much of that information has been used to determine hardiness zone ratings.

On Hardiness Ratings:

Hardiness ratings are based on the ability of plants to survive cold temperatures. They are imperfect but the best we have at present to objectively evaluate geographical limits of adaptability. Hardiness maps (see page xxiii) are based on minimum winter temperatures and must be interpreted cautiously. Many factors affect plant growth other than average minimum temperatures. For example, zone 8 in Athens, Georgia is a different world from zone 8 in central California. Although minimum temperatures may be similar, summer temperatures during the night, humidity and rainfall are quite different. Valleys and mountains in the same hardiness zone are different climatically and plants which survive in higher elevations may perish when they descend 500 feet. Microclimates exist even in a small garden, and plants which performed poorly in one location often perk up when moved to a more sheltered environment.

Heat tolerance is more difficult to evaluate than cold tolerance. Plants respond to cold by dying; to heat by languishing. However, heat tolerance, or summer hardiness ratings are equally important in predicting plant performance. European garden literature is a rich source of information but descriptions must be taken with a grain of salt. Similarly, descriptions of plant habit in the North and West may not mirror performance in the South or East. This is primarily due to differences in summer hardiness. In this text, I have attempted to provide summer hardiness ratings for all species based on experimentation, observation, existing literature, and discussions with gardeners. The southern hardiness range listed is one in which the species performs well, if factors such as shade/sun, drainage, etc. are properly provided. Plants may survive south of that rating, but performance is significantly reduced. The ratings are not perfect, but hopefully add to the body of horticultural knowledge.

On Garden Design:

Design is an important aspect of gardening. Great garden designers are born, not made, and nurture through observation and experience. Principles of design abound and even I try to adhere to some of the basics. Most importantly, the design should be pleasing to the owner and not planned with others in mind. Select one or two dominant colors which appeal and use colors which complement, rather than distract, from each other. The aim of color is to tie plants together and then wed the planting to the site. One of the reasons for the popularity of gray and silver foliage, as well as white flowers, is their ability to bring the planting together. I am the first to admit that I am a poor designer. I garden with a palette of mixed colors. To me, the most important part of design is that the plants perform well in the site. Good performance is defined by persistent, fresh foliage, vigorous growth, and copious flower production. Selection on the basis of plant performance is more important than selection based on the color wheel. To totally ignore design, however, is to relegate a garden to a collection of plants.

Water should be included in every garden. The presence of water, be it a birdbath, fountain, pond, or stream does more to soften and define a garden than all other features combined. I am always learning about garden design and someday will discourse competently on hues, shapes, feelings, and combinations. Until then, however, I will enjoy the eclectic combination of plant material around my garden pond.

On Plant Nomenclature:

Plant names are no different than any other names; some are long and complicated, others are short and sweet. A scientific name defines a single species only, but a common name may describe a dozen or more. A valid scientific name is valid throughout the world, regardless of language or politics. The science of nomenclature is practiced by taxonomists who attempt to bring order out of chaos. Because one of their goals is to validate current scientific names and replace incorrect ones, scientific names are constantly being changed. Two main problems occur when taxonomist meets gardener. The first occurs when a new scientific name replaces one of long standing. According to some authorities, *Chrysanthemum morifolium* is now *Dendranthema grandiflora*; *Vinca rosea* is *Catharanthus roseus*; *Helleborus corsicus* has become *H. argutifolius*; and *Euphorbia polychroma* is *E. epithymoides*. At times, it seems like a change in nomenclature is accomplished just to keep someone busy, however, if the new name is agreed on by taxonomic authorities, it should also be accepted by horticulturists and gardeners. This brings up the second problem. Taxonomists don't always agree on valid nomenclature. Names accepted by one authority aren't necessarily accepted by other equally respected authorities due to valid differences of opinion and methodology. That leaves everyone else in a muddle. In general, *Hortus III* was used as the authority for scientific names in this text. However, *Hortus III* was published in 1976 and many changes have occurred since then. Several other respected texts (see Bailey, *Manual of Cultivated Plants;* Royal Horticultural Society, *Dictionary of Gardening;* Thomas, *Perennial Garden Plants;* Wyman, *Encyclopedia of Gardening*) and recent monographs were also consulted to sort out nomenclature.

Plants are listed by genus, species, variety and cultivar. A genus is a closely related group of plants consisting of one or more species. Species within a genus have more characteristics in common with each other than they do with species in other genera. Often genera are closely related and differences are difficult to discern. Although *Silene* and *Delphinium* are obviously different, *Silene, Agrostemma* and *Lychnis* may be confused. The genus name begins with an upper case letter and is underlined or written in italics.

A species is difficult to define but may be thought of as a type of plant distinct from other types by identifiable features. The unique characteristics are reproducible from generation to generation through seed. A species name begins with a lower case letter and is underlined or written in italics.

Often individual plants may be slightly different from other members of the species and the definable characteristic is reproduced each generation. This group of plants is known as a variety and has enough similarities with others to be in the same species but is sufficiently different to be grouped as a separate variety. Often varieties are geographically distinct and have their own range. Varieties breed relatively true from seed, passing on their definable differences from parent to offspring. Varieties are preceded with "var." and underlined or written in italics. For example, *Muscari comosum* var. *monstrosum* infers that a group of plants of *Muscari comosum* differs in some way to be placed in var. *monstrosum*.

A cultivar refers to a cultivated variety and may be the result of hybridization, random mutation, or plant selection. For our purposes, cultivar differs from variety in that the definable factors that make a cultivar unique are not passed on from generation to generation by seed (although seed firms maintain homozygous lines so seed-propagated cultivars may be offered). Cultivars are propagated vegetatively by tissue culture, cuttings, grafting or divisions. Cultivars begin with upper case letters and are surrounded with single quotation marks. For example, *Lychnis coronaria* 'Abbotswood Rose' has lighter pink flowers than the species. Seeds produced by plants of 'Abbotswood Rose' do not produce similar plants. The distinction between variety and cultivar diminishes when varieties are given cultivar names. For example, var. *alba* is a common variety of many species and usually refers to the presence of white flowers. If those plants are given a cultivar name such as 'White Knight' or 'Snow White', it is impossible to know if plants are reproducible sexually or asexually. Unfortunately, in horticultural and gardening circles, the terms cultivar and variety are used interchangeably.

Hybrids occur by spontaneous marriage between species or genera (natural hybridization) or as a result of breeding programs of individual gardeners and nurseries. Characteristics from each parent may be found in the offspring. Interspecific hybrids are designated by a multiplication sign (×) and are usually only reproducible vegetatively. For example, *Polygonatum* × *hybridum* is a hybrid between *P. multiflorum* and *P. biflorum* and is reproduced by division of the rootstock. Intergeneric hybrids occasionally occur and are designated by an uppercase multiplication sign (X) before the name. × *Heucherella alba* is a hybrid between *Heuchera brizoides* and *Tiarella cordata* var. *collina*. The × is not sounded.

I have attempted to sort out the nomenclature where possible. There is still a long way to go. Comments from readers are welcome.

On Common Names:

I like common names. Names like cardinal flower, resurrection flower, pussytoes, and blackberry lily are far more "user friendly" than *Lobelia cardinalis*, *Lycoris squamigera*, *Antennaria dioica*, and *Belamcanda chinensis*. They also bring with them part of the history of discovery and use of the species. Lily-of-the-valley tells me more about the plant I am about to buy that *Convallaria majalis*, while lungwort describes the philosophy of naming plants more than *Pulmon-*

aria officinalis. Common names may describe the flower, such as pincushion flower (*Scabiosa*); leaves, spotted geranium, (*Geranium maculatum*); origin, Persian buttercup (*Ranunculus asiaticus*); medicinal properties, self-heal (*Prunella vulgaris*); or the discoverer, Stokes aster, (*Stokesia*). Unfortunately, the same common name may be used for more than one species or a single species may be known by several common names, depending on area of the country. Although scientific names have been documented, few efforts to standardize common names have been attempted. One such attempt was *Standarized Plant Names*, 1942, to which I referred wherever possible. Many species and hybrids, however, were not assigned common names in that text. Other reference books and serious gardeners were consulted and a common name has been included for most species. Other names may be equally appropriate. Assistance from readers to provide appropriate missing common names is appreciated.

On Pronunciation:

Most people like to pronounce names with some degree of confidence. Scientific names are intimidating and often people will not say them for fear of sounding ignorant. Pronunciation is something that one feels confident about only with continued use. If scientific names are seldom part of one's gardening vocabulary, proper pronunciation will always be difficult. Pronunciation is also subjective. It does not matter if *paniculata* is pronounced (pa-nik-ew-lah' ta) or (pa-nik-ew-lay' ta). I prefer to pronounce *Stokesia* as (stoks' ee-a), in recognition of Dr. John Stokes, for whom the genus was named. However (stow-keys' ee-a) is commonly used and equally correct. I have provided pronunciation guides for most genera and specific epithets principally based on *Dictionary of Plant Names* (Coombes, 1985). Other references are available which use different formats.

How to Use this Book.

    Generic entries are provided with a pronunciation guide, common name and family.

    Each **specific epithet** (the species term) has a pronunciation guide, common name, and average height and width of mature flowering plants. The height and width are guides to help with placement in the garden. Climate, soils, rainfall, irrigation practices and fertility will influence these guidelines. The next line provides season of flowering (based on zone 6–8), flower color, origin and hardiness range.

Genus	Pronunciation	Common name	Family
↓	↓	↓	↓
Baptisia	(bap-tiz-i-a)	Wild Indigo	Fabaceae

Species	Pronunciation	Common name	Avg height/spread
↓	↓	↓	↓
-australis	(ow-strah-lis)	Blue Wild Indigo	3–4'/4'
Spring	Indigo Blue	Eastern United States	Zones 3–9
↑	↑	↑	↑
Flowering season	Flower color	Origin	Hardiness range

    A **quick reference** table is provided for genera with three or more cultivated species. Easily identifiable differences among species may be located.

    Descriptions for each species and known cultivars and varieties are listed. Not every cultivar or variety has found its way into the book, but most of the presently available selections are present.

    Related species are described briefly. In general, related species are not as available to the gardening public but have worthy garden characteristics. Cultivars of related species are listed similarly to main species, except that the "cultivar" heading does not occur.

A **quick key** to separate species in the genus is provided for genera with two or more species. I have tried to refrain from including too much botanical "jargon", however, in some cases technical terms were necessary. The keys are based on observation and available literature. In some cases, they are precise and well done. In others, such as *Hosta* and *Lilium*, where many more hybrids exist than species, the key is a rough guide only. In general, cultivars and varieties are not included in the keys. A small glossary of technical terms is provided in the back of the book.

Additional reading is listed if the reading is specific to that genus. Most citations may be located in university or public libraries. Additional general reading is also listed in the bibliography.

Line drawings accompany the text of numerous species. All drawings are shown with reduction from actual life size (e.g., 67% means that the drawing is 67% of actual life size).

Drawings of inflorescences and leaves including leaf bases, leaf shapes, leaf apices, leaf types, and leaf arrangements may be found on the facing and subsequent pages.

Leaf Bases

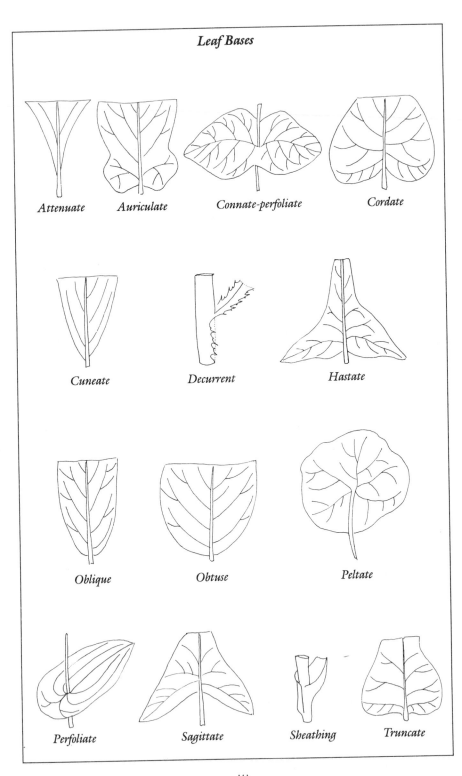

Attenuate   Auriculate   Connate-perfoliate   Cordate

Cuneate   Decurrent   Hastate

Oblique   Obtuse   Peltate

Perfoliate   Sagittate   Sheathing   Truncate

Leaf Shapes

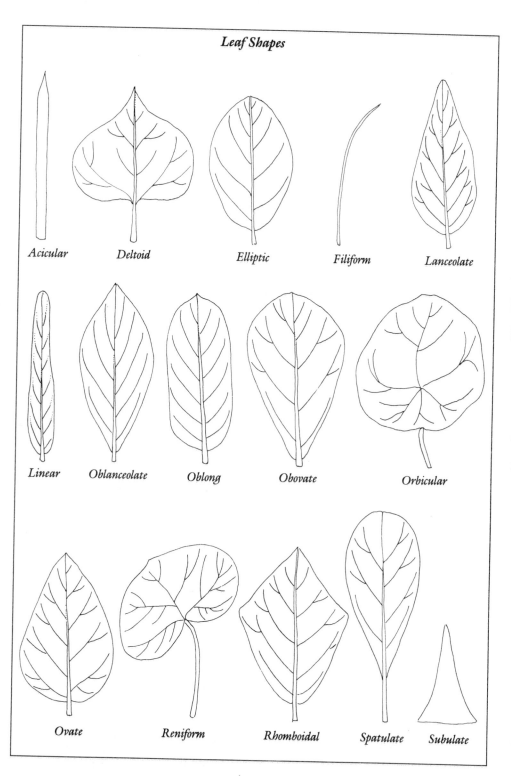

Acicular   Deltoid   Elliptic   Filiform   Lanceolate

Linear   Oblanceolate   Oblong   Obovate   Orbicular

Ovate   Reniform   Rhomboidal   Spatulate   Subulate

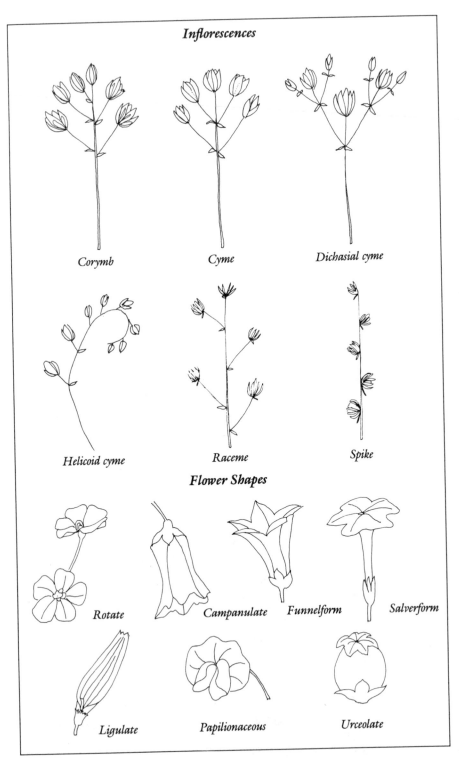

Inflorescences

Corymb

Cyme

Dichasial cyme

Helicoid cyme

Raceme

Spike

Flower Shapes

Rotate

Campanulate

Funnelform

Salverform

Ligulate

Papilionaceous

Urceolate

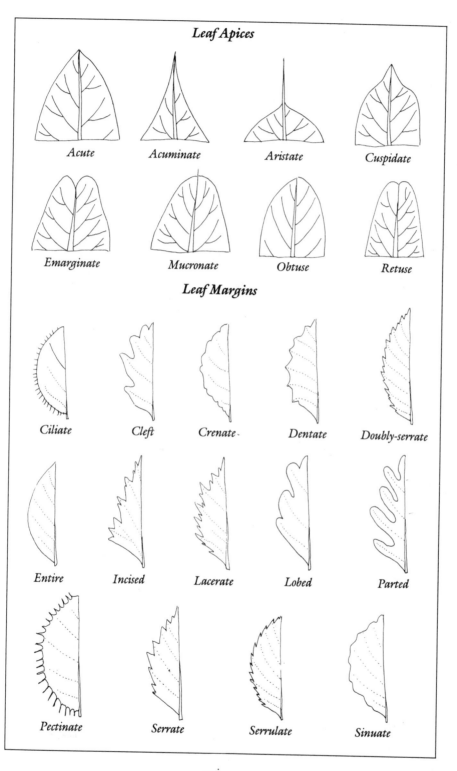

Leaf Apices

Acute   Acuminate   Aristate   Cuspidate

Emarginate   Mucronate   Obtuse   Retuse

Leaf Margins

Ciliate   Cleft   Crenate   Dentate   Doubly-serrate

Entire   Incised   Lacerate   Lobed   Parted

Pectinate   Serrate   Serrulate   Sinuate

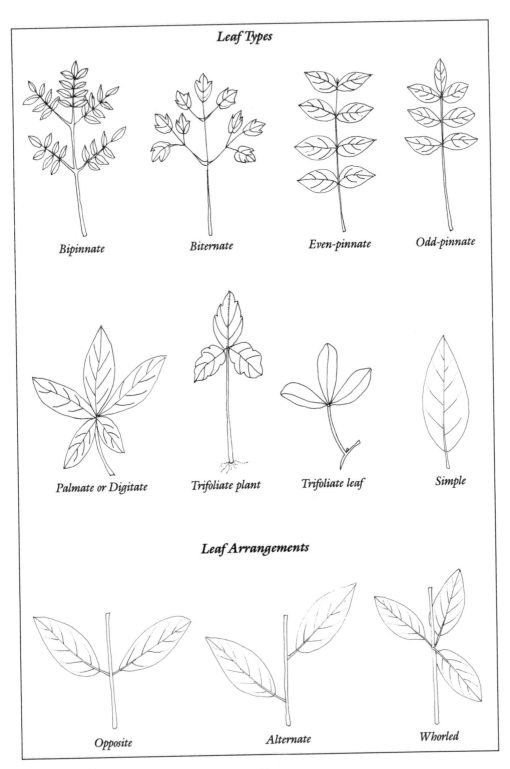

Leaf Types

Bipinnate   Biternate   Even-pinnate   Odd-pinnate

Palmate or Digitate   Trifoliate plant   Trifoliate leaf   Simple

Leaf Arrangements

Opposite   Alternate   Whorled

Zones of plant hardiness.

HERBACEOUS
PERENNIAL PLANTS

A

Acanthus (a-kanth' us)   Bear's Breeches   Acanthaceae

The genus contains approximately 20 species of which three or four are particularly ornamental. The leaves are simple, opposite, and often have thorny margins. The flowers are held in long, erect spikes and each flower is subtended by a showy, spiny, leaf-like bract. The spikes are lovely, albeit somewhat unnerving, but the ornamental value of the genus resides in the handsome foliage. Once established, *Acanthus* is almost indestructible and will colonize an area with its invasive roots. If one tires of bear's breeches and wishes to remove same, it is next to impossible not to leave some root pieces behind, which, like amoebae, will regenerate and recolonize their old homesite.

Acanthus is a popular genus on the West Coast and occasionally seen in the Gulf Coast states but is not sufficiently winter hardy for use throughout the country. The leaves are hardier than the flowers and some species will survive to zone 7 (6 with protection), but will not flower. Plants do well in full sun or partial shade and are relatively drought resistant. The foliage is evergreen; however, in severe winters, it becomes tattered and torn.

The most effective means of propagation is by 2–3″ long root cuttings taken in the spring. Insert vertically in a well-drained medium and keep moist and warm. Shoots appear in 3–5 weeks. Plants can be divided in early spring but adequate moisture is necessary to insure establishment. Fresh seed germinates in about 3 weeks if kept moist and warm (70–75°F).

Quick Reference to Acanthus Species

	Height (in.)	Spines on leaves	Leaf color
A. mollis	30–48	No	Dark green
A. perringii	12–24	Yes	Gray green
A. spinosus	36–48	Yes	Dark green

1

-mollis (mol' lis)		Common Bear's Breeches	30–48"/36"
Late Spring	Purple	Southern Europe	Zones 8–10

In the fifth century B.C., this most common species was immortalized in the design of the sculptured leaves on Greek Corinthian columns. The lustrous green, 8–12" wide foliage is wavy, heart shaped, and best of all, has no spines. This large coarse plant, having a spread of up to 3', may be used as a specimen or in groups of 3 to 5 plants. The flower stems rise an additional 3–4' and bear numerous white and purple flowers in mid- to late spring. The foliage is more winter hardy than the flowers and often the leaves emerge in the spring but the plant produces no flowers. The bracts surrounding the flowers have 5–7 veins and are painfully sharp. In the heat of north Georgia (zone 8), the plant has flowered poorly and the magnificent plantings seen in southern California cannot be duplicated.

Cultivars:

var. *latifolius* has 3–4' tall stalks of mauve pink flowers, larger leaves and is more robust and cold tolerant than the species.

-spinosus (spine-o' sus)		Spiny Bear's Breeches	36–48"/36"
Late Spring	Mauve	Southern Europe	Zones 7–10

The main difference between this species and the previous is the presence of spiny leaf margins which appear a good deal more lethal than they really are. The 10" diameter leaves are lanceolate, and more deeply divided than those of *A. mollis*. The flowers are similar except that three to four veins occur on the purplish bracts rather than five to seven found in common bear's breeches. If late freezes occur, *A. mollis* is killed to the ground while this species is little affected. The flowers are produced consistently each year and the leaves remain fresh all season. Plants also tolerate warm, humid summers better than the previous species—a definite advantage for southern gardeners.

Cultivars:

var. *spinosissimus* is a man-eater and should only be grown by masochists or those who can command someone else to do the pruning, training and actual gardening of such vicious plants. The leaf spines are white and the divisions are much narrower than those of the species. I have enough trouble with belligerent people, why tolerate belligerent plants. *Hortus III*, the reference text from the Bailey Hortorium of Cornell University, has reclassified *A. spinosus* to *A. mollis* var. *spinosissimus*, and deleted *spinosissimus* as a variety. To me, there are enough differences between the two forms to retain the variety classification and I have done so.

Related Species:

A. perringii (*A. dioscoridis* var. *perringii*) is only 1–2' tall and has rosy-red bracts. The leaves are sessile (no petiole), gray green, and are usually, but not always, spiny. Good drainage is essential. Being native to mountainous areas of Asia Minor, it is likely hardy in zones 7–9, although insufficient plants have been evaluated to provide confident hardiness ratings.

Quick Key to Acanthus Species

    A. Leaves spiny or apparently so
        B. Plants 3–4′ tall, leaves with petioles ....*A. spinosus*
        BB. Plants 1–2′ tall, leaves sessile.............................*A. perringii*
    AA. Leaves without spines... *A. mollis*

Additional Reading:

Rix, Marilyn. 1980. The genus *Acanthus* L., an introduction to the hardy species. *The Plantsman* 2(3):132–140.

Achillea (a-kil-lee′ a)   Yarrow   Asteraceae

    Although there are approximately 100 species, less than a dozen are truly ornamental. They range in height from 4″ to 4′ with flowers of almost every hue. Leaves of all species are alternate and, with the exception of *A. ageratum*, sweet yarrow, and *A. ptarmica*, sneezewort, the foliage is deeply divided into a fine fern-like appearance. In several species, the foliage has a heavy spicy odor and a gray-green tint. The outer ray flowers are pistillate (female only), and may be yellow, white, or pink while the inner disc flowers are bisexual (male and female together), and usually yellow. The flower heads (inflorescences) are flat compound corymbs.

    Some species of yarrow are, at times, considered weeds, particularly those which multiply rapidly from invasive rhizomes. This characteristic, however, is only true for one or two species and most others behave themselves and stay at home. Unless otherwise noted, all species should be grown in full sun and well-drained soils. They tolerate poor soils (if well-drained) and many of the upright species will grow too tall and lanky if fertilized or grown in rich soil. The flowers of most species make excellent fresh or dried specimens but the pollen must be visible before the flowers are cut or vase life will be significantly reduced.

Quick Reference to Achillea Species

	Height (ft.)	*Flower color*	*Foliage color*
A. × 'Coronation Gold'	2–3	Yellow	Gray-green
A. *filipendulina*	3–5	Yellow	Green
A. *grandifolia*	2–3	White	Gray-green
A. *millefolium*	1–2	Various	Green
A. × 'Moonshine'	1–2	Sulphur	Gray-green
A. *ptarmica*	1–2	White	Green
A. *tomentosa*	½ –1	Yellow	Gray-green

3

-× 'Coronation Gold'		Coronation Gold Yarrow	2–3'/3'
Late Spring	Yellow	Hybrid	Zones 3–9

This hybrid is the best upright yellow yarrow available today and resulted from crossing *A. filipendulina* with *A. clypeolata*. Unfortunately, it is often incorrectly listed as a cultivar of *A. filipendulina*. The plant is shorter than *A. filipendulina*, better branched, and does not require staking. It requires less maintenance and should be the plant of choice for landscapers. The inflorescences are 3–4" across and look like shiny golden plates.

Flowering begins in late May in north Georgia and continues for 8–12 weeks. The foliage is gray-green and has a strong aromatic smell. It tolerates a wide range of climates and soils and is grown in gardens from Manitoba to Florida.

'Coronation Gold' is popular as a cut flower throughout the world. It is interesting to note the differences in stem and flower size between northern and southern climates. In north Georgia, over 50 flowering stems per plant are produced while the same plants growing in Holland yield fewer than 15 stems but each one is 1½ –2 times longer with larger flowers.

Propagate by terminal cuttings in spring or early summer or divide in spring or fall every 3–4 years. Seed purchased as 'Coronation Gold' will likely be *A. filipendulina* or one of its cultivars.

-*filipendulina* (fi-li-pen-dew' lye-na)		Fern-leaf Yarrow	3–5'/3'
Summer	Yellow	Caucasus	Zones 3–9

The foliage is deeply cut and feathery but bears little of the gray-green tint that is so appealing in *A.* × 'Coronation Gold'. This is a handsome plant but when grown in rich soils or when over fertilized, it usually requires staking, a job I abhor. The flat yellow flower heads are 5" across and make excellent cut flowers.

Cultivars:
'Gold Plate' has deep yellow flowers on stems up to 5' tall.
'Parker's Variety' bears golden yellow flowers on 3–4' tall stems. Both produce large numbers of flowers and have better stem strength than the species but may require support in areas with hot, humid summers.

Plants may be propagated by spring division, terminal cuttings in early summer, or by seed. Seed sown in a mixture of 1:1 peat:vermiculite and placed at 70–72°F in a humid area germinate within 21 days. The cultivars mentioned are available from seed.

-*grandifolia* (grand-i-fo' lee'-a)		White Yarrow	2–3'/2'
Summer	White	Southeast Europe	Zones 5–8

This is a particularly lovely species which I first admired in England and one which fills the need for a good upright white-flowered yarrow. I looked forward

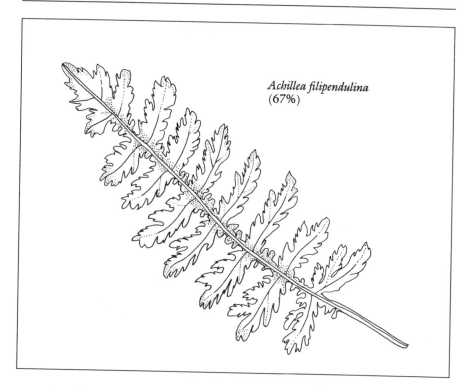

Achillea filipendulina
(67%)

to sowing the seeds I had collected when I returned home. The foliage is gray-green, lacy and deeply cut while the flowers are held on strong stems in a 3–4" diameter flat inflorescence. It is a far better white than found in any cultivars of common yarrow, *A. millefolium*, and should be offered in the United States by some enterprising nurserymen. I hope someone does it soon as my seeds did not survive the rigors of being dry cleaned with my jacket.

Once established, plants are commonly propagated by seed or division similar to *A. filipendulina*.

-*millefolium* (mil-lee-fo' lee-um)   Common Yarrow   1–2'/5'
Summer   White to Cerise Red   Europe   Zones 3–9

Common yarrow is "common" because of its ability to spread rapidly and take over any ground available. In Europe, it is often discarded as a troublesome weed not to be included on the grounds of any self-respecting gardener. Yet the same people will find fresh and dried flowers of common yarrow in florist shops where they are widely used in colorful bouquets. This species was cultivated in Europe before 1440, used as a remedy for toothache, and mixed in ale in place of hops to increase the inebriating quality of that drink. It was thought to have a magical quality similar to our "apple a day keeps the doctor away"; and was said to grow in churchyards as a reproach to the dead, "who need never have

5

Achillea millifolium
(54%)

come there if they had taken their yarrow broth faithfully every day while living"
(Coats, 1956). The main use, however, was that of a herb to heal wounds and
supposedly was named after Achilles, who is said to have used it to staunch the
wounds of his soldiers. And everyone thought this was just a common old
flower!

The habit is matlike and the dark green foliage is deeply cut. In early summer, the flower stalks rise about two feet and are much stronger where night
temperatures consistently stay below 70°F. Where night temperatures are too
warm, the stems do not acquire enough carbohydrates to "fatten up" and many
topple. Plants fill in rapidly and those placed four feet apart produce an unbro-
ken mat in 2 years. If planted two feet apart, they fill in by the end of the first
year.

Cultivars:

'Cerise Queen' is the best of the cerise-red flowered cultivars and performs well
throughout the country. It grows about 18″ tall and provides bright drifts
of color.

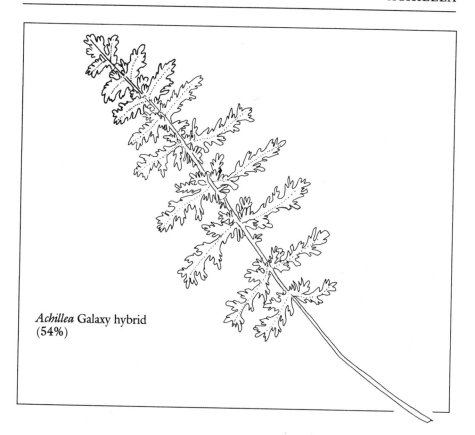

Achillea Galaxy hybrid
(54%)

'Fire King' and 'Fire Beauty' have dark red flowers with little difference between
   them.
'Red Beauty' bears cerise-red flowers on 2' tall stems in mid summer.
'Rose Beauty' has rather nondescript rose-pink flowers on 2' tall stems.

All cultivars may be propagated from seed but the seed companies have a long
way to go before gardeners or commercial people use the seed of some cultivars.
Seed is notoriously variable and it is not uncommon that 'Rose Beauty' will
have 4 or 5 different colors. In our studies, 'Cerise Queen' seed yielded at least
6 colors, five of them poor. It is just as easy to divide good specimens to retain
the desired colors and I do not recommend seed at this time.

Related Species:
   Galaxy hybrids are exciting new hybrids resulting from crossing *A. taygetea*
and *A. millefolium*. The foliage is similar to that of *A. millefolium* but the flower
heads are larger and the stems much stronger. The only problem I have seen is
the tendency of the flowers to fade, particularly when temperatures are above
80°F. In our trials, 'Beacon' and 'Great Expectations' faded less than others. In

7

England, little fading is seen. Additional testing is needed to assess the merits of these hybrids, but based on preliminary evaluations, they are welcome additions.

'Appleblossom' is a vigorous 3' tall plant with peach-colored flowers.
'Beacon' stands 2–3' tall and bears rich red flowers with yellow centers. It is the best cultivar I have seen.
'Great Expectations' produces primrose yellow flowers on 2' high stems.
'Salmon Beauty' bears large heads of salmon flowers on 3' tall stems. Other cultivars are being developed and I believe this series will do well in most gardens in North America. All are easily propagated by division.

| - × **'Moonshine'** | | Moonshine Yarrow | 1–2'/1' |
| Summer | Sulphur yellow | Hybrid origin | Zones 3–8 |

This hybrid, between *A. clypeolata* and *A. taygetea*, was introduced by Alan Bloom of Bressingham Gardens in Diss, England. 'Moonshine' is similar to *A.* × 'Coronation Gold' except in size and shade of flower color. The inflorescences are flat-topped, dense, pale yellow and 2–3" in diameter while the gray-green

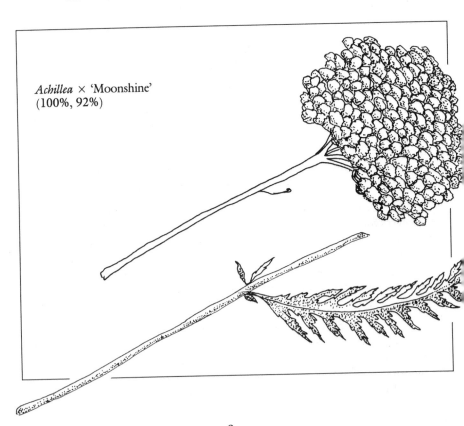

Achillea × 'Moonshine'
(100%, 92%)

foliage is deeply dissected. It is one of the most popular yarrows in American landscapes and is often recommended because of habit and interesting flower color. The flowers appear in early June (late June in New England) and continue until September. It is, however, much more perennial in the North than in the South. In the southeast where summer days are frequently punctuated by late afternoon rains and high humidity, 'Moonshine' tends to "melt out". This is not suprising considering that one of its parents, *A. taygetea*, is also susceptible to many foliar diseases. 'Moonshine' does best in the Southeast during summers with little rainfall. Spraying for diseases such as *Botrytis* and various root rot organisms such as *Pythium* is helpful and should be practiced in July and August. Dan Franklin, one of the finest landscape architects in the city of Atlanta simply treats the plant as an annual, enjoys the early summer beauty and removes plants as they decline in late summer. Regardless of the region of the country in which it is grown, excellent drainage is necessary to ensure longevity more than 2 years.

This is one of the finest hybrid yarrows to be developed in many years and, if sited properly and grown well, should continue to be a popular plant for commercial landscapers and gardeners.

Propagate by division any time during the growing season.

-ptarmica (tar' mah-ca)		Sneezewort	1–2'/1'
Early Summer	White	Europe	Zones 3–9

I can think of few other common names in the plant kingdom as ugly as sneezewort. Hearing the name for the first time certainly doesn't endear this species to anyone. The common name is derived from the fact that "the floures make one neese exceedingly". The leaves and roots were also dried, reduced to powder and used as an inexpensive substitute for snuff.

The species is unique among yarrows due to the lack of dissected leaves. The foliage is finely toothed, sessile (no petiole), and linear to lance-shaped. The species itself is of little ornamental value but a number of good cultivars are available. The cut flowers are occasionally used as a substitute for baby's breath. It is an aggressive plant and will spread considerably in good soils.

Cultivars:

'Globe' has small button-like blossoms on 12–18" tall stems.

'The Pearl' is the most popular cultivar and bears a profusion of double white flowers on 2' high stems. The flowers are cream colored but in warm climates, plants sprawl and are weedy looking.

'Perry's White' is taller (up to 30"), with flowers similar to the species but opening about a week earlier.

All double-flowered cultivars produce some single flowers as well. Up to 30% single flowers may be produced depending on weather and cultivar.

Propagate by division in the spring.

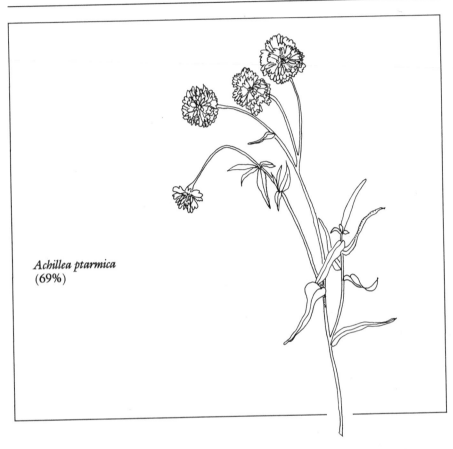

Achillea ptarmica
(69%)

-tomentosa (tow-men-tos′ a)		Woolly Yarrow	6-12″/18″
Early Summer	Yellow	Europe	Zones 3–7

The common name provides an excellent description of the deeply-cut, light green foliage which is covered with long hairs, providing a truly woolly appearance. The rock garden is a particularly suitable location, however, plants also make good subjects for the front of the border. It is most handsome in the spring when the hairy new growth begins to clamber over rocks and invades small niches. Many sulphur-yellow flowers, similar to, but smaller than those of *A.* × 'Moonshine', are produced in June and continue throughout the summer.

Unfortunately, plants are intolerant of hot, humid conditions and cannot be recommended for areas south of zone 7. Although they will survive in zone 8, plants perform well only through early summer and decline by mid to late July, unlikely to be seen again the next year. This is not a species for southern landscapes unless frequent fungicide applications are made. I grow it in zone 8 as an annual because I enjoy the woolly texture and the flowers enough to replace it each spring. Not everyone is as tolerant.

Cultivars:

var. *aurea* has golden yellow flowers on 3–8″ tall stems.
'King Edward VIII' bears pale yellow flowers on 10–12″ tall stalks.
'Moonlight' is taller than the species (up to 18″) but otherwise is not particularly different.

All of the above are usually propagated by division but the species and var. *aurea* may also be seed propagated.

Related Species:

A. chrysocoma, Grecian yarrow, is similar to *A. tomentosa* but the leaves are more hairy and appear to be coated with white fur. The flat topped corymbs are golden yellow.

Quick Key to Achillea Species

    A. Flowers yellow
       B. Leaves gray-green
          C. Flowers bright yellow, plants 2–3′ tall .... *A.* × 'Coronation Gold'
          CC. Flowers sulphur yellow, plants 1–2′ tall .... *A.* × 'Moonshine'
       BB. Leaves green, little gray color apparent
          C. Plants 3–5′ tall .... *A. filipendulina*
          CC. Plants 3–12″ tall .... *A. tomentosa*
    AA. Flowers pink, red, or white
       B. Leaves deeply cut
          C. Leaves gray-green, plants 2–3′ tall, upright habit,
             flowers white .... *A. grandifolia*
          CC. Leaves dark green, plants 1–2′ tall, mat-like habit,
             flowers usually pink or red, occasionally white .... *A. millefolium*
       BB. Leaves not divided, linear-lanceolate .... *A. ptarmica*

Acidanthera (a-sid-an-the′ ra)   Abyssinian Gladiolus   Iridaceae

There are approximately 20 species of tender bulbs in the genus but only one is commonly available.

-bicolor (bi′ ko-lor)   Abyssinian Gladiolus   2–3′/1′
Late summer-fall   White with purple throat   Ethiopia   Zones 8–10
(Syn. *Gladiolus callianthus*)

This is one of the loveliest of the summer-flowering bulbs (actually a corm) and it is unfortunate that the species has such a limited range. Although perennial in Athens, Georgia, it must be lifted in the fall north of zone 8. The corms should be treated like those of *Gladiolus* and dug in the fall after flowering but before the first severe frost, and dried in a warm room. Remove cormels, dead roots, and stems, and store corms and cormels in a dry, warm place (60–70°F) until spring. One of my gardening friends, Sharon Illingworth, who lives about 30 miles south of Thunder Bay, Ontario, Canada, starts them inside in early May and sets them out at the end of the month. This way she is able to enjoy the late flowers before frost cuts them down. Those who live in areas where it is perennial must be patient in the spring as it is one of the slowest plants to emerge. It is a good species to combine with some of the spring-flowering plants which go dormant in the summer such as *Mertensia* and *Doronicum*. *Acidanthera* has barely emerged when these species are at their peak. As they decline, it fills in those areas vacated due to summer dormancy. Unfortunately, flowering declines if corms are not lifted and divided every year. Even in Athens, I consider them annuals because flowering the second year is reduced and is non-existent the third year.

The swordlike, mid green leaves are topped with long tubed, star-shaped, fragrant 2″ diameter white flowers with a purple throat. Each flowering stem consists of 4–6 flowers arranged in a loose spike. The species is often grown for cut flowers and, when placed in a floral preservative, displays excellent vase life.

Cultivars:
'Muralis' is similar to the species but more vigorous, growing 3½′ tall.

Aconitum (ak-ko-ny′ tum)   Monkshood   Ranunculaceae

Aconitum has a number of common names, one of which is monkshood, so called because of the enlarged sepal which resembles a hood, under which the rest of the floral parts are hidden. Roots were used as poison bait for wolves, thus accounting for another popular common name, wolfsbane. All aconitums have poisonous roots, leaves, and stems. Warnings concerning their poisonous properties have been sounded since the late 1500's. In *A New Herbal*, William Turner writes "Let oure Londiners which of late have receyved this blewe wolfes bayne . . . take hede that poyson of the rote of this herbe one daye do not more harme than the freshness of the flower hath done pleasure in seven yeres, let them not saye but they are warned." It may even have been used to rid oneself of an unwanted husband or wife, but "it was considered rather a vulgar poison and was not employed by persons of high rank, who probably thought Socrates' hemlock more distinguished." (Coats, 1956). The turnip-shaped tuberous roots, however, are the most toxic and should not be planted near root crops such as potatoes or horseradish in case of accidental harvesting. The "poison" yielded by *A. napellus* is the drug aconite which was used worldwide as a heart sedative.

Regardless of the morbid properties, aconitums are excellent garden plants. The flowers are arranged in terminal racemes or panicles and flower in summer to early fall. Flowers are generally various shades of blue but several species such

12

as *A. vulparia* and *A. orientale* have yellow flowers, and rose colored flowers occur in *A. pyramidale*. The leaves are alternate, dark green and usually palmately divided. The leaves superficially resemble those of *Delphinium* but the flowers of the two genera are distinctly different.

Aconitums should be planted in full sun but will tolerate afternoon shade, particularly when planted near the southern boundary of their range (zone 7). They also tolerate moist soils but abhor swampy conditions. *Aconitum* must have cool nights to flourish which is why it languishes in southern regions of the country. If summer night temperatures do not regularly fall below 70°F., they should not be planted. One of the few disappointments I have had in gardening in the South is the absence of the stately spires of *Aconitum*. It did well in southern Ontario (zone 4) but try as I may, I cannot grow monkshood in north Georgia (Zone 8).

Most species are at least 3' tall and look out of place in the front of the garden, however *A. ivorine* (*A. septentrionale* 'Ivorine'), a 2–3' tall plant with ivory-colored blossoms in early summer, may be planted in the foreground. Flowering time for most of the monkshoods is late summer and fall, however, the 6' stately dark-purple spires of *A. henryi* open with the summer phlox and daylilies. *Aconitum* produces good cut flowers but care should be taken not to allow sap from the cut stem on open wounds.

Plant the tuberous roots in the fall to establish the root system before the first hard frost. Set the crowns just below the soil surface about 12–18" apart. Do not disturb established plants as they do not transplant well. Plan where you would like them to be for the next ten years for that is where they should stay.

Seed propagation is particularly difficult because the seed develops a deep dormancy upon ripening. Sow seed as soon as collected from the plant. Germination of old seed will occur, but very slowly (12–18 months is not uncommon). Seed grown plants take 2–3 years to flower. To propagate vegetatively, the brittle tuberous roots can be separated in late fall or early spring.

Quick Reference to Aconitum Species

	Height (ft.)	Flower color	Leaves divided all the way to base
A. × *bicolor*	3–4	Various	Yes
A. carmichaelii	2–3	Dark blue	No
A. napellus	3–4	Dark blue	Yes

-× bicolor (bi-kol' or)		Bicolor Monkshood	3–4'/2'
Summer	Various	Hybrid	Zones 3–7

(Syn. *A. cammarum*, *A. stoerkianium*, *A. napellus* 'Bicolor')

Plants listed under the cultivar name 'Bicolor' (usually *A. napellus* 'Bicolor') are likely a cross between *A. variegatum* and *A. napellus*. The growth habit is

13

quite variable depending on the dominant parent in a particular cultivar. The leaves are 2–4″ long and divided into 5–7 segments.

Cultivars:

'Bicolor' is 3–4′ tall and has blue and white flowers borne on wide branching panicles derived fron A. *variegatum*.

'Bressingham Spire' is 2½–3′ tall with violet blue flowers in dense upright panicles suggesting the influence of *A. napellus*. This cultivar is particularly valuable because staking is not required.

'Newry Blue' is 4–5′ tall with navy blue flowers and has the same upright flowering habit as 'Bressingham Spire'.

'Spark's Variety', a 4–5′ tall dark blue cultivar, is similar to 'Bicolor' in flowering habit. Some authorities believe this to be a cultivar of *A. henryi*. Staking may be required, particularly if grown in too much shade.

-carmichaelii (kar-my-keel′ lee-eye)		Azure Monkshood	2–3′/3′
Late Summer	Dark blue	Central China	Zones 3–7

(Syn. *A. fischeri*)

The leaves are thicker and more leathery than those of *A.* × *bicolor* and not as deeply dissected. It is a sturdy plant which seldom needs staking and has dark blue flowers appearing in late summer and early fall. Afternoon shade and sufficient moisture are necessary for plants to be at their best. When planting, large amounts of organic matter should be incorporated in the planting hole. This species flowers about 2 weeks later than *A.* × *bicolor* and is often referred to as the fall flowering aconitum. The flowers persist well into the fall. A planting incorporating Japanese anemones, late monkshoods, and autumn sedums such as *S.* × 'Autumn Joy' is truly breathtaking.

Cultivars:

'Arendsii' (syn. *A.* × *arendsii*) is a hybrid between *A. carmichaelii* and its var. *wilsonii*. Now available in the United States, it definitely deserves to be used more. Plants bear large helmets of intense blue and stand 3–4′ tall. The stems are sturdy enough to be self supporting and, everything considered, is the best late flowering aconitum in cultivation.

'Barker's Variety' has deep blue flowers and comes true from seed.

'Kelmscott Variety' has lavender blue flowers and is similar in habit to 'Barkers Variety'. Both grow to a height of 6′ under ideal conditions.

var. *wilsonii* is up to 6′ tall with 12″ long loose panicles of deep blue flowers.

-napellus (na-pel′ lus)		Common Monkshood	3–4′/1′
Late Summer	Dark blue	Europe	Zones 3–8

Common monkshood has been in the trade for many years and is probably one of the parents of *A.* × *bicolor*. The leaves are divided to the base and divided

14

again into linear or lance-like segments. The flowers are in spike-like terminal racemes. The popularity of *A. napellus* has declined with the introduction of newer garden cultivars but is still an outstanding plant.

Cultivars:

'Carneum' is a pink-flowered form that is sometimes offered as 'Roseum'. The pink color adds a new dimension to *Aconitum* but plants must be grown where night temperatures are consistently cool or flowers fade to a washed out white.

Quick Key to Aconitum Species
  A. Plants usually greater than 5' tall ....*A. carmichaelii* var. *wilsonii*
  AA. Plants usually less than 5' tall
     B. Leaves dissected all the way to base
        C. Inflorescence dense, not usually branched, flowers single
           color
           D. Plants approximately 3' tall .... *A.* × *bicolor* 'Bressingham Spire'
           DD. Plants approximately 4–5' tall .... *A. napellus*
        CC. Inflorescence usually branched, flowers bicolored ....
                                                              A. × *bicolor* 'Bicolor'
     BB. Leaves dissected but not all the way to base .... *A. carmichaelii*

Additional Reading:

Gilbert, Susan. 1985. Monkshood. *Horticulture* 63(9):50–53.

Mussel, H. 1986. A study of the cultivars of *Aconitum napellus* and *A. variegatum* complex according to the characteristics for destination of the inferior taxa. *Acta Horticulturae* 182:89–93.

Actaea (ak-tee'-a)   Baneberry   Ranunculaceae

   The three common species of *Actaea* are grown for their compound leaves and colorful berries. Unfortunately, the berries are poisonous, which accounts for the common name, baneberry. For this reason plants should not be grown where children and pets play. Baneberries are woodland species and do well in shady locations, particularly in moist, humus rich soil. The white flowers appear early in the spring in terminal racemes and give way to ¼" long oval berries in late summer and early fall. The leaves are alternate, and 2–3 times ternately compound.

   Seed should be sown when fresh, as old seed is much more difficult to germinate uniformly. In sowing this and other genera of Ranunculaceae, place the moist seed tray at about 70°F for 3 weeks, then transfer to freezing conditions (28–30°F) for about 5 weeks. After the cold treatment, remove the tray from the freezer and place at 40–50°F until germination occurs. All this is more easily accomplished by sowing in the fall and allowing snow cover or mulch in winter to maintain slightly freezing temperatures. Cool spring temperatures complete the requirements. A more rapid means of propagation is by root division in the spring.

Quick Reference to Actaea Species

	Height (ft.)	Flower stalks thickened	Color of berries
A. alba	2–4	Yes	White
A. rubra	2–4	No	Red
A. spicata	2–4	No	Black

-alba (al' ba)		White Baneberry	2–4'/3'
Late Spring	White	Eastern North America	Zones 3–7

Syn. *A. pachypoda*

The ternately compound leaves are similar to those of *Astilbe*. The fringed flowers are borne in 2–4" long terminal racemes on green flower stalks well above the foliage. The flower stalks (pedicels) become thicker and turn a pinkish red as the white berries develop. Although the fruits of *A. alba* and *A. rubra* usually are different colors, there is a red-fruited form of *A. alba*, making the shape of the pedicel the best means of distinguishing the two species. This is a handsome plant for the shady area of a woodland setting or border. The deep green leaves appear fresh well into the late summer and the berries provide interest into late fall. Abundant moisture is required in areas of hot summers. I have been coaxing mine along for a few years now, but I fear the end is at hand.

-rubra (rew' bra)		Red Baneberry	2–4'/3'
Spring		White North America	Zones 3–7

The flowers appear about a week earlier and are larger and not as fringed as those of the previous species. The ¼" long red berries are borne on slender green pedicels which turn red as they mature. The berries are particularly poisonous and roots are violent purgatives, irritants, and emetics. The leaves are usually more hairy than those of *A. alba* but except for the color of fruit and shape of pedicels, few differences exist. Plants require the same growing conditions as *A. alba*.

Cultivars:
'Neglecta' is a white berried cultivar, but is difficult to find in the nursery trade.

Related Species:
   A. spicata, black baneberry, is similar to *A. rubra* but has jet black berries (also very poisonous) carried on short black slender pedicels.

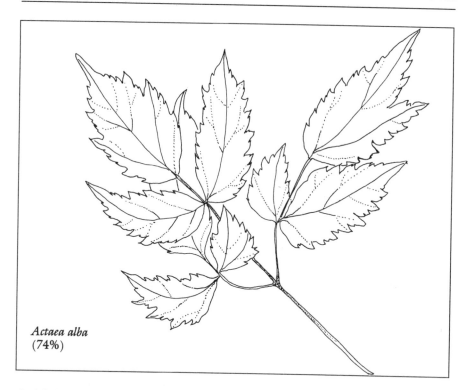

Actaea alba
(74%)

Quick Key to Actaea Species

  A. Pedicels swollen, fruit usually white .... *A. alba*
  AA. Pedicels slender, fruit usually not white
      B. Fruit usually red ....*A. rubra*
      BB. Fruit usually black .... *A. spicata*

Adenophora (a-den-off' or-a)   Ladybells   Campanulaceae

    The ladybells are often confused with members of *Campanula* but are unique in having a thick disc-like structure at the base of the style of the flower. If you don't relish the thought of tearing apart flowers to find such mundane organs, it is helpful to know that *Adenophora* has numerous branched, slender stems and nodding bell-shaped lilac-blue flowers. The leaves are alternate, and sessile or have short petioles. Plants prefer a well-drained soil in full sun or partial shade. In Montreal, I regarded *Adenophora* as an innocuous weedy member of gardens. Although better behaved in Georgia, I still have trouble getting excited about it. More tolerant of heat than many of the campanulas, it may be included in the southern garden where other members of the Campanulaceae must be excluded. There are about 50 species, however, the only readily available members are *A. confusa* and *A. lilifolia* (often incorrectly listed as *A. liliifolia*).

17

-confusa (con-fuse' a)		Common Ladybells	2–2½'/2'
Late Spring	Blue	China	Zones 3–8

(Syn. *A. farreri*)

This 2–2½' tall species bears ¾" long, nodding bell-shaped, deep blue flowers in late spring. The leaf bases are 2–3" wide and tapered. The flowers have entire petals that open in early June and persist for about 3–4 weeks.

Seed is fine and should be mixed with sand or talcum powder to insure even distribution. Press seed in gently, do not cover. Keep seed tray at 70–75°F soil temperature and moist at all times. Germination takes 2–3 weeks. The roots are deep and fleshy and therefore difficult to divide or move without significant damage.

Related Species:

A. lilifolia, lilyleaf ladybells, is not as tall (up to 2') and the flowers are not as intense blue. The petals are finely serrated and the leaves are narrower (approximately 1" wide). This species tolerates heat better than *A. confusa* and is a better plant for southern gardeners.

Additional Reading:

Bailey, L.H. 1953. *The Garden of Bellflowers*. The Macmillan Co., N.Y. 155 p.
   This classic book provides information about the many genera known as bellflowers, including *Adenophora*.

Adonis (a-don' is)	Adonis	Ranunculaceae

There are about 20 species but only *A. amurensis* and *A. vernalis* are perennial throughout most of the country. The leaves are alternate, dissected and light green. The plants are erect but normally do not exceed 18" in height and are most effective as rock garden plants or in the front of a small border. They must be planted in masses as one or two plants do not provide enough "flower power". Although said to perform better at a basic pH, they don't seem particularly fussy about soil as long as it is well-drained. An area that receives some afternoon shade should be chosen in the South, although full sun north of zone 6 is satisfactory. They are relished by slugs and spring application of slug preventative reduces damage.

Approximately 6 weeks of temperatures below 40°F are necessary for the rhizomes to break dormancy in the spring. Both species go dormant by midsummer. Plant late-emerging perennials such as *Platycodon* or *Acidanthera* or summer annuals to cover the vacant area.

If fresh seed is sown in the spring, and if seedlings are grown in a cold frame through the summer and transplanted to the garden in the fall, plants will flower

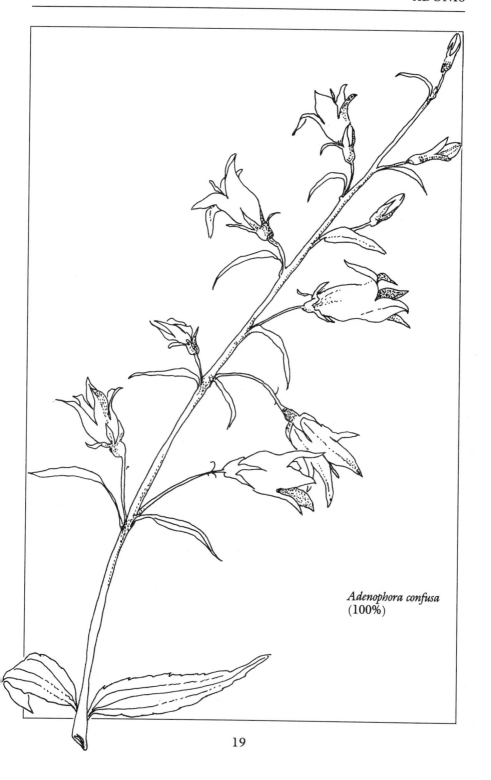

Adenophora confusa
(100%)

in the spring. Division is not required but may be accomplished in late spring after the foliage dies down.

Quick Reference to Adonis Species

	Height (in.)	No. of leaves	Flower color	Flowering time
A. amurensis	9–12	Few	Yellow	Early Spring
A. vernalis	12–15	Many	Yellow	Late Spring

-amurensis (am-ew-ren' sis)	Amur Adonis	9–12"/12"
Early Spring Yellow	Japan, Manchuria	Zones 4–7

Flowers appear as early as February in southern gardens and progressively later further north. The broad, 3–6" long stem leaves are cut into 3 sections to the base. Each section in turn is divided into linear segments. The 2" wide flowers are usually buttercup-yellow but may occasionally be white, rose, or have red stripes. Each flower has 20–50 petals slightly longer than the sepals and appears just before the leaves fully emerge.

If the weather remains cool when flowers open, they persist for up to 6 weeks, less if hot weather comes along. The golden flowers contrast well with the reticulated iris (*I. reticulata*), crocus, and other spring flowering bulbs.

Cultivars:

'Flore-plena' is a commonly grown double cultivar and is much showier than the species.

'Fukuju Kai' has fully open sulphur yellow flowers and is the earliest to bloom.
Other cultivars having copper, orange, pink, and white flowers have been developed by Japanese nurserymen, but have not been widely distributed.

-vernalis (ver-nah' lis)	Spring Adonis, Pheasant's Eye	12–15"/12"
Spring	Yellow Europe	Zones 4–7

This species is more winter hardy (zone 3 with protection) than the former and flowers 3–6 weeks later. The many stem leaves are sessile (no petioles) and are 1–2" long. The flowers have fewer petals than A. amurensis (10–15), are slightly toothed, and about 2½" wide. They open flat as a dinner plate, as if knowing their time in the sun was fleeting, to be enjoyed while possible.

Related Species:

A. apennina is similar to A. vernalis but has larger flowers (up to 3") and the lower leaves are rounded and sheathlike.

Quick Key to Adonis Species
   A. Stem leaves few, petioled, stem branched, petals 20–50 ..... *A. amurensis*
   AA. Stem leaves many, sessile, stem not branched, petals 10–15 ....*A. vernalis*

Agapanthus (ag-a-pan' thus)   African-lily   Liliaceae

Agapanthus is a rhizomatous plant with fleshy roots and elongated leathery leaves. Most species have strap-shaped, glossy dark green 2–3' long leaves. The flowers are carried in a rounded umbel on a thick scape and appear in late summer. In favorable climates, plants are extremely tough and durable. In areas of Britain, southern Europe and throughout New Zealand, *Agapanthus* is common and long lasting, being used as edgings, roadway dividers and hedging.

Although species such as *A. praecox* (formerly *A. umbellatus*) and *A. campanulatus* are fully hardy in areas of California and Florida, the hardiest and most available forms of *Agapanthus* are the hybrids, particularly the popular 'Headbourne Hybrids'. In north Georgia (zone 8), it is difficult to overwinter *Agapanthus*, yet there are areas as far north as zone 5, where winter temperatures may reach –10°F, where they overwinter. Moderation of temperatures by a lake effect, sandy well-drained soils, and snow cover help create this unusual situation. For the vast majority of gardeners in this country, however, *Agapanthus* should be treated as potted plants for deck, porch or around a garden pool to be brought into a frost-free area during the winter.

Allow the crowns to dry out over the rest period and begin adding water as spring approaches. The crowns should be set approximately 2" below ground level, watered well and left undisturbed. During the growing season, plants require copious amounts of water and must not be allowed to dry out.

Cultivars:

Many beautiful garden forms and hybrids have been developed but few have gained much popularity except as cut flowers. I list but a few of the better selections.

'Alice Gloucester' has purple flower buds and stems and bears large, warm white flowers in mid- to late summer.
'Headborne Hybrids' arose during the 1950's and 60's from Mr. Lewis Palmer of Headbourne Worthy near Winchester, England. As a mix, they have 2–3" long deep violet to pale blue flowers. Many of the single colored hybrid clones arose as a result of selections from Mr. Palmer's work.
'Isis' bears large inflorescences (6" across) of lavender blue flowers.
'Loch Hope' is by far the finest blue agapanthus in cultivation today. It is late flowering and produces flowers of the deepest violet atop 4–5' tall stems. In many of the older blue selections, the flowers fade to an unsightly reddish purple. This is not the case with this hybrid as the flowers maintain their deep color until they fall from the plant.
'Snowy Owl' is an excellent clone with creamy white flowers on 3' high stems.

21

Ajuga (a-jew' gah)   Bugle Weed   Lamiaceae

There are approximately 40 species of low-growing ground covers, however, only three are particularly useful to North American gardeners. They grow in any reasonably well-drained soil and although tolerant of full sun, growth is more rapid in partial shade. *Ajuga reptans* can become a persistent weed particularly if planted on the edge of a lawn but other slower growing species are available. Flowers of *Ajuga* are usually violet-blue although pink- and white-flowered cultivars have also been developed. A large drift of *Ajuga* in full bloom is spectacular but the foliage is the main reason for its popularity. In the South, crown rot (caused by *Sclerotium rossii*) is a major problem, particularly with *A. reptans*. Entire plantings may die or large patches develop infection. Planting in well-ventilated areas, dividing every 2–3 years, and application of fungicides help reduce this problem.

Seed should be sown in late summer for fall planting or in November for spring planting. Cultivars will not come true-to-type from seed but cuttings and divisions may be used. Division may be accomplished any time the ground is workable. Tissue culture techniques have also been developed.

Quick Reference to Ajuga Species

	Height (in.)	Stoloniferous (Y or N)	Stems (erect or prostrate)
A. genevensis	6–12	N	Erect
A. pyramidalis	6–9	N	Erect
A. reptans	4–12	Y	Prostrate

-genevensis (gen-e-ven' sis)		Geneva Bugle Weed	6–12"/9"
Summer	Various	Europe	Zones 4–9

This upright species is becoming more popular because it spreads less vigorously than *A. reptans* but grows faster than *A. pyramidalis*. If constant moisture is provided, it tolerates more sun than *A. pyramidalis* or *A. reptans*. The dark green basal leaves are coarsely toothed, hairy, and about 3" long. The upper leaves are 1–3" long, sessile and only slightly serrated. The 2" tall flower spikes are usually blue but may be pink or white. Although most *Ajuga* grow in zone 3, this species should receive winter protection in zone 4.

Cultivars:

var. *brockbankii* is a smaller, more vigorous form of the species with deep blue flowers and shorter stolons.

var. *rosea* has rosy-pink flowers but is otherwise identical to the species.

-pyramidalis (pi-ra-mid-ah' lis)		Upright Bugle Weed	6–9"/9"
Late Spring	Blue	Europe	Zones 3–9

(Syn. *A. alpina*)

This handsome plant incorporates the fine flowers and dark foliage of *A. reptans* without the spreading habit. The basal rosette is slightly toothed and hairy. The flower spikes are 4–6" long and the large purple bracts appear to press against the blue flowers. Although the plant does not spread as rapidly as *A. reptans*, it does produce short stolons late in the season in response to short days.

Cultivars:

'Crispa' (syn. 'Metallica-crispa') has deep blue flowers and brownish red crinkly foliage with a metallic luster. It is an outstanding garden plant.
'Pink Beauty' is 4–5" tall with light pink flowers in May and June.

-reptans (rep' tanz)		Common Bugle Weed	4-12"/24"
Late Spring	Violet	Europe	Zones 3–9

Much of the breeding and selection in this genus has been accomplished with *A. reptans* and remarkable advances in foliage color have resulted. Regardless of cultivar, *A. reptans* is stoloniferous and can spread rapidly. This characteristic makes the species an excellent ground cover and a large clump in flower is a spectacular sight. Plant where its invasive qualities are welcome, such as on a bank or under the dappled shade of trees. Do not plant it as an edging to the lawn or the insidious disease of "buglelawn" will occur. One of the symptoms includes the appearance of small islands of green foliage soon forming a large archipelago in an ocean of lawn. Weapons to destroy these islands include shovels, sprayers, or as one gardener did, simply expanding the flower bed to include all the bugleweed in the lawn. His lawn became smaller every year. The best prevention is proper planning; plan to keep the *Ajuga* away from all grassy areas.

If all else fails, remember that the ingestion of leaves of *A. reptans* is a mild narcotic. After trying some of the leaves, buglelawn will not seem as serious.

Cultivars:

Selections for flower color.
var. *alba* has creamy white flowers.
'Catlin's Giant' has tall (up to 8" long) spikes of blue flowers and bronze-green foliage.
'Pink Beauty' bears 4–5" long inflorescences of deep pink flowers.
'Pink Spire' is a fine green-leaved cultivar bearing 7" long pink flower spikes.
var. *rosea* produces rose flowers.

Selections for leaf color, all have blue to violet flowers.

'Atropurpurea' has dark bronze-purple leaves which color best in full sun. It is
an excellent landscape plant to provide drifts of bronze.

'Bronze Beauty' is similar but has metallic bronze foliage.

'Burgundy Glow' has foliage with shades of white, pink, rose and green. In the
fall, the older leaves turn a deep bronze and the young leaves have a rosy
hue. The combination is interesting if your eyes can stand the clashing
hues.

'Cristata' is probably one of the ugliest little plants available today. The leaves
are crinkled and distorted and the whole plant looks like crumpled spinach.

'Gaiety' has bronze purple leaves and lilac flowers.

'Multicolor' (syn. 'Rainbow') is similar to, but more vigorous than 'Burgundy
Glow' but the foliage colors are deeper. Sometimes comments concerning
leaf colors are best left to the gardener. This is one of those times.

'Silver Beauty' has gray-green leaves edged with white and is particularly handsome.

Quick Key to Ajuga Species

    A. Plants stoloniferous
      B. Plants vigorously stoloniferous, stems prostrate, hairless .... *A. reptans*
      BB. Plants weakly stoloniferous, stems upright, with long hairs............
                                                  A. pyramidalis
    AA. Plants not stoloniferous.................................. *A. genevensis*

Alchemilla (al-kem-ill′ a)　　　　　Lady's Mantle　　　　　Rosaceae

The genus received its name because of its popularity with alchemists of old
and was reputed to have many healing powers. Today we know it as a wonderful
low-growing shade tolerant plant with sprays of small yellow flowers in the
spring. The foliage is light green, pubescent and soft to the touch, particularly
on the underside. The apetalous (no petals) flowers are about ¼″ wide and
range from green to yellow.

Alchemilla requires partial shade and consistent soil moisture to thrive.
Plants will be stunted if placed in full sun or allowed to dry out. Cool climates
are preferable but they do quite well as far south as zone 7 providing there is
ample shade and moisture. I have grown lady's mantle in zone 8 and it is lovely
to those who have never seen large drifts grown under favorable conditions, however, the luxuriant growth taken for granted further north is never attained.

Fresh seed germinates readily but purchased or old seed should be given a
cold treatment similar to *Actaea*. *Alchemilla* self-sows readily which helps increase the planting size. Plants should be divided in early spring prior to flowering.

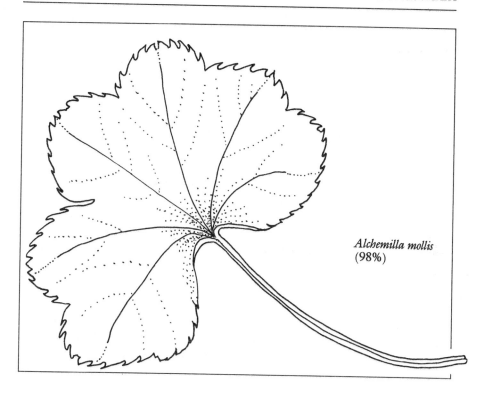

Alchemilla mollis
(98%)

Quick Reference to Alchemilla Species

	Height (in.)	Leaf color	Flower color
A. alpina	6–8	Green with white margins	Green
A. mollis	12–18	Light green	Yellow-green

-alpina (al-pine′ a) Mountain Mantle 6–8″/12″
Spring Green Europe Zones 3–7

This species is not used enough in the United States and although the flowers are not outstanding, the silver edges of the deeply cut 2″ wide foliage and the low neat habit make this a wonderful garden plant. Self-seeding is common, and if this becomes a problem, the seed heads should be removed prior to maturity. This is more important in the North than in the South. It is also native to Greenland and cold hardy in most of the northern states and Canada but not as heat tolerant as A. mollis.

Related Species:

A. conjuncta is a closely related but more robust species, growing 12–18″ tall.

25

A. pubescens is a little larger (8–10″) than *A. alpina* and has 7-lobed kidney-shaped leaves which are silky beneath.

-mollis (mol′ lis)		Lady's Mantle	12–18″/24″
Spring	Yellowish	Asia Minor	Zones 4–7

The common lady's mantle is a splendid ground cover and will grow in almost any moist, shady area except a bog. The dense pubescence gives the foliage a soft velvet feel and the yellow-green starry flowers which are held above the foliage make long-lasting cut flowers. The leaves have shallow lobes and are particularly pretty after a soft rain when the captured droplets glisten in the sun. This species is too large for the rock garden but can be used sucessfully to edge a path or border. The densely hairy leaves create a problem in areas such as the Southeast where thundershowers punctuate hot summer afternoons. The water trapped in the leaves and crown does not dry out during the night and provides excellent breeding grounds for a number of foliar diseases. Use of a fungicide during wet, rainy periods partially alleviates the problem.

Related Species:

A. vulgaris, common lady's mantle, is similar to *A. mollis* but is less pubescent and has smaller, greener flowers. The foliage is also more deeply lobed. Most of the plants of *A. vulgaris* sold in the United States are probably *A. mollis*.

Quick Key to Alchemilla Species

    A. Leaves light green, densely hairy, shallow rounded lobes .... *A. mollis*
    AA. Leaves with white margins, slightly hairy, deeply lobed .... *A. alpina*

Additional Reading:

Reed, Christopher. 1987. Lady's mantle: refined company for many plants. *Horticulture* 65(1):16.

Allium   Ornamental Onion   Liliaceae

The genus *Allium* contains approximately 500 species including onion (*A. cepa*), garlic (*A. sativum*), and chives (*A. schoenoprasum*). Although ornamental forms of chives such as 'Forescate' have been developed, the presence of these tasty but breathy members of the onion family has given the ornamental alliums a bad name. The species are bulbous or rhizomatous (*A. unifolium*) and are all characterized by the presence of a superior ovary, cymose umbels of small flowers and the emission of an onion or garlic smell when crushed. Scientists in several locations have tried to eliminate the odor from alliums, particularly the culinary species, but I, for one, hope they have little success. An allium without odor is like a book without a cover. The odor occurs only when plants are

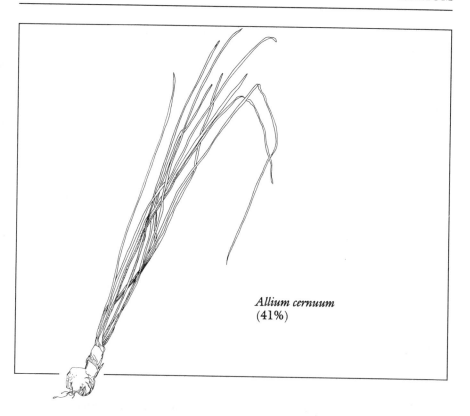

Allium cernuum
(41%)

broken or crushed and is not given off spontaneously. In fact, the flowers of some members have a mild fragrance of violets.

Allium has been placed in the Liliaceae because of the superior ovary but some taxonomists argue that the presence of the umbellate inflorescence should place *Allium* in the Amaryllidaceae. Others yet argue that a separate family, Alliaceae, should be created for all genera with a superior ovary and an umbellate inflorescence. Others which would be included in such a reorganization are *Agapanthus, Brodiaea,* and *Triteleia.*

The ornamental alliums range in size from the 2–3″ high plants of *A. circinatum* to the 4′ tall scapes of *A. giganteum*. Although many alliums bear lilac-blue flowers, some species send up umbels of white (*A. neapolitanum*), pink (*A. murrayanum*), yellow (*A. moly*), or interesting multicolors (the very un-allium looking *A. siculum* var. *dioscoridis*). Most species bear 3–8 linear leaves (except *A. karataviense*) which die back before or soon after flowering.

In general, the planting depth of the bulb is approximately 3 times the diameter. Bulbs should be fall planted in full sun and in well-drained areas. As lovely as many of these species are, they are poor plants if not combined with other perennials or annuals. Because the foliage dies during or immediately after flowering, many gaps in the garden soon exist. Other plants growing around them camouflage the empty spaces. An area devoted strictly to alliums (or any genera of bulbs) is a collection, not a garden, and should be avoided by a gardener.

Quick Reference to Allium Species

	Height (in.)	Flower color	Fragrant flowers	Flowering time
A. acuminatum	8–12	pink	no	early summer
A. aflatunense	24–36	lilac	no	late spring
A. caeruleum	12–24	blue	no	late spring
A. christophii	12–24	violet	no	summer
A. giganteum	36–60	lilac	no	late spring
A. karataviense	6–12	lilac	no	late spring
A. moly	12–15	yellow	no	early spring
A. neapolitanum	8–12	white	yes	early spring
A. ostrowskianum	8–12	rose	yes	early summer
A. sphaerocephalum	18–36	purple	no	late spring
A. triquetrum	8–15	white	no	summer

-acuminatum (a-cum-in-ay′ tum)		Pink Wild Onion	8-12″/12″
Early Summer	Pink	Western North America	Zones 4–7

Two or three narrow leaves emerge from a round bulb, above which an 8″ scape holds erect, star-shaped flowers with pointed segments. Many ½″ long flowers form a loose umbel approximately 2″ wide. The flowers range from deep rose to lilac-pink and bloom for about 2 weeks starting the end of May. Plants do best in dry areas and in hot, rainy, climates such as the Southeast, do not often persist more than 2 years. Plant in a well-drained sunny location.

It is a pretty plant when used in colonies of at least a dozen bulbs. Bulbils which form at the base of the bulbs result in a slow-spreading colony.

-aflatunense (a-fla-tun-en′ se)		Persian Onion	2–3′/2′
Late Spring	Lilac	China	Zones 4–8

This is one of the taller alliums and produces 4″ diameter spherical umbels of star-shaped flowers atop 3′ tall scapes. Often thought of as a smaller version of *A. giganteum*, it lacks the majesty and grandeur of the latter. The bulbs, however, are available at ⅓ the cost. The strap-shaped basal leaves are up to 4″ wide and disappear soon after the flower appears.

This is one of the few species in the genus truly at home among other plants in the border. Plants do well in any sunny well-drained location, however, they are susceptible to root rot organisms prevalent in heavy soils. Results in zone 8 have been variable. Some years plants are outstanding, others years, disappointing. The cut flowers are excellent and persist nearly 2 weeks.

Seed should be sown in moist seed trays and placed at about 70°F for 2–4 weeks, then placed at 30–40°F for an additional 4–6 weeks. After the cold treatment, bring the tray to 50–60°F. until germination occurs. Keep moist at all times.

Cultivars

'Purple Sensation' has darker purple flowers than those of the species.

Related Species

Hybridization of *A. elatum* × *A. aflatunense* in Holland has resulted in tall (3–4') plants with large globe-shaped flower heads. Cultivars include 'Gladiator', 'Lucy Ball' and 'Rienpoortvliet'.

-caeruleum (ce-rue' lee-um)		Blue Globe Onion	12–24"/18"
Late Spring	Blue	Russia	Zones 2–7

(Syn. *A. azureum*)

The deep blue flowers are held tightly in a 1–2" diameter umbel. The leaves are 3-sided and 6–12" long. The flowers, which open in late May in zone 7 and about 2 weeks later in zone 3, persist for about 2 weeks and make excellent dried flowers. Unfortunately, it is difficult to establish in most American gardens as it comes from the steppes and deserts of Central Asia and requires hot, dry conditions to flourish. Similar to many other allium flowers, this is also an excellent cut flower.

Occasionally bulbils are formed within the inflorescence and may be used for propagation. Seed should be treated as with *A. aflatunense*.

Related Species:

A. cernuum, wild nodding onion, is native to United States and bears nodding umbels of lilac-pink flowers. Bulbs are easy to grow and make a wonderful early summer show when placed in groups of three to six. Deadhead immediately after flowering.

-christophii (kris-tof' ee-eye)		Downy Onion, Star of Persia	15–24"/24"
Summer	Violet	Turkey, Afghanistan	Zones 4–8

(Syn. *A. albo-pilosum*)

Although short in stature, this is one of the largest flowering species in cultivation. Up to 100 metallic blue star-shaped flowers are carried on a spherical umbel often 10–12" in diameter. The stems and the margins of the strap-shaped leaves are covered with white hairs which are responsible for the common name. The leaves die before the flowers have completely opened.

When in flower, there is no more eye-catching member of the genus. It is also one of the best alliums for long-lasting dried flowers, literally looking good for years. A sunny well-drained area at the front of the border is necessary for best performance.

Propagate by seed similar to *A. aflatunense*.

Related Species

'Globemaster' is a recent hybrid between *A. elatum* and *A. christophii*. Hundreds of violet flowers are formed on 3' tall stems. The flowers are sterile and remain fresh for many weeks. Unfortunately, bulbs are presently only available for commercial cut flower growers in Europe but may be available for gardeners in the 1990's.

-giganteum (gi-gan′ tee-um)		Giant Onion	3–5'/2'
Late Spring	Lilac	Central Asia	Zone 4–8

This is, as the name implies, the giant of this genus. The bulb itself is 2–4" in diameter and resembles a large, misshapen ball. In early spring, 6 to 9 broad (5–8" wide) gray-green leaves emerge as a rosette followed by a thick, strong scape carrying the many lilac flowers. By the time the scape is 6–12" long, the leaves lie on the ground. Three to four weeks are required for the scape to grow to a final height of 4' but the wait is justified. Over 100 individual flowers, each ½" long, are held closely together in a dense, 4" diameter rounded umbel.

Plant in groups of three, more if you can afford the pricey bulbs, in full sun and well-drained soils. It is an excellent late spring and summer flower for the back of the border and because the leaves disappear soon after flowering, there is no "dead time" waiting for the leaves to wither as with tulips and daffodils. Plantings as far south as zone 8 have been excellent and if mulch is applied, the bulbs appear to be cold tolerant to zone 4. In zone 8, flowering occurs in mid-May but not until early June in Michigan (zone 4). As a cut flower it is outstanding, and has gained much popularity with florists and designers.

Propagation is accomplished by separating the two portions of the bulb which tend to split after 2 years.

Related Species:

A. elatum, native to central Turkey, has 3' tall scapes bearing large many-flowered lavender unbels. The oblong dark green leaves are 8–12" long and 2–3" wide.

A. stipitatum is similar, bearing 3–4' tall scapes topped with globular lilac flowers. It differs in that the petals reflex downward and wither after flowering, while those of *A. giganteum* are persistent. The leaves are narrower, about 1–1½" wide. This is also a magnificent species. Var. *alba* bears creamy white flowers.

-karataviense (ka-ra-tah-vee-en′ se)		Turkistan Onion	6-12"/15"
Late Spring	Silver-gray	Turkey, Afghanistan	Zones 4–9

This unique species is grown for the foliage as much as for the flowers. The thick, gray-green leaves (usually 2) are up to 4" wide and mottled purple, particularly underneath and near the base. The leaves may be more ornamental than the flower, which is a rather washed out silver-lilac. The dense umbels are 8–12″ across and compete with those of *A. christophii* for the largest in the genus. The plant is particularly suited to open, windy locations because of the strong, thick 6″ tall scape which carries the flowers. The leaves and seed capsules persist well after the flower has abscised and remain handsome until mid-June.

Seed-propagated plants (accomplished as with *A. aflatunense*) require about 3 years to flower.

-moly (mah′ lee)		Lily Leek, Golden Onion	12–15″/12″
Late Spring	Yellow	Southern Europe	Zones 3–9

Even before the time of Homer, the lily leek was endowed with magical properties. Reference to the "Moly" can be found in the *Odyssey*, in which Ulysses walked unharmed under its protection. It has been looked upon as a good luck charm for many years and this combination of magic and beauty makes the plant difficult not to include in the garden. The two flat, lance-like leaves are blue green and up to 2″ wide and 8–12″ long. The small ½″ diameter star-shaped flowers are held in a 2″ wide open umbel and are a lovely shade of golden yellow. A dozen bulbs planted in a sunny well-drained area quickly increase to form a golden vista in late spring and early summer.

Propagate by bulb offsets or seed. Seed propagated plants will flower in one year.

-neopolitanum (nee-ah-pol-i-tay′ num)		Naples Onion	8-12″/12″
Early Spring	White	Southern Europe	Zones 7–9

Two to three linear leaves, about ½ to ¾″ wide and keeled, are held in a basal rosette resembling daffodil foliage. The scape carries a loose, many-flowered umbel (2½″ across) of starry white flowers with rosy stamens. The individual flowers are about ¾″ in diameter and are among the most fragrant in the genus. It is one of the earliest to flower, opening the end of April and persisting for about 4 weeks. It is not reliably hardy in zone 6, but if heavily mulched, will overwinter. Mulch should also be applied further south to reduce temperature fluctuations in the soil. Plant about 5″ deep in a sheltered corner of the garden, preferably at the foot of a low, south-facing wall.

The fragrance of the flowers has made this a popular cut flower as well as an excellent species for greenhouse pot plant production. Cover 4–5 bulbs with an inch of soil in a 5″ diameter pot and place at 45°F for 8–10 weeks. Bring to a warm area and enjoy the flowers.

Cultivars:

var. *grandiflorum* has 3″ diameter umbels and is more vigorous than the species. It is used for forcing in pots and cut flower production and is more ornamental than the species.

Related Species:

    A. cowanii is similar but only about 6″ tall, and is now thought to be a form of *A. neapolitanum*. It performed poorly in our trials in Georgia, but was planted in highly exposed areas.

-ostrowskianum (o-strow′ sky-aye-num)		Ostrowsky Onion	8-12″/9″
Early Summer	Rose	Turkey, Afghanistan	Zones 3–9

    This is an excellent species for the patio planter or front of the garden. The 2–3 linear leaves are flat, bluish green, and somewhat limp. The star-shaped flowers are held in a 2″ diameter many-flowered umbel. They have a mild pleasant fragrance but the onion smell is particularly noticeable when the leaves and stem are crushed. The flowers become thin and papery as they age and persist for many weeks while the foliage remains 3–4 weeks after flowering. Plant in a sunny, well-drained area.

Cultivars:

'Zwanenberg' has carmine-pink flowers which are a little brighter than those of
    the species.

Related Species:

    A. oreophilum is a similar species and some writers consider the two to be the same. *A. oreophilum* is only 1–4″ tall and has channelled leaves. Apart from size, however, there is no difference in garden culture or performance.

-sphaerocephalum (sfay-roe-sef′ a-lum)		Drumstick Chives	18–36/15″
Late Spring	Purple	Europe	Zones 4–9

    This is one of the finest alliums for cut flowers and for use in the border. The 3–5 hollow, semi-cylindical leaves resemble inflated chive leaves. The oval to round 2″ diameter flower heads consist of 50–100 flowers. Each flower bud is green and with maturity, flowers turn purple, giving the inflorescence a two-tone effect. Flowers open in mid-June and persist for 2–3 weeks. The stamens are longer than the petals and provide an airy feel to the flower heads. It is excellent in hot climates and performs well in zone 8. The flowers are persistent on the plant and as a cut flower, last up to 10 days in water. I cannot understand why this species has been so overlooked and underused in American gardens.

    Plant multiple bulbs 6″ apart and 6″ deep in a sunny exposure. One or two plants are not effective and a grouping is essential.

    Bulblets can be separated after 2–3 years and seed may be treated similar to *A. aflatunense.*

-triquetrum (tri-kwee′ trum)		Three Cornered Onion	8-15″/12″
Summer	White	Western Europe	Zones 5–9

    This is easily recognizable by the three-sided scape which supports a 2½″ diameter inflorescence of six to eight ½″ long pendulous, white flowers, borne primarily on one side of the inflorescence. Each bell-shaped flower has a central stripe of green and the stigma is deeply 3-parted, another characteristic useful in separating the three cornered onion from others. The flowers are fragrant, but not nearly as sweet as those of *A. neapolitanum*. The foliage consists of three to four 1″ wide, keeled leaves. It is common in hedgerows in England and New Zealand.

Plant bulbs in well-drained soils in full sun. Seeds germinate readily and can create a weed problem the following spring if growing conditions are conducive. Many gardeners remove the flowers as soon as they have wilted. Propagate by the many bulblets formed after the first year or by seeds treated similarly to those of *A. aflatunense*.

Cultivars:

var. *pendulinum* has larger flowers borne on all sides of the umbel. It is more useful as a cut flower than the species.

Related Species:

A. ursinum, ramsoms, is about 10″ tall and bears 15–20 white flowers in flat 2″ diameter umbels in late spring. The strongly scented plants consist of two to three elliptical leaves with long petioles. Plants are more tolerant of shade than most alliums.

Quick Key to Allium Species

    A. Flowering plants usually taller than 2 feet.
        B. Leaves half-rounded, hollow, upright .... *A. sphaerocephalum*
      BB. Leaves flat or keeled, not half-rounded or hollow
          C. Leaves 3–4″ wide, plants 2–3′ tall .... *A. aflatunense*
          CC. Leaves 5–8″ wide, gray-green, plants 3–5′ tall .... *A. giganteum*
  AA. Flowering plants usually less than 2′ tall
      B. Flowers lilac, blue, or violet
        C. Flowers lilac or blue
          D. Flowers lilac, leaves flat, mottled purple, 2–4″ wide ....
                                        A. karataviense
         DD. Flowers blue, leaves triangular, not mottled, ½ to ¾″
             wide .... *A. caeruleum*
      BB. Flowers yellow, white, or pink
        C. Flowers white
          D. Flowers star shaped, upright, scape round....... *A. neapolitanum*
         DD. Flowers bell shaped, nodding, scape three sided... *A. triquetrum*
        CC. Flowers yellow, pink
          D. Flowers yellow, plants 12–15″ tall...................... *A. moly*
         DD. Flowers pink, plants 8–12″ tall
            E. Leaves narrow, green, flower segments recurved at
             tips .... *A. acuminatum*

EE. Leaves flaccid, gray-green, segments not recurved . . . .
A. ostrowskianum

Additional Reading:

Harper, P. 1976. The ornamental onion. *Horticulture* 54(8):19–22.

Moore, Harold E. Jr. 1954. The cultivated alliums. *Baileya* 2(3):103–113.

Moore, Harold E. Jr. 1954. The cultivated alliums II. *Baileya* 2(4):117–123.

Moore, Harold E. Jr. 1955. The cultivated alliums III. *Baileya* 3(3):137–149.

Moore, Harold E. Jr. 1955. The cultivated alliums IV. *Baileya* 3(3):157–167.

Amsonia (am-sown' ee-ah)   Blue Star Flower   Apocynaceae

This North American genus contains some fine low maintenance, resilient species for the garden. Light blue, star-shaped flowers are held in terminal panicles above the alternate leaves. There are approximately seven species in the genus including difficult to find but lovely Arkansas amsonia, *A. hubrectii* and the pale blue-flowered *A. ludoviciana*. *A. angustifolia*, downy star flower and *A. tabernaemontana*, blue star flower, are excellent garden plants and offered by most nurseries.

-angustifolia (an-gus-ti-fo' lee-a)   Downy Amsonia   1–3'/3'
Spring   Pale blue   Southeastern United States   Zones 7–10

(Syn. *A. ciliata*)

An excellent plant for southern gardens, the hairy foliage, which emerges in early spring, remains healthy all season. With maturity, the linear to linear-lanceolate dark green leaves lose much of their silkiness. However, if the plant is cut back after flowering, the new growth returns as feathery as before. The leaves are crowded toward the upper end of the stems and the margins slightly curled back toward the underside of the leaves. The starry flowers are pale blue and persist for 3–4 weeks. This species and *A. tabernaemontana* are two of the few herbaceous species which provide fall color in the garden. The foliage turns a lovely golden yellow and lasts until frost.

Plant in full sun or light, dappled shade and provide sufficient moisture to survive dry periods. No serious pests occur, but the stems need cutting back at least once during the season to keep them from falling over.

Seed, division, and terminal cuttings taken during the spring are viable means of propagation. Store the seed at about 40°F for 4–6 weeks because untreated seed germinates irregularly. Chipping or cutting away a small piece of one end of the seed and soaking overnight in water also results in better germination. Division is not necessary for many years but is a quick way to increase a planting. Cut through the crown in late spring or fall so that each division

34

consists of at least one growing point. Terminal cuttings from lateral branches collected in May and treated with a rooting hormone (one labeled for herbaceous plants) root faster and more uniformly.

-tabernaemontana (tay-ber-nay-mon-tah′ na) Willow Amsonia 1–3′/3′
Spring Pale blue United States Zones 3–9
(Syn. *Tabernaemontana amsonia*)

This differs from *A. angustifolia* in that the leaves are wider, more evenly spaced along the stem, and are not as hairy as they emerge. It is native from Pennsylvania to South Carolina and as far west as Kansas, and having escaped from cultivation, can be found along roadsides. This species is more cold hardy than the previous and much more common. The lovely blue hues of the flowers and the fall color of the foliage are similar in both species.

Plants have alternate willow-like leaves and many ½–¾″ pale blue star flowers clustered in loose drooping terminal inflorescences in early summer. They are particularly lovely in the early spring as they break through the ground and rapidly extend to their mature stature. If grown in full sun, pruning may not be necessary, however, if grown in shade, prune at least once to maintain shape. Deep, moist soils and partial shade are ideal.

Cultivars:

var. *salicifolia* (sometimes listed as *A. salicifolia*) has leaves 5–10 times longer than they are wide and is less erect than the species. The flowers have a white throat and a small beard within.
Propagation is similar to *A. angustifolia*.

Related Species:

A. montana appears to be a smaller version of the above species. Plants do not require cutting back and hold their shape well.

Quick Key to Amsonia Species:
A. Plants hairy, particularly when young, leaves crowded on stem, margins curled back.................................. *A. angustifolia*
AA. Plants not obviously hairy, leaves spaced on stem, margins not curled back .... *A. tabernaemontana*

Additional Reading:

Taloumis, George. 1985. *Amsonia. Horticulture* 63(8):30–31.

Anaphalis (an-naff′ al-iss) Pearly Everlasting Asteraceae

Anaphalis produces masses of small white flowers in August and September, usually with a brownish yellow center, but the foliage is special throughout the

Anaphalis triplinervis
(81%)

growing season. The gray-white leaves create a cooling effect in the border and tone down the bright reds and oranges of plants beside them. They are particularly useful in areas which are too wet for other gray-green plants such as *Artemesia* and *Perovskia*. Plants in the genus are especially tough and withstand significant abuse. Although rich soil is not a prerequisite, it should be grown in evenly moist areas because the foliage looks shabby under dry conditions. They are also at home in the naturalized or wild flower garden in full sun to partial shade.

    The leaves are alternate, entire, and sessile. The flower heads are small and crowded at the ends of the branches. They can be cut and dried to make excellent "everlastings".

    Seed sown in late summer will produce flowering plants the next year but division is the most rapid means of propagation. Plants should be divided every 3–4 years.

Quick Reference to Anaphalis Species

	Height (in.)	Underside of leaves woolly	Flower color
A. cinnamomea	24–36	Yes	White
A. triplinervis	12–18	Yes	White

36

-cinnamomea (sin-a-mo' mee-a)		Pearly Everlasting	24–36"/24"
Late Summer	White	India	Zones 3–8

(Syn. *A. yedoensis*)

The 2–4" long gray-green lanceolate leaves have a cinnamon, woolly pubescence on their undersides. The rounded flower heads consist of dozens of ¼ to ½" diameter flowers which cover the plants like a carpet of snow. The common name refers to the long-lasting dried flowers. Under evenly moist conditions, it grows 3' tall and equally wide. This is a plant which takes a few years to appreciate but once its potential is expressed, gardeners cherish it for the late flowering and the gray foliage.

Related Species:

A. margaritacea is almost identical to this species but is native to North America. It grows 4' tall under optimum conditions and has slightly larger flowers. It is interesting to note that most of the tall growing *Anaphalis* offered by American nurserymen is *A. cinnamomea*, native to India, while the majority of everlastings in English gardens is our native *A. margaritacea*.

-triplinervis (tri-plee-ner' vis)		Three-veined Everlasting	12–18"/12"
Late Summer	White	Himalayas	Zones 3–8

This makes an excellent plant for the front of the garden or rockery and the dense, white, woolly pubescent leaves contrast and soften other green-leaved species. The stems have a more or less zigzag or wavy form (flexuous) which is especially evident if a few leaves are removed. The flowers, which open in July, are long-lasting and continue until frost.

Cultivars:

'Summer Snow' has clear white flowers over tufts of silvery gray foliage. The flowers are a "cleaner" white than those of the species.

Related Species:

A. nubigena is similar but only 6–9" tall.

Quick Key to Anaphalis Species

A.	Plant 24–36" tall, stems straight .... *A. cinnamomea*
AA.	Plant 12–18" tall, stems flexuous .... *A. triplinervis*

Anchusa (an-koo' sa)   Alkanet   Boraginaceae

There are about 30 species but few are suitable for the garden. All are biennials or short-lived perennials (living for 2–3 years) and provide flowers in the blue range, a color often difficult to find in the spring and summer garden. Members of *Anchusa* are characterized by the presence of alternate leaves, hairy stems, and flowers arranged together in the shape of a scorpion's tail (scorpioid cyme). *A. capensis* is approximately 1–2′ tall and is best treated as a biennial or an annual. The best species is *A. azurea*, available in a number of stately cultivars.

-azurea (a-zewr-ree′ a)		Italian Alkanet	3–5′/2′
Late Spring	Blue	Caucasus	Zones 3–8

(Syn. *A. italica*)

This tall growing, coarsely hairy species is a beautiful background specimen for the late spring garden. The 4–8″ long entire leaves are sessile or attached to the stem by the clasping base. The bright blue flowers are ½–¾″ across and persist for about four weeks. It performs best in deep soil in full sun. In the South, plants may reach 4′ in height and require support. Plants may become invasive in rich soils and too lanky if fertilizer is applied.

Cultivars:
Various selections were made between 1900 and 1931 and some of these are still popular today.

'Dropmore' was selected in 1905 and the deep blue flowers are still in demand. It reaches a height of 4′ and is one of the more commonly offered cultivars.
'Little John' is a compact version of the species (1½′ tall) with dark blue flowers and a compact habit.
'Loddon Royalist' is only about 3′ in height and has lovely gentian-blue flowers.
'Opal' was raised in 1906 and has azure blue flowers. This and 'Dropmore' are untidy in habit and occupy a great deal of garden space.
'Royal Blue' is similar to 'Loddon Royalist' but has a deeper blue color.

Propagation is mainly by root cuttings. Take ½–¾″ diameter cuttings, 2–3″ long, in early spring, place horizontally in moist, loose, well-drained soil at 65–75°F (also see *Anemone* × *hybrida*.) If seed is used, sow ½″ deep, place at 70–75°F and cover to maintain high humidity.

Anemone (a-nem′ o-nee)	Windflower	Ranunculaceae

Anemone is a diverse genus of approximately 70 species including fibrous and tuberous-rooted species. They are used for greenhouse potted plants, florist cut flowers and garden plants. One can find anemones blooming in spring, summer and fall and most grow in ordinary garden soil. In 1629, John Parkinson wrote in *Paradisi* that "the sight of them doth enforce an earnest longing desire in the minde of anyone to be a possessour of some of them at the least, for . . . is of it selfe alone almost sufficient to furnish a garden with their flowers for almost halfe the yeare . . ." Most species have compound leaves and apetalous (no petals) flowers consisting of showy sepals. The tuberous types (*A. blanda*, *A. coronaria*) are best planted in mid- to late October approximately 3″ deep. All species appreciate shelter from the afternoon sun and do poorly if allowed to dry out. The early spring-flowering tuberous species are usually dormant by the time the hot sun of summer arrives.

Propagation by seed is possible but for most, division is the quickest and surest method of multiplication. For tuberous species, the tubers may be lifted in early June and divided. Ripe seed should be rubbed in dry sand to remove the cottony down adhering to the seed. Species lumped under *A. japonica* (*A. vitifolia*, *A. hupehensis*, *A.* × *hybrida*) are rampant growers and easily increased by division in the fall. Root cuttings are also a good method of propagating many species of *Anemone*.

Quick Reference to Anemone Species

	Height (in.)	Tuberous (Y or N)	# of sepals	Flower color	Flowering time
A. blanda	6–8	Y	9–14	Blue	Early Spring
A. canadensis	12–24	N	4–5	White	Spring
A. coronaria	7–15	Y	6–20	Various	Early Spring
A. × *hybrida*	30–48	N	6–11	White, pink	Fall
A. × *lesseri*	15–18	N	5–8	Rosy red	Early Summer
A. magellanica	6–8	N	5–10	White	Early Spring
A. nemerosa	6–8	N	5–9	White	Spring
A. sylvestris	10–18	N	5–8	White	Spring
A. vitifolia	18–36	N	5–7	White, pink	Fall

-blanda (blan′ da)   Grecian Windflower   6–8″/8″
Early Spring   Dark blue   Greece   Zones 4–8

The Grecian windflower is one of the earliest harbingers of spring. The small stature makes plants most suitable for naturalizing or for filling in small areas of the garden. The large, rounded tuber produces deeply cut foliage resulting in a fern-like appearance. Although the flowers of the species are dark blue, cultivars are available in sky blue, white, pink or purplish red. The narrow sepals are about ½″ long and the flowers nearly 2″ across. The flowers last but 2 weeks and give rise to hairy seed heads composed of achenes. These fruiting bodies last 3–4 weeks but are not particularly attractive and should be removed. The tubers are planted 1–3″ apart in dappled shade and in soil amended with organic matter. In the South (south of zone 7), it does not spread as rapidly as in the North nor is it as long-lived. One to two years is necessary to establish the tubers, especially if they are dried out when purchased. Once established, however, plants will self-sow and the seedlings will flower the second year. Provide winter protection with leaves or pine boughs in zone 4.

Cultivars:

'Blue Star' has dark-blue flowers about 2–2½″ in diameter.
'Bridesmaid' and 'White Splendor' both bear flowers of pure white. There is little difference between them.

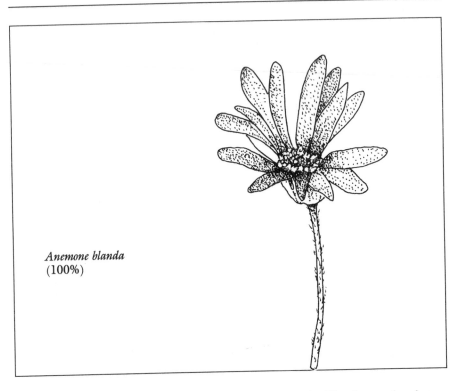

Anemone blanda
(100%)

'Pink Star' and 'Rosea' have differing shades of purple. The former has larger
   flowers than the latter.
'Radar' is one of the finest cultivars and has large mauve flowers with white
   centers.

Related Species:
   A. apennina, Apennine windflower, is similar but not as cold hardy. Plants
have larger leaves and lighter blue flowers.

-canadensis (kan-a-den' sis)	Meadow Anemone	12–24"/spreader
Spring White	Northern United States, Canada	Zones 3–7

(Syn. *A. pennsylvanica*)

   The common name is particularly appropriate because the species will spread
and fill an entire meadow. That it is invasive is probably its only flaw, and if
placed in a difficult corner or other area where it can run, it will reign supreme
in the spring and into early summer.
   The light green leaves are 5–7 parted and broader than long. They are hairy
beneath and the leaf segments are toothed. Each clear white flower is almost 2"
across and consists of 4–5 sepals.
   Plants do best in partial shade but tolerate full sun. It is native to low lying

areas and thus requires moist conditions to become established. As long as its exuberant habit can be enjoyed, this is an excellent plant for those who think they can't grow anything.

Propagate by division any time from May to September.

-coronaria (ko-ro-nah' ree-a)		Poppy Anemone	7-15"/8"
Early Spring	Various	Mediterranean	Zones 6–9

Gardeners seldom see the actual species any more, for it has been replaced with more colorful hybrids. All *A. coronaria* strains have finely divided foliage and rounded sepals in various colors. Regardless of the pedigree, they make lovely spring garden plants as well as good cut flowers. They may be planted in the North (zone 6) as late as October and in the South in November for early spring flowering. Further north than zone 6, pot the tuber at the beginning of March and plant outside after threat of frost, and flowers will emerge in late May and early June. Research in Georgia (zone 8) has shown that planting as late as December does not affect the number of flowers (4–5 flowers/plant). The flowering season was also extended a few weeks with late planting. However, plantings in January, Febuary, and March resulted in few flowers of questionable quality. This was probably because insufficient cold was accumulated by the tubers. This research also indicates that corms are best treated as annuals, dug up and discarded after flowering. Flower production declines and corms die after two or three years in the ground. Corms of *A. blanda* or *A. coronaria* are relatively inexpensive and can be replaced at nominal cost. Soak corms overnight in water prior to planting, and place 3–4" deep.

Cultivars:

'De Caen' hybrids were developed early in the 18th century around the Caen and Bayeux districts of northern France and became known as the De Caen anemones. The flowers are single, saucer shaped and available as 'Florist Mix' or as separate colors. 'The Bride', white; 'Mr. Fokker', violet-blue; and 'Sylphide', violet rose are only a few of the cultivars which have been developed within the De Caen series.

'Hollandia' (syn. 'His Excellency') has scarlet sepals with white bases surrounding a black center.

'Mona Lisa' series is a relatively new strain of poppy anemone which is much preferable to the 'De Caen' series. Separate colors as well as a mixture have been developed. The flowers are larger, the stems are 1½ to 2 times longer and the vase life of the cut flowers is longer. They are presently available for greenhouse forcing but should soon be available to the general public.

'St. Brigid' series has semi-double flowers and is available as a mixture or in separate colors. 'Lord Lieutenant', purple blue; 'The Admiral', blue; and 'The Governor', crimson scarlet are available in this series.

'St Piran' was developed in Cornwall, England and bears long stems of single and semi-double flowers. They are only available in a mix.

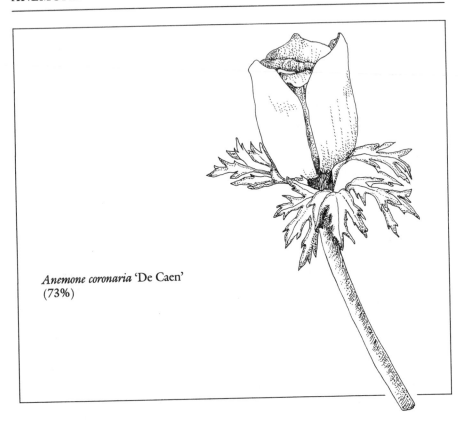

Anemone coronaria 'De Caen'
(73%)

-× *hybrida* (hi-bred' a)   Hybrid Anemone, Japanese Anemone   2½–3'/2'
Fall   White, pink   Hybrid origin   Zones 4–8

The nomenclature of *Anemone* is rather confused but nowhere is it as befuddled as with Japanese anemone and the various hybrids. Probably most plants sold as *A. japonica* are masquerading under that name and are actually hybrids. Many of these hybrids are wonderful garden plants and provide much needed color in late summer and early fall gardens. They perform best in well-drained soils and partial shade. They are often slow to establish but are free-flowering after the second year. Some absolutely wonderful hybrids are available and although my preferences in anemones reside with the single forms, many cultivars are also available with semidouble or double flowers. The only defect with many of the cultivars is that they are 4–5' tall and may need some support to look their best.

Cultivars:
var. *alba* bears single, clear white 2–3" diameter flowers and stands 3' tall.
'Alice' has semidouble light pink flowers and is 2–2½' tall.

'Honorine Jobert' has graced gardens since the beginning of the American Civil War and is still the most popular and highly sought white anemone today. It is 3–4' tall and the clean white sepals contrast beautifully with the yellow stamens in the center. The flowers are only 2–3" across, not as large as some of the newer clones, but the plant is floriferous and worthy of a place in the garden.

'Lady Gilmore' is a recent introduction with 4" wide semidouble rosy-pink flowers. The outside of the flower is darker than the inside, a trait found in many pink cultivars.

'Luise Uhink' was bred by the German nurseryman, Wilhelm Pfitzer, but is little known in this country. This is unfortunate as it has 4–5" diameter single white flowers on 4' tall stems and is a prolific flowerer.

'Margarete' has semidouble to double deep pink flowers and is 2–3' tall.

'Max Vogel' is one of the most impressive pink flowering anemones I have observed. It stands about 4' tall and carries dozens of single, 4–5" wide, clean pink flowers. It is truly outstanding.

'Prince Henry' ('Prinz Heinrich') has deep rose, semidouble flowers and is smaller than most of the hybrids but still stands nearly 3' tall.

'Queen Charlotte' bears lovely pink semi-double flowers which measure 3" across. It grows about 3' tall and was also bred by Pfitzer in Germany.

'September Charm' may be a cultivar of *A. hupehensis*. It bears single rose-pink flowers which are darker on the outside than inside. Average garden height is 2–3'.

'Whirlwind' is 4–5' tall and has 4" wide semi-double pure white flowers.

Propagation by division in the spring is a simple matter. Root cuttings may also be used with anemones by taking thick sections of root approximately 3–4" long from lifted plants and placing vertically in a moist well-drained medium. Cover the tops of the root section with a thin layer of sand or vermiculite and place in a cold frame or unheated greenhouse. This method of propagation should be accomplished when the plants are dormant in the winter.

Related Species:

A. hupehensis, native to China, has 5–7 rosy-mauve sepals, grows 2–2½' tall and flowers a week or so earlier than *A. × hybrida*. The cultivar 'Splendens' has purple to pink flowers. The semidouble form (20–25 sepals) is likely the historic *A. japonica* introduced to England in 1844 by Robert Fortune. This is properly called *A. hupehensis* var. *japonica*.

-× *lesseri* (les' sa-ree)	Lesser's Anemone	15–18"/12"
Early Summer	Rose-red Hybrid	Zones 5–8

This hybrid between *A. multifida* and *A. sylvestris* bears 5" wide palmately divided leaves. The 1½–2" diameter flowers are in shades of yellow, white or rose but the species is red to rose colored. It is best for the front of the border

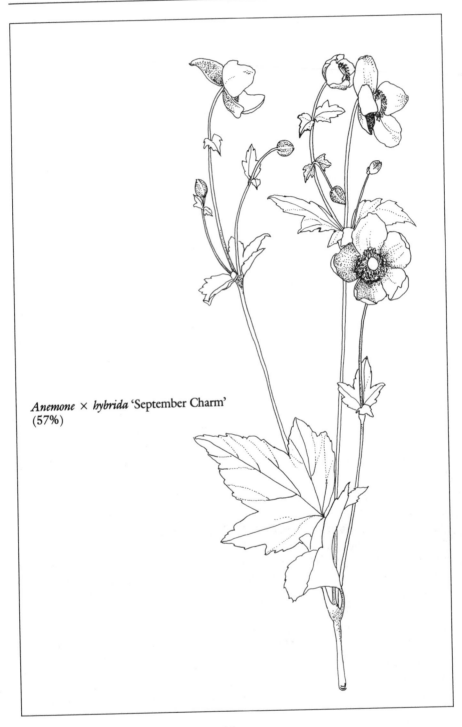

Anemone × *hybrida* 'September Charm'
(57%)

and like other species, should have afternoon shade. The plants are heat tolerant and perform well in the South.

Propagate by division only.

-*magellanica* (ma-jel' lan-i-ca)   Magellan Anemone   6–8"/6"
Early Spring   White   Chile   Zones 2–7

The main claim to fame of this low-growing garden species is its cold tolerance, which allows it to be grown as far north as Alaska. The hairy leaves are much divided and plants are covered with numerous 1" creamy-white flowers on 12" long scapes.

Plants are not difficult to grow in rich soil in sun or light shade.

-*nemerosa* (nem-o-ro' sa)   Wood Anemone   6–8"/8"
Early Spring   White   Europe   Zones 4–8

The foliage is three times divided into deeply toothed linear segments. The flowers are about 1½" wide and often tinged rose on the margins. Plants are single stemmed with leaves borne halfway up the stem, and terminate in a solitary flower. It has a worm-like rhizome which branches extensively. Plants are extremely variable in size, color, and even structure of the flowers. There are usually 5–8 sepals but forms without sepals and others with 50 or more are known. The common flower color is white, but a number of clones have blue or pink flowers and a yellow-flowered variant has also been described. *A. nemerosa* performs best in slightly acid soil (pH 5.5–6.5) containing liberal amounts of peat or leaf mold and in dappled to deep shade.

Cultivars:

Many cultivars and varieties have been described but, unfortunately, few are available to the general gardener.

Blue flowers:
var. *allenii* is about 1' tall and has large (2" diameter), deep lavender-blue flowers. The reverse is streaked with purplish red dots of varying intensity.
'Blue Beauty' is the tallest of the blue forms growing 15–18" tall and bears perfect sky blue cup-shaped blooms. It is the best blue form of the species.
var. *caerulea* is about 6" tall with sky blue ¾" wide flowers. The flower reverse is paler blue.
var. *robinsoniana* has 1½" diameter bright lavender-blue flowers. It grows 12–14" tall and is one of the oldest varieties still offered by perennial growers.

Pink flowers:
var. *rosea* is 10–14" tall and carries nodding 1" wide light rose flowers with a paler reverse. It is slow to increase vegetatively and seed production is poor.

45

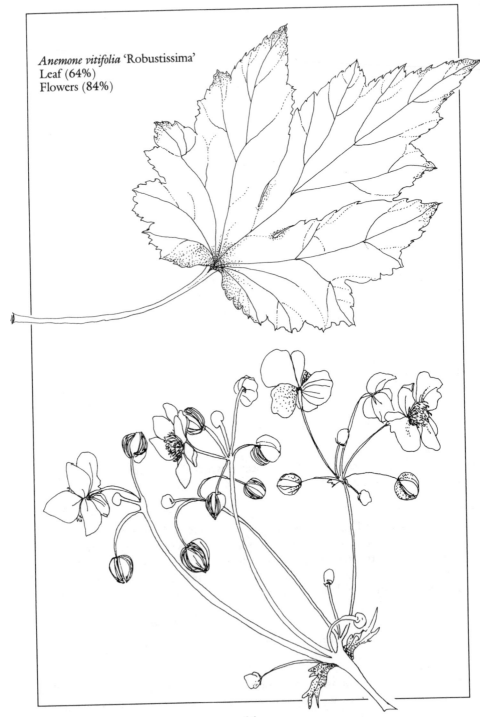

Anemone vitifolia 'Robustissima'
Leaf (64%)
Flowers (84%)

White flowers:

'Lychette' is one of the best white-flowered cultivars and bears large 2" diameter flowers which are pure white above and beneath. There are green blushes around the bases of the 6–8 sepals. Plants grow 20" tall.

'Lady Doneraile' is similar to 'Lychette' but only 10" tall.

'Flore Pleno' stands 10" tall and has double flowers. It is an excellent garden plant.

var. *grandiflora* has the largest flowers, sometimes attaining 3" in diameter. It is vigorous and grows 20" tall in rich soil.

'Vestal' has pure white sepals surrounding a center filled with broad stamen filaments.

Related Species:

A. quinquifolia, American wood anemone, was initially considered to be a variety of *A. nemerosa* (*A. n.* var. *quinquifolia*). It is native from Quebec to Georgia and common in moist rich woodlands. The white flowers are ¾–1" across and appear in spring. This is a lovely addition to the shaded woodland garden.

A. × *semanii* is a yellow-flowered hybrid between *A. nemerosa* and *A. ranunculoides*. Plants have a sprawling habit and the yellow color is variable.

Additional Reading:

Toubol, Ulrich. 1985. Clonal variation in *Anemone nemerosa*. *The Plantsman* 3(3):167–174.

-sylvestris (sil-ves' tris)		Snowdrop Anemone	10–18"/12"
Spring	White	Europe	Zones 4–8

One of the prettiest spring anemones, it combines light green, 3–5 parted leaves with fragrant 1½–2" diameter, dainty, white flowers. The 5-sepaled flowers are slightly nodding when fully open and are solitary on the flower stalk. The lovely flowers give way to interesting white, woolly fruit. *A. sylvestris* requires light soil and partially shaded area for best performance. The major drawback is that it runs freely, particularly in loose soils, and can overrun less aggressive plants. Plantlets, however, are not difficult to remove and gardening friends will be more than happy to accept a few.

Cultivars:

var. *macrantha* has larger and more abundant flowers.

'Flore pleno' is a double-flowered white cultivar but is not nearly as pretty as the species.

Related Species:

A. virginiana, thimbleweed, is a native woodland species with greenish white to white 1" wide flowers. Flowers consist of 5 sepals and appear in early spring. Plants grow about 2' tall and are particularly suited to the woodland garden. Thimbleweed is hardy from zone 3 to 8.

| *-vitifolia* (vit-a-fol' ee-a) | Grape leaf Anemone | 18–36"/18" |
| Fall | White | Nepal | Zones 5–8 |

(Syn. *A. tomentosa*)

As with many of the fall-flowering anemones, confusion as to the true identity of *A. vitifolia* runs rampant. It is, however, an exceptional plant. The leaves are lobed rather than divided as in the forms of *A.* × *hybrida*. One of the best characteristics is the clumping habit. The foliage is outstanding, remaining healthy and dark green from spring to frost, an exceptionally valuable trait. Similarly to *A. sylvestris*, the plants are stoloniferous and dozens of new plantlets emerge in the spring. In the spring, I curse as I remove intruders from the garden but I always leave a few clumps knowing the pleasure I will derive throughout the gardening season.

The single, white flowers have 7–8 sepals and are one of the earliest fall-flowering anemones. Three to five flowers are held on strong scapes 1½–2' above the foliage. Flowering begins in early August, plants are at their best in August and September and continue to flower sporadically into October. White, woolly fruit remains attractive throughout the winter.

Cultivars:

'Robustissima' produces mauve-pink flowers held well above the foliage. It is more winter-hardy than the species and can be grown in zone 3.

Quick Key to Anemone Species

    A. Flowering stems bearing solitary flower
      B. Leaves on flower stem sessile .... *A. coronaria*
      BB. Leaves on flower stem petioled
        C. Fruit woolly .... *A. sylvestris*
        CC. Fruit not woolly, usually smooth
          D. Sepals 9–14.. *A. blanda*
        DD. Sepals usually 5–9
          E. Flowers usually white, sometimes blue .... *A. nemerosa*
          EE. Flowers usually red .... *A.* × *lesseri*
    AA. Flowering stems branched, bearing 3–5 flowers
      B. Plants 6–8", spring flowering .... *A. magellanica*
      BB. Plants taller, summer or fall flowering
        C. Flowers 1–1½" across, flowers early summer .... *A. canadensis*
        CC. Flowers 2–3" across, flowers late summer and fall
          D. Leaves 5-lobed, not divided into 3 leaflets............ *A. vitifolia*
          DD. Leaves not lobed, divided into 3–5 leaflets........ *A.* × *hybrida*

Additional Reading:

Chatto, Beth. 1986. Japanese Anemone. *Horticulture.* 64(10):18–19.

Antennaria (an-ten-ar' i-a)   Pussytoes   Asteraceae

About 15 species are used in gardens, primarily because of the gray foliage. The flowers are dioecious, meaning that male and female occur on separate plants. Flowers are nondescript but are surrounded by dry, chaffy scales which provide the color. However, the gray foliage is the most valuable garden asset. Plants tolerate poor infertile soils and hot, dry locations. They are best suited for the front of the garden.

-dioica (die-o-i' ka)   Common Pussytoes   4-10″/18″
Early Summer   White   Europe   Zones 3–8

Plants send up crowded corymbs of light green flowers with pinkish tips which resemble the toes of your favorite pussycat. The spatulate basal leaves are about 1″ long and gray-green (some call them silver). The foliage becomes less gray-green as the season progresses and may be almost green by midsummer. Plants are stoloniferous and fill in rapidly. If not used as a ground cover, they should be divided every 2 years. Although tolerant of poor soil, good drainage reduces the incidence of root rot.

Cultivars:

var. *minima* is only about 1″ tall and forms a dense carpet.
var. *rosea* has rosy-red flowers and is 8–10″ tall.
var. *tomentosa* has creamy white flower heads on 3″ tall stalks.

Propagate by division in the spring or by seed. The seeds are very small and should be mixed with fine sand to insure even distribution in the seed tray. Provide temperatures of about 72–75°F and maintain consistent soil moisture. Transfer seedlings to 60°F for subsequent growth.

Related Species:

A. rosea (syn *A. dioica* var. *rosea*), rose pussytoes, has fluffy pale pink flowers rising 3–4″ above the permanently gray-green foliage. It is far more decorative than the species.

Anthemis (an' them-is)   Golden Marguerite   Asteraceae

Of the 80 species in the genus, few are worth growing and fewer yet are available in the United States. All have strongly scented, alternately arranged foliage which is divided 2–3 times. Flowers of some species are white (*A. cupaniana, A. nobilis*) but most have yellow or orange flowers borne singly on long stems. All need full sun and well-drained soils for best results. Most tolerate relatively poor soils and, in fact, become too leggy if fertilized heavily. The genus is most suitable for northern climates and while *A. tinctoria* prospers during spring and early summer in southern gardens, it usually collapses into a messy heap making it rather useless south of zone 7.

Propagation is easy by division and is necessary within 2–3 years for all species listed. Seeds germinate readily and are available for some cultivars of *A. tinctoria*.

Quick reference to Anthemis species

	Height (in.)	Foliage color	Flower color
A. cupaniana	6–9	gray-green	white
A. marschalliana	12–18	silver-green	yellow
A. tinctoria	24–36	green	yellow

-cupaniana (kew-pan-ee-ah' na)	Dwarf Camomile	6–9"/36"
Early Summer White	Italy	Zones 5–8

Plants form dense gray-green mats providing wonderful contrasts to other plants in the garden. They are most useful as edging or placed strategically at the front of the border. The 2" diameter white daisies are borne on 6" flower stems above the ferny, aromatic leaves. This species remain relatively compact compared with others. Good drainage reduces rotting problems during cool, rainy winters.

-marschalliana (mar-shal-ee-ah' na)	Marshall Camomile	12–18"/24"
Early Summer Yellow	Caucasus	Zones 5–7

(*A. biebersteiniana*)

Plants are dressed in finely divided silvery foliage atop of which are borne 2–3" diameter golden yellow daisy flowers. The pinnately segmented foliage has long hairs and is silky to the touch. If spent flowers are removed immediately, flowering will continue throughout the summer. This is a better species for the South than *A. tinctoria*.

-tinctoria (tink-to' ree-a)	Golden Marguerite	2–3'/2'
Summer Yellow	Europe	Zones 3–7

This is the most common *Anthemis* available and, with proper culture, is an excellent border plant in northern United States and Canada. The 3" long parsley-like toothed leaves are somewhat downy beneath. The stem is angled and the 1½″ diameter flowers are single, yellow and plentiful.

If grown in rich soil, plants attain 3′ in height and require staking. Cut back the plant severely after flowering to encourage basal growth, and divide every 2 years.

Cultivars:

A. tinctoria and *A. sancti-johannis* (a similar species with deep orange-yellow flowers) have hybridized freely and some of the listed cultivars may be hybrids between them.

'E. C. Buxton' is a superb 2–2½′ tall cultivar which bears off-white daisies with lemon yellow centers.

'Grallagh Gold' ('Beauty of Grallagh') bears yellow orange flowers and is only 2′ tall. It has superseded 'Perry's Gold', an older, taller, golden yellow form.

'Kelway' ('Kelwayi') has bright yellow flowers.

'Moonlight' bears light yellow blossoms.

'St. Johannes' has bright orange flowers. The three previous cultivars are more compact than the species but dwarfer cultivars are still most welcome.

Sharon Illingworth, of Thunder Bay, Ontario, Canada takes cuttings from overwintered young shoots in early spring and roots them in vermiculite, covered with plastic bags. Roots are formed within 14 days and transplants are ready by early June.

Quick Key to Anthemis Species

A. Plants 6–18″ tall, flowers white or yellow
  B. Flowers yellow, foliage silky, usually taller than 12″ ... *A. marschalliana*
  BB. Flowers white, foliage glabrous, usually less than 12″ tall ....
                                          A. cupaniana
AA. Plants 2–3′, flowers yellow to orange .... *A. tinctoria*

Aquilegia (ack-wi-lee′ gee-a)   Columbine   Ranunculaceae

A garden without columbine is simply incomplete. The genus consists of approximately 65 species, many of which are outstanding garden plants. The flowers, which may be nodding or upright, consist of 5 petals with a short broad tube in front and backward projecting spurs. The 5 sepals are often the same color as the petals but may be different in some species and hybrids. The compound pinnate foliage is held on long petioles. All columbines are spring or early summer flowering and prefer a rich soil in light to moderate shade with plenty of moisture. Many species are short lived, particularly if drainage is poor, and should not be counted on for more than three years. Several columbines reseed freely, particularly *A. canadensis* and *A. vulgaris* but the hybrid cultivars do not come true from seed. Natural hybridization occurs among species, so

Aquilegia × *hybrida*
(68%)

they should be planted in separate areas of the garden if one does not want illegitimate seedlings among the parents. In my opinion, the hybrids ('McKana', 'Biedermeier', 'Mrs. Scott Elliot') are not nearly as stately as many of the species; however, they often satisfy the needs of the "bigger is better" gardeners.

Propagation of the species is not difficult from seed, particularly if the seed is fresh. As the seed ages, a deep dormancy develops and a cold treatment (6 weeks at 40°F.) is necessary to insure uniform germination. Many of the named cultivars of the hybrids and the species may be purchased from seed.

Quick Reference to Aquilegia Species

	Flower color (sepals/petals)	*Spurs straight(S) hooked(H) curved(C)*	*Spur length (in.)*	*Flower nodding(N) upright(U)*
A. alpina	blue/ blue(white)	H	¾–1	N
A. caerulea	blue/white	S	1–2	U

	Flower color (sepals/petals)	Spurs straight(S) hooked(H) curved(C)	Spur length (in.)	Flower nodding(N) upright(U)
A. canadensis	yellow/red	C	½–1	N
A. chrysantha	yellow/pale yellow	H	2–2½	U
A. flabellata	white/white	H	¾–1	N
A. × hybrida	various	S	2–6	U
A. longissima	yellow/pale yellow	S	4–6	U
A. vulgaris	blue/blue	H	½–¾	N

-alpina (al-pine' a)		Alpine Columbine		1–3'/2'
Spring	Blue	Switzerland		Zones 3–8

This species belies its name as some of the most vigorous and stately plants in my garden are *A. alpina*. All columbines appear to be taller in the South compared with the same plants in the North and this columbine is only 1–1½' in northern areas but is 2½–3' in the South. The gray-green foliage is deeply divided into linear lobes. The abundant nodding flowers have short hooked spurs, flared 2" wide sepals, and are usually blue throughout although the petal tube may sometimes be white. This is, without question, one of the finest species available for the garden.

Propagation from seed is easy and although a cold treatment is beneficial, it is not necessary.

Cultivars:

var. *alba* is a white form whose flowers contrast well with the gray green foliage.
var. *superba* is larger than the species but otherwise similar.

Related Species:

A. × 'Hensol Harebell' is a hybrid between *A. alpina* and *A. vulgaris* and bears deep blue flowers well into summer.

-caerulea (ce-ru' lee-a)		Rocky Mountain Columbine		1–2'/2'
Spring	Blue/white	Rocky Mountains		Zones 3–8

This long-spurred blue and white-flowered species isn't much different than many of the hybrids of the same color. The flowers are upright and 2–3" across. The Rocky Mountain columbine, however, has been an important parent in the evolution of long-spurred hybrids. The spurs are straight or outward curving and are often tipped with green. Although not as vigorous as many of the other species or hybrids, it is longer lasting, 4–5 years in the garden not being uncommon.

Aquilegia caerulea
(100%)

Cultivars:
   Some catalogs provide an impressive list of cultivars but most belong with the hybrids, of which *A. caerulea* is only one of the parents.

'Mrs. Nicholls' has 3″ wide Cambridge blue outer petals and whitish blue inner petals. It is an old cultivar and, unfortunately, difficult to find.
var. *ochroleuca* (syn. 'Albiflora') has creamy white flowers but is otherwise similar to the species.

Propagation is similar to *A. alpina.*

Related Species:
   A. × *helenae* is a hybrid between *A. caerulea* and *A. flabellata*. It has the blue and white flowers of *A. caerulea* and the short ½″ long spurs of *A. flabellata.*

-canadensis (kan-a-den′ sis)	Canadian Columbine	2–3′/1′
Early Spring Yellow/red	Eastern United States, Canada	Zones 3–8

Aquilegia canadensis
(56%)

This is one of my all-time favorite spring flowering plants. To be sure, they are not as spectacular as many of the hybrids but have a certain grace and elegance that puts them in a class of their own. Native to much of eastern North America, it is found in moist, shady areas. Plants look best in clumps of three or more and reseed to double the area within 2–3 years. The 1½" long nodding flowers appear in early spring and remain in bloom for approximately 6 weeks. The short spurs are slightly curved but do not have the obvious hook seen in *A. vulgaris* or *A. flabellata*. In my garden, plants range from light pink/yellow to blood red/yellow. In climates with cooler nights the sepals are decidedly redder. It has somewhat evergreen foliage in southern climes and new growth begins as soon as temperatures rise above 40°F. Due to its vigor, it is one of the few columbines that can be placed at the back of the bed or used to hide a distracting object such as an electrical box or fire hydrant (although my dog is not fooled and has not yet learned the meaning of respect).

Propagation by seed is easy. Do not be surprised to find plants emerging quite a distance from the initial planting. If fresh seeds are needed, wait until the seeds loosen and turn jet black. Plants will flower the second year from seed. Thinning the plants by transplanting young plants rejuvenates the clump as well as increases numbers.

This species also shows a relative disdain for that voracious enemy of columbine—the leaf miner! Based on observations over the years, there is little doubt that when grown side by side, *A. canadensis* is less susceptible to leaf miner damage than many other species and certainly much less susceptible than the hybrids.

Cultivars:
'Corbett' is a recent selection found near Corbett, Maryland. It has pale yellow flowers.

Related Species:
A. formosa, Formosa columbine, is similar to *A. canadensis* but is taller and has sepals longer than the spurs.

-chrysantha (kris-anth' a)	Golden Columbine	2½–3½'/1'
Spring Yellow	New Mexico	Zones 3–9

The flowers are 2–3" across and the petals are a deeper yellow than the sepals. The long spurs spread away from the flower. This is a tall, loose grower which has been used as one of the parents of the long-spurred hybrids. If provided with sufficient moisture, no staking should be necessary.

Cultivars:
var. *alba-plena* has pale double yellow flowers often tinged with pink and about 1¾" across.
var. *jaeschkanii* and *nana* are dwarf varieties (1½' tall), the former bearing yellow flowers and red spurs while the latter is the same color as the species.
'Silver Queen' has 3" diameter white flowers.
'Yellow Queen' bears 2–3" wide lemon-yellow flowers.

-flabellata (flay-bel-lah' ta)	Fan Columbine	8-18"/1'
Spring White	Japan	Zones 3–9

The leaves are unique in that they are thicker and darker than most species and the round leaf segments are fan-shaped and often overlap. Plants have been described as "squat", however, the term compact is kinder and more accurate. It is an excellent plant for the front of the garden or the rockery. The white nodding flowers are often tinged pink and the spurs are conspicuously hooked. The terminal flower opens first followed by those in the lower axils.

Cultivars:
'Akitensis' has large, rounded, blue-green leaves, above which are short-stemmed blue and white flowers.

'Mini-Star' is a dwarf 6–8" tall cultivar with blue sepals and white petals.

var. *nana* is similar in habit and flower to the above cultivar. They appear to be different names for the same thing.

var. *nana alba* is a white-flowered dwarf variety.

var. *pumila* has mauve sepals and white petals. It grows about 4" tall and is an effective plant for the front of the garden.

All may be raised from seed.

Related Species:

A. bertolonii, alpine rock columbine, is only 4–9" tall and bears rich blue-violet flowers. This is wonderful dwarf columbine for the front of the border or rock garden.

- × *hybrida* (hy-brid' a)	Hybrid Columbine	18"–3'/1'
Spring	Various	Hybrids	Zones 3–9

The hybrids are particularly popular and with good reason. The flowers are large, upright, and in a wide range of colors. There are two generally accepted divisions in this group, long-spurred and short-spurred hybrids. Crosses involving *A. canadensis*, *A. chrysantha*, *A. caerulea*, and *A. formosa* became known as the long-spurred hybrids and are most popular.

The recent upsurge in passion for hybrid columbines began with the McKana hybrids, an All America bronze medal winner in 1955, which brought large flowers and pastel shades to the gardener. McKana hybrids superseded 'Mrs. Scott Elliott', another excellent strain. The breeding of hybrids continues at a furious pace and many excellent cultivars are available today.

Cultivars:

'Biedermeier' is a 9–12" compact blue and white cultivar, but other colors are also available in the mix. Often referred to as nosegay columbine.

'Crimson Star' grows 2½' tall with crimson sepals and white petals.

'Dragonfly' consists of a mix of colors on 18–24" tall plants.

'Musik' ('Music') series, is available in a potpourri of colors. Growing 18–20" tall, plants are excellent for the front or middle of the garden.

'Nora Barlow' is a most interesting and unusual cultivar. Flowers are fully double and look more like small dahlias than columbines. The sepals are reddish pink with white margins and plants grow 2–2½' tall.

'Song Bird', also known as the 'Dynasty' series is the work of the late Charles Weddle, one of this country's finest plant breeders. The plants are 2–3' tall and come in vibrant colors which are truly impressive. One of the finest in the series is 'Cardinal' with rich violet sepals and white petals.

'Spring Song' consists of 3' tall plants with spurs up to 3" long. The flowers are available in mixed colors and some are nearly double.

Many of the older long-spurred hybrids were crossed with *A. vulgaris* to yield the short-spurred hybrids. These are more popular in Europe than in the United States and are smaller in stature and bear smaller flowers.

Many hybrids are available from seed but self-sown seed will not necessarily resemble the parent. Leaf miner can be a serious pest and is more disruptive to the hybrids than to many of the species. If leaf miner becomes very invasive, the easiest contol is to simply cut the plants down to the ground after flowering and destroy the leaves. New growth will soon appear. An all-purpose systemic insecticide may be applied in early spring as a preventative measure but is not effective once the damage is evident.

-longissima (long-gis' si-ma)		Longspur Columbine	2–3'/2'
Early Summer	Yellow	Southern United States	Zones 4–9

The obvious attributes of this species are the very long (4″) slender spurs on pale yellow flowers. A grouping of 5–6 plants makes an impressive display. Unfortunately, though vigorous, it is a short-lived perennial seldom persisting more than 2–3 years.

Cultivars:

'Longissima Hybrids' resulted from crosses among some of the long-spurred hybrids and *A. longissima* and contains different colors.

'Maxistar' is the most common cultivar available and has larger but similar flowers to the species.

-vulgaris (vul-gah' ris)		Granny's Bonnet	1 ½–2'/1'
Early Summer	Blue	Europe	Zones 3–8

So much natural interbreeding among *A. vulgaris* and other species has occurred that it is becoming more and more difficult to find the true *A. vulgaris*. There is a great deal of variability but in general the flowers are blue or violet, with short incurved spurs which end in small knobs. It does not possess the classic statuesque form of *A. alpina*, the sparkle of *A. canadensis*, or the airiness of *A. longissima*. However, it is a durable performer and has persisted well in The State Botanical Garden of Georgia. Although I am surely in the minority, I believe that some of the ugliest flowers in the plant kingdom are the doubles and near triple cultivars of *A. vulgaris*.

Cultivars:

var. *alba* is a good single white flowered form.

var. *nivea* also has single white flowers and pale gray foliage. It is vigorous, often attaining 3' in height. Var. *nivea* is sometimes referred to as Munstead White Columbine, in reference to Gertrude Jekyll's fondness for the plant.

Quick Key to Aquilegia Species

A. Spurs small, generally less than 1″ long
    B. Flower red and yellow, spurs straight or slightly curved .. *A. canadensis*
    BB. Flower not red and yellow, spurs hooked
        C. Leaves divided into 3 rounded and fan-shaped leaflets . .*A. flabellata*
        CC. Leaves deeply divided, leaflets linear to somewhat
            rounded
            D. Flowers 2–3 to a leafy stem, leaflets linear............. *A. alpina*
            DD. Flowers many to stem, leaflets more or less rounded . *A. vulgaris*
AA. Spurs longer than 1″
    B. Flower usually blue and white, spurs 1–2″ long .... *A. caerulea*
    BB. Flower usually yellow, spurs longer
        C. Spurs 2–3″ long, sepals much longer than petals ......*A. chrysantha*
        CC. Spurs 4–6″ long, sepals slightly longer than petals .... *A. longissima*

Additional Reading:

Dewolf, Gordon. 1984. Columbine. *Horticulture* 62(6):12–13.

Arabis (ar′ a-bis)   Rock-cress   Brassicaceae

About 100 species are distributed over the northern hemisphere and most are alpine species. Those cultivated are effective for the front of the garden as they are all less than 12″ tall. The principal species in the trade is *A. albida*, wall rock-cress, but others also have garden value. *A. alpina* has smaller rosettes than *A. albida*, is less hairy, and more compact (especially var. *compacta*). *A. blephar-ophylla* (a native of California) has rose-purple flowers but is quite tender and needs winter protection in much of the country. *A. procurrens* grows to 9″ tall, has entire evergreen leaves, and larger white flowers. *A. soyeri* is about 10″ high with white flowers while *A. sturii* is only 2–3″ tall with glossy leaves and relatively large white flowers. A compact, white flowering species with potential in the United States is *A. ferdinandi-coubergi*. The species has gray-green foliage but the variegated form ('Variegata') is most eye-catching in early spring.

The majority of species are cool climate plants and perform far better in the North than in the South. In hot weather, the centers tend to "melt out" and the stems become long and spindly. I have been successful with *A. procurrens* and *A. albida* in Georgia but neither spread vigorously during the summer. All species should be planted in full sun, preferably in areas where drainage is excellent.

All are easily propagated by division, cuttings, or seed.

-albida (al-bee′ da)		Wall Rock-cress	8–10″/18″
Early Spring	White	Mediterranean	Zones 4–7

(Syn. *A. caucasica*)

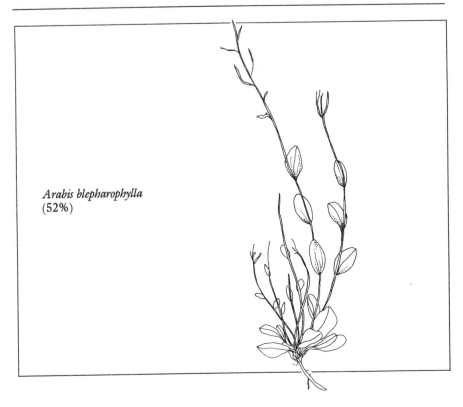

Arabis blepharophylla
(52%)

The plant forms a loose mat and the hairy, succulent foliage is particularly effective climbing over rocks or cascading down walls. The numerous white flowers are held in a loose raceme in early spring. Plants should be cut back severely after flowering or branches will be nude except for the terminal leaves by midsummer. The subsequent year's performance is also enhanced by late spring pruning. In the North, plants make a wonderful spring show and form large clumps which need division every 2–3 years. In north Georgia, flowers are present by the end of February and persist until the end of April. Plant in the fall in the South for enjoyment the following spring (similar to a pansy) as plants tend to decline in the summer heat south of zone 7.

Cultivars:

var. *flore-plena* is an excellent plant because the flowers are mostly sterile and little seed is produced. The lack of seed production results in more persistent flowers.

'Rosabella' has rose-colored flowers which become paler as temperatures rise in the spring.

'Snowball' bears white flowers over 4–6″ tall plants.

'Snow Cap' is a large white-flowered cultivar more ornamental than the species.

var. *variegata* has yellow-white stripes on the leaves. It is an interesting variety but the leaf color detracts from the flowers and the plant is too "busy."

Armeria (ar-meer' i-a)   Sea Thrift   Plumbaginaceae

Armeria consists of approximately 50 species, several suitable for edging, the rockery or front of the garden. Flowers appear in solitary, dense, globe-shaped heads high above the foliage on leafless stems. They tolerate sunny locations but benefit from afternoon shade, particularly in the South. The foliage is tufted, similar to tufts of grass. Few obvious differences exist between many of the species and horticultural classifications are principally based on stature and size of leaves.

Propagation is by division and seed. Seeds placed under warm (70–75°F), moist conditions germinate in 14–21 days.

Quick Reference to Armeria Species

	Height (in)	Leaves > 1" wide	Flower color
A. *juniperifolia*	2–4	No	Lilac
A. *maritima*	6–12	No	Various
A. *plantaginea*	12–18	Yes	Pink

-*juniperifolia* (jew-ni-pe-ri-fo' lee-a)	Pyrenees Thrift	2–4"/6"
Summer	Lilac	Spain	Zones 4–8

(Syn. *A. caespitosa*)

This low-growing plant is occasionally offered by rock garden plant specialists but deserves greater use. It is densely tufted with peculiar 3-angled leaves seldom longer than ¾". The small pale lilac flower heads are only about ⅜" across and held on 1" long scapes. Place in a sunny location and well-drained soil.

Cultivars:

var. *splendens* has flattened leaves and bears bright pink nodding flowers on 2–3" long scapes.

-*maritima* (ma-ri' ti-ma)	Common Thrift	6–12"/10"
Summer	Pink	Europe	Zones 4–8

This diverse species contains over 20 botanical varieties. Common thrift has pink, mauve-red, lilac, or white flowers depending on the variety or cultivar. The specific epithet is derived from the species's salt tolerance and plants may be found growing on coastlines where few others can survive the saline conditions. As the common name implies, it is the most common species of the genus and has undergone extensive selection. The 1–1½" diameter flower head, which

61

consists of many tiny flowers attached to the central flower dome, persists for about 3 weeks in the North, a week less in the South. The plant forms a tuft of narrow, 4–8″ long linear leaves, each of which has one prominent vein running lengthwise. It is relatively easy to grow, however in the South, it should be shaded from afternoon sun.

Armeria maritima is also grown as a flowering potted plant. Approximately 12 weeks are required from seed to produce a flowering plant under greenhouse conditions. No cold treatment is necessary to induce flowering.

Cultivars:

'Alba' is about 5″ tall with a creamy white flower, unusual in this species. It is handsome in the garden but, unfortunately, the white flowers discolor faster than colored flowers and decline more rapidly in heavy rains or winds.

'Dusseldorf Pride' grows 6–8″ tall and carries large wine-red flower heads. It is gaining a large following in this country.

var. *laucheana* produces 20–40 leaves resulting in a highly tufted rosette. It is about 6″ tall and has outstanding deep rose-pink flowers.

'Robusta' is the most vigorous form I have seen. It grows 12–15″ tall and produces 3″ wide pink flower heads.

var. *rubra* is a rather washed out reddish form and is 6–8″ tall.

'Ruby Glow' is 8–10″ tall with ruby-colored flowers similar to 'Dusseldorf Pride'.

'Splendens' is 8–10″ tall and bears intense red flowers, and is one of the most ornamental cultivars.

'Vindictive' is a compact free-flowering cultivar growing 6″ tall and bearing bright rosy-red flowers.

Related Species:

A. × 'Bloodstone' is a 9″ tall hybrid (probably between *A. maritima* and *A. plantaginea*) with exceptionally bright red flowers. This is an excellent plant for the front of the garden.

Seeds sown under high humidity and warm conditions produce seedlings ready to transplant in 3–4 weeks. They can be overwintered in a cool greenhouse or outside and flower in the spring. Division is risky; more plants are damaged than reproduced.

-plantaginea (plan-tag′ i-nee-a)	Plantain Thrift	12–18″/12″
Summer Pink	Central and Southern Europe	Zones 4–9

The pink flower head is approximately ¾″ across and more oblong than the rounded flower shape of *A. maritima*. The leaves are much wider (1–2″ across) than the previous species, resembling those of plantain. They are mostly erect and have 3–7 veins running lengthwise.

Armeria plantaginea
(50%)

Cultivars:

'Bees' Ruby' is one of the most spectacular of the plaintain thrifts. The intense
bright cerise flowers are carried on smooth 18″ tall stems.
var. *leucantha* is a white-flowered form.

Related Species:

A. pseudoarmeria (syn. *A. cephalotes*), pinkball thrift, is similar and has large, 1–2″ diameter, pink flower heads. Except for the youngest leaves, the foliage is limp and flaccid and appears to be in constant need of water.

Quick Key for Armeria Species

    A. Leaves over 1″ wide, lance-shaped, usually fewer than 10 ..*A. plantaginea*
    AA. Leaves less than ¾″ wide, linear, usually more than 10
        B. Plants 6–12″ tall ....*A. maritima*
        BB. Plants 2–6″ tall ....*A. juniperifolia*

Artemisia (are-ti-meez′ ee-a)   Wormwood   Asteraceae

This large genus (about 200 species) contains 4–5′ tall plants which become woody with age, as well as mat-formers which never grow over 18″ tall. Some of the famous members of this noble genus are *A. dracunculus*, tarragon; the symbol of the Old West, the tumbling sagebrush, *A. tridentata*; and the cause of much heartache and headache, absinthe, *A. absinthium*. All species except *A. lactiflora* are characterized by having small, alternate leaves and inconspicuous, often dioecious flowers (male and female flowers on separate plants). The leaves of most species are finely divided, and are highly aromatic when crushed. Smelling crushed leaves is one of the best ways to determine the difference between plants of this genus and gray-leaved plants of closely related genera such as *Senecio*. Many species are from arid regions and are particularly suitable for dry, sunny areas and make few soil demands. In the South, however, where summers are humid and hot, many of the mat-forming species tend to open their centers and fall apart. The shrubby forms are more useful as they can be rejuvenated from time to time with hard pruning. This gives the pruner a wonderful sense of power and teaches the prunee to behave. Most of the ornamental species have silvery-green foliage and are used as a foil for harsh colors in the garden, providing a cool note in hot, sunny weather. Applying fertilizer, particularly nitrogen, causes more harm than good to most species and tall, spindly growth results. Except for *A. lactiflora*, plants are best grown lean and dry.

The method of propagation differs for herbaceous and shrubby species. In general, herbaceous species are divided in the fall or early spring. Cuttings with a small piece of stem attached may also be taken in late summer and placed in a clean bed of peat, sand and peat or vermiculite. This is also the main propagation method for the shrubby species. Take 3–4″ long semi-hardwood cuttings in late summer or fall and place in a cold frame in peat:sand mix (50:50). A rooting hormone is beneficial. Roots should be present in 3–4 weeks. *Artemesia* may be propagated under intermittent mist but cuttings rot quickly so plantlets must be removed as soon as roots form.

Quick Reference to Artemisia Species

	Height (ft)	Woody	Silver foliage
A. abrotanum	3–4	Yes	Yes
A. absinthium	2–3	Yes	Yes
A. lactiflora	4–6	No	No
A. ludoviciana	2–4	No	Yes
A. schmidtiana 'Nana'	½–1	Yes	Yes

-abrotanum (a-broe′ tan-um)   Southernwood, Old Man, Lad's Love   3–4′/18″
Summer   Gray foliage   Southern Europe   Zones 5–8

This species has light gray-green, finely divided, fragrant foliage. Under good cultural conditions, plants grow 4′ tall. The foliage is softly hairy at first and becomes less so later in the season. Some people like to plant it near a garden bench or a path so that the foliage can be brushed against to take advantage of the fragrance. Prune back hard in spring and early summer if necessary, otherwise plants will look weedy by midsummer.

-absinthium (ab-sin′ thee-um)   Wormwood, Absinthe   2–3′/2′
Late Summer   Gray foliage   Europe   Zones 3–9

Many artemesias have been used as herbal remedies and as local curatives for various ailments. A. absinthium was used to cure stomach aches and intestinal worms. Perhaps it is best known, however, as an important ingredient in the preparation of absinthe, a dry, bitter spirit containing 68% alcohol. Scientists discovered that A. absinthium contains absinthin which caused a disorder known as absinthism. Effects of absinthism included delirium, hallucinations, and permanent mental illness. First made by Pernod in 1797, production was banned in Switzerland, then France, but continued to be manufactured in Spain until 1939. The effects of absinthe were graphically displayed by the French painter, Degas, in his famous painting, "Absinthe". Absinthe may still be purchased today, but is an imitation and contains no parts of the absinthe plant.

This woody artemisia has deciduous, finely divided silvery-gray foliage. The 2–5″ long leaves are more silvery than the previous species but not as fragrant. The flowers are tiny, gray and carried on long branched panicles. Plant in a dry, well-drained location in full sun.

Cultivars:

'Lambrook Silver' is about 2½′ tall and more silvery than the type. If necessary, cut back heavily in the summer to discourage floppiness. This is the best artemisia for the North and the gray, finely divided foliage provides an effective break for green-leaved plants in the garden.

65

Related Species:

A. × 'Powis Castle' is a cross between *A. arborescens*, a finely cut but marginally hardy species, and *A. absinthium*. It blends the hardiness of the latter with the beauty of the former. Plants are sterile and uniform. Unfortunately, few plants are available in the United States but it is too fine a plant not to be offered in the near future. Hardiness zones have not yet been established but plants are likely cold hardy to zone 5 and heat tolerant to zone 8. This is one of the finest artemesias I have seen.

A. stelleriana, beach wormwood, is native to eastern North America and resembles annual dusty miller. Plants are cold hardy to zone 3. The white, silky silky divided leaves are densely hairy and plants grow 10–12″ tall. Many ¼″ wide yellow flowers are borne in narrow panicles.

-*lactiflora* (lak-ti-flo′ ra)		White Mugwort	4–6′/4′
Late Summer	Cream	China, India	Zones 5–8

This is the oddball of the group, having green foliage, conspicuous flowers, and growing best in moist areas. The 8–9″ long leaves are pinnately compound and each leaflet is about 3″ long, coarsely lobed and toothed. The rosette is evergreen in milder zones. Under suitable growing conditions, it easily attains 6′ and requires staking. The magnificent cream-white flowers are borne in large 1–2′ long plume-like panicles and persist well into the fall. This is an ideal background plant whose late season flowers provide a nice change from the daisies so abundant at that time. It is also useful for cut flowers. Plants do best in sunny locations and, unlike other species, prefer moist soil.

Propagate by division every 3–4 years.

-*ludoviciana* (loo-do-vik-ee′ aye-na)		White Sage	2–4′/2′
Late Summer	Gray foliage	North America	Zones 4–9

This deciduous, non-woody species provides compact growth and good silver foliage color. It differs from most other gray-leaved species in having entire, rather than dissected leaves. The 2–4″ long leaves are white-woolly beneath and neath and almost hairless above. The stems are white and branched towards the top. The gray flowers are produced in late summer on narrow, branched, compound panicles. The roots run underground, resulting in large clumps. This is an excellent species for southern gardens as it tolerates warm temperatures, is less prone to disease, and grows back quickly after pruning.

Cultivars:

'Latiloba' has wide (3″ across) gray-green leaves with 3–5 lobes near the ends. It stands 12–24″ high and makes an effective ground cover. It is not as heat tolerant as the species.

'Silver King' is the best cultivar and is more compact, hardy to zone 3, and offers excellent deep silver foliage. The flowers are mostly male and the plumes sport red fall color not found in the species.

'Silver Queen' produces sparse female flowers and silvery leaves with deeply cut jagged margins.

Propagate by division in late summer or fall and cuttings in late spring and summer.

Related Species:

A. purshiana, pursh sagebrush, is similar to 'Silver King' but only 2–3' tall with narrower, less divided leaves. It also flowers about a week earlier and more profusely. It is listed as a synonym of *A. ludoviciana* by some authorities.

-schmidtiana (shmit-ee' aye-na)	Silvermound Artemisia	15–24"/18"
Summer Gray foliage	Japan	Zones 3–7

The species is about 2' tall but seldom seen in gardens. It is represented by the dwarf form 'Nana' and usually sold as 'Silver Mound'. The finely cut silver foliage grows in a silky cushion with small, drooping yellow flowers. The handsome mounding habit has resulted in this plant being immensely popular in the North. The mounded shape is retained most of the season in the Northeast and Canada but, unfortunately, it "melts out" in hot summers and is disappointing in zones 7–8. Melt out also occurs in the Midwest, only later. The center of the plant opens and any semblance of a mound is lost, making it a particularly poor choice for southern gardens. It is rather woody at the base and cuttings consisting of the leaf, petiole and a piece of the stem should be taken in the summer.

Quick Key to Artemisia Species

    A. Leaves green or nearly so
        B. Leaves coarsely divided, slightly aromatic, plants 4' or
            taller, flowers showy .... *A. lactiflora*
      BB. Leaves finely divided, fragrant, plants 3–4' tall, flowers not
            showy .... *A. abrotanum*
   AA. Leaves silvery, pubescent
        B. Leaves entire, or lobed at ends, not divided .... *A. ludoviciana*
      BB. Leaves divided
          C. Leaves coarsely divided into lobes, plants 2–3' tall ... *A. absinthium*
         CC. Leaves finely divided, plants 6–12" tall .... *A. schmidtiana* 'Nana'

Additional Reading:

Mitchell, Irene. 1978. The plant and painting that shocked Paris. *Horticulture* 56(4):32–37.

Sheldon, Elisabeth. 1987. Shades of gray. *Horticulture* 65(12):37–43.

Arum (ar′ um)　　　　　Arum　　　　　Araceae

Approximately twelve species belong to this genus and all are characterized by a spadix consisting of unisexual flowers, the females at the base, the males above them and sterile flowers between. The spathe is the showy part and envelops the spadix in the spring. More and more woodland species are being offered to gardeners for use in shady, moist areas and some of the most handsome foliage to be found on any garden plant belongs to *A. italicum* 'Pictum'.

-italicum (ee-ta′ li-kum)	Italian Arum	12–20″/18″
Spring　　Creamy white	Southern Europe	Zones 6–9

Arum italicum is a woodland species native to Italy, the Mediterranean and south to the Canary Islands. The habit is unusual to most gardeners in that new foliage appears late in the fall (November in my garden) and remains over winter. The leaves are followed by creamy flowers in spring which look like small Jack-in-the-Pulpit (*Arisaema triphyllum*) flowers. They disappear in summer and are replaced with strong columns of bright orange-red berries as ornamental as any part of the plant. Although most at home in the woodland garden, plants are particularly handsome at the front of any shade area. The 12″ long, hastate (like an arrowhead) leaves are at their best in late fall and winter. For this reason, it is an exceptional plant for the winter garden. Combined with the winter foliage of *Bergenia* or *Heuchera*, and the architectural forms of ornamental grasses such as *Miscanthus*, the garden may be enjoyed 12 months of the year.

Cultivars:

'Marmoratum' has broad gray-green leaves marbled with splotches of yellow-green. The leaves are larger than those of the more common 'Pictum' and the yellow-green spathe is purple at the base. Unfortunately, it is difficult to find in the trade.

'Pictum' is the best form of this species and has dark green leaves which are narrowly spear shaped and conspicuously blotched with gray and cream. It grows approximately 18″ tall, spreads by tuberous roots, and is an excellent but slow growing ground cover. In the fall, shiny clustered spikes of bright orange berries brighten the landscape.

Propagate the species and cultivars by division after leaves appear in fall. Seed of the species must be stratified (provided with cool, moist conditions) in the fall and left until spring at which time some germination may occur. Seed often requires a year to germinate.

Aruncus (ah-run′ kus)　　　　Goat's Beard　　　　Rosaceae

Only two or three species occur and each possesses excellent qualities for the garden. Male and female flowers occur on different plants (dioecious) and are carried in tall showy panicles. The light green foliage is bipinnately compound.

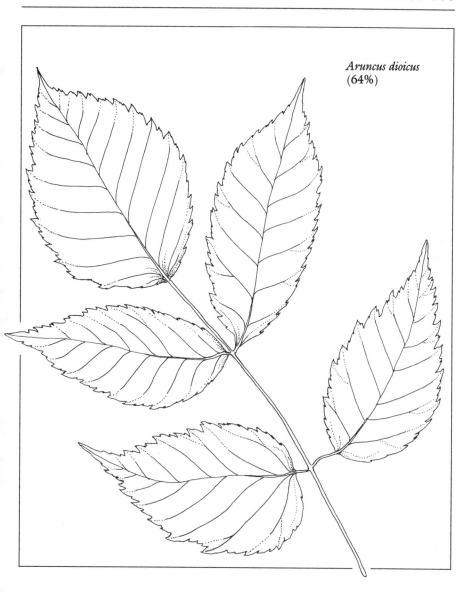

Aruncus dioicus
(64%)

Shade and moisture are necessary for best growth and flowering in southern areas of the country (zone 5 to 7), although plants may be grown in full sun further north. If placed in too much sun or too little moisture, the leaf margins turn brown and crispy.

Propagate by division in the spring or by seed collected fresh and placed in a warm (70–75°F), humid area. Germination will occur in two to three weeks. If seed is old, place at 40°F for about 4 weeks prior to putting them in the warmth.

-dioicus (die-o-eye' kus)	Goat's Beard	4–6'/6'
Late Spring Creamy white	Europe, Asia, North America	Zone 3–7

(Syn. *A. sylvester, Spiraea aruncus*)

This is a spectacular plant when given sufficient moisture, dappled shade, and plenty of room. The 2–3' long leaves are tri-pinnately compound and each lanceolate leaflet is sharply doubly serrated. In the northern states, plants are far more tolerant of afternoon sun than in the South. I have tried to grow goat's beard in Athens, Georgia for many years and have not succeeded. It is either too hot or I can't provide sufficient moisture or both. Because of these experiences, I don't recommend its use south of zone 6 (although it will survive in zone 7 and 8). Where well grown, however, large plume-like compound panicles of small (1/8") creamy flowers appear in late spring and provide a magnificent sight. Plants occur as male or female forms and the male plumes are more feathery and upright than the drooping seed-ladened females. Plants form large clumps in rich soils but unfortunately many of today's smaller gardens can not afford the space.

Cultivars:

'Kneiffii' is only 3' tall with foliage deeply cut into threadlike segments. Although not as dramatic, it is a useful, handsome plant for smaller areas

Related Species:

A. aethusifolius, native to Korea, is a relative newcomer to the perennial trade and is a true miniature. It attains a mature height of 8–12", has deeply cut leaves and a panicle of creamy white flowers. Plants tolerate partial shade, and are most at home in the rock garden or the front of the border.

A. astilboides is also a smaller version of the species, and although difficult to find in the American trade, is worth the hunt. The leaves are more deeply serrated and the inflorescence less compond. The main difference compared to *A. dioicus*, however, is that it is only 18–24" tall.

Asarum (a-sar' um)	Wild Ginger	Aristolochiaceae

Asarum contains about 60 species, most of which are native to north temperate areas. The common name comes from the ginger-like smell that arises from the roots when bruised or cut. The plant which provides true ginger, however, is *Zingiber officinale*. Wild ginger spreads by rhizomes and is generally less than 1' tall. All species prefer woodland conditions of slightly acid soils, heavy shade, constant moisture and good drainage. They are used mainly as shade tolerant ground covers and the urn-shaped flowers borne underneath the glossy foliage are seldom seen by the uninitiated. Some taxonomists have split this genus into 2 main sections, placing evergreen species in the genus *Hexastylis* and the deciduous species in *Asarum*. I have retained all species under *Asarum*.

70

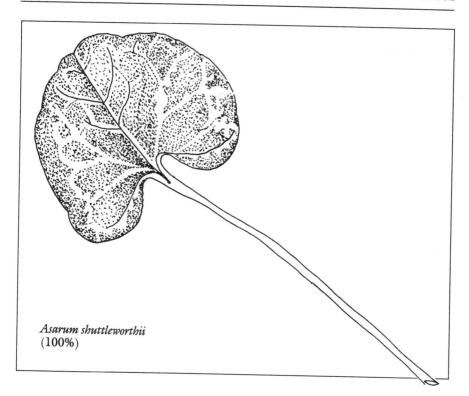

Asarum shuttleworthii
(100%)

Species may be propagated by seed although the most foolproof method is division in spring or early fall.

-europaeum (eur-o' pay-um)   European Wild Ginger   6–8″/8″
Spring   Dull brown   Europe   Zones 4–7

This is an excellent ground cover for the woodland garden. The 2–3″ wide heart-shaped leaves are leathery, glossy dark green, and evergreen in most areas. Although the flowers are not particularly showy, it is fun to poke around under the foliage and discover the distinctive urn-shaped blooms. Being hidden from flying insects, the flowers are pollinated by ground hugging insects. This is one of the hardiest species and easiest to establish in the North, but does not tolerate high temperatures associated with southern summers. Plants require moist, shady conditions.

Related Species:

A. canadense, Canadian wild ginger, has 2 large glossy, deciduous leaves up to 7″ across held on 6–12″ pubescent petioles. The rhizomes are more aromatic than those of *A. europaeum* and have been used as a substitute for ginger. Plants are more heat tolerant then *A. europaeum* and revel in the heat of zone 8.

71

A. hartwegii, Sierra wild ginger, is a western representative, native to Oregon and California. The green leaves have conspicuous silver veining and it has become known as cyclamen leafed wild ginger. Excellent drainage is necessary.

A. shuttleworthii (also known as *Hexastylis shuttleworthii*), mottled wild ginger, has beautiful mottled evergreen foliage. Plants are not as winter hardy, but are more heat tolerant than the previous species. It is native from Virginia to Alabama and Georgia. 'Callaway' (selected at Callaway Gardens, Pine Mountain, GA) is more vigorous and the leaves are even more mottled than the species.

A. virginianum (syn. *Hexastylis virginianum*) is native to Virginia and the Carolinas and has evergreen, heart-shaped, 2–3″ long dark green leaves with white spots on the upper side.

Additional Reading:

Scott, B. 1988. Wild ginger. *American Horticulturist* 67(4): 11–14.

Asclepias (as-klee′ pe-as)   Silkweed, Milkweed   Asclepidaceae

A. tuberosa, butterfly weed, is the only species worthy of inclusion in the formal garden although wild flower purists get excited about one or two others.

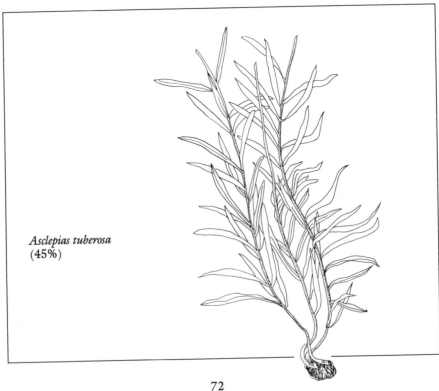

Asclepias tuberosa
(45%)

Anyone who has farmed and tried to rid the fields of the common milkweed, *A. syriaca*, knows how tenacious members of this genus can be. The inflated pods of the common milkweed are occasionally used as dried ornaments. Rather than growing it for the pods, collect them from roadside weeds or the fields of your friendly neighborhood farmer. He will be most appreciative. All members of this genus have milky sap, inflated seed pods (follicles), and silky seeds.

| *-tuberosa* (tew-be-ro' sa) | Butterfly Weed | 2–3'/2' |
| Spring   Orange | Eastern North America | Zones 4–9 |

The orange flowers of butterfly weed are so vibrant that they seem to jump out at you. There is a good deal of variation in flower color and I've seen plants ranging from pure yellow to dark red at the edge of woods in north Georgia. Mature plants do not transplant well, and removing plants from the wild should not be attempted. The 4–4½" long leaves more or less spiral up the stiff stems and are spaced closely together. The stems are topped by umbels of many small flowers in spring and continue to bloom at least six weeks in the garden. Flowers have a good vase life when cut and although some gardeners flame the base of the stem, vase life will not decline if flameing is not accomplished. Cutting the mature flowers also results in additional flowering three to four weeks later. Flowers allowed to remain give way to narrow 3–6" long ornamental follicles which provide an additional dimension to the plant. They should be removed before they split because the seeds spill out at that time, and ornamental soon

Asclepias tuberosa
(64%)

gives way to messy. Butterfly weed is slow to emerge in the spring and patience is a must.

Seed germination is highly variable and results as low as 5% to as high as 90% have been reported. If fresh seed is collected, cleaned, and sown immediately, 50–80% germination will result. Old seeds, or seeds that are purchased, germinate more uniformly if sown in a well aerated soil mix, watered well, covered with plastic, and placed in the refrigerator or other cool place for about six weeks. A good deal of variation in flower color results in seed sown material. Root cuttings can be used to increase colored forms which have merit (See *Anemone × hybrida*).

Related Species:

A. incarnata, swamp milkweed, has alternate 3–6″ long leaves and clusters of white and pink flowers atop 2–4′ tall plants in late spring and summer. Performance is best under moist soils but well-drained sites are also tolerated.

Additional Reading:

Borland, Jim. 1987. Clues to butterfly milkweed germination emerge from a literature search. *American Nurseryman* 165(3):91–92, 94–96.

Aster (as′ tur)   Aster   Asteraceae

This large genus consists of over 600 species and while many are weed-like, horticultural improvements have greatly enhanced the garden value of asters in recent years. Many species native to the United States have common names such as New York Aster and New England Aster and perhaps it is this familiarity with the native asters that have held back the popularity of the named cultivars in this country. Although several useful species are native to the U.S., credit for much of the improvement must be given to English and German nurserymen. Many selections were raised in the late 1890's and new ones continue to be introduced every year.

The leaves are alternate and the daisy flowers are borne either singly or in multiple flowered panicles or corymbs. Species and their cultivars range in height from 6″ (*A. alpinus*) to the giant 8′ *A. simplex*, however, so much breeding work has been accomplished with *A. novi-belgii* that cultivars of that species alone are now available in heights from 6″ to 6′. Flower color of most species is white or in the blue-purple range (although many pink cultivars have been selected). An exception is *A. linosyris*, an 18″ tall, late summer flowering species whose bright yellow flowers have resulted in the common name of Goldilocks.

Division is the easiest means of propagation. The outside portions of the clumps should be split and replanted in early spring or fall. The center of stronger growing species become bare within 1–2 years and if not divided every few years, plants will degenerate and lose their ornamental usefulness (an exception to this is *A. amellus*, which should be left undisturbed for 2–3 years). Terminal cuttings of most species can also be rooted. Collect 1–2″ long cuttings with two to three leaves in the spring or early summer and insert in a clean mixture of sand and perlite and rooting will occur within 2–3 weeks. This is the best and sometimes the only method to clean up prized plants which suffer from aster wilt caused by *Verticillium vilmorinii*. Since the fungus resides in the root-stock, terminal cuttings of new growth may result in healthy plants. *A. novi-belgii* types are most susceptible while *A. novae-angliae* is least affected. The other major problem of New England and New York asters is powdery mildew (*Erysiphe cichoracearum*). Some cultivars are more susceptible than others but fungicides should be applied to all cultivars starting around July 1 to reduce infection.

Asters are useful for fall flowering but some flower in the summer and may reflower in the fall if spent blossoms are removed immediately. Tall varieties need staking and should be avoided if one is anti-staker. This is still a major drawback to asters, particularly the New England and New York types. Regardless of where they are grown, most cultivars must have support or they look shabby. Staking can be reduced and even eliminated in many medium size cultivars if plants are grown in full sun and pinched back once or twice in spring and early summer. This is a good practice for all tall flowering plants and results in more compact, dense plants. Pinch back 2–3" of growth from each growing point no later than June 15 in the North and July 1 in the South or you may remove the developing flowers.

Plants which are sold under the name of China aster are *Callistephus chinensis*. These are beautiful plants but are annuals and not to be confused with the perennial asters.

Quick Reference to Aster Species

	Height (ft)	Flowers single or in clusters	Flowering time
A. alpinus	½–¾	Single	Summer
A. amellus	2–2½	Single, Cluster	Early Fall
A. divaricatus	1–2	Cluster	Summer
A. × frikartii	2–3	Cluster	Early Fall
A. novae-angliae	4–6	Cluster	Early Fall
A. novi-belgii	1–6	Cluster	Early Fall
A. sedifolius	2–3	Cluster	Fall
A. tataricus	3–6	Cluster	Late Fall
A. thompsonii	1–3	Cluster	Early Fall
A. tongolensis	1–2	Single	Summer

-alpinus (al-pine′ us)   Alpine Aster   6–9"/1'
Summer   Purple   Europe   Zones 4–7

This is an excellent front of the garden specimen for cooler areas of the country. It is a variable plant bearing solitary, 1–2" diameter purple flowers with

75

yellow centers. The foliage is gray-green in the spring but loses the gray color in the summer, particularly in the South. It is not tolerant of hot, humid climates and thus is not a particularly long-lasting species, 3–4 years being an average life span.

Cultivars:

var. *albus* has white flowers but is a rather spindly grower.
'Dark Beauty' has dark blue, almost purple flowers and is similar to var. *superbus*.
'Goliath' is so called because of the 2½–3″ diameter light blue flowers. It is taller than the species and grows to 15″.
'Happy End' offers rose-pink flowers and a compact habit.
'Wargrave Variety' has pale pink flowers which, unfortunately, tend to fade in bright sun.

Seed germinates readily when placed in moist, warm (70–75°F) conditions.

-amellus (a-mel′ lus)		Italian Aster	2–2½′/2′
Early Fall	Purple	Italy	Zones 5–8

Plants have pubescent stems and leaves which produce a rough appearance and feel. The leaves are entire, sessile and about 5″ long. The large, 2–2½″ diameter purple flowers consist of 20–30 narrow petals with orange-yellow centers. They are borne singly or in dense corymbs in early fall and bloom continuously to frost. The species itself, however, is seldom seen and improvements have been made to reduce height, increase color range, and reduce floppiness. Most of the new cultivars are 1–2′ tall and do not need staking unless overfertilized or if temperatures become exceptionally high. It is a particularly fine species for zones 5 and 6 and is good, but not as spectacular, in the heat and humidity of zones 7 and 8. *A. amellus* is one of the parents of the hybrid *A.* × *frikartii*.

Cultivars:

'King George' is an exceptionally fine selection offering deep purple flowers on 2–3′ tall stems. It is floriferous and requires no support.
'Nocturne' is often cited as a pink-flowered form but appears to be more bluish purple than pink. Although not as floriferous as 'King George', it is nevertheless a good selection.
'Pink Zenith' and 'Lady Hindlip' bear pink flowers with yellow centers on 2–3′ tall stems. The former is darker pink and shorter (2′) than the latter.
'Rudolph Goethe' was selected in 1914 and is still popular today. It bears violet flowers on 2–3′ tall stems.
'Sonia' is probably the best pink-flowered form and produces many 2″ diameter rich pink flowers with yellow centers on plants 1–2′ tall.

Related Species:

A. × alpellus is a cross between *A. alpinus* and *A. amellus*. Plants are 12–15″ tall and bear blue ray flowers around orange centers. It is sometimes offered as *A*. 'Triumph'.

-divaricatus (di-var-i-cah′ tus)		White Wood Aster	1–2′/3′
Summer	White	North America	Zones 4–8

(Syn. *A. corymbosus*)

This spreading aster is native from Maine to Georgia but is seen far more in European gardens than in this country. It bears many thin, purple-black, cascading branches, at the end of which are corymbs of small (¾″ diameter), star-like white flowers with yellow centers. The blossoms may be small, but they are so plentiful that the plant is covered with clouds of flowers from mid-July through September. The leaves are about 3″ long, heart shaped, and coarsely toothed.

It is one of the few asters which tolerates shade and may be planted at the front of the border to grow through other plants. Flowers are particularly pretty running in and among bergenias, a combination made popular by Gertrude Jekyll, the Grand Dame of English gardening. In hot summers, in the Midwest

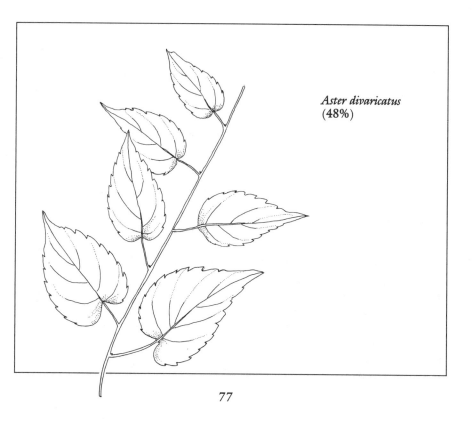

Aster divaricatus
(48%)

77

Aster × *frikartii* 'Monch'
(92%)

and further south, it tends to be leggy. Stems can be cut back to 12″ in mid-June.

Division, terminal cuttings taken in the spring, or seed sown in the spring or fall are appropriate methods of propagation.

- × *frikartii* (fri-kart′ ee-eye)	Frikart's Aster	2–3′/3′
Summer	Lavender	Hybrid	Zones 5–8

A. × *frikartii* was raised in Switzerland around 1920 and is the result of crossing *A. amellus* × *A. thompsonii*. The large flowers of *A. amellus* combined with the long flowering season of *A. thompsonii* provide one of the best and most popular asters today. Interestingly, it is a little taller than either parent. The dark green, pubescent foliage is mildew resistant and remains disease free throughout the season. The 2–3″ diameter, lavender-blue flowers start in late June in the South, late July further north and continue for about eight weeks. Plants should be placed in full sun and fertilized sparingly.

Cultivars:

Four selections were named from the original hybrid, but 'Eiger' and 'Jungfrau' are seldom seen in the United States. 'Monch' and 'Wonder of Staffa', however, are easily obtained.

'Monch' is reputed by many garden authorities to be the best *A*. × *frikartii* clone. It bears lavender blue flowers and stands 2½–3' tall with a 3' spread. Plants differ from 'Wonder of Staffa' in being less prone to falling, and having darker blue flowers.

'Wonder of Staffa' supposedly has lighter blue flowers than 'Monch' but the differences between these cultivars have been overstated. It is a challenge, to say the least, to distinguish between the flowers of each cultivar even when placed side by side. 'Wonder of Staffa' may be slightly taller (although I have seen little difference) than 'Monch' and in warm climates might require more support. Perhaps differences in cultivars have been obscured over the years as the demand continued to rise. It is possible that some material is seed propagated to keep up with demand or that stock blocks have been mixed up on occasion. Nevertheless, both cultivars are excellent garden plants and well worth the space in any sunny garden.

Seeds of Frikart's aster are available but the resultant flowers occur in many different shades of lavender and blue. Division is most appropriate.

-novae-angliae (no'vay-ang' glee-aye)		New England Aster	4–6'/4'
Late Summer	Violet-purple	Eastern United States	Zones 4–8

This common wild flower is one of the largest and prettiest in the genus but is seldom seen, having been superseded by improved cultivars. The entire, 4–5" long leaves are numerous, very hairy and clasp the stem. The flowers are 1½–2" across and consist of 40–50 ray flowers surrounding a yellow center. They are useful for cutting and last longer in water than those of *A. novi-belgii*, New York aster.

Cultivars:

'Alma Potschke' is an excellent 3–4' tall bright rose selection. The flowers are 1–2" across and have slightly curled petals. It is more compact (but still requires support) than other selections and less prone to topple.

'Barr's Pink' has 1½" wide bright rose-pink, semi-double flowers on 4' tall stems.

'Harrington's Pink' was developed by Mr. Millard Harrington of Williamsburg, Iowa, and is one of the most popular asters today. This 3–5' tall plant bears large (1½" diameter) salmon-pink flowers and is one of the latest to bloom.

'Lyle End Beauty' has lovely cerise flowers but grows 4–5' tall and must be supported.

'Mt. Everest' is 3' tall with good, clear white flowers.

Aster novae-angliae 'September Ruby'
(78%)

'September Ruby' has 1″ diameter, deep ruby red flowers on 3–5′ high stems. If planted in rich soils or overfertilized, heights up to 5′ are not uncommon for this cultivar. Although classified as a late bloomer, flowering begins in late May in north Georgia and continues through late June. If the flowers are removed, it blooms again in September. Flowering is 3–4 weeks later in the Northeast but seldom do flowers peak in the fall. This is true with many so called fall-flowering asters.
'Treasure' is about 4′ tall with violet-blue flowers.

-novi-belgii (no′ vee-bel-gee′ eye)   New York Aster, Michaelmas Daisy   1–6′/3′
Late Summer   Violet   Eastern United States   Zones 4–8

There are literally hundreds of cultivars of this common roadside weed. Some of the common traits include smooth or nearly glabrous leaves which clasp the stem and flowers with 15–25 ray flowers. The flowers are not as good for cutting as the New England asters but provide excellent color in late summer and fall. They are called Michaelmas daisies because they bloom around September 29, St. Michael's Day, in the British Isles.

Cultivars:

Dwarf cultivars (less than 15″ tall). Many of the dwarf cultivars are excellent for the front of the garden and, best of all, require no staking.
'Audrey' bears 1″ wide lilac flowers on 12″ tall plants.
'Buxton's Blue' is only 4–6″ tall but produces many small dark blue flowers.
'Jenny' bears red flowers on 12″ tall stems.
'Prof. Kippenburg' is 9–12″ tall and carries lavender-blue semi-double flowers. This excellent cultivar has withstood the test of time.
'Snowsprite' has semi-double white flowers with a yellow center. It grows 15″ tall.

Medium cultivars (less than 4′). Many require staking, especially those with large flowers.
'Ada Ballard' has double lavender-blue flowers atop 3′ tall stems.
'Arctic' bears double white flowers.
'Eventide' produces 2″ wide semi-double, violet-blue flowers on 3–4′ high plants.
'Ernest Ballard' has reddish pink semi-double flowers up to 3″ wide. Many of the medium size cultivars are the result of the work of Mr. Ernest Ballard of Colwall, Malvern, England. One of his traits was breeding large (1–3″ diameter) flowers on 2 ½–3′ tall plants. Most Ballard family members have at least one cultivar as their namesake.
'Patricia Ballard' has semi-double rose pink flowers.

Tall cultivars (over 4′). I recommend none for the South and hesitate to recommend them at all. They are too tall for most gardens, require extensive support, and can become invasive. If grown well, however, they are show stoppers. They are exceptional in flower and can be grown as long as they are pinched at least once in the spring or early summer and then supported.
'Cardinal' has deep rosy-red flowers surrounding a yellow center.
'Climax' is a 5′ tall giant with outstanding large (3–4″ across), light blue flowers in early fall.
'Fellowship' bears large clear semi-double pink flowers on 4–5′ tall stems.
'White Lady' is 5–6′ tall with clear white flowers and an orange-yellow center.

Propagate all cultivars by division.

Related Species:

A. × *versicolor*, bicolor aster, resulted from a cross between *A. laevis*, smooth aster, and *A. novi-belgii*. Plants grow 3′ tall with ray flowers which open blue or white and change to purple.

-sedifolius (say-di-fo' lee-us)		Rhone Aster	2–3'/3'
Fall	Lilac	Southern Europe	Zones 4–7

(Syn. *A. acris*)

This relatively unknown aster has rough hairy, linear, entire leaves and many stems resulting in a bushy habit of growth. Each stem terminates in a corymb of 30–40 small (1–1¼"across) starry blossoms. The individual flowers are not particularly ornamental but the plants are literally covered in a sea of lavender blue. The ray flowers are widely spaced around the yellow center.

Plants tolerate most soils, assuming drainage is adequate, and should be grown in full sun.

Cultivars:

'Nana' is the most common form, the species seldom being seen anymore. It is 18"–2' tall and the flowers are only slightly smaller (1") than those of the species.

Division is the surest and easiest means of propagation but seed sown and placed at 70–75°F under constant moisture germinates readily.

-tataricus (ta-tar' ri-cus)		Tatarian Daisy	3–6'/3'
Late Fall	Blue	Siberia	Zones 4–8

This tall upright plant seldom requires stalking. Although it will reach heights of 6' or more, seldom does growth exceed 3–4' the first year. The erect stems are covered with straight bristly hairs (hispid) and the entire, lanceolate leaves are large (the basal leaves are up to 6" wide and 2' long), and sessile. Flower stems branch near the top resulting in many blue to purple ray flowers with yellow centers. One of the best features of this aster is its late flowering. Although many asters flower until frost, they often look tired and worn out. This species does not start flowering until late September or early October and still looks fresh in November. It is an excellent late-flowering garden plant.

Related Species:

A. macrophyllus, bigleaf aster, native to the eastern United States, is about 4' tall and flowers in August and September. It produces 8–10" long serrated, heart-shaped (cordate) basal leaves with long petioles. The uppermost leaves become less cordate and are sessile at the top. The 1" diameter pale blue to violet flowers are held in a rounded many-flowered corymb. It does not flower as late as *A. tataricus*.

-thomsonii (tom-son' ee-eye)		Thompson's Aster	1–3'/2'
Late Summer	Lilac	Western Himalayas	Zones 4–9

The leaves are coarsely toothed and the 1–2" diameter lilac flowers are borne on long slender flower stems. One of the outstanding characteristics is its long

82

Aster tataricus
(45%)

blooming period and, as one of the parents of *A.* × *frikartii*, this trait was passed on to that hybrid.

Cultivars:

'Nanus' is only 12–18″ tall and is essentially the only form of *A. thomsonii* represented in gardens. It resembles a dwarf *A.* × *frikartii*. The 1–3″ long, pointed foliage is gray-green and the starry, blue flowers are about 1–1½″ in diameter. This is an excellent plant for the front of the garden where late color is desired.

-tongolensis (ton-go′ len-sis)   East Indies Aster   1–2′/1′
Summer   Violet Western China   Zones 5–8

(Syn. *A. subcoeruleus*)

Rosettes of dark green hairy leaves and solitary, 2″ diameter violet-blue flowers with bright orange centers are characteristics of this aster. The strong stems carry the flowers well and no support is necessary. Plants are stoloniferous and significant clumps can form under suitable conditions. Unfortunately, this

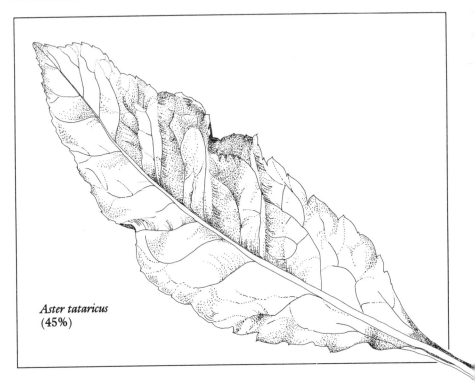

Aster tataricus
(45%)

summer-flowering aster is not long-lived and survives only 2–3 years in the South, perhaps a little longer in zone 5.

Divide after flowering to keep plants vigorous.

Cultivars:

'Berggarten' has 2–3″ diameter violet-blue flowers with an orange-yellow eye. Flowers appear in June.

'Napsbury' has lovely blue flowers with orange centers.

'Wartburg Star' bears 1½″ diameter lavender-blue flowers with orange centers.

Related Species:

A. yunnanensis, Yunnan aster, is native to western China. Plants are not stoloniferous and have a habit similar to *A. alpinus*. They bear pale blue to mauve flowers with yellow centers on 9–12″ tall plants.

Quick Key to Aster Species

    A. Flowers usually solitary on flower stem

       B. Plant 6–9″, stem leaves lanceolate ....*A. alpinus*

      BB. Plant taller than 1′

      C. Leaves coarsely hairy, leaves and stem rough .... *A. amellus*
     CC. Leaves often pubescent, but not rough............... *A. tongolensis*
  AA. Flowers numerous on flower stem
    B. Leaves entire, ray flowers blue or lilac
      C. Over 10 flowers per stem .... *A. sedifolius*
     CC. Less than 5 (sometimes only 1) flower per stem......... *A. amellus*
    BB. Leaves toothed
      C. Base of upper stem leaves clasping stem
        D. Leaves pubescent or rough..................... *A. novae-angliae*
       DD. Leaves smooth or nearly so .... *A. novi-belgii*
     CC. Base of stem leaves petioled, not clasping.
        D. Plant dwarf (at least garden cultivar),
          1–1½′ tall .... *A. thompsonii* 'Nanus'
       DD. Plant 2–3′ tall
         E. Ray flowers blue............................. *A.* × *frikartii*
        EE. Ray flowers white........................... *A. divaricatus*

Astilbe (as-til′ bee)   False Spirea   Saxifragaceae

Astilbes have enjoyed immense popularity in recent years and are excellent plants for shady, moist conditions. If grown in areas to their liking, they are plants of incomparable beauty. The individual flowers are small and without much merit, but the striking plume-like inflorescences range from 6″ to 2′ tall. There are about 25 species, some of which are less than 1′ tall and useful for the front of the garden or rockeries while others are over 4′ in height and better suited for the back of the border. None require staking and all are long lasting under good garden conditions. The mid to deep green foliage is 2 or 3 times divided into groups of three and is often copper colored when young (particularly red-flowered hybrids). The biggest enemy of *Astilbe* is dryness but ample moisture and rich soil result in a rewarding planting. If the soil dries out, the foliage develops brown margins and whole leaves may wither and die prematurely. Plants are particularly effective grouped around the edge of ponds or other water features in the garden.

Astilbes can also be used as potted plants forced into flower in the greenhouse. Plant the crowns in 6″ pots in late summer and allow them to establish good root and foliage systems during the fall. Place them in a cold frame or bury under straw mulch so they receive approximately 3 months of sub 40°F temperatures. At that time, bring the pots inside and water and fertilize as foliage and flowers appear. Astilbes also make excellent cut flowers if harvested when half open.

Propagate from divisions in spring or fall. Some of the species may be raised from seed but the hybrids must be propagated vegetatively. Seed should be sown in moist sand-peat mixture and placed at 70–75°F for 2 weeks followed by 40°F for 4 weeks.

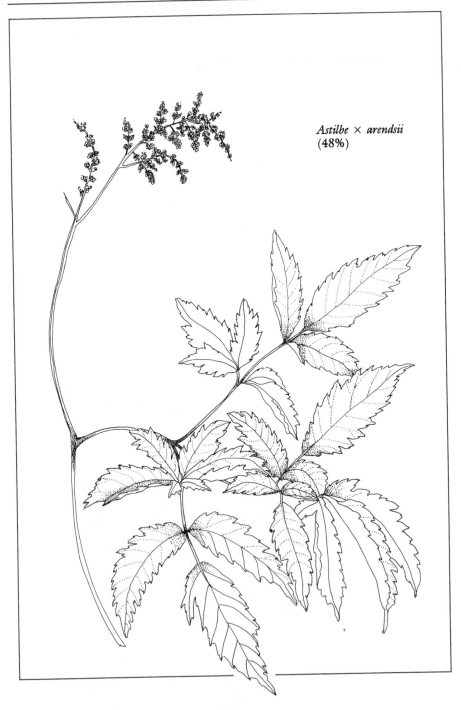

Astilbe × *arendsii*
(48%)

Quick Reference to Astilbe Species

	Height (in)	Flowering season	Flower color
A. × arendsii	24–48	Late Spring	Various
A. chinensis var. pumila	8–15	Summer	Red-pink
A. × rosea	24–36	Summer	Salmon, pink
A. simplicifolia	12–18	Summer	Pink, white
A. taquetii 'Superba'	24–48	Late Summer	Lilac

-× *arendsii* (ah-rendz' ee-ie)	Astilbe	2–4'/2'
Late Spring Various	Hybrid origin	Zone 4–9

Over 95% of the astilbes sold in this country probably belong to this group of hybrids. Not enough can be said about the accomplishments of Georg Arends (1862–1952), of Ronsdorf, West Germany, who studied and hybridized such genera as *Bergenia, Sedum, Phlox* and *Campanula*. His passion, however, was *Astilbe*. One of his first introductions (1903), using *A. chinensis* and *A. japonica*, was a light pink cultivar called 'Peach Blossom', still enjoyed by gardeners today (this has since been reclassified as *A. × rosea* to designate hybrids of *A. chinensis* and *A. japonica* parentage only). Additional clones arose from crosses among other species including *A. grandis, A. thunbergii, A. davidii,* and *A. astilboides*. In 1933, a major breakthrough came with the appearance of a bronze leaf, red-flowered cultivar later named 'Fanal'. He continued crossing combination after combination and between 1902 and 1952 introduced over 74 cultivars, many of which are available in American nurseries today. Astilbes also caught the attention of other nurseries such as the Lemoine Nursery in Nancy, France and Bressingham Gardens in Diss, England. Over fifty cultivars may be found today ranging from those with copper to dark green foliage; flower colors from clear white to blood red; and flowering times of early June to mid-August.

Cultivars:

It is impossible to name all cultivars within the confines of this book but the following list includes some personal favorites as well as other popular varieties. All cultivars may be divided in early spring.

White flowers:
'Bridal Veil' is about 2½' tall with off-white flowers.
'Deutschland' bears dense flower spikes on 2' tall plants.
'Irrlicht' has rosy white flowers over dark green foliage. It grows 2–2½' tall.
'Prof. van der Wielen' has loose flower spikes on 3' high plants.

87

'Snowdrift' is a sport of 'Irrlicht' and produces clear white flowers over 2½' tall stems.

'White Gloria' is an early-flowering cultivar about 2' tall.

Pink to salmon flowers:

'Bressingham Beauty' has arching plumes of clear pink flowers on 3½' tall plants.

'Cattleya' bears orchid-pink, long blooming flowers on 3' high plants.

'Emden' is completely covered in soft pink flowers over 2–3' tall plants.

'Erica' is about 3' tall and has large open panicles of clear pink flowers.

'Europa' is an early-flowering cultivar bearing pale pink flowers over 2' tall plants.

'Finale' is 2–2½' tall and produces light pink late-flowering panicles.

'Ostrich Plume' bears many bright pink arching spikes over 3' tall plants.

'Rheinland' is popular and has early clear pink flowers on 2' tall plants.

Red to magenta flowers:

'Fanal', first offered in 1933 is by far the most popular. It is small (2' in height), early to flower, and produces blood red blooms above dark bronze leaves.

'Federsee' adapts well to dry conditions. Plants produce 2' long panicles of carmine-rose flowers.

'Garnet' is about 2' tall and bears carmine-red blooms.

'Glow' is only 1–1½' tall with intense red flowers.

'Jo Ophorst' has late-flowering, stiff magenta spikes on 3' tall plants.

'Purple Blaze' is large (4–4½' tall) with large purple blooms appearing in late summer.

'Red Sentinel',an early-flowering cultivar, produces red flowers on 3' tall plants.

'Spinell' bears salmon red flowers atop 3' tall stems.

Related Species:

A. biternata, false goat's beard, is the only astilbe native to North America. Plants grow 3–5' tall and bear large panicles of creamy white flowers in late spring and summer. Partial shade, rich soil and ample moisture are necessary for best performance. It closely resembles *Aruncus dioicus*, goat's beard, but has 3-lobed terminal leaflets and only 10 stamens per flower. *Aruncus* is not lobed and flowers contain many stamens.

-chinensis (chin-en' sis)		Chinese Astilbe	1 ½–3'/2'
Summer	Rosy purple	China	Zones 3–8

The species is seldom seen in gardens, being represented by the dwarf variety *pumila* which makes an excellent ground cover for a moist, shaded area. It is obvious that not all material labelled as var. *pumila* has been propagated vegetatively or originated from the same parent stock block. I have seen this variety as an 8" groundcover and also as a 2–2½' border subject. Some of the variations can be attributed to climate and presence of soil moisture (plants will be taller and more vigorous in constantly moist soils than in those that dry out), how-ever, even in the same climatic zones and in relatively similar moisture regimes, variation in height is considerable. Regardless of habit, stiff, rose spike-like pan-icles, persisting for 4–6 weeks, are produced atop deeply incised bronze-green foliage. Although garden performance is better in moist soils, it is one of the more drought tolerant astilbes.

- × *rosea* (ros' ee-a)   Rose Astilbe   2–3'/2'
Summer   Pink Hybrid   Zones 4–8

The result of crossing *A. chinensis* and *A. japonica*, a 3' tall white-flowered species, this hybrid has the habit of *A. japonica* and the flower color of *A. chi-nensis*. The original hybrid is seldom seen in gardens, having been superseded by various selections.

Cultivars:

'Peach Blossom' is 3–4' tall and produces salmon-pink blooms clustered in large racemose panicles.
'Queen Alexandra' is a deeper pink but otherwise similar to 'Peach Blossom'. These cultivars are both excellent for damp places, and intolerant of drought conditions. They were some of the first hybrids raised by Georg Arends.

-*simplicifolia* (sim-pli-si-fo' lee-a)   Star Astilbe   1–1½'/2'
Summer   White   Japan   Zones 4–8

This dwarf species has undergone considerable selection and hybridization, having caught the attention of Arends in 1911. Although leaves of most garden species are pinnately compound, leaves of *A. simplicifolia* are simple and about 3" long. It forms compact mounds of mid-green, glossy, deeply cut foliage which gives rise to white starlike flowers in airy, open panicles in June and July in the South and July and August in the North. The seed heads are nearly as ornamental as the flowers and provide an additional 1–2 months of useful gar-den effect.

Cultivars:

Most cultivars are likely hybrids between *A. simplicifolia* and other species, but resemble *A. simplicifolia*. They are slower to establish than the *A.* × *arendsii* hybrids and require about 3 years to reach mature size.

var. *alba* has white flowers which are "cleaner" than those of the species.
'Atro-rosea' has 18–20" tall bright rose salmon plumes.
'Bronze Elegance' produces rose pink blooms in August over bronze foliage.
'Sprite' is the most popular cultivar and is the result of *A. simplicifolia* × *A. glaberrima* var. *saxossa*. It has airy, shell-pink blooms over bronze foliage and grows 12–18" tall. The rust-colored seed heads are particularly handsome.

-taquetii (ta-get' ee-eye)		Fall Astilbe	2–4'/2'
Late Summer	Lilac	Eastern China	Zones 4–8

This species is represented in gardens by the vigorous, late flowering 'Superba'. Compact columnar panicles to 4' tall extend the flowering season of *Astilbe* into late summer and early fall. In north Georgia, flowering ceases in mid-July whereas those of *A.* × *arendsii* hybrids finish 2–4 weeks earlier. Further north, flowering may continue into late August and early September. The flowers are more dense than those of the *A.* × *arendsii* hybrids, but unfortunately are only available in a single color. An excellent cut flower, it lasts over a week in water. The seed heads retain the majesty of the flower spires and persist throughout the winter.

Quick Key to Astilbe Species

    A. Leaves simple or in 1 group of 3 (1-ternate) .... *A. simplicifolia*
    AA. Leaves compound in 2–4 groups of 3 (2–4 ternate)
        B. Axis of inflorescence densely woolly
            C. Height 6–18", dense upright panicles, rose-purple ....
                A. chinensis var. *pumila*
            CC. Height 2–4', loose panicles, various colors ....*A.* × *arendsii*
        BB. Axis of inflorescence slightly hairy
            C. Height 2–3', airy panicles, usually pink, late spring to
                summer flowering ....*A.* × *rosea*
            CC. Height 2–4', dense upright panicles, lilac, late summer
                to fall flowering............................. *A. taquetii* 'Superba'

Additional Reading:

Lacy, Allen. 1987. The ascent of astilbes. *Horticulture* 164 (6):44–49. This provides an excellent account of Arends and his love of astilbes.

Astrantia (a-stran' tee-a)	Masterwort	Apiaceae

This interesting genus encompasses about 10 species although none is common in American gardens. Plants are useful for moist, shady areas and benefit from copious amounts of organic matter. The white to pink flowers are surrounded by a "collar" of bracts which produce a starlike effect. The flower head is a compound umbel and consists of both sterile and fertile flowers, The sterile flowers have long flower stalks (pedicels) and the fertile flowers are short stalked. They persist for 10–14 days as a cut flower and are produced commercially as such in the Netherlands, California and parts of the Midwest. Night temperatures are too warm to grow *Astrantia* much further south than Georgia-Tennessee unless at higher altitudes. Cool night temperatures, partial shade, and consistent soil moisture are necessary for best performance. *Astrantia major*, the most common garden species, is well known in flower gardens in Europe, particularly the British Isles, and is now finding its way over here. It is about time!

Astrantia is easily increased by division of the black roots in autumn or early spring. It also spreads by runners just below the surface.

-major (may-jor)   Great Masterwort   2–3'/1.5'
Late Spring   White-pink   Europe   Zones 4–7

The 2–3" diameter flowers are greenish white with a collar of green bracts and borne in a many flowered umbel. The basal leaves have a petiole, 3–5 deeply cut lobes and are toothed, while the leaves on the flower stem have widely expanded petioles which clasp directly to the stem and are seldom toothed. The bracts are often tinged purple which give the overall effect of pink flowers. Plants spread rapidly under good growing conditions and produce a formidable clump.

Cultivars:

'Involucrata' offers a unique flower form due to its extra long collar of pink bracts. Plants are sometimes offered under the name 'Shaggy', a most apt description of the flowers.

'Sunningdale Variegated' is most handsome in the spring when the margins of the light green leaves are splashed with yellow and cream. The variegation fades in summer. This is an elegant plant.

Related Species:

A. carniolica, lesser masterwort, is similar but smaller (1–2' tall) than A. major. The purple flowered cultivar, 'Rubra', has maroon flowers which contrast well with the greenish bracts surrounding them.

Aubrieta (o-bree' sha)   Rock Cress   Cruciferae

The genus consists of about a dozen species and although there are probably some hybrids lurking here and there, most of the garden plants belong to A. deltoidea. Aubrieta is closely related to Arabis, also commonly known as rock cress. The differences are not obvious and with the introduction of many cultivars, it is more difficult for the uninitiated to tell them apart. In general, Aubrieta is more compact with smaller foliage having 1–2 teeth on each side of the blade. The flowers are larger and have a cylindrical calyx (sepals) below the petals about half as long as the petals. Flowers of Aubrieta are lilac to red with a few blue forms, while flowers of Arabis are usually white or pink. A summary follows.

	Habit	Petal length	Flower color	Foliage toothed	Sepals tubular
Aubrieta	more compact	3/4"	lilac, red	yes	yes
Arabis	less compact	1/2"	white, pink	no	no

Both genera have alternate, silver-green, pubescent, evergreen foliage.

Aubrieta is not tolerant of warm nights, often declining in warm climates, and should be treated similar to *Arabis*. Many of the cultivars can be propagated by seed and those not available from seed may be propagated by terminal cuttings or division.

-deltoidea (del-toi' dee-a)   Rock Cress   6–8"/2'
Spring   Lilac   Sicily to Asia Minor   Zones 4–8

This species performs best where sunny conditions and well-drained soils are present. The foliage is somewhat wedge shaped with large teeth. The ¾" long, red to lilac flowers are clustered in racemes that emerge from the leaf axils. After the plants flower in the spring, the stems continue to grow and become leggy by midsummer. It is important to cut them back to 6–8" and allow new growth to emerge, otherwise stems will be naked in the middle with a few leaves on the end. This is especially true in the South if plants are allowed to deteriorate.

Cultivars:

'Aurea' has golden-green foliage and blue to violet flowers.

'Aurea Variegata' has green leaves with yellow variegation. It is otherwise similar to 'Aurea'.

'Barker's Double' has double purple-blue flowers.

'Campbellii' has double rose-purple flowers.

'Carnival' is very free flowering and produces hummocks of purple violet flowers.

'Dr. Mules' is similar to 'Carnival'.

var. *graeca* has large leaves and light blue flowers.

'J.S. Baker' bears bluish flowers with a white eye.

'Parkinsii' produces lavender blooms with a white eye.

var. *rosea splendens* has bright rose flowers which do not fade with age.

'Royal Blue' has dark blue flowers.

'Royal Red' bears flowers in shades of red and magenta.

'Vindictive' has large (up to 1" wide) rosy-red flowers.

Seed is available for many cultivars and germinates in about 2 weeks under moist, warm (70–75°F) conditions. Division, however, is the easiest means of propagation. Stem cuttings may also be taken from new growth in the spring or after cutting back in late spring or early summer.

Aurinia (ow-rin' ee-a)   Basket-of-Gold   Brassicaceae

There is general agreement among taxonomists that this plant should be called *Aurinia* rather than the old name of *Alyssum*, although from the gardener's point of view, it matters not at all. Of the approximately seven species, *A*.

saxatilis is the most popular because of the intense yellow early spring flowers. I grew this species with ease in East Lansing, Michigan and Guelph, Ontario. but had little success in north Georgia. In the South, if planted in early fall, performance is beautiful the first spring but plants gradually melt out during the summer. Planting under the shade of summer flowering perennials may help it return in subsequent years but it should be replanted each fall for best form and color.

-saxatilis (saks-ah′ ti-lis)		Basket-of-Gold	12″/18″
Spring	Yellow	Eastern Europe	Zones 3–7

(Syn. *Alyssum saxatile*)

When *Aurinia* is in flower, the canary yellow flowers can be seen shimmering across the length of a football field. It requires full sun and excellent drainage and should be cut back after flowering. The foliage is gray green and spreads into clumps rapidly. It is a classic rock garden and wall plant.

Cultivars:

'Ball of Gold' has a globose habit and grows about 8″ tall.
'Compactum' is similar to 'Ball of Gold' but more compact.
'Citrinum' has lemon gold flowers and grows 12–15″ tall.
'Flore'('Flore-plena') has double flowers but is generally less vigorous than the singles.
'Sunny Border Apricot' has apricot colored flowers,
'Tom Thumb' is only 3–6″ tall but vigorous.

Seed germinates in 2–3 weeks in moist, warm (70–75°F) conditions. Seeds are available for the species and a few cultivars but division in the fall is the easiest method of propagation. Cuttings may also be taken in the spring or fall.

B

Baptisia (bap-tiz' i-a)   Wild Indigo   Fabaceae

Baptisia contains about 35 species and comes from the Greek word *bapto* meaning "to dip", referring to the flower extract once used as a substitute for indigo. *B. australis* was often used for blue dyes while *B. tinctoria* was a source of yellow dye in the southern United States. Flowers may be white (*B. alba*, white wild indigo, *B. leucantha*, prairie wild indigo), cream (*B. bracteata*, cream wild indigo), yellow (*B. megacarpa*, streamside wild indigo, *B. tinctoria*, yellow wild indigo) or blue (*B. australis*, blue wild indigo, *B. minor*, lesser wild indigo). *Baptisia* produces racemes of pea-like flowers over alternate, gray-green, 3-parted compound leaves. The genus is native to the United States and tolerates warm temperatures and partial shade. Plants grow best in deep, rich soils although they tolerate poor soils.

Quick Reference to Baptisia Species

	Height (ft.)	Flower color	Flowering time
B. alba	2–3	White	Late Spring
B. australis	3–4	Blue	Spring
B. tinctoria	2–4	Yellow	Early Summer

-alba (al' ba)   White Wild Indigo   2–3'/3'
Late Spring   White   Southeastern United States   Zones 5–8

This species is appearing more frequently in southern gardens and should make its way north before too long. It grows best in full sun but tolerates partial shade. The 12″ long lateral racemes of ½″ long white flowers persist 3–4 weeks. The flowers often are blotched purple and are not as erect or dense as those of

94

B. australis. The seed pods are cylindrical, yellow-brown, and persistent. This is a useful specimen for the smaller garden where an easy to grow, long-lived plant is desired.

Propagation by seed is slower and more difficult than *B. australis* and a scarification treatment is beneficial. Division of the roots may be accomplished in early spring or fall. Care must be taken to make a clean cut of the roots with a sharp knife and provide abundant water upon transplanting.

Related Species:

B. leucantha, prairie wild indigo, is the western representative of the species. Upright white racemes occur in late spring atop blue-green foliage. Plants do not do as well in the East as *B. alba*.

B. pendula is similar to *B. alba* but the upright racemes give way to pendulous seed pods in late spring. The stems have a purple blue tint and are a little taller than those of *B. alba*. They are excellent backdrops to lower growing spring perennials. This may simply be a variety of *B. alba*.

-australis (ow-strah' lis)		Blue Wild Indigo	3–4'/4'
Spring	Indigo Blue	Eastern United States	Zones 3–9

This is the best species for the garden. In the early spring, it is one of the first plants to emerge and the gray-green leaves quickly fill out into a substantial sized bush. The 10–12" long flowering stalks arise in the spring, carrying 1" long, indigo-blue pea-like flowers which last for about 4 weeks. Although the flowers are violet-blue, there is much variation when plants are raised from seed. Flowers will vary from light to deep indigo blue, the latter much preferable to the former. Two to 2½" long brown to black pods appear in early summer and remain until the plant dies back in the fall. The pods become dry by midsummer and the seeds inside rattle around and should be collected at this time. Arrangers find these pods attractive and use them as dried ornaments. In my partially shaded gardens, I must support my plants. If grown in full sun, however, no staking is required. The plant spreads by rhizomes and consumes considerable garden space. It does not require dividing from the plant's point of view, but division every 4–5 years may be beneficial to ease overcrowding.

The flower looks a little like lupine flowers but the leaves and habit are much different. Some people also confuse it with *Thermopsis* which has dark green rather than blue-green leaves, and yellow flowers. Although *B. australis* is cold hardy to zone 3, the leaves turn black with the first hard frost.

The key to successful seed propagation is to harvest the seed as they turn black and sow when fresh. Seed propagation is less erratic when seeds are given a scarification treatment. Piercing or scraping the seeds with sandpaper or other abrasive substance is useful. This allows moisture and oxygen to penetrate the seed coat. Acid scarification is used commercially but should be performed only by trained individuals. Once the seeds have been treated, place them in a peat-

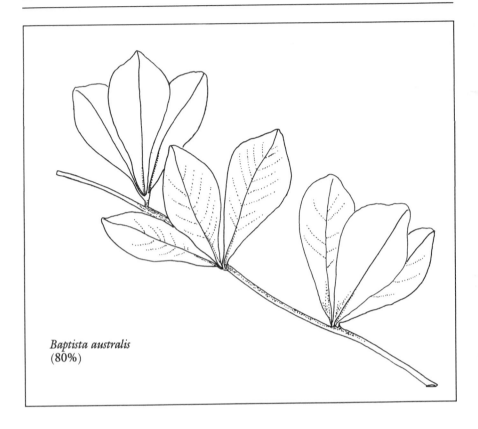

Baptista australis
(80%)

vermiculite mix in a moist, warm environment. Germination of over 90% occurred regardless of acid and mechanical scarification, cold and hot water soaking or cold stratification. (See additional reading). A cold treatment (40°F) is
also useful and can be accomplished in a cold frame or in a refrigerator or in-
cubator. The fleshy roots may also be divided between October and March.

-tinctoria (tink-to' ree-a)		Yellow Wild Indigo	2–4'/1'
Early Summer	Yellow	Eastern United States	Zones 5–9

This species is not particularly suitable for a formal garden but is at home in
a meadow garden or sunny informal area. The upper leaves are nearly sessile
(with very short petiole) and the terminal flowers are only about 2–3" long.
There is also considerable variation within the species and flowers range from
clear yellow to cream colored.

Related Species:
B. *perfoliata*, Georgia wild indigo, and B. *arachnifera*, hairy wild indigo, an
endangered species in Georgia, have yellow flowers and simple, perfoliate leaves
(the stem passes through the leaf) rather than compound leaves.

Quick Key to Baptisia Species
  A. Leaves simple, perfoliate .... *B. perfoliata*
  AA. Leaves compound, leaf stalk present
    B. Flowers blue, white
      C. Flowers blue, pods inflated............................ *B. australis*
      CC. Flowers white, pods cylindrical .... *B. alba*
    BB. Flowers yellow .... *B. tinctoria*

Additional Reading:
Dirr, Michael A. 1987. *Baptisia australis. American Nurseryman* 165(5):166.

Belamcanda (bel-am-kan' da)   Blackberry Lily   Iridaceae

   The most common species of blackberry lily is *B. chinensis,* which bears seed pods as ornamental as the flowers.

-chinensis (chin' en-sis)   Blackberry Lily, Leopard Flower   3–4'/2'
Summer   Orange, red spotted   China   Zones 5–10

   In early to midsummer, stems bear loosely arranged clusters of 3 to 12 orange flowers, each peppered with gaudy red spots from which one of the common names, leopard flower, is derived. The flowers are about 2″ across and the petals and sepals barely distinguishable from each other. The 6 segments are narrow at the base and are, unfortunately, very fleeting. The pear-shaped seed pods are persistent and contain the shining, black, round seeds for which the blackberry lily is named. In the fall the black seeds line up like kernels of corn inside the open pod and are an attractive part of the autumn garden. The stoloniferous roots give rise to about six sword-like clustered leaves that resemble those of *Gladiolus.* Plant in full sun in a well-drained soil and mulch heavily north of zone 5. Iris borer can be a problem but removal of dying or decaying leaves will greatly reduce the problem.
   I have seen dwarf forms at Longwood Garden but plants raised from that seed grew almost as tall as the species in my Georgia garden.
   Seeds germinate within 3 weeks if provided with moist warm conditions. Rootstocks may be divided in early spring.

Related Species:
   B. flabellata has gray-green leaves and unspotted yellow flowers. Plants are often sold as 'Halo Yellow'.

Bergenia (ber-gen' i-a)   Bergenia, Pigsqueak   Saxifragaceae

   The genus contains about eight, glossy, leather-leaved species, most of which flower in early spring. Plants tolerate full sun in the North but prefer afternoon

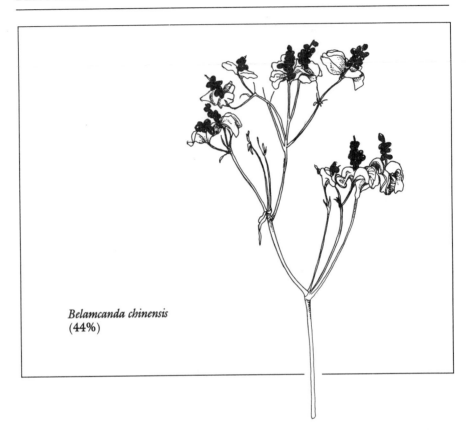

Belamcanda chinensis
(44%)

shade in the South. They are evergreen although the foliage is often damaged in harsh winters. When planted in groupings of 10 or 20, the cabbage-like leaves of bergenia make an impressive sight. The flowers of most species are rose to red colored but hybrids exist with pink and white flowers. The flower buds, however, are less cold hardy than the foliage and may abort during particularly cold winters. This should not deter one from using bergenia because the foliage is as attractive as the coarse flowers. The large, shiny leaves are often used to provide greenery for florist bouquets since they persist for a long time after cutting.

Bergenia can be propagated easily from seed or by division in early spring.

Quick Reference to Bergenia Species

	Height (in.)	Flower color	Leaf shape	Flower season
B. cordifolia	12–18	Rose-pink	Heart	Early Spring
B. crassifolia	12–18	Rose-pink	Oval	Early Spring

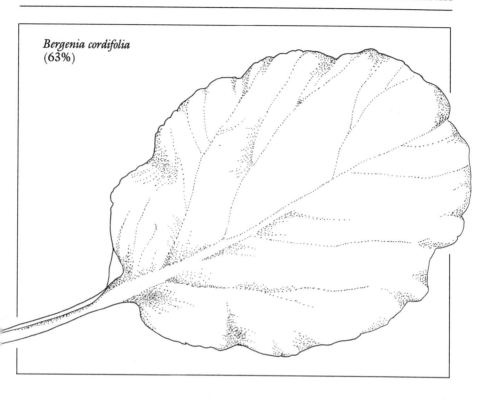

Bergenia cordifolia
(63%)

-cordifolia (kor-di-fo′ lee-a)	Heart-leaf Bergenia, Megasea	12–18″/12″
Early Spring	Rose-pink	Siberia	Zones 3–8

This is the most common species available and is a vigorous grower. The 10″ long, glossy evergreen leaves are leathery, waxy and thick. They turn a deep burgundy with the advent of cold weather, and if not buried by snow, make an effective show in the winter. However, even in my north Georgia garden, the purple foliage becomes damaged and is not particularly attractive in the winter. The panicles consist of a dozen or so flowers but do not rise much higher than the foliage. To provide the best show, plant in groups of at least 10 plants in partial shade.

Cultivars:

'Perfecta' has rosy red flowers held well above the foliage and has performed well in many regions of the country. Plants are far superior to the species.

Related Species:

B. × *smithii* (syn. *B.* × *newryensis*) encompasses some of the more common garden cultivars. Plants of this hybrid arose from crosses between *B. cordifolia* and *B. purpurascens*, purple bergenia.

'Abendglut' (Evening Glow), raised by Arends nursery in Germany, is becoming more popular in this country. It is shorter and more prostrate than most other clones and richly colored in the winter.

'Bressingham Bountiful' is vigorous with much-branched infloresences of pink flowers.

'Bressingham Salmon' bears salmon flowers.

'Bressingham White' produces clean white blooms.

'Distinction' has pink flowers on long brownish red pedicels.

'Morning Red' is 8–12″ tall with carmine red flowers.

'Profusion' is an excellent pink hybrid. 'Profusion' and 'Distinction' were among the original cultivars raised near the turn of the century by Mr. T. Smith of Northern Ireland. Their rounded foliage is characteristic of the *B. cordifolia* parent.

'Pugsley's Purple' grows 2′ tall and is a late, purple-flowering hybrid.

'Sunningdale', one of the better hybrids for winter color, is approximately 12″ tall with excellent foliage color all year.

'Silberlicht' (Silver Light), also raised by Arends, has pink-tinged white flowers with red centers and shiny dark green foliage. Both this and 'Abendglut' have *B. ciliata* in their pedigree and are less cold hardy.

B. purpurascens is about 15″ tall and has larger (petals ¾ –1″ wide) deep magenta flowers.

'Ballawley' is a massive plant with 8–12″ wide leaves. It makes a wonderful ground cover in areas where moisture is available. Plants are grown more for the foliage than the magenta flowers, which are not freely produced.

-crassifolia (kra-si-fo′ lee-a)		Leather Bergenia	12–18″/12″
Spring	Purple	Siberia	Zones 4–8

There are few differences between this species and *B. cordifolia* and they serve the same garden function. The toothed undulating leaves are obovate (like a hen's egg with the broad part above the middle) rather than heart shaped. The flowers are held higher above the foliage than those of *B. cordifolia* and the inflorescence is more branched. The leaf blade of *B. crassifolia* runs down along the petiole (decurrent) rather than being two obviously distinct parts of the leaf (i.e. petiole and blade) as in heart leaf bergenia. Performance is better in the North than the South.

Quick Key to Bergenia Species

    A. Leaves cordate (heart-shaped), petioles long and thick .... *B. cordifolia*

    AA. Leaves obovate, blades decurrent on petioles .... *B. crassifolia*

Additional Reading:

Beckett, Kenneth A. 1983. *Bergenia. The Garden* 108(12):480–484.

De Wolf, Gordon. 1983. *Bergenia. Horticulture* 61(3):8–9.

Yeo, Peter F. 1961. Two bergenia hybrids. *Baileya* 9:20–28

Yeo, Peter F. 1962. *Bergenia* × *Smithii*, the correct name for *B. cordifolia* × *B. purpurascens. Baileya* 10:110–111.

Bletilla (ble-til' la)   Bletilla   Orchidaceae

    Few plants in the orchid family are suitable for the outdoor garden; *Bletilla* is one of them. These terrestial orchids produce pseudobulbs useful for propagation while terminal flowers, consisting of similar sepals and petals, are produced on racemes. The bulbous roots should be planted no deeper than 2" below the surface.

-striata (streye-ah' ta)		Hyacinth Bletilla	8-12"/10"
Spring	Purple	China	Zones 5–9

(Syn. *B. hyacinthina*)

    Three to six pleated papery leaves emerge early in the spring and look rather nondescript, but later give rise to rosy-purple sprays of orchid-like flowers. Racemes consist of about 6–10 flowers, each measuring 1–1½" across and persisting for 2–3 weeks.
    Partial shade and well-enriched soil are ideal, allowing a single plant to enlarge into a fine garden clump in a few years. They are suited to growing in large containers on the patio or deck. This method is most useful for gardeners north of zone 5 who can bring the container in for the winter to be returned outside in the spring. It is too fine a species to ignore simply because winters are cold. I like the idea of having orchids in my garden and *Bletilla* adds a touch of class to any deck or border planting.
    The only problems I have seen result from late frosts. Leaves emerge so early that the ends often get nipped resulting in tattered tips. Summer drought causes poor initiation of flowers resulting in little or no flowering the following spring. Late frosts occasionally result in death of the flowers.

Cultivars:

var. *alba* has creamy white flowers which contrast better with the dark green
    leaves than the purple flowers of the type.
'Albostriata' is the most ornamental form and has white stripes along the length
    of each leaf. Purple flowers similar to the species are produced and the foli-

age remains ornamental all season. Best growth occurs in a rich, cool, moist soils.

Propagate by division of the pseudobulbs. They are tuber-like structures about ¾" in diameter. Separate them from the mother plant in the fall or simply divide the clump with a sharp shovel.

Boltonia (bowl-tone′ ee-a) Boltonia Asteraceae

Most species of *Boltonia* are native to the United States and easy to grow. They produce vast numbers of daisy-like white or purple flowers in late summer. The leaves are alternate, lance-shaped, and sessile. Many species are too large and lanky to be considered for anything but the wild flower garden.

-*asteroides* (ass-ter-oide′ ees)		White Boltonia	5–6′/4′
Late Summer	White, purple	Eastern North America	Zones 4–9

The 3–5" long, blue-green leaves are entire, broadly lanceolate and narrowed at both ends. The numerous ¾–1" wide flowers are held in large billowy terminal panicles. Although the species produces showy flowers, it is too large, floppy, and weedy for my liking and should not be grown in the formal garden. However one of the finest garden plants is a selection of this "weed".

Cultivars:
'Snowbank' is a cultivar of which I am most fond. It is about 3–4′ tall and does not require staking when grown in full sun. In partial shade, however, plants will not be as compact and require support. The simple foliage is blue green, and the top half of the plant is blanketed by clear white daisies with yellow centers. In my garden, flowering begins in early August and continues well into September. Although plants perform best in deep, moist, organic soils, plants have tolerated two severe Georgia droughts with only occasional watering. 'Snowbank' associates well with other late summer and fall bloomers such as *Perovskia atriplicifolia*, *Sedum* × 'Autumn Joy', *Eupatorium purpureum* and *Lespedeza thunbergii*.

Propagation is by division in the spring; a small shovel of basal rosettes yields dozens of offspring. Divide every 3–4 years. Seed of the species may be collected and will germinate readily. Seed of 'Snowbank' will not come true.

Related Species:
B. incisa, Siberian boltonia, is 2–3′ tall and bears lilac flowers.

B. indica (*Astermoea mongolica*), Japanese boltonia, produces ½" diameter double white flowers throughout the summer on 2–4′ tall plants.

B. latisquama, violet boltonia, native from Missouri to Oklahoma, is similar

102

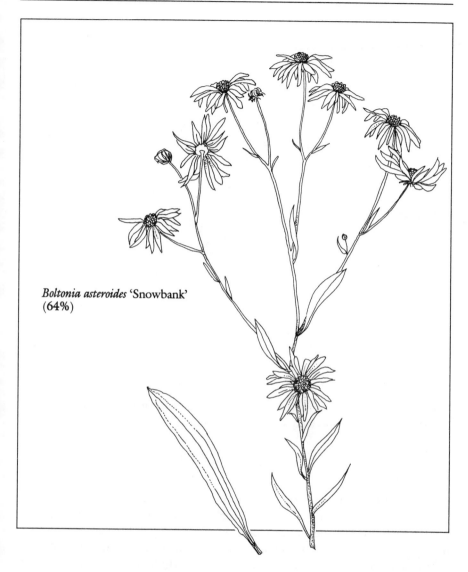

Boltonia asteroides 'Snowbank'
(64%)

to *B. asteroides* in habit but is about 4' tall and has larger, purple flowers. A dwarf form, var. *nana*, also occurs.

Borago (bor-rah' go)   Borage   Boraginaceae

Most species of borage are annuals but the flowers are such a lovely shade of blue, it is worth the effort to include at least one species. Borage has long been used as a pot-herb and young leaves were often (and still are) included in salads.

103

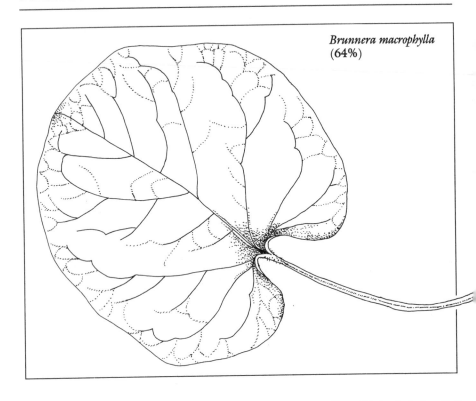

Brunnera macrophylla
(64%)

Medicinal properties attributed to borage (mainly *B. officinalis*) included relief for stomach distress and a curative for local inflammation.

-laxiflora (laks-i-flo' ra)		Borage	1–2'/1'
Early Summer	Blue	Corsica	Zones 5–9

Most appropriate for wall or rock gardens, this borage bears light blue, drooping flowers about ¾" across similar in shape to flowers of tomatoes (rotate). The loose racemes are produced in late spring and persist for approximately 4 weeks. The many stems are covered with short backward-pointing bristles and the 4–6" long leaves are rough and coarsely hairy. Plants need deep mulching in the fall in most parts of the country.

Propagate by division in the spring, by seeds sown in the fall, or by 2–3" long terminal cuttings in summer.

Brunnera (brunn' er-a)	Brunnera	Boraginaceae

The genus contains three species but only one is of ornamental interest. *Brunnera* is most at home in moist, shady areas and does particularly well along shaded stream banks or water features in the garden. After flowering in the spring, large, basal heart-shaped leaves are produced. The flowers and inflorescence remind me of forget-me-nots (*Myosotis*) and the leaves are similar to Virginia bluebells (*Mertensia virginica*).

-macrophylla (mak-ro-fil′ a) Heartleaf Brunnera 12–18″/20″
Spring Light blue Caucasus Zones 3–7

(Syn. *Anchusa myosotidiflora*)

The azure blue flowers arise early from the soft light green foliage and continue into early summer. Plants branch from the base, spread quickly and produce mounds of lovely, cool foliage. The basal leaves are much larger (up to 6″ across) and held on longer petioles than those near the top, resulting in a light, airy effect in the landscape. The ¼″ diameter flowers have a yellow center and are carried in a loose 1–2″ wide panicled raceme.

In the South, heavy shade and consistent moisture are necessary for vigorous growth. In the North, morning sun is welcome but moisture must still be maintained. I have seen moist woodlands covered with these plants and their quiet understated beauty is soothing to the soul.

Cultivars:

'Hadspen Cream' produces light green leaves with irregular creamy-white borders. If subjected to full afternoon sun, the leaf margins turn brown.
'Langtrees' has dark green leaves with silver-white spots on the border. It is more tolerant of dry conditions than other cultivars.
'Variegata' is characterized by large clear white borders which sometimes take up the whole leaf. It is intolerant of drought and prefers cool, moist, shady areas. It is a most handsome plant if grown well.

Propagate by seed sown in moist, warm (70–75°F) medium in late summer and transplant in the fall. Root cuttings handled similar to *Anemone* × *hybrida* are the best means of propagating the cultivars.

Buphthalmum (buf-thahl′ mum) Oxeye Asteraceae

Although the genus features rather common yellow, dark-centered daisies, they have their moments of glory. The name is derived from *bous*, ox and *opthalmos*, eye, in reference to the appearance of the disc of the flower head. I suppose I have not seen enough oxen eyes but it doesn't look a great deal different than most other daisies. They are best in moist areas and tolerate poor soil. The large blossoms make reasonably good cut flowers. The foliage is alternate, dark green, and toothed. All species may be easily propagated by division in early spring or immediately after flowering. Seeds germinate in 14–21 days if placed in warm (70–75°F) moist conditions.

Quick Reference to Buphthalmum Species

	Height (ft)	Leaf shape	Flower diameter	Leaves scented
B. salicifolium	1–2	Long, narrow	1–2″	No
B. speciosum	3–5	Heart-shaped	2–3″	Yes

-salicifolium (sa-li-si-fo′ lee-um)		Willowleaf Oxeye	1–2′/2′
Late Summer	Yellow	Southeastern Europe	Zones 3–7

The toothed leaves are long and narrow, like those of a weeping willow, and usually have white pubescence on the undersides. The terminal, solitary flower heads are about 2″ wide. The stems are slender and, without support, the plant will topple. Like most daisies, flowering continues for many weeks if spent flowers are removed.

Cultivars:

'Sunwheel' is the only cultivar I have observed and is about 2′ tall with golden yellow flowers from July to September.

-speciosum (spee-see-o′ sum)		Scented Oxeye	4–5′/3′
Late Summer	Yellow	Southeastern Europe	Zones 3–7

(Syn. *Telekia speciosum*)

This species is seldom seen in gardens because of its coarse, gangling, large habit. However, it is excellent as an accent or back of border plant and provides a pleasing effect for many months. The large leaves are pubescent, sessile, double toothed, and strongly aromatic. The flowers are larger than the previous species measuring up to 3″ in diameter. It is a vigorous grower and spreads rapidly.

C

Camassia (ka-ma' see-a)   Quamash   Liliaceae

Camassia was used extensively by the Indians of the Northwest as a food staple and bitter wars were fought over possession of the Quamash grounds. All are native to North America, extending from the West Coast to Georgia, yet are underused in gardens in this country. The foliage is long, lance-like and grassy, and flower stems are erect and up to 4' tall. The star-shaped flowers (blue, purple, white, or cream colored) consist of six petal-like segments, and appear at about the same time as the late tulips. They are inhabitants of rich meadows, wet in spring and dry in summer. Plants tolerate some shade but perform better in full sun. Plant in the fall approximately 3 times deeper than the diameter of the bulb and in groups of at least a dozen. Nothing looks worse than one lonely flowering bulb.

The foliage is not as persistent as that of daffodils, and bulbs may be planted in the formal garden. However, they do look rather scruffy after flowering and are better planted in a slightly more out of the way area such as the naturalized garden, where enough can be planted to insure a good supply of cut flowers for indoors.

Bulb offsets are produced after several years, but natural production is slow. Wounding the bulbs greatly enhances offset production and is practiced commercially. Seed propagation is not difficult if seed is fresh. Seeds germinate readily but 3–4 years are required before plants flower.

Quick Reference to Camassia Species

	Height	# flowers open at once	Total flowers on stem
C. cusickii	3–4	many	30–100
C. leichtlinii	3–4	1–4	20–50
C. quamash	2–3	many	10–40

-cusickii (kew-sik′ ee-eye)		Cusick Quamash	3–4′/1′
Early Summer	Blue	Oregon	Zones 3–8

The bulbs are large and can weigh up to half a pound! Numerous, slightly wavy leaves about 15″ long and 1½″ wide appear in a basal cluster. The lovely pale blue star shaped flowers are approximately 1½″ across and held in long racemes on 3–4′ long scapes. Each narrow flower segment has 3–5 faint veins running its length.

This is the most cold-hardy species and grows as far north as zone 2 with suitable winter protection.

-leichtlinii (liekt-lin′ ee-eye)		Leichtlin Quamash	3–4′/1′
Early Summer	Various	California to British Columbia	Zones 5–9

This is the best species of *Camassia* for the garden. The foliage is broader than *C. quamash* but not as wide as *C. cusickii*. Plants are strong and stout and seldom need support except in windy areas. The flowers are large (up to one inch across) and may be white, cream, blue or purple. Each segment has 5–7 nerves (veins). When the flowers wither, they twist around the capsule before falling away. This is one of the few characteristics which distinguishes this species from others, clearly pointing out how few differences exist among members of the genus.

Cultivars:

'Atroviolacea' has single flowers of deep violet.
'Eve Price' is the finest cultivar I have seen and produces a magnificent clump of light blue spikes. Although presently difficult to locate, I hope it will soon be available in this country.
'Semi-plena' ('Plena') bears creamy-yellow double flowers.

-quamash (kwah′ mash)		Common Quamash	2–3′/1′
Early Summer	Various	Western North America	Zones 4–8

(Syn. *C. esculenta*)

The 12″ long leaves are linear and grass-like (about ½″ wide). The flowers are usually white or in various shades of violet with 3–5 nerves per segment. This is a particularly variable species and the segments making up the flowers may be closely or loosely spaced, often on the same raceme. The irregular flowers have 5 segments more or less on one side and the last one on the other. The flowers are persistent but don't twist around as in the former species. The colors are not as deep as in *C. leichtlinii*.

Cultivars:

'Flore-alba' is a handsome semi-double, white-flowering cultivar.

Quick Key to Camassia Species

   A. Leaves 1–1½" wide, flowers blue, 3–5 faint veins per segment . *C. cusickii*
  AA. Leaves less than 1" wide, flower color various, 3–7 nerves per
       segment
      B. Flowers all regular, few in bloom at once, withered
         segments twisted, soon deciduous........................ *C. leichtlinii*
     BB. Flowers irregular, many in bloom at once, withered
         segments not twisted, persistent.......................... *C. quamash*

Campanula (kam-pahn' ew-la)   Bellflower   Campanulaceae

    This fascinating genus consists of approximately 250 species, many of which are useful for the garden. Campanulas can get into one's blood and bring out the collecting urges in many people. The great horticulturist, Liberty Hyde Bailey, took immense pleasure in his garden which "was fully inhabited by bellflowers, representing genera and species of *Campanula*, and related plants . . .". The British authority Alan Bloom stated that he had "furtively accumulated 109 species and varieties of campanula before the nurseryman in me took control.". Shades of blue tend to dominate but flowers are often tinted with lilac, lavender, violet and other hues. Species with white and pink flowers can also be found. They range in height from low-growing rockery species to five foot tall monsters. The leaves are simple, usually alternate, and toothed. The basal leaves of the upright forms are usually different in size and shape than the stem leaves. The genus includes annuals (*C. americana, C. ramosissima*), biennials (*C. medium*), and even food crops (*C. rapunculoides*), but most are long-lived ornamental perennials. Although many wonderful species for the American garden occur, unfortunately most of the upright bellflowers do not perform particularly well in the South (*C. persicifolia* is one exception). This is certainly a generalization and at higher altitudes or in cooler microclimates in the South, experiences with some upright forms are more positive. Bellflowers do not appreciate night temperatures above 70°F, although the dwarf forms are more forgiving than the erect species.

    Propagation for all but double-flowered cultivars is easy by seed. Even most of the named cultivars come true from seed. Terminal stem cuttings, root cuttings, and divisions can be used when necessary. Most are sun-loving but a few of the rock garden plants benefit from partial shade.

    To quote L. H. Bailey once more is to understand some of the finer qualities of *Campanula*. "They are eminently plants for the garden-lover, for those persons who graciously accept cool nights and soft rains and dews, who respond to the milder sensations and derive sustaining satisfactions from gentle experiences. They are for those who love to grow plants for the joy of growing them..".

Quick Reference to Campanula Species

	Height (in.)	Habit (erect/low)	Flower color	Flower shape	Flower (nodding or upright)
C. alliariifolia	18–36	E	White	Bell	N
C. carpatica	9–12	L	Blue	Cup	U
C. cochlearifolia	4–6	L	Blue	Bell	N
C. garganica	5–6	L	Blue	Star	U
C. glomerata	12–18	E	Purple	Bell	U
C. lactiflora	36–60	E	Lilac	Bell	U
C. latifolia	48–60	E	Purple	Tubular	U
C. persicifolia	12–36	E	Blue	Saucer	U
C. portenschlagiana	4–6	L	Blue	Bell	U
C. poscharskyana	8–12	L	Lilac	Bell	U
C. pyramidalis	36–48	E	Blue	Bell	U
C. rotundifolia	6–12	L	Purple	Bell	N

-alliariifolia (a-lee-ah-ree-i-fo′ lee-a)	Spurred Bellflower		18–36″/24″
Summer	White	Caucasus, Asia Minor	Zones 3–7

(Syn. *C. lamiifolia*)

This is one of the few white-flowered species although white cultivars of other species are available. The plant forms a clump of attractive heart-shaped basal leaves above which 2–3′ long flower stems arise. The lower leaves are larger and have longer petioles than leaves further up the stem. The nodding, white, 1–2″ long flowers appear in each leaf axil and as they open, the stems arch over, taking up more room than anticipated. Plants are rather short lived (2–3 years) but reseed freely.

Being a floppy species, cut it back after flowering to keep in bounds. Plants are intolerant of summer heat and humidity and are poor choices for southern gardens. Full sun and well-drained soil are necessary for best growth. Fertilize lightly to restrict height.

Seeds sown in summer or fall germinate well but irregularly. Place seed in moist medium, and maintain high humidity and warmth (70–75°F).

-carpatica (kar-pa′ ti-ca)	Carpathian Harebell		9-12″/12″
Summer	Bright Blue	Eastern Europe	Zones 3–8

One of the most popular bellflowers in this country, Carpathian harebell tolerates a wide range of conditions and spreads readily as long as adequate drainage is provided. The numerous bell-shaped flowers are solitary and up to 2″ across. The leaves are triangular, toothed and dark green. Plants are excellent for the rock garden or front of the border and are covered with flowers in summer. I have not found this species particularly outstanding in my north Georgia garden but I haven't tried all available cultivars. I have been more successful in the South with some of the other smaller-flowered, low-growing species. All cultivars of C. *carpatica* prefer to have roots in cool soil, therefore, a summer mulch is useful, particularly in the South.

Cultivars:

var. *alba* has white flowers.
'Blue Clips' is compact, 6–9″ tall and bears blue flowers up to 3″ wide.
'China Cup' and 'China Doll' are about 9″ tall and have azure blue flowers. They
   are similar to each other.
'Jingle Bells' produces a mixture of white and blue flowers and grow 8–12″ tall.
'Turbinata' grows 6–9″ tall with purplish blue flowers on a compact frame.
'Wedgewood Blue' bears 2½″ diameter violet-blue flowers over 6″ tall plants.
'Wedgewood White' is one of the most compact white flowered cultivars.
'White Clips' is a fine plant but not particularly better than 'Wedgewood White'.
'White Star' is similar to var. *alba*. The flowers are a little cleaner white but
   plants are not as compact as 'Wedgewood White' .

Propagation of most cultivars is easiest by seed. Place the seed on top of medium and lightly cover with a thin layer of vermiculite. Keep the seed moist by covering with plastic and keep out of direct sun. Germination should occur within 3 weeks and seedlings can be transplanted 2 weeks later. Plants should be divided every other year to maintain habit and vigor.

Related Species:

C. *barbata*, bearded bellflower, is 4–14″ tall and bears blue, bell-shaped flowers which are bearded within. So many flowers are produced that it has been said to "flower itself to death."

-cochlearifolia (kok-lee-ah-ree-i-fo′ lee-a)	Spiral Bellflower	4–6″/12″
Summer	Blue-violet	European Mountains	Zones 6–7

(Syn. C. *pusilla*)

This is one of the campanulas with a virtually unpronounceable name, easily grown in spite of the fact that nobody can say it. Mat-forming plants, suitable for the front of the garden or along pathways, produce ¾″ diameter sky-blue flowers on wiry stems. Nothing more than good drainage and mid-afternoon shade are required for success.

Cultivars:

var. *alba* bears clear white flowers and is particularly vigorous.
'Miranda' is a vigorous grower which produces pale icy blue flowers.
'Pallida' has blue flowers up to 1″ in diameter.

Propagate by seed similar to C. *carpatica* or by division in spring or fall.

Related Species:
    C. sarmatica, Sarmatican bellflower, has nodding, pale blue, soft hairy flowers on one side of the flower stem. Plants grow 1–2' tall and bear velvety, gray-green leaves.

-garganica (gar-gah' ni-ca)	Gargano Bellflower		5–6"/12"
Spring	Blue	Italy	Zones 6–8

    This species was discovered in 1827 at the base of Mt. Garganica in Italy. Although treated by some authorities as a variant of *C. elatines* or *C. portenschlagiana*, it is usually offered as *C. garganica*. The basal leaves are kidney shaped while the stem leaves are heart shaped. Both are grayish green with rounded teeth. Star-like blue flowers with white eyes are produced in clusters in the leaf axils and persist for 2–3 weeks.
    This is an aggressive species and needs to be divided often. Full sun is preferable but partial shade is tolerated, particularly in the southern range of cultivation. It is a hardy rock garden plant which should be grown for the unique non-campanulate flowers, prostrate habit and gray-green leaves.

Cultivars:
var. *hirsuta* is a gray downy-leaved form with lighter blue flowers and longer
    stems than the type.
var. *hirsuta alba* has the same form as var. *hirsuta* but with white flowers.

Propagate by seed (similar to *C. alliariifolia*), terminal cuttings or division in early spring or fall.

-glomerata (glo-me-rah' ta)	Clustered Bellflower		12–18"/12"
Summer	Blue,purple	Eurasia	Zones 3–8

    The common name of this showy bellflower comes from the clustered arrangement of flowers atop the flowering stem. There may be as many as 15 flowers in a cluster (raceme) which persist for 2–3 weeks. Cut flower stems also last up to 2 weeks when placed in water. The ovate, toothed foliage is hairy above and below and varies in size. The stem leaves are 3–4" long, sessile or short petioled and usually narrower and more pointed than the 5" long basal leaves. Plants may be single stemmed or branched.
    Full sun in the North or partial shade in the South is recommended. Plantings in the State Botanical Garden of Georgia held up for approximately 3 years. Trialing in the Horticulture Gardens at the University of Georgia has shown that plants may be recommended for the Southeast as long as partial shade and water are present. For most aesthetic results, place in groups of at least three plants.

Cultivars:

var. *acaulis* is a dwarf early-flowering violet-blue form which is almost stemless and only 3–5″ tall.
var. *acaulis alba* has white flowers and is 8–12″ tall.
'Crown of Snow' is nearly 2′ tall and bears large white flower clusters.
var. *dahurica* (syn. *C. dahurica*, *C. speciosa*) has large deep-violet flowers (clusters 3″ across) and stands about 12″ tall.
'Joan Elliott' sends up many flowering stems of deep violet-blue flowers and is 1½′ tall.
'Purple Pixie' is about 1½′ high with lavender-blue flowers.
'Snow' is a clean white form and grows 2–2½′ tall.
'Superba' has violet flowers and grows 2½′ tall. It is vigorous and tolerates heat better than many other selections.
'Superba Alba' is a white form of the above cultivar.

Propagate using 2–3″ long terminal cuttings in summer after flowering. Seed is available for many of the cultivars as well as the species and should be treated similar to *C. alliariifolia*.

-lactiflora (lak-ti-flor′ a)	Milky Bellflower	3–5′/3′
Summer Lavender-blue	Caucasus	Zones 5–7

This tall bellflower has a bushy habit and sometimes reaches 5′ under optimum conditions. The 2–3″ long sessile serrated stem leaves are pointed and become smaller as they ascend the stem. The 1″ long bell-shaped flowers are milky-white (thus the common name) to pale blue and form 3–4″ long terminal panicles on each axillary shoot.

Although tolerant of full sun in northern climes, plants are more at home in partial shade and do not look out of place in a semi-shaded wild flower garden. A consistent moisture level is necessary for vigorous growth. Well-drained soils are necessary, especially in the South. Plants do not transplant well and direct sowing (i.e. sowing seeds directly in the garden) helps them establish. In fact, once established, plants multiply rapidly due to the prolific self-sowing tendancy. If a problem, flowers should be removed immediately after flowering, resulting in a second flush of flowers in the fall.

Cultivars:

var. *alba* is a 4–5′ tall white-flowering variety.
var. *coerulea* bears violet-blue flowers.
'Loddon Anna' is a strong 4′ tall plant with soft pale pink flowers. This is a lovely cultivar.
'Pouffe' is a dwarf cultivar raised by Alan Bloom. It stands only 10–18″ high and is covered with pale blue flowers for 4–5 weeks. Many of the taller cultivars are floppy; this is not.

'Prichard's Variety', bearing purple-blue flowers and growing 3–4' tall, is the most common cultivar available.

var. *rosea* has pink flowers.

'Superba' has large (1½–2") dark violet-blue flowers and is more vigorous than the type.

Propagate the species and varieties by seed or division; the cultivars by division. Treat the seeds similar to *C. alliariifolia*. All varieties exhibit a great deal of variation when raised from seed.

-latifolia (lah-ti-fo' lee-a)		Great Bellflower	4–5'/3'
Early Summer	Purple-blue	Europe	Zones 3–7

This erect perennial has a running rootstock which results in rapidly spreading clumps. The 5–6" long basal leaves are held on a long petiole but become smaller and virtually sessile as they ascend the stem. All are slender-pointed, double toothed and hairy. The erect, bell-shaped flowers are about 1½" long and held in a short leafy terminal raceme.

Plants are not as showy or as good garden specimens as the former species. Support is required to remain upright and plants are best placed in the rear of informal settings. We have had no success in establishing plants and I have seen few good stands south of zone 6. Where successful, seed capsules should be removed prior to maturity if new colonies are not wanted.

Cultivars:

var. *alba* has white flowers but is otherwise similar to the species.

'Brantwood' is violet colored and the best known cultivar of the species.

'Gloaming' has pale blue flowers and is particularly attactive.

'Macrantha' has larger flowers but otherwise is similar to the species.

'Macrantha Alba' is a good white form although not remarkably different from var. *alba*.

Propagate the species by seed or division in early spring. Seed normally germinates quickly but may first require 2–4 weeks of 40–50°F to assure a high germination percentage. Cultivars should be divided in early spring.

Related Species:

C. americana, tall bellflower, is native to moist shady areas in eastern North America. Although not as showy as other upright forms, the spikes of 1" wide, pale blue flowers associate well with other shade tolerant perennials. Unfortunately, plants are short lived and often treated as annuals or biennials.

-persicifolia (per-sik-i-fo' lee-a)		Peachleaf Bellflower	1–3'/2'
Summer	Blue-violet	Europe, North Africa, Asia	Zones 3–8

This popular European cut flower is becoming more familiar to American consumers and gardeners. The erect flowers are 1–1½" long and broadly bell

114

shaped, almost resembling a saucer. Flowers occur in various shades of blue in open terminal racemes. The evergreen, basal leaves are 4–8" long while the sessile stem leaves are 2–4" long. All are narrow, leathery, and have rounded teeth and certainly don't resemble peach leaves. Clumps increase in size by shoots arising from the base of the plant and new colonies are formed through self-sowing. Flower color, plant habit and size are variable.

In zones 3–6, this is an excellent garden plant. Garden performance in the South has been mixed. In zone 7, plants perform fairly well and persist for 3–4 years but in zone 8, flower color is faded and plants usually decline after 1 or 2 years.

Cultivars:
'Alba' has white flowers.
'Alba Coronata' bears semi-double white flowers.
'Alba Flore-plena' has fully double white flowers.
'Beechwood' bears pale, soft blue flowers.
'Bluebell' has single blue flowers and grows 2–3' tall.
'Coerulea Coronata' produces semi-double purple-blue flowers.
'Coerulea Flore-plena' has double flowers of the same color.
'Grandiflora Alba' has larger (2" diameter) white flowers.
var. *moerheimii* bears double white flowers and is similar to 'Alba Flore-plena' but is longer lived.
'Telham Beauty' is 3–4' tall with bell-shaped pale china-blue flowers. A most handsome cultivar.
'Snowdrift' also has large 2" diameter white flowers.

Propagate by seed (similar to *C. alliariifolia*), division, or terminal cuttings.

-portenschlagiana (por-ten-schlag-ee-ah' na)   Dalmatian Bellflower   4–6"/12"
Spring   Blue-purple   Southern Europe   Zones 4–8
(Syn. *C. muralis*)

This is a particularly effective plant for rock gardens, rock walls or as potted plants. In the British Isles, it scampers over walls and transforms rockeries and walls into glorious seas of blue. I use it in my garden, and although the performance does not compare to English standards, it makes an effective ground cover at the front of the bed. The 1–2" long foliage is triangular and forms low growing dark green mats. The 1" diameter bell-shaped flowers virtually cover the plant in late spring and early summer.

Although the flowers are smaller than those of *C. carpatica*, it is a better plant for the South. Plants persist for three to four years. They are not particularly fussy about growing conditions except drainage, which must be excellent.

Cultivars:
var. *alba* is a lovely white-flowered cultivar, otherwise similar to the species.
var. *major* has larger flowers than the type.

115

Propagation of the species is easy from seeds or divisions; cultivars are easily divided. The seeds are extremely small and should not be covered. Water from the bottom so seeds will not be washed away. A four week treatment at 35–40°F promotes germination.

Related Species:

C. × 'Birch Hybrid' resulted from a cross between C. *portenschlagiana* and C. *poscharskyana*, Serbian bellflower. Nodding cup-shaped purple blue flowers smother the 6″ tall plants. Effective for walls and crevices.

-poscharskyana (po-shar-skee-ah' na)		Serbian Bellflower	8-12″/12″
Spring	Blue-lilac	Yugoslavia	Zones 3–7

The long 18″ stems are prostrate resulting in excellent plants for dry walls, rockeries, or edgings of paths. The ½–1″ wide star-shaped flowers have deeply cut petals about 4 times as long as the flower tube. The 1½″ long leaves are rounded with wavy margins. This is a good species where a rapidly spreading, low-growing plant is needed for a sunny area.

Propagate by seed (similar to C. *alliariifolia*) or division in early spring or fall.

-pyramidalis (pi-ra-mi-dah' lis)		Chimney Bellflower	3–4'/3'
Summer	Blue, white	Southern Europe	Zones 3–7

This plant is grown as a biennial as it deteriorates badly after the second year. The 2″ long heart-shaped basal leaves have 6–8″ long petioles and dentate margins. Twelve to fifteen inch long, pyramidal, racemose panicles of bell-shaped blue flowers arise from the axil of each stem leaf. More flowers open at the base of the flower stem than at the top, resulting in the pyramidal shape of the inflorescence.

Similar to most other upright species, chimney bellflower does not tolerate heat and humidity and struggles as far north as zone 6. Regardless of locale, stems are brittle and the plant should be supported. If space permits, it is an effective species for patio containers.

Cultivars:

var. *alba* is similar to the type but with clear white flowers.
'Compacta' is a dwarf 2–3' tall form. It is easier to manage in the garden and requires less room than the type but lacks the characteristic pyramidal shape. Propagation is similar to other species.

Related Species:

C. × *fergusonii* (C. *pyramidalis* × C. *carpatica*) has erect 2' tall stems with blue flowers. It is seldom seen in North American gardens.

-rotundifolia (ro-tund-i-fo' lee-a)	Harebell	6-12"/12"
Summer Blue-violet	Northern Hemisphere	Zones 2–7

This species is circumboreal in distribution and is found in many regions of North America. It is known as the Bluebells of Scotland and well entrenched in song and verse in that country.

The 1" wide basal leaves are rounded, thus "rotundifolia", but often disappear by the time flowering occurs. The 2–3" long stem leaves are linear and grass-like. Many flowering stems are formed and several ½–1" wide, bell-shaped, nodding flowers are borne in each terminal raceme.

Performance is far better in mountain or northern climates, and plants are ideally suited to the northern United States and Canada. In the South, they are much more sprawling and weed-like.

Cultivars:

var. *alba* has creamy white flowers but is otherwise similar to the species.

'Flore-plena' has double blue flowers that are more persistent than other cultivars.

'Olympia' is a good bright blue-flowered cultivar with 12" tall stems. In our gardens at the University of Georgia, this was pretty the first year, weedy the second, and dead the third.

var. *soldanelliflora* is a unique semi-double variety whose blue flowers are split to the base into about 25 divisions. It is most appropriate for the northern States and Canada.

Propagate by seeds (similar to *C. alliariifolia*) or division.

Quick Key to Campanula Species
- A. Plants normally less than 1' tall
  - B. Flowers nodding
    - C. Plants less than 6", stem leaves slightly toothed or absent, basal leaves ovate .... *C. cochleariifolia*
    - CC. Plants greater than 6", stem leaves entire and linear, basal leaves kidney-shaped to rounded .... *C. rotundifolia*
  - BB. Flowers upright
    - C. Flowers star-shaped
      - D. Blue flowers small with white center, stem leaves round toothed .... *C. garganica*
      - DD. Blue flowers large, stem leaves sharply toothed .. *C. poscharskyana*
    - CC. Flowers not star-shaped
      - D. Flowers large (1½" wide), broadly cup-shaped, solitary .... *C. carpatica*
      - DD. Flowers smaller, bell-shaped, few to a stem... *C. portenschlagiana*
- AA. Plants normally greater than 1' tall
  - B. Flowers white, nodding............................... *C. alliariifolia*

117

BB. Flowers not white (in species), upright
  C. Stem leaves linear to narrowly lance shaped . . . . *C. persicifolia*
  CC. Stem leaves oval or rounded in shape
    D. Flowers in dense, clustered head . . . . *C. glomerata*
    DD. Flowers in spike-like or racemose inflorescences
      E. Flowers widely bell shaped to saucer shaped,
        inflorescence pyramidal in shape . . . . *C. pyramidalis*
      EE. Flowers narrowly bell shaped to tubular,
        inflorescense long spike-like
        F. Lower stem leaves sessile or nearly so,
          inflorescence 3–4″ long . . . . *C. lactiflora*
        FF. Lower stem leaves long petioled, inflorescence
          1–2″ long . . . . *C. latifolia*

Additional Reading:
Books:

Bailey, L. H. 1953. *The Garden of Bellflowers*. Macmillan Co.

I strongly recommend this book for any would-be Campanulite. It is an excellent reference to the campanulas and other bellflowers (including *Adenophora*, *Platycodon*, and *Codonopsis*). Unfortunately, it is out of print and will have to be found in a good library or in an used book store specializing in garden books.

Manuscripts:

Sheldon, E. 1988. Try campanulas for diversity. *American Horticulturist* 67(6): 22–26, 32–35.

Canna (kan' na)   Canna Lily, Indian Shot   Cannaceae

Approximately 50 species occur in the genus but finding a true species in the garden is well nigh impossible. The plants which adorn gardens today are known as *C.* × *generalis*, *C.* × *hybrida*, or just plain garden hybrids. They resulted from crosses among *C. glauca*, gray canna; *C. speciosa*; *C. iridifolia*, Peruvian canna; *C. warscewiczii*, and the native *C. flaccida*, southern marsh canna. Suffice it to say the nomenclature is rather confusing and I prefer "garden hybrids". Nomenclature aside, many beautiful hybrids are available which out-perform their parents 100 times over.

Cannas placed in rich, well-drained soil in full sun begin to flower in mid-summer and continue well into the fall, depending on cultivar. In most of the country, the rootstocks must be lifted after frost has knocked down the leaves. Allow the roots to dry in a warm area for a few days and then store them in moist (not wet!) peat moss where temperatures will remain above 40°F. In zones 8–10, the plants may be overwintered in the ground but no damage will be done if rootstocks are lifted. In the spring, start the rhizomes indoors in pots about 4 weeks before the date of the last frost. Do not plant them too early as they are tender and may be killed by late frosts. Plant single colors *en masse* 1' apart for maximum effect.

Cultivars:

There are hundreds of cultivars with single to multiple colored flowers and green, bronze or purple foliage. Heights range from 1½' to 7'. Canna specialists are continually releasing new cultivars.

A List of 10 Reliable Hybrid Cultivars:

	Height (ft.)	*Leaf color*	*Flower color*
'Black Knight'	3	Bronze	Dark red
'Lucifer'	2	Green	Red and yellow
'Orange Beauty'	4	Green	Orange
'Pfitzer Chinese Coral'	2	Green	Red
'Pfitzer Crimson Beauty'	1½	Green	Crimson-red
'Pink President'	3	Green	Pink
'Richard Wallace'	4	Green	Yellow
'Rosamunde Cole'	3½	Green	Red
'The President'	3	Green	Red
'Wyoming'	4	Bronze	Orange

Propagation of cultivars is accomplished by division of the rootstock. On the roots are many dormant buds, and at least one bud must be present to reproduce the plant. The strongest buds yield the strongest plants. Large clumps can be produced by using root pieces with multiple buds. Seed is available for a number of cultivars and germination is easy if the seed is first soaked in water for 24 hours to soften the hard coat. The seeds are so hard that natives of the West Indies were said to have used them for shot, thus its other common name, Indian shot. Seeds germinate in 14 days and plants may flower the first year.

Caryopteris (ka-ree-op' te-ris)   Bluebeard   Verbenaceae

Although this genus consists of woody species, plants die back to ground each winter and may be treated as herbaceous perennials. Violet-blue flowers that almost encircle the stem appear in late summer and fall on the current season's growth. There are six species, of which two are valuable and overlooked garden plants.

Quick Reference to Caryopteris Species:

	Height (ft.)	Flowers whorled all the way around stem
C. × clandonensis	3–5	No
C. incana	3–5	Yes

-× **clandonensis** (klan-don-en′ sis)		Blue Mist	3–5′/4′
Summer	Blue	Hybrid origin	Zones 5–9

This hybrid, between *C. indica* and *C. mongholica*, was raised in West Clandon, England, (thus its specific epithet), in 1930. The opposite leaves are narrow, up to 3½″ long and the undersides are gray-white.

They are usually entire but occasionally may be coarsely toothed. Up to 20 flowers are held in a tight 1–2″ diameter cyme and two cymes are borne in each of the upper 3–4 leaf axils. The inflorescences lean toward the outside of the plant giving the appearance of the flowers being one-sided.

Full sun and well-drained soils result in maximum performance. The flowers are a welcome late summer relief from the many yellow daisies which flower at that time.

Cultivars:

'Arthur Simmonds' was raised in the garden of the late Arthur Simmonds of West Clandon, Surrey, England. Plants are 2′ tall and consist of dull green 1–2″ long leaves and bright blue flowers.

'Blue Mist' has gray-green foliage and light blue flowers.

'Dark Knight' bears the darkest blue flowers of any cultivar.

'Ferndown' has dark green foliage and dark blue flowers. Raised in Ferndown Nurseries, Dorset, England.

'Heavenly Blue' is of American origin and has darker green leaves, deeper blue flowers, and is altogether a superior plant to *C. × clandonensis*. Seed propagation of this cultivar has resulted in much variation, making it more difficult to distinguish. 'Blue Mist' and 'Dark Knight' may have resulted as sports of 'Heavenly Blue'.

'Kew Blue' resulted from a seedling of 'Arthur Simmonds' and was raised in Kew Gardens. Flowers are a darker blue than 'Arthur Simmonds'.

'Longwood Blue' was selected at Longwood Gardens, Kennett Square, PA. Plants have silvery foliage, bear sky blue flowers in late summer and grow 1½–2′ tall.

Propagate by terminal cuttings in spring or early summer.

-*incana* (in-cah′ na)		Common Bluebeard	3–5′/4′
Late Summer	Blue	China, Japan	Zones 8–9

(Syn. *C. mastacanthus*)

There are few obvious differences in the foliage between this and the previous species. The leaves of this species are not quite as gray-green or as long (only 1–3″) and linear, and are always coarsely toothed. The flowers are violet-blue and held in cymes in the upper leaf axils. Each cyme has many more flowers than *C.* × *clandonensis* and totally envelop the stem. It is much more ornamental and the flowers are not one-sided as in the previous hybrid. Flowering begins in early August and persists for at least 8 weeks. We have experimented with this species in the cut flower trials at Georgia and the flowers are excellent and long lasting.

Plants require full sun and well-drained soils. The main drawback is the relative lack of cold hardiness and plants are not suitable north of zone 8. Even in zone 8, mulch should be applied around the base of the plant. The first hard frost kills back the top growth and plants may be cut back to 18–24″ any time thereafter.

Propagate by seed in warm, humid conditions. Two to three inch terminal cuttings of new growth also root readily.

Quick Key to Caryopteris Species

    A. Leaves 2–3½″ long, flowers one sided on stem, flowers bright
       blue, foliage gray-green . . . . *C.* × *clandonensis*
    AA. Leaves 1–3″ long, flowers envelop stem, flowers violet-blue,
       foliage green . . . . *C. incana*

Catananche (kat-a-nan′ ke)   Cupid's Dart   Asteraceae

The common name comes from the fact that the plants were once used by the ancient Greeks as an important ingredient in love potions and its presence in bouquets is still used to symbolize love. Flowers are useful for fresh or dried cut flowers. Plants should be placed in full sun in well-drained soils. There are five species in the genus but only one, *C. caerulea*, is worthy of mention.

-*caerulea* (se-ru′ lee-a)   Blue Cupid's Dart   18–30″/12″
Summer   Blue   Southern Europe   Zones 3–9

The foliage is mostly basal and narrow, and usually entire or with a few small teeth. Each leaf is woolly-pubescent on both sides with three veins running the length. The 8–12″ long leaves may be gray-green, particularly when young. The blue dandelion-like flowers are about 2″ in diameter and borne singly on long naked flower stems. Each ray flower is strap shaped while the disk flowers (the center) are darker blue. The yellow stamens provide a pleasing contrast.

Cultivars:

var. *alba* is a white-flowering form which is not nearly as handsome as the type. 'Bi-color' may be the solution for those who can't decide between white- and

121

blue-flowered cultivars. It has white petals with a dark center, and is often used for dried floral bouquets.

'Blue Giant' has dark blue flowers decorating a 2' tall stout plant.

'Major' produces lavender-blue flowers and is nearly 3' tall.

'Perry's White' is similar to var. *alba* and may even be the same clone.

Propagation of the species is not difficult from seed. If sown in March or April, plants will flower the first year. Barely cover the seed in the seed tray. Cultivars can be raised by root cuttings (see *Anemone* × *hybrida*) in the spring.

Caulophyllum (kaw-lo-fill' um)   Blue Cohosh   Berberidaceae

This little-known genus contains 2 species, only one of which is occasionally offered by nurserymen. They are plants for the shade garden and thrive in moist conditions but do poorly if allowed to dry out. They may be propagated by seed or division in the fall or spring.

-thalictroides (tha-lik' troi-deez)   Blue Cohosh   12–18"/12"
Spring   Yellow-green   Eastern North America   Zones 3–9

This woodland plant is native from southeastern Canada to Alabama and Mississippi. The thickened rootstock sends up fleshy grayish green stems which bear 1–2 pinnately compound leaves. The leaf is 3-lobed at the base with each lobe deeply cut into three 1–4" long narrow segments. The small, ½" long yellow-green flowers are rather nondescript and held in a loose panicle. The main reason for including this species in the shade garden, however, is the appearance of the blue grape-like berries in late summer which stand erect above the foliage. The berries remain even after the foliage has withered and provide a rich, deep blue for the late fall landscape.

Centaurea (sen-tor' ree-a)   Cornflower, Knapweed   Asteraceae

Centaurea contains approximately 500 species and about a dozen are useful garden plants. A number of excellent annual species occur such as *C. cyanus* (bachelor's button), *C. americana* (purple basket flower), and *C. moschata* (sweet sultan). The latter two species produce excellent cut flowers. *C. cineraria* (dusty miller) is a popular gray-leaf bedding and edging plant. The cornflowers are a diverse group of plants but all have overlapping scales immediately beneath the petals as one of the identifying characteristics of the genus. The leaves are alternate and may be once or twice divided.

All prefer full sun and good drainage. If placed in too much shade, plants become lanky and weedy. They are easily propagated from seed and no particular problems with germination should be encountered if the seed is fresh.

Many of the hardy species can also be propagated from divisions and should be divided every 2–3 years.

   Centaurea is a genus awash in ancient Greek folklore. It is said to have healed Chiron the Centaur. This, in itself, may not seem reason enough to name a genus after such an event because as we all know, most Centaurs were wild and lawless. Chiron, however, unlike most of his kind, was wise and just. He was a magnificent teacher and having been healed by that innocuous cornflower, went on to teach many Greek heroes, including Achilles. Next time you see a bachelor's button, think of Chiron.

Quick Reference to Centaurea Species

	Height (ft.)	Flower color	Flower diam.(in.)	Foliage color (top)
C. dealbata	1½–2½	Lavender	2½–3	Green
C. hypoleuca	1½–2	Rose, pink	1½–2	Gray-green
C. macrocephala	3–4	Yellow	3–3½	Green
C. montana	1½–2	Blue	1–2	Green
C. nigra	1–1½	Violet	1–1½	Green
C. pulchra	2–3	Pink	3–3½	Gray-green

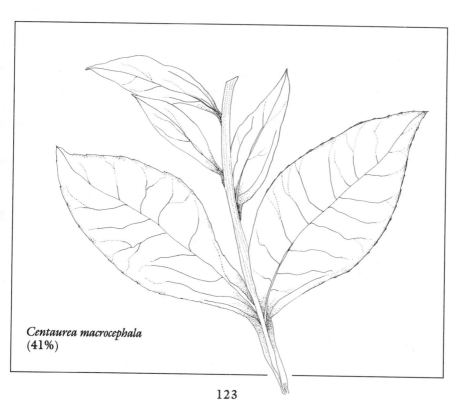

Centaurea macrocephala
(41%)

123

-dealbata (deel-bah′ ta)		Persian Cornflower	1½–2½′/1½′
Late Spring	Lavender	Asia Minor, Persia	Zones 3–7

The foliage is up to 2′ long, coarsely cut into pinnate lobes with long whitish hairs on the underside. The deeply fringed flower heads are solitary and carried atop a slender stem bearing small, sessile, entire leaves. The bracts at the base of the petals (involucre bracts) are deeply fringed like the flowers. The 2–3″ diameter flowers appear in late spring in the South (early summer in the North) and continue for approximately 4 weeks. The warm days and nights in zones 7 and 8 tend to make them stretch and require staking. In zone 8, plants melt out in the summer and decline within 3 years. They are better plants for the North where their stems are thicker and less likely to fall over.

Cultivars:

'Sternbergii' is more compact in plant habit and flowers longer than the species. The flowers have clear white centers surrounded by rosy petals.

-hypoleuca (high-po-loo′ ka)		Knapweed	1½–2′/1½′
Summer	Rose purple, pink	Armenia	Zones 4–7

There is little difference between this species and the previous except that it is more compact and the leaves are grayer. The flowers are smaller (1½–2″ diameter) although named cultivars may have flowers up to 4″ across.

Cultivars:

There is a great deal of confusion concerning the parentage of 'John Coutts', an excellent lavender-colored *Centaurea*. It was originally thought to be a cultivar of *C. dealbata* and is usually offered as such in catalogs. Further study by Graham Stuart Thomas, the noted British plantsman, changed it to *C. hypoleuca* and some catalogs offer it as such. Other nurseries have decided that it really does not matter and offer it as *C.* 'John Coutts'. The bottom line to the gardener is that if you obtain 'John Coutts', you will have a good garden performer.

-macrocephala (mak-ro-ceph′ a-la)		Armenian Basket Flower	3–4′/2′
Summer	Yellow	Armenia	Zones 3–7

This is one of my favorite plants when grown in a favorable environment. The large bright yellow flowers are 3–4″ in diameter and are excellent cut flowers. They last up to 10 days in water and are well established in European florists' shops. The coarse 5–6″ long leaves are entire with wavy margins. The involucre bracts (see *C. dealbata*) are brown and papery and add to the coarse appearance of the flower. In Michigan (zone 5), it reaches 4′ tall with full yellow flowers and deep green leaves. On the other hand, in our trials in North Georgia (zone 8), it struggles to reach 3′ and the flowers are small and persist but a short time.

-montana (mon-tan' nah)		Mountain Bluet	1½–2'/1'
Early Summer	Blue	Europe	Zones 3–8

In the North, this plant is a weed—a very pretty weed, but one nevertheless. I remember this plant taking over almost the entire garden in Montreal and the difficulty in removing it. Where we could keep it confined, it was lovely, but little did we suspect the travelling ways when so innocently planted. Even aware of its dark side, I still enjoy the bluets for their rich blue flower color and unique flower shape. It is a cool season species, and does not have the same vigor in the South as in the North. Regardless of locale, it is stoloniferous and will be somewhat of a rover. Plants perform best in high pH soils.

The 2–2½″ diameter flowers consist of long ray petal flowers around the margin and short disc flowers in the center. The outer ray flowers are tubular and the ends are divided into 3–5 short segments. The normal color of the flowers is deep blue with a reddish center. Another lovely characteristic of this species is the black margin around each involucre bract (see *C. dealbata*). The bracts overlap like shingles and add to the value of the flower. The foliage is entire and silvery-white when young.

Cultivars:

'Alba' has white flowers.
'Rosea' ('Carnea') bears pink flowers.
'Violetta' produces amethyst flowers.

-nigra (ni' gra)		Hardhats	1–1½'/1'
Summer	Violet	Europe	Zones 3–7

Having escaped from cultivation, plants can be found in fields throughout the eastern United States. The flowers and petioles are dark violet and the solitary, ball-like flowers are responsible for the common name. This is a coarse, somewhat weedy species but the violet color contrasts well with the whites and pale yellows of summer.

Cultivars:

'Rivularis' is similar to the species but more compact.
'Variegata' has leaves edged with creamy white and is most striking.

Related Species:

C. kotschyana, Kotschy's cornflower, grows 3' tall and bears deep purple to blood red flowers. Plant in full sun in well-drained soil.

-pulchra (pul' kra)		Pink Knapweed	2–3'/2'
Summer	Rose-pink	Kashmir	Zones 4–7

This species is seldom seen in the United States but one I am hoping will be here soon. In Holland, I have seen fields of this plant grown for cut flower production and, in parts of Europe, is an outstanding garden plant. In *Hardy Plants of Distinction*, Alan Bloom states "the real aristocrat amongst centaureas is surely *C. pulchra* 'Major'". It is similar in habit to *C. macrocephala* and without the flower, the two may be confused. The pinnately compound leaves are entire, smooth and grayish green. The flowers resemble those of *C. macrocephala* in that they are large (3″ in diameter), borne singly on stout stems, and full. It is less hardy than *C. macrocephala* but limits of hardiness have not been established with certainty in North America.

Cultivars:
'Major' is larger and more vigorous than the type and is a better garden plant.

Quick Key to Centaurea Species
    A. Leaves entire
        B. Flowers blue or violet
            C. Flowers blue, ray flowers on margins very different than
                ray flowers near center .... *C. montana*
            CC. Flowers violet, ray flowers similar .... *C. nigra*
        BB. Flowers yellow or rose
            C. Flowers yellow, foliage green on both sides .... *C. macrocephala*
            CC. Flowers rose to pink, foliage gray-green.................. *C. pulcra*
    AA. Leaves cut once or twice, not entire
        B. Leaves smooth above, white hairy beneath................. *C. dealbata*
        BB. Leaves gray-green on both sides .... *C. hypoleuca*

Centranthus (ken-tran′ thus)   Red Valerian, Jupiter's Beard   Valarianaceae

The genus consists of about a dozen species but few are used in American gardens. They are fair border plants and grow in alkaline soils in full sun. The name comes from *kentron*, spur, and *anthos*, flower, because the corolla (the petals) is spurred at the base.

-ruber (rew′ ber)		Red Valerian	18–36″/24″
Spring	Pink-red	Europe	Zones 5–8

This old-fashioned, neglected garden plant is the best of the genus. The sessile, opposite blue-green leaves are about 4″ long, and sometimes toothed at the base although more often entire. The individual flowers are only ½″ long but numerous flowers occur on the terminal cymes in late spring and summer. Red valerian thrives on infertile, chalky soils.

The white cliffs of Dover, England take on a red hue in spring as the precariously perched plants flower profusely up and down the limestone cliffs. In fact, there are few nooks and crannies in northern Europe that this plant does not inhabit. In the United States, it is not as nomadic but may still occasionally be found on roadsides and outcroppings. Insects and pests are non-existent and little more than irrigation and sunshine are required. Cut flowers last about one week in water.

Cultivars:

var. *albus* produces clean white flowers and is an excellent plant.
var. *coccineus* has deep red flowers.
var. *roseus* bears rose-colored flowers.

Propagation is easy by seed and in most seed collections, reds, whites, and sometimes rose-flowered plants will occur. Plants flower the first year from seed. Division in the spring or fall is necessary to maintain true colors.

Cephalaria (seff-al-ay' ri-a)   Cephalaria   Dipsacaceae

Although consisting of 30 large, coarse species, the genus is seldom encountered in the United States. However, one species is striking enough to be of use in gardens where room is available.

| *-gigantea* (gi-gan' tee-a) | Tatarian Caphalaria | 5–6'/4' |
| Summer | Yellow | Caucausus | Zones 3–7 |

(Syn. *C. tatarica*)

C. *gigantea* is particularly tall and if pinched early, may also grow 5' wide. The striped stem carries dark green pinnate leaves, each leaflet having toothed margins and hairy undersides. The primose-yellow flowers produced at the end of the 2' tall wiry stems are flattened and scabiosa-like (at one time this species was in the genus *Scabiosa*). The 2" diameter flowers heads are made up of many 4-parted florets and the marginal florets are enlarged and radiate outwards. Flowering persists on and off throughout the summer.

Plants look best at the back of the garden where their coarseness may be reduced but where their attributes may still be enjoyed. The flowers provide a lovely soft yellow not often found in gardens. Place in full sun and provide adequate moisture. If allowed to dry out, the leaf margins turn black and the foliage quickly deteriorates. Plants decline in the fall and should be cut back after flowering.

Propagation by seed is easiest if seed is placed in sand at 40°F for approximately 6 weeks. After 6 weeks, sow seed and sand in peat:vermiculite mix under warm (70–75°F), humid conditions. Divisions may also be used; plants need dividing every 2–3 years to maintain vigor.

Related Species:

C. *alpina*, yellow cephalaria, differs mainly in the marginal flowers which are not enlarged and are a truer yellow. Sometimes plants offered as C. *alpina* are simply variants of C. *gigantea*.

127

Cerastium (ser-ass′ ti-um)   Snow-in-Summer   Caryophyllaceae

The genus is so confusing that taxonomists can not decide if there are 40 or 100 species; probably the number is somewhere between. The main species found in gardens, however, evoke emotions of love or hate from gardeners. When in flower, the plants literally look like shiny mounds of snow in summer. Perhaps because I watch *Cerastium* "melt out" in summer in the South, I appreciate it more than most. In England, it is rampageous, and has been described as a "thug and a strangler..", and an " unpromising race of weeds.." by Alan Titchmarsh in *The Rock Gardeners Handbook*. Few areas in this country enjoy the luxury of it being a weed. In any event, *Cerastium* provides several excellent species for the wall, rock garden, or borders along paths and if plants gets out of hand, simply "tear them up by the roots . . . or burn by the barrow-load" (Titchmarsh).

Ideally, full sun is required in the North and partial shade in the South. Shear off the flowers after they fade to maintain plant vigor. The fact that it will grow in pure sand is a telling reminder that drainage should be excellent and feeding minimal.

Propagate by seed collected in summer, by divisions in spring or fall or by softwood cuttings.

-tomentosum		Snow-in-Summer	6–8″/12″
Late Spring	White	Italy, Sicily	Zones 2–7

This is the most common species and the silvery leaves and bright white flowers are a welcome sight in late spring and early summer. Plants do not tolerate heat well and the centers decline where summers are hot and humid. The leaves are ½–¾″ long and the tips resemble the end of a spatula (spatulate). The petals are deeply divided so there appear to be ten petals instead of five. It spreads by underground runners and quickly fills in an area or covers a wall.

This is a fine, tough plant for northern areas and is often cursed by its own performance. Where it does well, people take it for granted and belittle its contributions to the spring garden. In the South, gardeners hold their breath in the summer hoping that it will establish itself well enough to provide another show next spring. Unfortunately, they are often disappointed.

Cultivars:

'Columnae' and 'Silver Carpet', which may be the same, both more matted and more compact than the type.

'Yo-yo' has a compact growth habit and does not spread as rapidly as the species. With a name like that, it should be a hit.

Sow seeds on the top of the peat:vermiculite mix but do not cover. Place the tray in warm (70–75°F) humid conditions. Germination occurs in 14–21 days, after which the seedlings should be placed at 55–65°F. Division may be accomplished anytime during the growing season.

Related Species:
C. biebersteinii, taurus chickweed, is similar except that leaves are larger (1–1½" long, ⅕" wide), and are not spatulate. The petals are deeply notched at the ends and about twice as long as the calyx. The foliage is silvery-gray because of the long white hairs covering the plant.

Ceratostigma (ser-at-os' tig-ma) Leadwort Plumbaginaceae

This genus of 7–8 species has alternate, rather bristly leaves. There are two excellent garden species, one commonly available, and one which deserves greater use in the American landscape, particularly in the South.

Quick Reference to Ceratostigma Species

	Height (in.)	Fall color
C. plumbaginoides	8–12	Yes
C. willmottianum	24–36	No

-plumbaginoides (plum-bah-gi-noi' deez) Leadwort 8-12"/18"
Late Summer Blue China Zones 5–9

(Syn. *Plumbago larpentae*)

The 1–2" long alternate leaves have short petioles, and are borne on many branched angular stems which die back to the ground in the fall. The deep gentian blue, ¾" diameter flowers are arranged in terminal heads, and flower from late summer well into fall.

Plants look equally good in Athens, Georgia and Columbus, Ohio. They tolerate full sun but afternoon shade results in open plants which spread more freely. As a ground cover in sunny areas or as a plant to ramble over small rocks, it is difficult to beat. In the fall, the foliage turns bronze-red and although plants won't compete with red maple or kochia for fall color, they are quite striking. Leaves emerge late in the spring so patience is important. Plants in zone 5 should be mulched.

Propagate by cuttings, spring division or seed. Seed germinates more uniformly if placed in sand in a plastic bag, and stratified for 4–6 weeks at 40°F. Root cuttings may also be used (See *Anemone* × *hybrida*).

-willmottianum (wil-mot-ee-a' num) Willmott's Leadwort 24–36"/2'
Late Summer Blue Western China Zones 8–10

This shrubby member may grow 5' tall, although 2–3' is more realistic. The 2" long pointed leaves have coarse hairs on both sides and taper at the base while the 5-lobed flowers, violet-blue with a rosy red tube, persist for 6–8 weeks. The leaf buds are covered with short scales in this species but are naked in the previous.

This is a most interesting plant, being a subshrub similar to *Caryopteris* and *Perovskia*. The leaves are smaller than those of the previous species yet the plant is twice as tall. The greatest drawback is the relative lack of cold hardiness, but is a fine plant in areas where hardy.

Propagation is similar to *C. plumbaginoides*.

Quick Key to Ceratostigma Species

    A. Plants slow growing, less than 18″ tall, foliage turns red in the fall, buds without scales.............................. *C. plumbaginoides*

  AA. Plants greater than 18″ tall, foliage remains green in the fall, buds scaly... *C. willmottianum*

| *Chelone* (chel-o′ nee) | Turtle-head | Scrophulariaceae |

The flowers of the 4 species in this genus are rather reptilian in appearance and if you squint your eyes and count to 10, you may see the resemblance to a turtle head. The sessile flowers are inflated and held in a terminal spike. The species are native to North America and prefer partial shade and rich, moist soil. They are particularly useful for bog gardens and stream bank areas with acid soil. Pinching the shoot tips in the spring results in better performance in all species.

Quick Reference to Chelone Species

	Height (ft.)	Flower color
C. glabra	2–3	White
C. lyonii	2–3	Rose-pink
C. obliqua	2–3	Deep rose

-glabra (gla′ bra)	White Turtle-head		2–3′/2′
Summer	White tinged with red	United States	Zones 3–8

(Syn. *C. obliqua* var. *alba*)

Native from Newfoundland to north Georgia, and west to Minnesota, plants are making their way into gardens in increasing numbers. The opposite, dark green, lanceolate leaves have short petioles and are obscurely veined. The flowers are white with a red to rose tinge and are borne in a dense, terminal spike for three to four weeks in late summer.

Plants do well in full sun and constantly moist areas, but do poorly south of zone 7, although if moist conditions are provided, heat tolerance is much improved. This species is handsome because of the contrast of flowers and foliage not seen in other species.

Sow seed in moist peat:vermiculite and cover with ¼" of fine peat. Place the tray at 40°F for six weeks for best germination. Bring out to 60°F and maintain moisture. Seed germinates in 10–14 days and may be transplanted to larger containers in 4–6 weeks. Vegetative cuttings (4–6" long) may also be used in the spring and summer. Division is possible in early spring and fall.

-lyonii (lie-on' ee-eye)		Pink Turtle-head	2–3'/1½'
Summer	Rose-pink	Southeastern United States	Zones 3–8

The 3–7" long leaves are smooth, pointed, and evenly toothed. They differ from the other species by being broadly ovate and long petioled. The 1" long rose-pink flowers have a yellow beard on the lip of the outermost petals and are held in a dense terminal spike. Flowers persist for about 4 weeks in the summer.

This is the most common turtlehead in North America but, similar to the previous species, is most suitable for cool climates. It should be planted in full sun, although afternoon shade is not detrimental in moist, rich soils. It tolerates

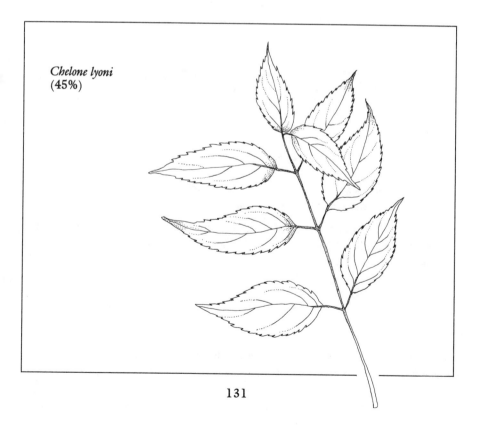

Chelone lyoni
(45%)

131

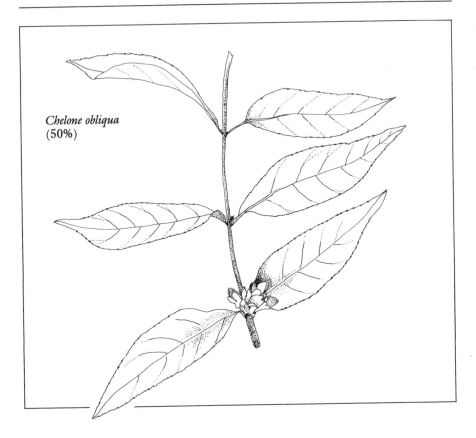

Chelone obliqua
(50%)

basic soils better than the other species of *Chelone*. With sufficient moisture, large clumps develop within 3–4 years.

Propagate similar to *C. glabra*.

-obliqua (o-blee′ kwa)	Rose Turtle-head	2–3′/2′
Late Summer, Fall Deep rose	Southeastern United States	Zones 6–9

Plants have smooth, large (up to 8″ long) and prominently veined leaves which are sharply toothed and broadly lanceolate. Some references claim that this is much shorter than *C. lyonii*, but I have seen little difference between them. The flowers are also similar to those of *C. lyonii* but are deeper rose.

While *C. lyonii* is native to the mountains of the Southeast, *C. obliqua* is native to wetlands, and is less cold hardy. Late flowering makes it a desirable addition to an area where moisture is plentiful.

Plants look lovely flowering alongside *Anaphalis, Aster, Anthemis* and *Sedum* in the fall garden. The upright habit, rosy-red flowers and handsome foliage make it a perfect companion for many plants.

Cultivars:

'Bethelii' has many more flowers on each spike and the deep rose color is more vibrant than the species.

Propagate similar to *C. glabra*.

Quick Key to Chelone Species

    A. Petioles very short, leaves lanceolate
      B. Flowers white, often tinged with pink.......................... *C. glabra*
      BB. Flowers rose to deep rose .... *C. obliqua*
    AA. Petioles long, leaves ovate.. *C. lyonii*

Chiastophyllum (ky-as' to-fy-lum)   Cotyledon   Crassulaceae

This is a monotypic genus, having only one species, *C. oppositifolium* (syn. *Cotyledon simplicifolia*). I first discovered this little gem in England a few years ago and was intrigued with the unique plant. From the 3 to 4 pairs of rounded, opposite, fleshy basal leaves emerge upright inflorescences of dangling chains of pea-like yellow flowers in spring and early summer.

The plant is most suited for draping over walls or in a rock garden and requires excellent drainage and afternoon shade. The species occurs in limestone outcroppings in its native habitat, therefore garden soils should be well limed. A grouping of three or four will definitely draw attention if well grown. Plants presently being tested in the Horticulture Gardens in Athens (zone 8) are struggling. Although I have not seen plants elsewhere, I believe they are hardy in zones 5 to 7.

Propagate by division in the spring or late summer. Seed propagation requires that the tiny seeds be mixed with sand and then spread out on the seed container. Place the container at 60–70°F for 2–3 weeks, then transfer to 40°F for 4–6 weeks. After cooling, remove and germinate at 65–75°F. This is more easily accomplished by sowing in flats in the fall, placing outside in a cold frame, and waiting until spring after Mother Nature has done her job.

Chionodoxa (ky-on-o-dox' a)   Glory-of-the-Snow   Liliaceae

Chionodoxa contains a wonderful group of spring-flowering bulbs which, in their native habitats, even bloom through the snow. Flowering occurs in March-April when bulbs are planted approximately 3" deep in the fall in full sun or partial shade. *Chionodoxa* is often confused with *Scilla* (squills) however, the perianth (flower segments) pieces are obviously united at the base whereas those of *Scilla* are not.

133

-luciliae (loo-sil' ee-aye)   Glory-of-the-Snow   4–6"/4"
Early Spring   Blue with white eye   Asia Minor   Zones 4–9

This is the best species of the genus. The two linear leaves arise in the spring followed by three to six wide open flowers on each flower stem. Each intense blue flower is about 1" wide with a large white center. If weather remains cool, flowers persist for 3–4 weeks. Warm weather accelerates flowering (as in all spring bulbs) and results in reduced flowering time.

Bulbs require good drainage and if planted on sides of hills or banks, they soon spread to make a spectacular display. They are also at home in the garden but at least 50, preferably one hundred or more, should be planted together.

Cultivars:

var. *alba* has white flowers on 6" tall stems and var. *rosea* has pink flowers on 8" high stems. Other than flower color, they are similar, although not as pretty as the species.

var. *gigantea* has large (2" diameter) blue flowers and var. *tmolusii* produces late flowering blue and white flowers. These varieties have recently undergone some taxonomic hair splitting and are now considered distinct species.

Related Species:

C. sardensis, Sardenian glory-of-the-snow, has 6–8 sky blue flowers which have no white disc (or very diminutive) at the throat of the flower. Some gardeners find that the lack of white center intensifies the flower color, however, I feel the white of *C. luciliae* provides interest as well as beauty. It flowers about a week earlier than *C. luciliae*.

× *Chionoscilla allenii* is a natural intergeneric hybrid between *C. luciliae* and *Scilla biflora* but is seldom offered in the trade. It is similar in habit to *Chionodoxa* but is subject to fungal diseases which attack *Scilla*.

Propagation is by offsets, small bulbs which form around the older bulbs, just after flowering. Fresh seed should be sown in seed flats at 65–70°F. If seed dries out, cold moist stratification (35–40°F) for 4–6 weeks provides more uniform germination.

Chrysanthemum (kris-anth' e-mum)   Chrysanthemum   Asteraceae

The chrysanthemum is one of the oldest cultivated plants in existence. Chrysanthemums provide a common bond with the people of China who lived 500 years before the birth of Christ. As happens with plants in cultivation that long, breeding efforts have changed the natural form and size so that some species exist in habits (eg. cascading forms, tree forms), colors, and flower shapes entirely different from the species. This is particularly true for the decorative *C. × morifolium* (*Dendranthema grandiflora*). Although most people think of the fall-flowering "mum" as the only plant in the genus, over 100 species are recorded, including many useful garden plants. A number of common wild flowers such as ox-eye daisy (*C. leucanthemum*) and Nippon daisy (*C. nipponicum*), green-

Chrysanthemum × superbum
(47%)

house flowers such as marguerite daisy (*C. frutescens*) and commercially grown cut flowers like the pungent feverfew (*C. parthenium*) are commonly cultivated. Species flower in summer and fall and almost every color of flower but blue is available. Several miniatures such as *C. atlanticum*, with lovely white daisy flowers, and *C. hosmariense*, grow less than one foot tall while underused annuals including *C. carinatum*, rainbow daisy, and *C. segetum*, corn daisy, offer additional possibilities. The leaves of all species are alternate, but may be divided, lobed, or entire.

Chrysanthemums are best planted in full sun and need little more than adequate drainage to thrive.

Quick Reference to Chrysanthemum Species

	Height (ft.)	Flower color	Flower time	Leaf shape
C. coccineum	1–2	various	early summer	finely divided
C. × morifolium	1–3	various	fall	lobed

	Height (ft.)	Flower color	Flower time	Leaf shape
C. parthenium	1–3	white, yellow	summer	lobed, cut to midrib
C. × rubellum	2–3	various	fall	lobed
C. × superbum	2–2½	white	summer	coarsely toothed

-coccineum (kok-sin' ee-um)		Pyrethrum, Painted Daisy	1–2'/1'
Early Summer	Various	Western Asia	Zones 3–7

(Syn. *Pyrethrum roseum*)

This species is not only a fine garden plant in cool areas of the country, but also the source of pyrethrum, an insecticide widely used for control of whiteflies in the greenhouse. The finely divided leaves are a vivid green; the lower ones about 10″ long and attached to the stem by a long petiole while the upper are sessile. Above the handsome foliage rise wiry stems supporting solitary 3″ wide flowers. Most of the flowers are in shades of red or white with yellow centers and occur as singles or doubles.

Plants can be placed in full sun in the North but should be protected from afternoon sun in the South. Painted daisies do not tolerate heat particularly well and, unfortunately, are not good garden plants south of zone 7. In fact, one of the common complaints of gardeners is that plants look beautiful the first year and decline rapidly the second. Another problem is that they often require support, but with the advent of good dwarf cultivars, this problem will be largely overcome. Flowers last 2–4 weeks but plants are not long lived, requiring replanting or dividing every 2 years to maintain vigor.

Cultivars:

'Atrosanguineum' bears single, dark red flowers and is the darkest red of any the cultivars.
'Brenda' produces cerise-red flowers with a yellow eye.
'Eileen May Robinson' has single pink flowers.
'Evenglow' is one of the best selections, producing rich salmon-red single flowers.
'Kelway's Glorious' produces single, dark red flowers.
'Pink Bouquet' produces double pink flowers.
'Robinson's Variety' bears double rose-colored flowers.
'Sensation' has double red flowers.

Some excellent dwarf cultivars are presently being introduced to this country which should result in many more painted daisies in American gardens.
Seed germinates readily in warm (70–75°F), humid conditions or divisions may be taken in early spring or fall.

| - × *morifolium* (mo-ri-fo' lee-um) | Chrysanthemum | 1–3'/3' |
| Fall   Various | China, Japan | Zones 5–9 |

(Syn. *Dendranthema grandiflora*)

The fall-flowering mums are complex hybrids which have been derived over hundreds of years using wild species in China and Japan. *C. indicum* and *C. morifolium* are probably the parents of the thousands of cultivars available today. I remember seeing my first fall chrysanthemum show many years ago in run-down display greenhouses in Hamilton, Canada and the colors, habits, and flower shapes were absolutely phenomenal. I have seen many such shows since but perhaps because it was my first visit to the "land of the mum", I have not seen any better. There are many shapes and sizes of flowers for outdoor culture as well, although not the diversity of forms capable of being grown under protection.

All fall mums flower in response to the length of the night. As fall approaches the night length increases and when it reaches a certain number of hours (critical night length), the flowering response is triggered. The difference between late-flowering and early-flowering mums is simply the number of weeks of critical night length required to flower. Obviously it is important to purchase early-flowering cultivars in areas where frost comes early. In the North, florists' mums received as gifts may be planted outdoors but these decorative forms usually require too many weeks of long nights before frost and often freeze before flowering. In the South, early- and late-flowering mums can be used. There is no relationship between quality of flower and flowering time.

The importance of night length was made very obvious to me when I moved south and noticed chrysanthemums flowering in April. It took me some time to realize that in southern latitudes, long early spring nights occur when temperatures are warm enough for plant growth. In the North, plants do not respond to the long nights of early spring because they are still shivering in the ground. Although plants flower in the South in the spring, they make a poor display and should not be allowed to do so. Flowering stems should be pinched to encourage vegetative growth.

Plant mums in full sun and well-drained soil. They are heavy feeders but should be fertilized no more than 3 times a year. If fed too heavily, it is impossible to keep the height down. Except for dwarf cultivars, cut the plants back heavily once or twice (up to 3 times in the South) to keep plants compact and encourage flowers. Don't cut back later than August 1 in the North or August 15 in the South or all the developing flowers will be removed. Aphids and spider mites are serious pests and pesticides should be used when necessary.

Some relatively new hybrids (1937) referred to as Korean hybrids were developed by an American breeder, Mr. A. Cumming, and were the result of crossing an early flowering cultivar with *C. coreanum*. They are variously colored, well branched and go under names such as 'Venus' and 'Apollo', with coral pink and dark red flowers, respectively.

137

Cultivars:

The hundreds of cultivars of hardy mums are often classified by flower shape.

Cushions: Double-flowered forms with compact growth, usually less than 20″ tall.

Daisies: Single daisy-like flowers with yellow centers.

Decoratives: Taller forms with larger double or semi-double flowers than cushion mums.

Pompons: Free-flowering plants with small ball shaped blooms, usually less than 18″ tall.

Buttons: Plants with small double flowers (less than 1″ across), usually less than 18″ tall.

The 'Minn' series of hardy mums was developed at the University of Minnesota to provide cultivars which flower in the North before frost. 'Minn Yellow' and 'Minn Gold' are examples of this fine series.

All mums can be propagated by divisions in spring and fall. In fact, division once every three years is advisable. New plants may also be propagated by 2–4″ long terminal cuttings taken from vegetative stems in spring and summer.

Related Species:

C. × 'Mei-kyo' produces many small (2″ diameter), double rose-colored flowers with yellow centers. They do not open until late October in my garden and continue until frost. It is hardy in zones 6–9.

C. *nipponicum*, Nippon daisy, native to Japan, is an excellent garden specimen. Large 3–4″ diameter white flowers with green centers open in September or October and flower until frost. Plants range from 3–5′ tall.

-parthenium (par-then′ ee-um)	Feverfew, Matricaria	1–3′/2′
Late Summer	White, yellow	Caucasus	Zones 6–8

This excellent cut flower is highly branched and often covered with ¾″ diameter, button-like flowers. The pinnately lobed foliage is strongly scented which may explain why few insects bother it and why many people don't like it. Each leaf is 2–3″ long, slightly hairy, and toothed.

This is one of those "old-fashioned" plants which is presently undergoing a renaissance as a cut flower and a bedding plant. In 1597, Gerard's *Herball* listed feverfew as a plant which was very good for "them that are giddie in the head". Roman legend states that it saved the life of a man who fell from the Parthenon during its construction, thus accounting for the specific name *parthenium*. (I don't think I believe it either). The foliage is also supposed to be very good fried with eggs. Please let me know.

Plants are not fussy as to soil but should be placed in full sun. The dwarf forms can be used as an edging while the larger forms are excellent as border plants. In the South, dwarf forms tend to melt out, particularly if allowed to dry out, and cannot be recommended for that area of the country. Even when cut back, the new growth declines in the heat and humidity. However, when kept well watered, an excellent crop was produced in the cut flower trials at the University of Georgia.

Cultivars:

var. *alba* has single white flowers on 2′ tall stems.
var. *aureum* has yellow foliage which turns green with the advent of flowers. It grows 8–12″ tall and is known as golden feather.
'Crispum' is a uniquely foul form with foliage curled like parsley.
'Golden Ball' is an 18″ tall yellow, double-flowering cultivar.
'Santana' is only 10–12″ tall with creamy white flowers. Plant performance has been erratic in our garden (zone 8), growing poorly in some years and well in others. It has done well in more northerly areas.
'Snowball' is 2–3′ tall with white double flowers.

Propagate similar to *C. × morifolium*. Seed may also be used.

-× *rubellum* (roo-bell′ um) Hybrid Red Chrysanthemum 2–3′/3′
Late Summer Various Hybrid origin Zones 4–9

This free-flowering, little known species is a likely a hybrid, however, the parentage is obscure. It is similar to *C. zawadskii*, Siberian daisy, and is considered to be a variant (var. *latilobum*) of that species by some authorities. The compact plants are much branched and each leaf is deeply 5 lobed and about 4″ long. The leaf segments are coarsely toothed and quite hairy, particularly on the underside. The pink to rosy-red single flowers are 2–3″ across and held singly or in a few flowered inflorescence well above the foliage. The ray flowers, which are narrow and separated from each other, surround a small yellow center.

It flowers earlier than the hybrid fall mums and is not fussy about soil but should receive as much sun as possible. The flowers are fragrant and make pleasant additions to garden bouquets.

Cultivars:

'Clara Curtis' is the best and easiest to locate cultivar. It grows 2–3′ tall and is covered with 3″ diameter deep pink daisy flowers with raised yellow centers.
'Duchess of Edinburgh' has muted red flowers on 2′ tall plants.

Propagate by division or cuttings similar to *C. × morifolium*.

Related Species:

C. weyrichii is an 8–12″ tall stoloniferous species. The 1–2″ wide pink flowers are carried over palmately parted, shiny green leaves. 'Pink Bomb' bears rosy pink flowers. 'White Bomb' has 2″ creamy white flowers on 12″ stems. Both flower in late fall.

- × *superbum* (soo-perb′ um)	Shasta Daisy	2–2½′/2′
Summer — White	Hybrid origin	Zones 4–9

The Shasta daisy is one of the most popular daisies because of availability and ease of cultivation. It was hybridized in 1890 by the American plantsman, Luther Burbank, by crossing *C. lacustre*, Portuguese chrysanthemum, and *C. maximum*, Pyrenees chrysanthemum, two similar daisy-flowering plants. Unlike other chrysanthemums, the leaves are coarsely toothed, not deeply lobed or divided. The lower leaves are up to 12″ long with short petioles while the upper leaves become shorter as they ascend the stem and are sessile. All the foliage is dark green and toothed. The 2–3″ diameter white flowers are borne singly and cultivars are available in single and double forms.

Plant in full sun with good drainage especially in areas where winter rain is common. It is a good plant for southern gardens; however, it is short lived and usually declines after 2–3 years. Divide or replace at that time.

Cultivars:

Singles:

'Alaska' is one of the oldest cultivars and still one of the best. The pure white flowers have yellow centers and are 3″ in diameter and borne on 2–3′ tall stems. It is cold hardy to zone 3.

'Everest' is similar to 'Alaska', but has 3–4″ diameter flowers and is 3–4′ tall.

'Little Miss Muffet' is only 8–12″ tall with 2–3″ wide creamy white flowers and a orange center.

'Majestic' has 3–4″ diameter flowers with small yellow centers borne on 3′ tall plants.

'Polaris' is a magnificent 3′ tall selection with 5–7″ diameter clean white flowers.

'Silver Princess' is a dwarf selection similar to 'Little Miss Muffet' and may be raised true from seed. These two cultivars can be used as bedding plants as they flower about 12 weeks from sowing and remain in flower most of the season.

'Snowcap' is a compact, bushy, low growing (18″–2′) weather tolerant plant. Rainfall and high winds don't affect it as much as the taller cultivars.

Doubles:

'Aglaya' has fringed petals which make the flower look like it has been attacked by caterpillers.

'Cobham Gold' has flowers which are creamy outside with a yellow raised center.

'Diener's Double' bears flowerw with frilled petals on 2′ tall stems.

'Esther Reed' flowers earlier than most cultivars and is only about 2′ tall.

'Marconi' is a popular cultivar with 4″ diameter clear white flowers on 3′ tall stems.

'Mount Shasta' is 2′ tall and has fully double flowers surrounding a raised center.

'Wirral Pride' is 2–3′ tall and flowers are obviously raised in the center.

All cultivars can be propagated by divisions in spring or fall and many cultivars can be obtained from seed.

Related Species:

C. uliginosum, (syn. *C. serotinum*), giant daisy, produces many two to three flowered clusters of 2–3″ wide white flowers with green centers. The foliage is 3–4″ long, coarsely toothed and sharply pointed. It is one of the tallest species and grows 4–7 feet.

Quick Key to Chrysanthemum Species

    A. Leaves toothed, not lobed or divided .... *C.* × *superbum*
  AA. Leaves lobed or divided
      B. Leaves lobed but not deeply divided
        C. Leaves very hairy beneath, late summer flower ...... *C.* × *rubellum*
       CC. Leaves glaucous or slightly hairy
          D. Leaves glaucous, not hairy, usually fall flowering ....
                                        C. × *morifolium*
        DD. Leaves slightly hairy, plant highly aromatic, late
            summer flowered .... *C. parthenium*
     BB. Leaves deeply divided, not merely lobed .... *C. coccineum*

Additional Reading:

Anderson, N.O. 1987. Reclassification of the genus *Chrysanthemum*. *Hort-Science* 22(2):313.

Associations:

National Chrysanthemum Society Inc., 2612 Beverly Blvd., Roanoke, VA., 24015. Publication: *The Chrysanthemum*.

Chrysogonum (kris-og′ o-num)   Goldenstar, Green and Gold   Asteraceae

    This genus is represented by one species, *C. virginianum*, a useful, shade tolerant ground cover.

-virginianum (vir-jin-ee-aye′ num)   Green and Gold   6–9″/12″
Spring   Yellow   Eastern United States   Zones 5–9

    This is such a popular plant in many parts of the country that nurseries cannot keep up with demand. The 1–2″ long toothed leaves are triangular and dark green. The ends of the petals are slightly notched and the brown stamens contrast well with the 1″ diameter bright yellow daisy flowers.

    Many catalogs state that plants bloom constantly all summer but in reality, they peak in early spring, flower on and off in May and June, and come to a standstill in the heat of the summer. This is particularly so in zones 7–9, although flowers are more persistent in northern gardens. Plants should be placed in moist, well-drained soil and heavy shade, particularly at the southern end of their range. *Chrysogonum* may be grown in full sun only if soils are constantly moist. Although cold hardy to zone 5, an application of mulch in that zone may be prudent. The much respected *R.H.S. Dictionary of Gardening* states that *Chrysogonum* is "of no striking beauty", but I strongly disagree. It certainly deserves a place in the wild flower or moist shade garden.

Division is the surest means of propagation, and should be accomplished in late spring every second year. Seed germinates within 3 weeks when sown in warm (70–75°F), moist conditions. Seedlings may also be found at the base of mature plantings and transferred to other areas of the garden.

Cultivars:

var *virginianum* is 4–6" tall and is most commonly offered in the trade.

var. *australe* is similar but has above ground stolons and shorter stems. Plants spread more rapidly than *C. virginianum* but the flowers are not as showy.

Chrysopsis (kris-op′ sis)	Goldaster	Asteraceae

This genus contains about 20 native species, two or three are occasionally found in the flower garden. As gardeners experiment with more native genera, this one should find a niche. All species have entire, alternate foliage and many golden yellow flowers. The most desirable species is *C. villosa*.

-villosa (vill-o′ sa)		Hairy Goldaster	3–5′/4′
Summer	Yellow	United States	Zones 5–9

The 1–2" long gray-green leaves are narrow and quite pubescent. The stems and leaf bases are bristly-hairy. The 1–1½" diameter golden-yellow daisy flowers occur on short flower stems in multibranched corymbs.

I have seen 4′ tall specimens in Georgia gardens absolutely covered with blooms from late summer until frost. When not in flower, it is a large, rather mundane green thing and when frost occurs, plants blacken immediately and should be cut back severely. Place in full sun and provide plenty of room. Plants are most adaptable and particularly drought tolerant. I recall visiting the garden of a friend who had moved two or three months before. We were in the midst of a drought, not uncommon that summer, and the garden had not been watered. Disaster greeted me; many plants had succumbed, but the 5′ tall, 4′ wide *Chrysopsis* was radiant with golden flowers.

Cultivars:

'Golden Sunshine' is 3–4′ tall, and produces 2" wide yellow flowers a little later than the type.

Propagate by divisions after 2–3 years or by seed harvested from the plants in the fall. Sow similarly to *Chrysogonum*.

Related Species:

C. falcata, (syn. *Pityopsis falcata*), sickleleaf goldaster, is only 5–12" tall with linear leaves and small (less than 1" across) flower heads. For those looking for small wild flowers, the plant has merit.

C. mariana (syn. *Heterotheca mariana*) grows 1–3' tall and bears many 1–1½" wide yellow flowers. Plants prefer sandy soils and good drainage and are as drought tolerant as *C. villosa*.

Cimicifuga (sim-me-sif-fyou' ga)   Bugbane   Ranunculaceae

The genus contains a number of native species which have become popular in recent years as more gardeners discover its attributes. About eight species occur and of the three most available, two are native to North America. *Cimicifuga* is slender, tall, and prefers a moist, shady location and rich, acid soil, similar to its native habitat at the edge of woods where leaf mold is plentiful. The species of garden value have white flowers with minute petals but much of the beauty is provided by the stamens. They are similar in habit to *Actaea* but the flowers are much more densely arranged on longer inflorescences and the fruits (berries in *Actaea*, follicles in *Cimicifuga*) are not ornamental. There are few obvious differences among *Cimicifuga* species and close inspection is necessary to distinguish one from the other. All species have ternately decompound leaves, meaning that the leaves are divided into three segments, three times. All species but *C. japonica*, Japanese bugbane, have small leaves on the flower stems and flowers arranged in long racemes. For identification purposes, determine if the pistils are stalked, as in *C. americana*, or sessile, as in *C. racemosa*. Looking for stalked pistils is not my idea of fun, but it may help identify a wayward bugbane.

Plants of *Cimicifuga* provide a tall, airy foil and provide a balance between spiked and rounded plants. Fall flowering hybrid anemones such as 'Queen Charlotte' combine magnificently with the white, wiry bugbanes. Plants with variegated leaves show off bugbane's dark green foliage.

The common name, bugbane, is a translation from *cimex*, a bug, and *fugo*, to drive away, from the use to which *C. foetida*, stinking bugbane, was put.

Quick Reference to Cimicifuga Species

	Height (ft.)	Flower time	Leaflet size (in.)	Inflorescense size (ft.)	Number of pistils
C. americana	2–6	mid	1–3	2–3	3–8
C. racemosa	6–8	early	3–4	3–4	1–2
C. simplex	3–4	late	1–2	2–3	2–3

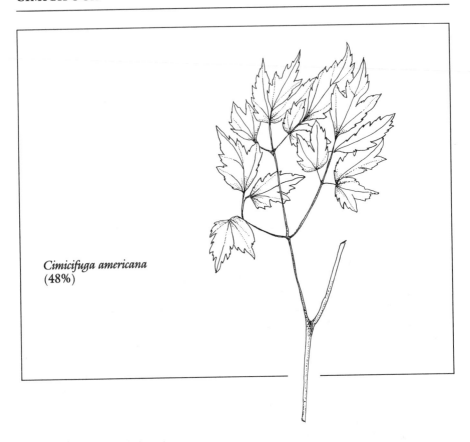

Cimicifuga americana
(48%)

-americana (a-me-ri-kah′ na)		American Bugbane	2–6′/3′
Early Fall	White	Eastern United States	Zones 3–8

Although not as common in gardens as the other species, it is easier to cultivate. Native from New York to Pennsylvania and as far south as the mountains of Georgia, plants are adaptable to a wide range of conditions. The 1–3″ long, rounded leaflets have 3–5 toothed lobes and heart-shaped bases. The flower stalks are sometimes branched near their base providing additional flowers as the season progresses.

Propagation by seed is difficult and best results are obtained with fresh seed. Even then, germination is erratic and seedlings emerge over a long time. After collecting the seed, place in sand in the cold (35–40°F) for 6–8 weeks. Sow seed and sand mixture on a 1:1 mix of peat:vermiculite and place in a warm (70–75°F), humid area. Plants can be divided but this should not be done for at least three years after planting. They have a deep root system and do not divide well.

Related Species:

C. japonica, Japanese bugbane, is 3–4' tall and bears long, branched racemes of white flowers. The foliage is similar to that of *C. americana* except that it is all basal and no leaves ascend the flower stems.

var. *acerina* has dark green maple-like leaves with long pointed lobes and purple stems. An outstanding variety.

-racemosa (ray-ce-mo' sa)		Snakeroot, Cohosh	6–8'/4'
Late Summer	White	Eastern United States	Zones 3–8

This is the aristocrat of the genus whose tall white spires provide an unforgettable sight in the late summer garden. The leaves are deeply cut and the 1–3" long leaflets are ovate and irregularly toothed. The long racemes reach 2' in length, and are often branched near the base of the terminal inflorescence. Flowers open in midsummer in zone 8 but not until late summer or early fall in zones 3 and 4. The flowers persist for about four weeks and the spent flower spires continue to be decorative for many more weeks.

There are fewer flower stalks produced on this species than others but its graceful, yet wiry form has made it popular in American gardens. The plants need a constant supply of moisture or leaf margins turn brown and plants become stunted.

Cultivars:

var. *cordifolia* (*C. cordifolia*) grows 4–5' tall. Leaves consist of 4–10" long leaflets, the terminal leaflet being heart shaped. Flowers are similar to those of the species.

Propagate similar to *C. americana*.

Related Species:

C. ramosa, branched bugbane, is taller than *C. racemosa* and more ornamental. Unfortunately, it is not easy to locate. It grows 6–7' tall and produces many long dense racemes of white flowers.

var. *atropurpurea* is 6–7' tall and bears many flower spires over dark purple foliage.

'Brunette' has deep bronze foliage and is only 3–4' tall. These two selections are outstanding and highly recommended.

-simplex (sim' plex)		Kamchatka Bugbane	3–4'/3'
Late Fall	White	Russia	Zones 3–8

(Syn. *C. foetida* var. *intermedia*)

Although Kamchatka bugbane does not have the majesty of the previous species, it has gained a significant following. The flower stalks are more arching than those of *C. racemosa* and the secondary stalks are often taller than the ter-

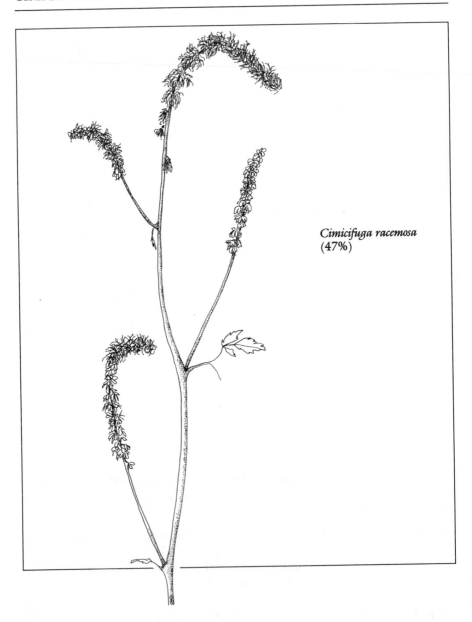

Cimicifuga racemosa
(47%)

minal raceme. Flowers of this species are generally the last of the bugbanes to open, a bonus for gardeners looking for late season color. Plants are more tolerant of basic soils than other species.

Cultivars:

'Elstead Variety' has finely cut dark green foliage, over which purplish brown flower buds open to pure white flowers.

146

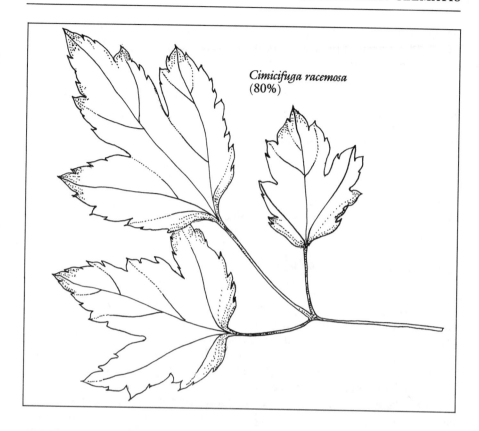

Cimicifuga racemosa
(80%)

'White Pearl' ('Armleuchter') has large (over 2' long), dense white flower spikes. Flowers open in late October in my garden.

Both cultivars are vast improvements on the species.

Propagate similar to *C. americana*.

Quick Key to Cimicifuga Species

    A. Height in flower 4' or less
        B. Number of pistils 3–8 .... *C. americana*
       BB. Number of pistils 2–3 .... *C. simplex*
   AA. Height in flower greater than 4', usually 6' or more......... *C. racemosa*

Clematis (klem' a-tis)   Clematis   Ranunculaceae

    Over 230 species of woody and herbaceous species have been described in this diverse genus. Certainly, the best known are the large-flowered vines and there is no lack of exceptional hybrids and species for the garden. One of the most vigorous climbers, *C. vitalba*, Dutchman's beard, traveller's joy, is quickly strangling many of the forests of New Zealand. It has been designated a noxious weed and eradication programs are being carried out. The genus also includes some fine herbaceous non-climbing species and they shall be discussed here.

The herbaceous species are not as showy as the climbers but are interesting garden plants with flowers of white or blue and heights ranging from 1–3'. The leaves are opposite and may be lobed, entire, or divided.

Quick Reference to Clematis Species

	Height (ft.)	Flower color	Number of leaflets
C. heracleifolia	2–3	Blue	3–5
C. integrifolia	1½–2	Blue	Entire
C. recta	3–4	White	5–7

-heracleifolia (he-ra-klee-i-fo' lee-a)	Tube Clematis	2–3'/3'
Late Summer	Blue	China	Zones 3–8

This subshrub has compound foliage, each leaf divided into three, 3–6" long leaflets with sharply pointed teeth. About 6–12 tubular, hyacinth-like blue flowers are produced in short axillary clusters. They have four reflexed sepals (there are no petals) and some flowers are male while others are perfect (male and female parts present). The 1" long fragrant flowers are produced in late summer and fall and followed by fluffy seedheads.

These are most interesting plants but sprawl everywhere by late summer and fall. They are vigorous growers and should not be fertilized unless necessary. Interplant closely with plants of equal size or provide support such as twigs to keep them from falling over. Plants prefer full sun and plenty of moisture.

Cultivars:
'Cote D'Azur' has lighter blue flowers but otherwise is similar to the type.
var. *davidiana* has wider flowers and less reflexed sepals than the species. The flowers are violet-blue and plants are 6–12" taller than the type. The foliage is heavily scented when dried and may be used in potpourri. This variety is one of the parents of C. × *jouiniana*, a vigorous yellow-white-flowered climber.
'Wyevale Blue' has darker blue flowers than the type.

Propagate by 2" long terminal cuttings in the spring and summer. Seeds may be cooled for 2–4 weeks at 40°F and then sown in a warm, humid area.

Related Species:
C. *stans*, japtube clematis, is similar but has ¾" long light blue flowers borne in terminal as well as axillary clusters. It is less woody and must be supported. It is not as good a garden plant as C. *heracleifolia* or C. *integrifolia*.

-integrifolia (in-teg-ri-fo' lee-a) Solitary Clematis 1½–3'/3'
Summer Blue Southern Europe Zones 3–7

The common name comes from the single, urn-shaped, nodding flowers borne at the ends of the stems. They are indigo-violet, 1–2" long with the sepals turned up at the ends. Flowering occurs in late summer about one to two weeks earlier than *C. heracleifolia*, followed by the appearance of ornamental, plumose seed heads. The 2–4" long leaves are sessile and entire (not trifoliate as in most species). The whole plant is slightly hairy.

Plants do not sprawl as much as the previous species but should still be supported. Place in full sun and do not allow to dry out as leaves blacken around the margins.

Cultivars:

var. *caerulea* has lighter blue flowers than the type.
'Hendersonii' has dark blue flowers and is the most popular selection. However, it is now believed to be a hybrid between *C. integrifolia* and *C. viticella* and should be called *C. × eriostemon*. Regardless of the name, it is a most interesting and handsome plant for the herbaceous garden.

Propagate similar to *C. heracleifolia*.

- recta (rek' ta) Ground Clematis 3–4'/3'
Spring White Southern Europe Zones 3–7

This is different than either of the previous species as it bears numerous, fragrant, white fringed flowers. They are borne in large terminal and axillary panicles in late spring and followed by silky fruits. The pinnately compound leaves are divided into 5–9 entire leaflets, each pointed and 1–3" long. Plants are best left to crawl along the ground but can be supported similar to other climbers. This species does not know whether to climb or crawl.

Cultivars:

'Flore-plena' has double flowers that persist longer than the type.
'Purpurea' bears purple leaves which make a wonderful contrast to the creamy white flowers

Propagate similar to *C. heracleifolia*.

Quick Key to Clematis Species

    A. Leaves divided, not entire
      B. Leaflets 5–9, flowers white.................................... *C. recta*
     BB. Leaflets 3, flowers blue............................ *C. heracleifolia*
   AA. Leaves entire, not divided.................................. *C. integrifolia*

Additional Reading

Evison, Raymond, J. 1979. *Making the Most of Clematis*. Floraprint Ltd, Nottingham, England. 78 pages.

Codonopsis (ko-don-op' sis)   Asia Bell   Campanulaceae

This little-used genus consists of about 20 species of herbaceous plants, often with twining stems. The nodding flowers are bell-shaped and have a distinctly unpleasant odor.

-clematidea (klem-a-tid' ee-a)		Asian Bell Flower	2–3'/2'
Summer	Light blue	Asia	Zones 6–8

The stems are erect when young but eventually begin to sprawl and twine. The ¾" long lanceolate to ovate leaves are entire, lightly pubescent and alternate. The 1" wide, nodding, light blue, bell-shaped flowers have lovely orange centers which are only seen if you take the trouble to pick them up and look inside. The flowers are usually solitary at the ends of the many branches. The lobes of the calyx (sepals) are about half the length of the corolla (petals).

Plants require a good deal of room because of their sprawling habit and are best planted on banks or other areas where the inside of the flowers can be admired. Otherwise they are not particularly outstanding. Place them in full sun to moderate shade and provide plenty of moisture.

Propagate by terminal cuttings or seed. Take 2" long terminal cuttings of basal shoots emerging in spring and root in a peat: vermiculite mix. Seeds should be covered lightly and placed in warm (70–75°F), humid atmosphere. Germination occurs within 2–3 weeks.

Related Species:

C. ovata is similar and often confused with *C. clematidea*. Plants are shorter (9–12") and less sprawling. The calyx is less than ½ as long as the corolla.

Convallaria (kon-val-air' ee-a)   Lily-of-the-valley   Liliaceae

The only species in the genus, *C. majalis*, is native to most of the Northern Hemisphere. The creeping rootstock allows rapid spread under optimum conditions. In the North, it is often looked upon as a benevolent, fragrant weed but as one travels further south, the creeping tendency is severely retarded and plants do not fill in as rapidly or as well. Growing up in Montreal, I loved and hated it with equal passion. Plants filled in everywhere and dynamite was needed to dislodge them. However, nothing compared to the thick fragrance of the flowers in the spring. Living in Georgia, where it struggles to send up a few flowers in the spring, I have decided that I know of no finer weed.

The 2–3 basal leaves are lanceolate-ovate and about 8" long. The arching, one sided racemes carry 5–8 drooping, white, wonderfully fragrant flowers

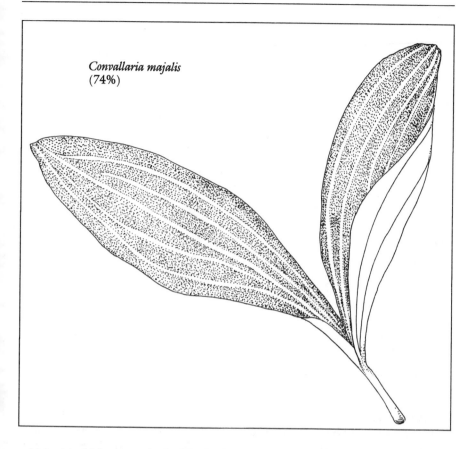

Convallaria majalis
(74%)

which should be brought inside the house to be fully enjoyed. The plants are about 12" tall in flower and thrive in Zones 2–5, do well in zones 6 and 7, and labor in zone 8. Grow in semi-shade and consistently moist conditions.

Cultivars:

'Fortin's Giant' ('Fortin's Variety') is 12–15" tall and has larger flowers (¾" long) than the species.

'Plena' has cream-colored double flowers, larger and more persistent than the type.

'Rosea' has light pink flowers but is otherwise similar to the species.

'Striata' has green leaves with pale white stripes and white flowers.

Propagate by division immediately after flowering.

Coreopsis (ko-ree-op' sis)   Tickseed   Asteraceae

Many of the 100 or more species are popular with gardeners today. They have opposite leaves, which may be entire or lobed, and yellow daisy-like flow-

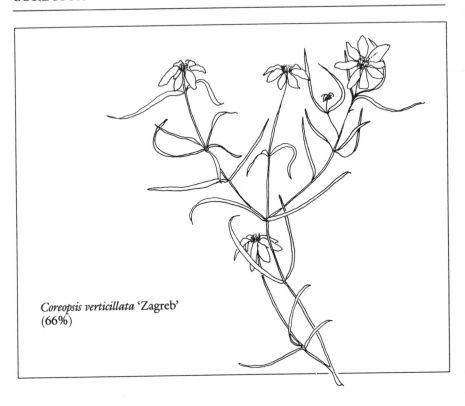

Coreopsis verticillata 'Zagreb'
(66%)

ers. A number of fine annuals exist, particularly *C. tinctoria*, plains coreopsis, as well as many wild flower species such as *C. tripteris*, Atlantic coreopsis, *C. integrifolia*, Chipola river coreopsis, and the large-flowered, pretty *C. major*, trefoil coreopsis, which brightens roadsides from Pennsylvania to Florida.

Many of the perennial species were once known as *Leptosyne*, a name no longer used, and the annual species were called *Calliopsis*, which seedsmen and nurserymen persist in using, resulting in unnecessary confusion within the genus. The name *Coreopsis* translates "like a bug", and refers to the shape and color of the seeds. This is likely how the common name, tickseed, evolved.

Coreopsis should be planted in well-drained soil in full sun. All perennial members can be propagated by division and several are easily raised from seed or terminal cuttings. Seeds germinate in 2–3 weeks if sown in a well-drained medium such as peat:perlite (1:1) in warm (70–75°F), moist conditions.

Quick Reference to Coreopsis Species

	Height (in.)	Flower time	Leaf shape
C. auriculata 'Nana'	6–9	Late Spring	entire
C. grandiflora	12–24	Summer	deeply cut

	Height (in.)	Flower time	Leaf shape
C. lanceolata	12–24	Summer	moderately cut
C. verticillata	18–36	Summer	thread-like segments

-auriculata (ow-rik-ew-lah' ta)   Mouse Ear Coreopsis   1–2'/1'
Spring   Yellow   Southern United States   Zones 4–9

The 1–2" diameter solitary flowers, made up of about eight yellow petals surrounding yellow disc flowers, are held well above the dark green, evergreen foliage. The rounded, pubescent leaves are 2–5" long and often have 1 or 2 small lobes at the base of the blade. It is stoloniferous, but does not spread rampantly.

Cultivars:

'Nana' is by far the best cultivar in the species and one of the best of the whole genus. There is nothing flashy but flocks of bright yellow flowers are produced in April and May. The foliage remains in good condition all season if moisture is provided. If plants dry out, however, the foliage self-destructs. Like the species, it is stoloniferous, but not invasive. This is a fine plant for the front of the border or along a path.
'Superba' has large (2–3" diameter) orange flowers with a maroon center and is good for cutting.

The species is easily propagated from division or seed. Cover seeds lightly and place seed tray in warm, humid area. Plants can be divided every two to three years to maintain vigor.

-grandiflora (gran-di-flo' ra)   Tickseed   1–2'/1'
Summer   Yellow   Southern United States   Zones 5–9

This is the mainstay of many a summer garden. The lowermost leaves are simple while the upper ones are often deeply 3–5 lobed. The flower heads are 1–2½" across and orange to yellow. It has a particularly long flowering season when handled properly, but unfortunately, plants are short-lived, lasting 2–3 years in the South and up to 4 years in the North.

Flowers on all species of *Coreopsis*, but particularly this one, must be dead-headed if plants are to flower to their potential. Flowering occurs late May to early August if spent flowers are removed, a tiring task but one well worth the fatigue. Don't get lazy and simply flick off the flower heads with your thumb or all that will remain above the foliage is naked flower stalks. Not only will the potential of the plants be unfullfilled by the lack of deadheading but the worn out flowers are wonderful candidates for disease. Many cultivars come true from seed and singles, semi-doubles, and doubles are now available.

153

Cultivars:

'Early Sunrise' is an especially compact, double yellow form available from seed. It won the prestigious All-America Award for 1989.

'Goldfink' produces many 2″ wide single yellow flowers with an orange center, only grows to about 9″ in height and is excellent for the front of the garden.

'Mayfield Giant' is an old cultivar with 2–4″ diameter gold-yellow flowers, grows 2–3′ tall and is useful for cut flowers.

'Sunburst' is about 2′ tall with large semi-double golden-yellow flowers.

'Sunray' is an exceptional selection which bears 2″ diameter double flowers for 8–12 weeks on 2′ plants.

'Goldfink' should be raised from cuttings or divisions but the others are available from seed. Many new seed types will be available in the near future, particularly from Europe. Propagate by divisions in the spring or fall, or from seed treated similar to *C. auriculata*.

-lanceolata (lan-cee-o′ lah-ta)		Lanceleaf Coreopsis	1–2′/2′
Late Spring	Yellow	Eastern United States	Zones 3–8

There is little difference between this and the previous species and some cultivars are hybrids between the two. Plants are rather variable but the flowers are always borne singly and are up to 2½″ across. The stems are leafy mainly at the base of the plant compared to *C. grandiflora* which is leafy throughout. The leaves are not as deeply cut as *C. grandiflora* and sometimes may be entire. It is a good garden performer, perhaps a little longer lived than *C. grandiflora* but not as floriferous. Comments concerning deadheading of *C. grandiflora* also pertain to this species.

Cultivars:

'Brown Eyes' is an excellent long-lived cultivar with single yellow flowers that have a maroon ring near the center. It has been in the Horticulture Garden at Georgia five years and is still thriving.

'Sternthaler' is similar to 'Brown Eyes' and has gold flowers with a brown ring over 12–18″ tall plants.

Propagate similar to *C. auriculata*.

-verticillata (ver-ti-si-lah′ ta)		Thread Leaf Coreopsis	18″–3′/3′
Summer	Yellow	Eastern United States	Zones 3–9

The combination of new cultivars with brigher, better colors combined with drought tolerance, long flowering time, and long life put this species at the top of the list among *Coreopsis*.

The sessile, 2–3″ long leaves are palmately divided into thread-like segments and therefore there is little leaf area from which to lose water under times of drought. The 2″ diameter, single flowers are borne in a few-flowered inflorescence (corymb) and held on slender stalks. Two or three plants grouped in a well-drained, sunny location grow into a sizable clump by the end of the summer. After the burst of summer flowering, cut off the flowers and an autumn flush follows. I have not been as successful with the species in north Georgia as expected. Hordes of flower buds are produced which proceeded to blacken and rot. This has not been the case, however, with several cultivars.

Cultivars:

'Golden Showers' ('Grandiflora') is 18–24″ tall, produces 2½″ diameter bright yellow flowers, and is larger in every way than the type.

'Moonbeam' is fast becoming the most popular cultivar. Plants are 18–24″ tall and bear many soft muted yellow flowers which never fail to catch the eye. Flowers open continuously from late June to October. They have performed well in gardens in zone 8.

'Zagreb' has deeper yellow flowers than 'Moonbeam', Compact upright plants are bushy, upright and only 8–12″ tall in the North. In the South, 18″ tall plants are not uncommon.

Propagate similar to *C. auriculata*.

Quick Key to Coreopsis Species

    A. Leaves divided or lobed, not entire
      B. Leaves finely divided, thread-like........................ *C. verticillata*
      BB. Leaves divided into broad segments, not thread-like
        C. Leaves deeply divided into 3 segments, plant leafy throughout......
                                                            C. grandiflora
        CC. Leaves divided shallowly, sometimes entire, plant leafy
            mainly near base .... *C. lanceolata*
    AA. Leaves entire
      B. Height 12–18″... *C. auriculata*
      BB. Height 6–9″ .... *C. auriculata* 'Nana'

Corydalis (ko-ri′ dal-is)   Corydalis   Fumariaceae

All 300 species produce 4-petaled irregular flowers and many have finely divided fern-like foliage. Although the genus is well represented throughout northern Europe, it is not particularly easy to find in the United States. Many species are ornamental but only *C. lutea*, yellow corydalis, is readily available.

-lutea (loo′ tee-a)		Yellow Corydalis	9-15″/18″
Spring	Yellow	Europe	Zones 5–7

The pale blue-green 1–4″ long leaves are two to three times pinnately compound, resulting in finely divided fern-like foliage. Many wiry stems push

155

through the soil terminating in small golden-yellow spurred flowers. The flowers superficially resemble those of the fringed bleeding heart, *Dicentra eximia*.

Plants bask in shady, moist areas and are tolerant of soils with basic pH. This is a most ubiquitous plant in the British Isles where it grows in cracks of walkways and fissures in walls and revels in areas scorned by more "uptown" plants. Our North American climate is not as much to its liking but corydalis is still a useful addition in the shaded rock garden.

The species is well known for its self-sowing tendencies, however, purchased seed is notoriously difficult to germinate because it is not fresh. Collect fresh seed and sow immediately. All seed should be sown in a seed tray in 1:1 mixture of peat:vermiculite and placed in a warm (70–75°F) area for 6–8 weeks. After the warm treatment, place at near freezing conditions for an additional 6–8 weeks. Warm the trays slowly and germination will occur, although erratically. Fortunately, nature takes care of these conditions. If seed flats are placed outdoors in late summer and allowed to overwinter under snow or other protection, germination will begin as the weather warms in the spring. Plants may also be divided in spring or fall.

Related Species:

C. sempervirens, rock harlequin, is a 2–4' tall biennial which naturalizes by reseeding. Flowers are pale pink to purple with yellow tips and the fern-like foliage is gray green. Plants are native from Newfoundland to Georgia and west to British Columbia.

Additional Reading:

Ownbey, G.B. 1947. Monograph of the North American species of *Corydalis*. *Annals Missouri Bot. Garden* 34:187–259.

Crocosmia (kro-caws' me-a)   Crocosmia, Montbretia   Iridaceae

Crocosmia is becoming more popular as new cultivars and hybrids emerge. The sword-like leaves arise from a corm and myriads of one-sided nodding flowers resembling small funnels are produced along the length of the arching flower stems. They are excellent as cut flowers and used commercially by florists in arrangements and bouquets.

Many of the colors available today are interspecific hybrids while others are intergeneric hybrids between *Crocosmia* and the little-known genus *Curtonus*. A good account of the *Crocosmia* hybrids can be found in the excellent text *Perennial Garden Plants*, by the English authority, Graham Stuart Thomas.

In the North, plants should be lifted in the fall and treated similar to gladioli. Plants can be propagated by division or by lifting and removing offsets from the corms. They become crowded after a few years and flowering will be much reduced if not divided after 2 or 3 years.

- × *crocosmiiflora* (kro-kos-mee-i-flo′ ra)   Crocosmia, Montbretia   2–3′/1′
Summer   Various   Hybrid   Zones 5–9

The hybrid occurred in the early 1880's when the French hybridizer Lemoine introduced a hybrid between *C. aurea*, a golden, large-flowered but tender species, and *C. pottsii*, a vivid red, hardy species. This was once listed as *Montbretia × crocosmiaeflora* by Lemoine and became known as *Montbretia*, a name which no longer has any botanical stature. Additional selections and hybridization in England resulted in free-flowering, brilliantly colored plants. The nodding to erect flowers are borne on a zigzag rachis (the central axis of the inflorescence which bears the flowers) and persist for up to 4 weeks. They have been included in our research on commercial cut flower production and produce 8–10 stems per plant for 2–3 years before requiring division.

Plant in full sun and in well-drained soils. The corms should be planted in spring about 3″ deep and 6″ apart.

Cultivars:

Most cultivars have been bred in England. A few have filtered our way and with luck, more will make it across the pond.

'A. E. Amos' is a brilliant orange-red but has not performed particularly well in north Georgia.
'Citronella' (Syn. 'Citrinum') has small, pretty, orange-yellow flowers above the light green foliage.
'Emily McKenzie' is truly impressive. It was introduced in the mid–1950's and I have yet to see a more vibrant cultivar. The large orange flowers contrast beautifully with the crimson throat.
'Solfatare', one of the oldest hybrids, was bred in the late 1800's by the French nursery, Lemoine. It is 2′ tall with apricot-yellow flowers and dark green leaves.

Related Species:

C. masonorum has 3′ long flower stems, narrowly lanceolate leaves and bright orange-red upright flowers, each measuring about 1½″ long.

'Firebird' was selected by Alan Bloom of Bloom's Nursery in England and has fiery orange-red flowers with a bright yellow throat and is eye-catching in its brilliance.
'Spitfire' is a cross between *C. masonorum* and *C.* × *crocosmiiflora* 'Jackanapes', a red and yellow bicolored cultivar. It is a large plant with stunning orange-red flowers with a yellow throat.

A new race of plants resulting from the hybridization of *Crocosmia* and *Curtonus paniculatus* (Syn. *Antholyza paniculata*) has also been introduced by Blooms of Bressingham. This bigeneric genus contains several stunning cultivars.

'Bressingham Blaze' has intense orange-red flowers on 3' tall plants.
'Emberglow' produces burnt orange-red flowers atop 2–3' tall plants.
'Lucifer' is exceptional and is covered with scarlet-red flowers in the summer. It
has been grown in the United States for a number of years and has proven
its garden value over and over.

Spider mites cause a great deal of damage to the foliage and discourage flowering. A number of chemicals are available and although I do not enjoy the idea
of spraying, these plants are worth the trouble.

Additional Reading:

Kostelijk, Pieter J. 1984. *Crocosmia* in gardens. *The Plantsman* 5(4):246–253.

Crocus (kro' cus)   Crocus   Iridaceae

"All the world loves a crocus. There can be no two opinions about this."
states Loiuse Beebe Wilder in her delightful book *Adventures with Hardy Bulbs*.
Most gardens boast a few plants in March and April, and while these plants are
surely exquisite gems to the gardener, they show but a fraction of the potential
of the 75 species in the genus. Crocus may flower in September, October, November, February, March, and April. In some places, they can even be coaxed
into bloom in December and January. The common crocuses of gardens are the
large-flowered hybrids of *C. aureus* and *C. vernus* and consist of innumerable
spring-flowering cultivars.

The genus also includes a plant of great historical interest—the saffron crocus, *C. sativus*. The bright yellow stigmas of this plant were dried and made into
"karcom" of the ancient Hebrews, and corms were widely cultivated by the
ancient Greeks and Romans. Saffron took on medicinal and culinary uses as well
as being an important dye and perfume. It is still cultivated today in some of
the far eastern countries but is difficult to grow well in this country because of
the need for a long dry period. There are however, many species more ornamental, and except for the interesting stories you can tell your garden visitors,
it probably is not worth the space.

The corm is covered by scaly leaves from which arise leaf and flower buds,
as well as buds which form the new corm over the old. The leaves are usually
channeled and appear before the 3-merous flowers with bright yellow or red
stigmas. Crocuses may be divided into two groups, the first consisting of late
winter and early spring-flowering species, and the second the autumn flowerers
(these are different from *Colchicum*, often refered to as the fall-flowering crocus
which has 6 stamens instead of the 3 found in *Crocus*). The first group should
be planted from September to November while the second must be planted no
later than August. Plant close together about 4" deep in full sun, in groups of
25 or more. They perform well in shady areas, particularly the early flowering
species, but are at their best in the sun. Flowers are short lived, persisting for

Crocus vernus
(100%)

only 1–2 weeks, but what glorious weeks they are. Naturalized in grassy mead-ows, crocus are a beautiful sight when drifts of flowers are in bloom. However, they should not be planted in lawns if the lawn is to be kept cut. Seldom is mowing finished for the year that the emerging buds of autumn-flowering spe-cies are not injured, and mowing starts in the spring before the leaves of the spring-flowering types have yellowed.

Propagation of all crocus can be accomplished by lifting the corms, dividing them into various sizes, and replanting in a larger area. Most species can also be raised from seed. Unfortunately, many animals love the corms as much as gar-deners love the flowers. Squirrels, chipmunks, rabbits, mice and birds can be an awful nuisance and desperate measures must sometimes be taken. As Ms. Wilder also concludes "It is easy to see what a rabid state of mind the gentlest and most humane of persons may be brought by the destruction of his beloved Crocuses. The gun in a sure hand is the most unfailing weapon."

Many of the differences between species are found in the covering of the corm, the color of the anthers and branching pattern of the styles. A good deal of careful study is necessary to discern the identity of unknown plants. Many species are not commonly found in home gardens, and botanical gardens are often worth a visit to appreciate the diversity of the genus, particularly those which flower in the fall.

Quick Guide to Crocus Species

	Flower color	Flowering season
C. ancyrensis	Yellow	Winter, Spring
C. biflorus	White, light blue	Spring
C. chrysanthus	Various	Spring
C. kotschyanus	Rose	Fall
C. speciosus	Blue	Fall
C. tomasinianus	Mauve	Spring
C. vernus	Various	Spring

-ancyrensis (an-see-ren' sis)		Golden Bunch Crocus	4–6"/6"
Early Spring	Yellow	Turkey	Zones 3–9

This is one of the earliest of the spring-flowering crocus to bloom, occasionally flowering in late January in southern gardens. The long, slender flowers are about 1" long, ½" broad and bright yellow inside and out, although occasionally the outer segments may be feathered with bronze. Normally, each corm produces 2–3 flowers and 3–4 narrow leaves which appear with the flowers.

Cultivars:

'Golden Bunch' was selected for its prolific flowering and may have up to 10 golden-yellow flowers per corm, 5 being average.

-biflorus (bi-flo' rus)		Scotch Crocus	4–6"/6"
Early Spring	White, Blue	Italy to Iran	Zones 5–9

This reliable plant flowers as early as February and often bears two flowers at once, thus accounting for the specific name, biflorus. Although not native to Scotland, it has become naturalized there as an escapee from gardens. Typically the flowers are white with a yellow throat and purple stippling on the outer petals. This combination gives the flowers a slight metallic sheen resulting in its other common name, cloth-of-silver.

Performance is better in dry summers than wet ones and, like all crocus, full sun is preferable to shade.

Cultivars:

'Adamii' bears flowers which are lilac inside and light brown outside with darker veining.

var. *alexandri* produces flowers of pure white with glossy purple outside but no yellow throat.

'Pusillus' has small flowers of white with an orange throat.

var. *waldenii* has small white flowers with a bluish base and is one of the best forms of the species. A grayish blue selection is sold as 'Fairy'.

| *-chrysanthus* (kris-anth' us) | | Golden Crocus | 4–6"/6" |
| Spring | Various | Greece, Asia Minor | Zones 4–9 |

One of the best known of the spring-flowering crocus species, this is available in a wide range of colors. It flowers earlier than the hybrids and provides a longer flowering season when combined with them. The wild species is yellowish orange throughout and has a honey-like scent. A distinguishing feature of the species is the black-tipped anthers, although some are more brown than black. Plants often bear more than one flower per corm and produce 3–6 narrow leaves.

Cultivars:

The following are but a few of the dozens of cultivars available. Refer to a reliable bulb catalog for additional selections.

'Advance' has blue-violet outer petals and lemon yellow inner petals.
'Bluebird' is lavender blue throughout with white tinges on the inside of all petals.
'E.A. Bowles', named after one of the authorities on this genus, has canary yellow flowers with bronze veining towards the base.
'Lady Killer' is lilac-white outside and violet-white inside.
'Snow White' bears white to yellow outer petals with a bluish purple veining at the base and white inner petals with a blotch of yellow.
'Zwanenberg Bronze' is yellow on the inside with an interesting bronze exterior.

| *-kotschyanus* (kot-shee-ah' nus) | | Kotschy's Crocus | 4–6"/6" |
| Fall | Rose-lilac | Europe to Syria | Zones 5–9 |

(Syn. *C. zonatus*)

The flowers open a little later than *C. speciosus* and the rose-lilac flowers appear before the leaves. The flowers have a white or deep yellow throat and usually have two deep orange-yellow spots at the base of the flower segments. The anthers are creamy white compared with the orange anthers of Dutch crocus (*C. vernus*).

Cultivars:

'Albus', a white-flowered form, is sometimes available.

-speciosus (spe-see-o' sus)		Showy Crocus	4–6"/6"
Fall	Light blue	Southern Russia, Western Turkey	Zones 5–9

This is the easiest fall crocus to grow. The lavender-blue petals and the large, much divided orange-scarlet stigma make the flowers particularly attractive. The outside of the segments is painted with three main purple veins. It is the earliest of fall crocus and emerges while the foliage is very short. The 3–4 leaves are broad, dark green, and grow 15" long after flowering.

It seeds freely and also increases by offsets. When first planted, locate them in a permanent place as corms do not like to be disturbed.

Cultivars:

var. *aitchisonii* has 1½" broad, pale lavender flowers.
var. *albus* has flowers of white.
'Cassiope' flowers about one week after the species and has rich blue petals with
  a yellow base.
'Oxonian' has large dark blue flowers.
'Pollux' has large violet-blue outer segments and is silver-blue on the inside.

Related Species:

C. goulimyi, native to southern Greece, produces star-shaped pale to deep lavender flowers with a white throat and pale yellow anthers. Flowers emerge with or slightly before the leaves in October and November. Corms increase rapidly by offsets. An excellent fall-flowering crocus.

-tomasinianus (tom-a-se-nee-aye' nus)		Tomasini's Crocus	4–6"/6"
Early Spring	Lavender-blue	Western Yugoslavia	Zones 5–9

Plants increase rapidly by self-sowing and this is one of the better species for large drifts and masses. Three to five leaves are present when the flowers appear, each leaf growing about 10" long. The flowers are lavender to silvery blue outside and when warmed by the sun, they unfurl to boast a soft amethyst center. It flowers early (about 1 week later than *C. ancyremcis*) and is excellent to naturalize with hellebores or snowdrops (*Galanthus*).

Cultivars:

'Albus' produces milky white flowers but is otherwise similar to the species.
'Barr's Purple' has flowers of soft lilac mauve.
'Ruby Giant' produces large blooms of deep ruby purple.
'Whitewell Purple' bears flowers of deep reddish mauve which contrast beautifully with the yellow stigmas.

-vernus (ver' nus)		Dutch Crocus	4–6"/6"
Spring	Various	Europe	Zones 3–9

(Syn. *C. albiflorus*)

The most popular crocus of gardens today, it is widely distributed in alpine regions from the Pyrenees to the Carpathian Mountains. The 3–4 narrow leaves usually have a white line running their length and eventually grow 12–14″ long.

Cultivars:

var. *albiflorus* bears small white flowers.
var. *leucorhynchus* has pale lavender flowers with white tips on the outside.
var. *leucostigma* has blue flowers with cream colored stigmas.
'Obovatus' has feathered purple veins on the outer segments giving it an interesting appearance.

The Dutch hybrids have been selected for size and color and include other parentage such as *C. aureus* and/or *C. tomasinianus* as well as *C. vernus*. Flowers are 2–4″ long, 1–3″ wide, and the color range is extensive.

There are numerous hybrids which should be perused at leisure from fall catalogs. Some I am familar with include:

'Enchantress' has lovely pale blue flowers.
'Peter Pan' has large white flowers.
'Pickwick' ('Mr. Pickwick') has lilac flowers with dark blue stripes on the outside. It is the most popular of the striped cultivars.
'Remembrance' has purple flowers with a dark blue flower tube. This cultivar is often forced in dish or bowl gardens for Valentine's Day.
'Yellow Mammoth' is an apt name for this very popular large-flowered bright yellow selection.

Quick Key to Crocus Species (not including cultivars)
   A. Fall flowering
      B. Flowers lilac to deep blue, style much dissected, anthers yellow .... *C. speciosus*
      BB. Flowers rose to lilac, style slightly divided near top, anthers white .... *C. kotschyanus*
   AA. Spring flowering
      B. Style divided or entire, not trilobed
         C. Style divided, flowers slender with pointed segments, leaves blunt, not tapering at end .... *C. tomasinianus*
         CC. Style entire, flowers broad with rounded segments, leaves tapering at ends .... *C. vernus*
      BB. Style trilobed
         C. Flowers yellow inside and out........................ *C. ancyrensis*
         CC. Flowers not yellow (except cultivars), anthers yellow
            D. Anthers tipped black or dark brown.............. *C. chrysanthus*
            DD. Anthers not tipped black or dark brown.............. *C. biflorus*

Cyclamen (cyke' la-men)   Hardy Cyclamen   Primulaceae

Most people are familiar with the greenhouse cyclamen (*C. persicum*), but a wealth of other useful species occurs in this genus. All arise from corms and have heart-shaped leaves and mottled foliage. The distinctive flowers have reflexed petals borne on slender stalks. In milder climates (Zone 7+), several species may be planted outside for fall and winter bloom. These include *C. cilicium*, with pale rose flowers in the fall and *C. coum*, with carmine pink flowers. The best, most hardy species, however, is *C. hederifolium*.

-hederifolium (he-de-ri-fo' lee-um)   Hardy Cyclamen   4–6"/12"
Fall   Pink, white   Southern Europe   Zones 5–9

(Syn. *C. neapolitanum*)

There are few garden scenes as delightful as a bed of pink and white hardy cyclamen gracing the base of a mature tree in a fall garden. One of the finest examples I have seen is at Snowshill Manor in the Cotswolds of England. The pointed flower buds arise in the fall before the foliage and open into glorious stands of warm pink and white. The ivy-shaped leaves are up to 4–6" long but more beautiful than any ivy. They are gray-green and have attractive patterns of purple marbling. The foliage persists all winter before going dormant in the spring.

Cyclamen should be planted in partial shade and out of afternoon sun in a soil amended with lime. Since they are dormant in summer, water should not be applied where cyclamen are resting or corm rot may occur. Annuals which do not wilt readily, such as begonias, are excellent for overplanting. Once planted, cyclamen need not be moved.

Propagate by seed or cormels. Dense plantings are the result of liberal formation of cormels, which may be divided in the fall after flowering has occurred. It is also interesting to watch how Mother Nature makes sure seeds are shed. As the flowers fall off, the flower stem bearing the seeds begins to twist and coil until the stem capsule is brought close to the ground. At that point, the seeds are released, ensuring they fall near the original planting.

Cultivars:

var. *album* has white flowers. This variety is often interplanted with the pink species and makes a beautiful combination.

Related Species

C. europaeum, European cyclamen, is cold hardy to zone 8 but more difficult to locate. It has small rosy red flowers with a faint fragrance of violets.

Cynoglossum (sy-no-gloss' um)   Hound's Tongue   Boraginaceae

The eighty species have hairy stems and alternate, long stalked basal leaves which were said to resemble the tongue of a dog; hence the common name.

The blue flowers are less than 1" across and held in coiled infloresences called scorpioid cymes. This genus differs from others in the Boraginaceae by having tubular flowers which mature into small nutlets covered with prickles.

None of the perennial species is easy to locate but *C. nervosum*, with dark blue flowers and *C. virginianum* with lighter blue flowers, are useful garden plants. The biennial, *C. amabile*, is 1–2' tall and has lovely funnel-shaped flowers of blue, pink, or white. 'Firmament' is more compact and particularly ornamental.

-nervosum (ner-vo' sum)		Hairy Hound's Tongue	2–2½'/2'
Spring	Blue	Himalayas	Zones 4–8

The leaves and stems are rough due to the presence of short stiff hairs. The 6–8" long basal leaves are narrowly lanceolate, entire and petioled while the upper leaves are more oblong and sessile. Branching sprays of intensely blue forget-me-not-like flowers are produced in the upper axils as well as on the terminal shoot. The ½" long flowers first appear in a rounded head which uncoils to a 6–9" long erect inflorescence. Flowers persist for about four weeks.

Plants require abundant water and do not tolerate dryness. They may be planted in full sun in the northern part of their range but afternoon shade should be provided in zones 7 and 8. Rich soils are beneficial but heavy doses of fertilizer cause plants to grow tall and weak. Growing plants well in the South is difficult because the hairy leaves trap water and the high temperatures and humidity result in foliar disease.

Propagate from seed or divisions in fall or spring. Seed requires no special treatment other than sowing in a warm (70–75°F), humid environment.

Related Species:

C. grande, Pacific hound's tongue, native to western North America, is occasionally seen in gardens in the West but seldom in the East. Plants are 1–2' tall with bright blue flowers and oval, hairy leaves.

165

D

Dahlia (dah' lia)   Dahlia   Asteraceae

Although approximately twenty species occur, few are seen in gardens today. The modern herbaceous garden dahlia is thought to be derived from three Mexican species, *D. pinnata*, Aztec dahlia, with double purple flowers; *D. coccinea*, fire dahlia, with single red flowers; and *D. rosea*, old garden dahlia, with single pink flowers. Since its introduction to Europe in the early 1800's, hundreds of cultivars have been raised, particularly in France, England, Germany, Holland, and United States. These efforts have resulted in plants ranging from one to eight feet tall with flowers up to 18" across. Plants may be purchased that bear huge spider-like flowers or tiny pompom-like balls. One of the more recent trends in dahlias is the use of seed propagated dwarfs for bedding plants. That they can be raised true from seed allows greenhouse operators to offer them far more inexpensively than previously.

There are so many shapes, colors, and sizes of flowers that they have been classified into different groups by the American Dahlia Society. They are classified as to type, size and color of flower. The bedding dahlias are usually in a group of their own. To obtain a listing and definition of various classifications and appropriate cultivars for each, consult the American Dahlia Society (listing at end of *Dahlia*).

Dahlias have tender tuberous roots, normally lifted at first frost. Although they can be left in the ground in zones 8–10 (assuming good winter drainage), some gardeners report that lifting the roots even in those zones results in better performance the following year. After lifting, soak the roots in a fungicide such as benomyl, and store in a cool area in moist but not wet peat moss or sand. Inspect them occasionally over the winter for rot and moisture.

Propagation is accomplished by separating the tubers at planting time. At least one bud or eye must be present on the separated piece of tuber, otherwise no growth will occur. Use a sharp knife for separation of the tubers. Dipping the knife in rubbing alcohol or peroxide before each cut reduces the spread of disease organisms. Cuttings from the base of the plant can also be used as propagation material. Take 1–1½" long terminal growth from the basal shoots, apply rooting hormone (available at most nurseries) and root in a warm, humid area. If cuttings are taken early in the season, plants should flower the first year.

Dahlias are certainly not low maintenance plants in most areas of the country. Many of the tall decorative types require support to prevent flopping. They are prone to mosaic, stunt, and ring spot viruses as well as fungal and bacterial problems. Insects feast on them, the worst being aphids and spider mites. However, many people would not have a garden without dahlias and are willing to spend the time necessary to show off their brilliance, because brilliant they are when properly grown. I have been fortunate in seeing two of the loveliest plantings anywhere. One of these was in Vancouver, British Columbia when my colleagues and I visited Queen Elizabeth Park. Brilliant beds of decorative, spider and anemone flowered dahlias shimmered in the late afternoon light and we marvelled at their uniformity and color range. On my return to Georgia, I looked at the gaps in my garden where I had yanked out my 4' tall lanky, spider mite-infested plants and again pondered the fact that certain species of plants simply are more content in some climates than others.

The beauty of the Vancouver planting was challenged by the dahlia garden at Anglesey Abbey near Cambridge, England, where a great semicircular swath of 3–5' tall plants boasted magnificent flowers of every shape and color. Each photograph I took was to be the last, but each new plant found me exclaiming and firing away with my Canon. I finally pulled myself from that glorious Garden of Eden, very proud of the self discipline I demonstrated. Running out of film and the onset of darkness also helped.

In the South, dahlias need to be sprayed every week for spider mites, something I am not willing to do. I must admit, that for me, dahlias are not worth the problems involved trying to raise them well. I no longer grow dahlias in my southern garden but now I have a great excuse to travel to Vancouver and England again.

Additional Reading:

Sorensen, P.D. 1969. Revision of the genus *Dahlia* (Compositae, Helianthae, Coreopsidinae). *Rhodora* 71:309–416.

Associations:

American Dahlia Society, 2044 Great Falls St., Falls Church, VA., 22043. Publication: *Bulletin of the American Dahlia Society.*

Delphinium (del-fin' ee-um)   Delphinium   Ranunculaceae

Delphiniums seen in today's gardens usually are hybrids whose development began in the late 1800's, although over 300 species of annuals, biennials and perennials occur. *Delphinium* is closely related to *Aconitum*, differing in having a spurred rather than a hooded sepal and four rather than two petals. Similar to *Aconitum*, *Delphinium* prefers more northern latitudes and are not good perennials in the South. The leaves are palmately lobed or divided and plants range from 9″ (*D. tatsiense*) to 6′ tall (*D. elatum*). Although blue is the dominant color in the genus, red (*D. nudicaule*) and yellow (*D. zalil*) flowers occur.

Larkspur is the common name for annuals of this genus but recent taxonomic changes have placed the two common annual species in the genus *Consolida*. The common larkspur, *C. ambiqua*, and the candle larkspur, *C. regalis*, are often listed as *D. ajacis* and *D. consolida*, respectively. Is it any wonder why so many people prefer common names?

In most areas of the country, delphiniums are short-lived perennials and often lose vigor after 2–3 years. Many excellent cultivars can be raised from seed and new plants should be grown for replacement each year. In the South, plants are placed outside in fall or early winter to flower in early spring. After flowering, they are pulled and replaced with annuals.

A well-drained soil with a basic pH (adding lime to the soil helps provide this condition) and full sun are preferable. They are heavy feeders and the use of well-rotted compost or manure in combination with granular fertilizer such as 5–10–5 or 8–8–8 results in stronger, more vigorous plants. The two common hybrids of delphinium are the *elatum* and *belladonna* types, both have hollow, brittle stems which, if not staked, will be ravaged by rain and wind. Removing spent flowers as soon as possible allows formation of secondary blooms in the fall.

Propagation of many named cultivars can be accomplished by seed. Germination is most successful if seed is collected fresh and sown as soon as possible. If this is not possible, store the seeds in the refrigerator (35–40°F) for four weeks. Germination should occur in 14–21 days. Another more reliable method of propagation is basal cuttings in the spring. Take 3–4″ long terminals of new shoots arising from the base of the plants. The base of the cutting should be solid (ie. not hollow) and white. They can be rooted in partial shade in sand or sand/peat mix in 3–4 weeks.

The major pest of *Delphinium* is slugs, which find delphinium shoots particularly hearty, while crown rot is a severe disease in poorly drained soils or where roots have been planted too deeply. Powdery mildew and various leaf blights can also be serious problems.

Quick Reference to Delphinium Hybrids

	Height (ft.)	Single/double flowers	Branched or single flower spike
D. × *elatum*	4–8	Single, double	Single
D. × *belladonna*	3–4	Single	Branched

| -× *elatum* (ay-lay' tum) | | Hybrid Bee Delphinium | 4–8'/3' |
| Summer | Various | Hybrid | Zones 2–7 |

These hybrids probably resulted from crosses between *D. elatum, D. exalta-tum,* and *D. formosum* and although early records were lost, *D. elatum* was surely one of the parents. Hybridization and selection by nurseries in England, Germany, and America resulted in groups of plants referred to as strains or series. Within these groups are plants with different flower colors but similarities in habit and culture. They include the Blackmore and Langdon strains, Pacific Hybrid series (also known as the Round Table series), Wrexham strain, New Century hybrids and others with equally imaginative names. All are characterized by having large, flat flowers on a central flower raceme.

Additional flowering spikes arise from the base especially if the first inflorescence is removed immediately after flowering. These are the aristocrats of the garden and where the weather is cool as in the Pacific Northwest and the Northeast, plants will last up to five years, performing better each year. In the Midwest and Central Plain states, 2–3 years of enjoyment is not uncommon.

Cultivars:

For simplicity's sake, cultivars are arranged by height. The following are but a small fraction of those available.

Tall (greater than 4'):

Pacific Hybrids:

'Astolat' has lavender-pink flowers with a black center.

'Black Knight' is the darkest of the series, bearing dark purple, almost black flowers.

'Galahad' has magnificent white flowers and is one of the latest of the series to flower.

'Guinevere' bears flowers with light blue inner petals which contrast with darker colors on the outer petals to give the impression of a bicolor.

'King Arthur' is a most impressive 3–5' tall dark blue-flowering selection.

'Summer Skies' is light blue with a white center. All the Pacific hybrids are usually raised from seed, therefore, variation in color is common.

Mid-Century Hybrids:

This relatively new strain bears flowers of pink ('Rose Future'), white ('Ivory Towers'), light blue ('Moody Blues'), and dark blue ('Ultra Violet'). They are 4–5' tall, have stronger stems than other tall delphiniums and are more resistant to mildew.

Giant Imperial Series:

'Blue Spires', 'Blue Bell', and 'Rosalind' belong to this series. They are often listed as perennials but are mainly derived from annual larkspur, *C. regalis*. Due to the short-lived nature of delphiniums in most parts of the country, there is often little difference in longevity between these and the hybrid types.

Independents:
Many delphiniums have been bred as independent cultivars, not closely allied to a particular strain or series and because of this, they are often more difficult to locate.

'Betty Hayes' has pale blue flowers with a white eye.
'Canada' is sky blue with a black eye.
'Cressida' bears pale blue flowers with a white eye but is taller and more vigorous than 'Betty Hayes'.
'Jack Tar' is very late-flowering and has large rich, dark blue flowers.
'Xenia Field' produces beautiful pale lavender flowers with a creamy white center.

Small (2½–3½' tall):
These require less staking and are most impressive in groups of 3–5 plants.

Connecticut Yankee Series:
Similar to the belladonna types, cultivars are more heavily branched than many of the previous selections.

'Blue Fountains' is one of my favorites because of its reliability even as far south as zone 8. Flowers are produced in various shades of blue, white and mauve.
'Blue Tit' bears indigo blue flowers with a black eye.
'Baby Doll' has pale mauve flowers with a yellow-white eye.

-× *belladonna* (bell-ah' don-a)	Belladonna Delphinium	3–4'/3'
Summer	Blue shades	Hybrid	Zones 3–7

The belladonna hybrids resulted from crosses between forms of *D. elatum* and *D. grandiflorum*, a two foot tall blue-flowered species. Most cultivars are shorter and more branched than *D.* × *elatum* cultivars. Instead of a central flower stem followed by smaller branches as in *D.* × *elatum*, many flower stems of belladonnas occur at the same time, although the central stem still dominates. Flowering occurs from midsummer to fall. Most cultivars have single, cup-shaped flowers which are often sterile.

Cultivars:
'Bellamosa' produces deep blue flowers on 4' tall plants.
'Bonita' has gentian blue flowers.
'Casa Blanca' has pure white blossoms.
'Clivenden Beauty' bears sky blue flowers and grows 3' tall.
'Lamartine' has deep violet flowers on 4' high stems.
'Moerheimii' has white flowers but is not as vigorous as 'Casa Blanca'.

Additional Reading:

Dodge, Michael H. 1984. Delphiniums: perennial blue bloods. *Horticulture* 62(1):27–31.

Associations:

The Delphinium Society, 11 Long Grove, Seer Green, Beaconsfield, Buckinghamshire, HP9 EYN, England. Publication: *Delphiniums*.

Dianthus (dye-an' thus)   Pinks, Carnations   Caryophyllaceae

To recreate Grandmother's garden, one need go no further than this genus for an excellent start. Pinks have been in gardens as long as there have been gardens. Most garden species are low growing and suitable for rockeries and border edging. Natural and planned hybridization of the 300 species have occurred so that today the parentage of many of the pinks is somewhat cloudy. Considerable selection of annual pinks (*D. chinensis*) has occurred and excellent cultivars are available. In many parts of the country, the annual pinks are hardy and overwinter. The modern day carnations used for corsages and cut flowers are selections of *D. caryophyllus* and require greenhouse conditions to grow properly. Perennial species may be hardy from zone 2 to zone 10, so there is no excuse for not having some *Dianthus* in the garden. Unfortunately, many are short lived and division every two to three years is required to keep plants vigorous and attractive. All should be provided with full sun, excellent drainage, and slightly alkaline soils.

Propagation of many species is relatively easy from seed but division is the most foolproof method for all of the garden species. Most can also be propagated by terminal cuttings.

Quick Reference to Dianthus Species

	Foliage color gray or green	Height (in.)	Flowers solitary, in 2's or clusters	Flower color
D. × allwoodii	gray	12–20	2's	various
D. alpinus	green	3–6	solitary	pink
D. barbatus	green	10–18	clusters	various
D. deltoides	green	6–12	2's	red, pink
D. gratianapolitanus	gray	9–12	solitary	rose, pink
D. knappii	green	15–24	clusters	yellow
D. plumarius	gray	18–24	2's	various

-× *allwoodii* (awl-wud' ee-eye)	Allwood Pinks, Modern Pinks	12–20"/12"
Summer	Various	Hybrid	Zones 4–8

This hybrid was raised in the 1920's by the English nurseryman Montague Allwood, who crossed a garden pink (*D. plumarius* hybrid) with *D. caryophyllus*.

Plants are highly variable but, in general, the foliage is gray-green and usually bears two flowers per stem. Plants flower for up to eight weeks, have a more compact habit than the *plumarius* types (which see), and are more vigorous, requiring division every 2–3 years. Many fine cultivars have been raised and although a few single-flowered forms are available, most are doubles. Some have been raised specifically for exhibition and are known as show or imperial pinks.

Cultivars:

Border Selections (10–18″ tall):

'Alba' has lovely, clear white flowers on 10–15″ tall stems.

'Aqua' grows 10–12″ tall with clear white double flowers.

'Baby Treasure' is a free-flowering plant and bears fragrant shell pink flowers with a scarlet eye.

'Constance' is a silver-pink form with red flecks on the petals.

'Doris' is one of the most popular cultivars and has wonderfully fragrant salmon-pink flowers with a deep pink eye. 'Doris' underwent a number of mutations resulting in two sports, 'Laura' and 'Doreen', both with orange-pink flowers.

'Helen' has a little deeper color than 'Doris' and is free blooming. A recent sport of 'Helen' is available as 'Danielle', a vigorous 10–12″ high plant bearing deep salmon flowers most of the summer.

'Ian' is a long-blooming plant bearing rich scarlet flowers but it is not quite as cold hardy as many other cultivars (zone 5).

'Robin' is one of the brightest of the garden pinks having bright coral-red flowers.

Miniatures (3-6″ tall):

The miniatures can be used to advantage in rock crevices and as fillers in the rockery but, unfortunately, are not particularly easy to locate in the trade.

'Alpinus' is the result of crossing *D.* × *allwoodii* with other dwarf species. It bears single, fragrant flowers and is exceptionally free blooming. Flowers are produced in a mixture of colors ranging from light pink to red and an occasional bicolor. Plants are also more cold hardy (zone 3) than the others.

'Dainty Maid' has single bright purple flowers with a red eye.

'Elizabeth' bears pink flowers with a small crimson eye.

'Essex Witch' is one of the most popular cultivars with flowers in a range of pink hues as well as whites and salmons.

'Fay' has bright purple flowers on 6″ tall stems

'Mars' bears double, rounded, deep pink flowers and grows 3–6″ tall.

'Wink' has lovely clear white flowers on 4″ high stems.

Propagate by division in spring or fall or take 1–2″ long terminal cuttings immediately after flowering. Root in a warm, humid area.

| *-alpinus* (al-pine' us) | | Alpine Pink | 3–6"/1' |
| Late spring | Pink | Austrian Alps | Zones 3–7 |

The grass green leaves are about 1" long and ⅕" wide with a prominent midrib. They are entire and form a loose matted clump which multiplies to cover large areas. The 1½" diameter flowers are large relative to the plant and literally hide the foliage for 4–6 weeks. The five petals are fringed and the scentless flowers usually have a white central disc.

This is a garden gem if soils are well drained, somewhat alkaline, and summers are not often above 85°F. It is an excellent rock garden or edging plant in moderate summers. Plant in moderate shade and minimize full afternoon sun. In my garden (zone 8), it was spectacular until the end of July whereupon it gave up, pooped out, and was not seen again. This is not uncommon in the southeastern states and cuttings and/or divisions should be taken each year.

Cultivars:

var. *albus* has white petals with small purplish spots.

Propagate vegetatively similar to *D.* × *allwoodii*. Seed germinates within 3 weeks if placed in warm (70–75°F), humid conditions.

| *-barbatus* (bar-bah' tus) | | Sweet William | 10–18"/1' |
| Late Spring | Various | Eastern Europe | Zones 3–9 |

Sweet William is as well known in Edmonton, Alberta as it is in Athens, Georgia. Since many of the cultivars are seed propagated, there is a great deal of variation even within cultivars. Although classified as a biennial, it self-sows so prolifically that it is always a guest in the garden. The 2–3" long lanceolate leaves are short-petioled and have a prominent midrib. The unscented flowers have toothed or fringed petals, often with a distinct eye of either a darker or different color than the petals. Although many of the species of *Dianthus* have only 1–2 flowers per stem, sweet williams have a characteristic flat-topped cluster of flowers (cymes).

In the southern states, plants act as true perennials, particularly if flowers are removed before seed is produced. Plants are not long-lived and decline if not divided every 2–3 years.

Lime should be added to the garden yearly to provide a basic soil. They are sun lovers like the rest of the genus, although in the South, partial shade is tolerated. It makes a desirable cut flower, having an excellent shelf life in water. More and more sweet williams are appearing in bouquets and on dining room tables as modern day florists learn of their excellent properties.

Cultivars:

'Blood Red' has one of the darkest red flower colors in the species and grows to 15" tall.

'Homeland' and 'Nigracans' are both deep red-flowered cultivars.

'Indian Carpet' is about 10" tall and occurs in various colors.

'Messenger Mix' is similar to 'Indian Carpet' but is about 15" tall and one of the earliest cultivars to flower.

'Newport Pink' bears deep pink flowers and is 10–12" tall.

'Pink Beauty' has soft salmon-pink flowers on 15" tall plants.

'Scarlet Beauty' bears flowers of rich scarlet.

Division is the surest means to maintain true colors, but terminal cuttings or starting plants from seed is not uncommon. Germination takes 7–14 days when seeds are placed in warm (70–75°F), humid conditions.

Related Species:

'Sweet Wivelsfield' is a hybrid between *D. plumarius* and *D. barbatus*. It is approximately 18" tall with single or double flowers and has a pleasant scent (from *D. plumarius*). Seed is available and although not well known in United States, the ease of propagation may stimulate gardeners to try it.

-deltoides (del-toi' deez)		Maiden Pinks	6–12"/24"
Summer	Red, rose	Europe	Zones 3–9

The species forms loose mats and is an excellent ground cover when planted in full sun or partial shade. Two types of stems are found; the 8–12" long flowering stems which are usually branched at the base as well as as near the top, and non-bearing stems which are prostrate and 4–6" long. The grass-like green leaves are narrow (less than ½" wide), and 3–6" long. They often have a rosy purple flush, especially at cooler times of the year. The ¾" wide, solitary flowers often bear a V-shaped pattern in the throat. They are purple to rose colored and borne at the end of the branched stems. Flowers persist for 8–10 weeks and can totally cover the foliage. Shearing the plants after flowering promotes more vigorous growth and additional flowers in the summer.

Plants spread rapidly under conditions of good drainage and moderately rich alkaline soil. The species is as good as many of the named cultivars, particularly in the South, where some of the larger-flowered cultivars melt out in the summer. Sifting a layer of sand:soil mix on the centers of the planting helps alleviate the problem.

Cultivars:

'Albus' has clear white flowers.

'Brilliant', 'Coccineus' and 'Fanal' have scarlet-red flowers.

'Flashing Light' bears deep ruby-red flowers.

'Red Maiden' has reddish purple flowers which totally cover the 6" tall plants.

'Rosea' bears flowers in various shades of pink.

'Vampire' and 'Wisley Variety' have carmine-red flowers with dark green foliage.

'Zing Rose' has large deep red flowers. While it is magnificent in flower, it is not as well adapted to the South as the type.

Propagation is not difficult from seed or cuttings. Remove 2" long side shoots after flowering with a bit of the main stem attached and place in warm, humid conditions. Seed should be treated as with *D. alpinus*.

-*gratianopolitanus* (grah-tee-ah-no-po-li-tay' nus) Cheddar Pinks   9–12"/12"
Spring   Rose, pink   Europe   Zones 3–9

(Syn. *D. caesius*)

    This is a fragrant but variable species. The common name refers to the Cheddar Gorge in Southwest England, one of the native habitats of this plant. This is also the location of the Cheddar Caves, well known for their delightful cheese. When my colleague, Dr. Michael Dirr, and I visited there, it seems we ate far more cheese than we saw native pinks. Man cannot live by pinks alone!
    The gray-green entire foliage is narrowly lanceolate (less than ⅛" wide) and forms compact tussocks. The 1" diameter flowers are carried singly or in twos and are usually rose, pink or any shade between. If the flowers are not allowed to produce seed, flowering will continue from spring to late summer. In the Horticulture Gardens at Georgia, plants were in full flower from late March to mid-May. There is a great deal of variation within seed-propagated plants but their fragrance and ease of culture make this species one of the best in the genus. In the South, this is an almost indestructible species.

Cultivars:

'Bath's Pink' is one of the finest soft pink cultivars I have seen. The flowers are fringed, 1" across and plants are particularly floriferous.
'Flore-plena' has double pink flowers which are interesting although not particularly ornamental.
var. *grandiflorus* has 1½" diameter rose-pink flowers.
'Karlik' is covered with wonderfully fragrant, deep pink fringed flowers.
'La Bourbille' ('La Bourboulle') has clear, single pink flowers over mounds of silver-green foliage.
'Petite' produces an interesting, tiny 4" tall tussock of gray-green leaves over which appear small pink flowers. For those looking for a truly dwarf dianthus, this is a good choice.
'Pink Feather' has pink flowers with feathery petals.
'Splendens' has deep red flowers.
'Spotty' is an interesting red and white bicolor. This lovely cultivar is worth trying.
'Tiny Rubies' is a double-flowered deep pink form which is becoming more popular in American gardens.

Propagate by seed or terminal cuttings. Treat similar to *D. alpinus*.

| -*knappii* (nahp-ee' eye) | | Hairy Garden Pink | 15–24"/15" |
| Summer | Pale yellow | Hungary | Zones 3–8 |

I remember first reading about this species in a catalog which stated that it was "very rare and uncommon, the only yellow-flowered species of pinks". The way this advertisement ran on, the plant was so rare that if I didn't purchase it, I would seriously add to its chances for extinction.

The truth is, that although *D. knappii* is the only yellow-flowered dianthus in cultivation, it is anything but rare. Plants are easy to grow from seeds (which are plentiful), are short lived, reseed themselves everywhere, have no fragrance, and their washed out yellow flowers are dismally unexciting.

The 2–3" long gray-green leaves are less than ¼" wide and carried on 4-sided upright stems. Eight to ten flowers are clustered in a inflorescence that persists for 4–6 weeks. It grows better and has brighter flower colors in the North than the South, where it dies after one or two years.

Propagate similarly to other species.

| -*plumarius* (ploo-mah' ree- us) | | Cottage Pinks, Grass Pinks | 18–24"/12" |
| Early Summer | Various | Eastern Europe | Zones 3–9 |

The wild species is seldom seen but closely resembles *D. gratianapolitanus*, differing by having petals which are more deeply cut and flowers in groups of two rather than solitary as in the latter species. The main value of the species is that it is the dominant parent of the garden pinks, so popular in today's gardens.

The garden pinks are also known as old-fashioned pinks. They are usually listed separately from the Allwood types, known as modern pinks, previously discussed under *D. × allwoodii*. The garden pinks grow more slowly than the Allwoods and need to be divided every 2–3 years.

Cultivars:

'C.T. Musgrave' bears white flowers with a green eye and is one of the few single flowered cultivars available.

'Dad's Favorite' is a double bicolor of white with red fringes on the petals.

'Essex Witch' is one of the most popular cultivars with flowers in a range of pink hues as well as whites and salmons.

'Excelsior' has carmine-colored flowers with a darker eye.

'Inchmery' has pale pink flowers on a 8–10" tall compact plant.

'White Ladies' produces clean, white, strongly scented flowers.

Quick Key to Dianthus Species

    A. Plants with 1–2 flowers per flower stem
      B. Foliage gray-green
        C. Flowers usually 1 per stem, petals less than ½ cut...................
                                              D. gratianapolitanus
        CC. Flowers usually 2 per stem, petals deeply cut.......... *D. plumarius*

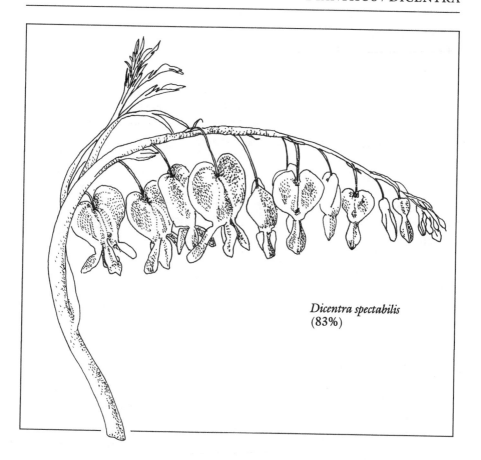

Dicentra spectabilis
(83%)

BB. Foliage green
    C. Leaves grass like, shorter than internodes, flowers 2 per stem . . . .
                                                       D. deltoides
      CC. Leaves longer than internodes, flowers 1 per stem . . . . *D. alpinus*
AA. Plants whose flowers are in clusters
    B. Flowers yellow . . . . *D. knappii*
    BB. Flowers not yellow . . . . *D. barbatus*

Dicentra (dy-sen′ tra)   Bleeding Heart   Fumariaceae

One of the most popular plants for the shaded garden year after year is the bleeding heart. The common name comes from the heart-shaped flowers whose inner petals protrude from the outer petals giving the appearance of a bleeding heart (rather a morbid name for such a lovely flower). The genus includes other colorful members with such imaginative names as Dutchman's breeches (*D. cucullaria*), golden eardrops (*D. chrysantha*), and squirrel corn (*D. canadensis*). In the garden, common bleeding heart, *D. spectabilis*, is the most popular but the virtues of fringed bleeding heart, *D. eximia*, and Pacific bleeding heart, *D. formosa*, are becoming better known and appreciated.

Plants of common bleeding heart were first introduced to England from Japan in the 1840's by one of the great plant explorers, Robert Fortune. There are about 15 species of *Dicentra*, characterized by deeply cut, compound leaves and flowers in racemes. All prefer rich moist soil in a shaded location. Propagation is accomplished by taking 3–4" long root cuttings (see *Anemone* × *hybrida*) in the summer or fall, division in the fall, or by sowing seed in late summer. Seed should be placed at 60–65°F for 2–4 weeks, 40°F for 4–6 weeks, and finally warmed slowly to 65°F until seed germinates. If placed in a seed flat in the fall and placed outside under mulch or snow, nature will take care of these requirements. Sometimes fresh seed may germinate well without any special treatment but if stored for more than two weeks, the above program should be followed.

Quick Reference to Dicentra Species

	Height (in)	Flower color	Dormant in summer	Inflorescence branched
D. eximia	9–18	Rose-pink	No	Yes
D. spectabilis	18–24	Rose-pink	Yes	No

-eximia (eks-ee′ mee′ a)	Fringed Bleeding Heart	9–18"/18"
Spring Rose-pink	Eastern United States	Zones 3–9

The fringed bleeding heart is native to forest floors from Georgia all the way up to New York. It is stemless: foliage and flowers arise directly from the scaly rootstock. The leaves are deeply cut, fern-like, and usually gray-green in cultivation. The inner petals of the 1" long rosy pink heart-shaped flowers protrude from the outer petals and are easily visible. Flowers are carried on long branched racemes resulting in a more floriferous species than common bleeding heart when optimal growing conditions are provided.

Cultivars:
Significant improvements have occurred as a result of breeding and selection programs in Europe.

'Alba' has lovely milky white flowers over light green foliage.

'Boothman's Variety' is a magnificent soft pink-flowered form with blue-green foliage.

'Silversmith' has white flowers flushed with pink and is quite different from other cultivars.

'Snowdrift' has pure white flowers without the pink tinge of 'Silversmith'.

'Stuart Boothman' is similar to 'Boothman's Variety' but the specimens I have seen have redder flowers and more glaucous foliage.

Related Species:

D. formosa, Pacific bleeding heart, is the western form of fringed bleeding heart and similar to the above. The main difference is that the inner petals barely protrude from the outer petals. Native from British Columbia to central California, it is more drought tolerant but less resistant to hot, wet summer weather than *D. eximia*. Considerable confusion exists as to the parentage of some of the newer cultivars. The debate is centered on whether the cultivars are selections of *D. eximia*, *D. formosa* or hybrids.

'Adrian Bloom' was a chance seedling from 'Bountiful' and produces ruby-red flowers.

'Bountiful' has soft rosy red flowers and finely cut foliage.

'Luxuriant' is almost certainly a hybrid between the two species and bears cherry red flowers over 15" tall blue-green foliage. I have had no success with this cultivar in zone 8.

'Sweetheart' appears to be a cultivar of *D. formosa*. Plants bear snow white flowers on 12" tall stems.

'Zestful' has large flowers of deep rose.

-spectabilis (spek-tah' bi-lis)	Common Bleeding Heart		18–24"/18"
Spring	Rose-pink	Japan	Zones 2–9

Common bleeding heart is difficult to beat when grown in partial shade and provided with adequate water. The leaflets are the largest of *Dicentra* species and the flowers, made up of white inner petals extending from rosy outer petals, look like they have been hung out to dry on the arching flower stems. It is a great joy to watch the foliage emerge in the spring and the flowers which follow soon after. If well watered, the foliage is attractive until early summer in the South and into the fall in the North. However, if rainfall is light or plants dry out, the foliage yellows and disappears by mid-June. This is one of the differences between this species and *D. eximia*, which does not go dormant.

Bleeding hearts can easily be forced in greenhouses or cool conservatories. Plants should be dug early in the spring when dormant, potted and brought into a cool greenhouse (55°F) for forcing. With the addition of heat and water, leaves appear in 10–14 days followed by open flowers four weeks later. It is one of the fastest species to force and is particularly appreciated on Valentine's Day.

The dormant rhizome is divided after flowering or 3–4" long root cuttings are taken in March and inserted in a cold frame in clean soil. Pot up or line out when young leaves are well developed and plant in the garden in the fall.

Cultivars:

'Alba' is the ever-present white form which is very impressive but not as vigorous as the type. The foliage is also lighter green.

'Pantaloons' is pure white and is a more vigorous selection of 'Alba'.

Quick Key to Dicentra Species

A. Leaves finely cut, flower stem branched, plants stemless .... *D. eximia*

AA. Leaves lobed, flower stem not branched, plants with leafy stems...........

D. spectabilis

Dictamnus (dick-tam' nus)	Gas Plant	Rutaceae

The genus contains only a few species but the main garden species is so outstanding that it makes up for lack of members. Gas plants are rich in volatile oils, which supposedly can be lit on a still, warm evening. I have gone through many a match, but have yet to see even a tiny spark. It is easy, however, to rub the leaves and smell the lemon fragrance present in the foliage.

Regardless of what is rubbed or ignited, this is an exquisite plant when established. The alternate leaves are glossy green and the plants are long lived. Two-year-old plants are usually purchased and require at least two more years to look their best.

-albus (al' bus)		Gas Plant	3–4'/3'
Early Summer	White	Europe, Asia	Zones 3–8

(Syn. *D. fraxinella*)

The alternate pinnate leaves are divided into 9–11 finely toothed leaflets about 2" long which are covered with translucent dots. The 1" long white or purple flowers have long exserted stamens and are held in a long terminal raceme. Although plants are up to 4' tall, the bases of the stems are woody and support is unnecessary.

Plants should be placed in a well-drained, sunny location and left undisturbed. Over a number of years, large clumps bearing magnificent displays of flowers develop. Unfortunately this plant is not comfortable in all parts of the country, and cool nights are necessary for best performance. I have a number of plants in the Horticulture Gardens at Georgia and although they improve every year, at their present growth rate, they will never reach the proportions of which they are capable. However, the plant is so lovely that I recommend it for southern gardens, but patience is a definite virtue. I look forward to its appearance each spring more than any other plant in the garden.

Cultivars:

var. *purpureus* has flowers of soft mauve-purple with darker veins on the petals. It is most attractive.

Propagation is time-consuming with *Dictamnus*. They are difficult to divide and the resulting injury may considerably damage the parent plant. Root cuttings have been used successfully (see *Anemone* × *hybrida*) but the donor plant must be disturbed to harvest the roots. Although feasible commercially, it is not a good technique for the home gardener. The most common method is to gather the seeds in late summer (do this before they are ejected all over the garden) and plant them in a container and place outdoors. Keep the seed container moist. Don't expect germination until the following spring, at which time some seedlings should emerge. Do not throw away the seed flat as seedlings will continue to emerge for an additional 12 months. This is one of the species which has been the subject of a good deal of seed research at Georgia, and as yet we have been unable to force the seeds any faster than Mother Nature.

Digitalis (dij-i-tah' lis)　　　　Foxglove　　　　Scrophulariaceae

If one surveyed flower gardens for foxglove, one would probably assume that only a single species, *D. purpurea*, existed in the genus. There are, however, over 20 species and three or four deserve a place in the shaded garden. Common foxglove is biennial but others are true perennials, and although not as spectacular, are fine garden plants nevertheless. The flowers are borne in tall colorful racemes which dominate the garden. The leaves of all foxgloves occur in rosettes as well as along the stem. Soil requirements are minimal but plants perform well in soils rich in organic matter. They should be planted in partial shade and not be allowed to dry out.

The name digitalis means finger-like and they were called finger flowers because "they are like unto the fingers of a glove, the ends cut off" (Parkinson, *Paradisi*).

Quick Reference to Digitalis Species

	Height (ft)	Flower color
D. ferruginea	4–5	Rusty red
D. grandiflora	2–3	Yellow
D. lutea	2–3	Yellow
D. × mertonensis	3–4	Rose
D. purpurea	4–5	Purple, white

-*ferruginea* (fe-roo-gin' ee-a)　　Rusty Foxglove　　4–5'/1½'
Early Summer　　Brown-red　　Southern Europe　　Zones 4–7

This biennial has leafy spikes that arise from a rosette of lance-shaped mid-green leaves. The brownish red pendant flowers are borne on 2–3' long racemes. The lower lip of the flower is considerably longer than the other lobes.

Place in areas of partial shade where plants will not dry out. I have had little success with this species in north Georgia, but I have seen it in flower further north. It is interesting if not spectacular.

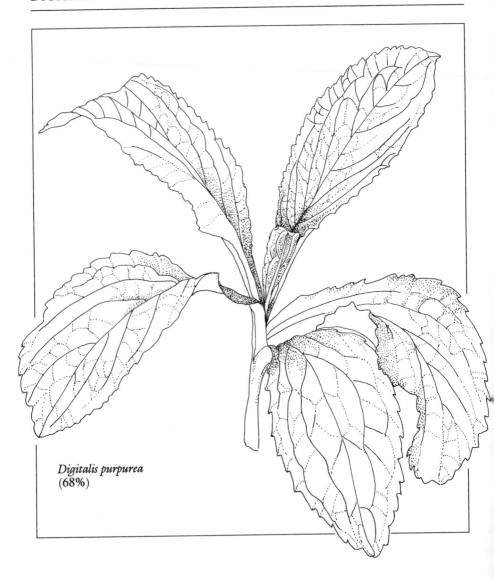

Digitalis purpurea
(68%)

Cultivars:

'Gigantea' has large yellowish brown flowers and grows 4–5' tall.
'Krik-Island' bears pure yellow flowers on 3–5' tall plants.

Propagate the species by seed similar to *D. grandiflora* in the spring or fall. A minimum of 2 years is necessary to flower.

Related Species:

D. parviflora, native to Spain, bears 2½–3' tall cylindrical racemes of small reddish-brown flowers in late spring and early summer.

-grandiflora (gran-di-flo' ra)   Yellow Foxglove   2–3'/1½'
Summer   Yellow   Europe   Zones 3–8

(Syn. *D. ambigua*)

This perennial bears hairy, toothed, dark green sessile leaves. The 2" long pendant flowers are yellowish on the outside and netted with brown on the inside. The species name refers to the large flowers, however, other species are much more ornamental than this one.

Seed germinates rapidly under warm conditions (70–75°F) and high humidity.

Related Species

D. lanata, Grecian foxglove, has 1" long pale yellow flowers held in erect dense racemes. The flowers are almost white with purplish netting within. It differs from the above species by being somewhat smaller (1–2' tall) and by having the lower lip of the flower longer than the other flower segments. It is more or less perennial and although not particularly showy, is a fine species.

-lutea (loo-tee' a)   Straw Foxglove   2–3'/1'
Summer   Yellow   Europe   Zones 3–8

The 4–6" long serrated glossy leaves are oblong to lanceolate. The ¾" creamy yellow nodding flowers are borne on one-sided branched racemes.

Cultivars:

var. *australis*, the smaller-flowered Italian form, is often used in place of the species. There is little difference in garden appearance or performance between the variety and the type.

Propagate similar to *D. grandiflora*.

Related Species:

D. obscura, native to Spain and northwest Africa, is 16–20" tall with entire, linear leaves and nodding beige-yellow flowers with red veins within.

- × mertonensis (mer-ton-en' sis)   Strawberry Foxglove   3–4'/2'
Summer   Rose   Hybrid   Zones 3–8

This hybrid was raised at the John Innes Horticultural Institute in 1925, in Merton, England, by crossing *D. purpurea* and *D. grandiflora*. The offspring is tetraploid (twice the number of chromosomes of either parent) and the 6–8" long leaves and 2½" long flowers are bigger than those of either parent. It inherited the perenniality from *D. grandiflora*, however, the bienniality of *D. purpurea* results in plants which persist for only 2–3 years.

This is one of my favorite plants for a number of reasons. It is one of the few spike-like flowers in a rose-colored shade. Unlike many other species in the genus, the foliage always looks fresh. Even when not in flower, the large, mid-green velvety leaves catch the eyes of the passers-by. In flower, the tall spires of coppery-rose flowers are interesting as well as ornamental. This species received a Gold Medal Award for excellence from the University of Georgia Horticultural Gardens in 1987.

Seed propagation is not difficult (see *D. grandiflora*). Dividing plants every two years is necessary to maintain vigor.

-purpurea (pur-pewr' ree-a)	Common Foxglove	4–5'/3'
Spring — Purple, White	Europe	Zones 4–9

The wrinkled, somewhat downy oblong leaves form a large rosette the first year followed by many flowering stems the next spring. The basal leaves have long petioles and the smaller stem leaves become sessile as they ascend the stem. The 2–3" long pendulous flowers are usually lavender with large purple and white spots inside and held on a long one-sided raceme.

This old-fashioned plant is still the most stately of the foxgloves and, when in flower, cannot be rivaled. One of the finest displays I have seen was a display of potted foxgloves at Longwood Gardens in Kennett Square, Pennsylvania. Plants had been raised in greenhouses and placed in large decorative urns when the flowers were at their peak. The 5' tall displays beckoned to the crowds passing by and those who stopped to admire them knew they were privileged to have visited that day.

Plants require a good deal of water to "strut their stuff" and should be placed in a moist, semi-shaded area. Flowering begins in early spring and persists for about four weeks, after which the spent flower stalks should be removed. Unless sprayed with fungicides, the foliage becomes ragged by late summer. Since plants are biennials and will likely not survive the winter, they should be replaced with annuals after flowering. I leave mine in the garden long enough to release seed for next year's plantlets.

Although this species is the source of the powerful drug digitalin, used for heart diseases, this was only discovered in the late 18th century. Prior to that, all sorts of fabulous medicinal poperties were attributed to these plants. In the 13th century, leaves were used to treat "scrofulous complaints" and this is thought to be the origin of the family name to which it belongs.

Cultivars:

var. *alba* is a white form of the species and is particularly pretty when naturalized at the edge of woods.

var. *campanulata* has large bell-shaped flowers near the top of the raceme

'Excelsior Hybrids' produce their flowers around the entire flower stalk and are held more upright than those of the species. Plants grow 5–7' tall.

'Foxy' is similar but is only about 2½' tall and has more side shoots. Flowers are produced the first year from seed.

'Shirley Hybrids' are similar to the type but are 4–5' tall. Propagate from seed in the spring or fall. Allow 2 years for flowering.

Quick Key to Digitalis Species

A. Middle lobe of flower longer than other lobes
  B. Plants 4–5' tall, flowers brownish-red................... *D. ferruginea*
  BB. Plants 2–3' tall, flowers yellowish......................... *D. lanata*
AA. Middle lobe of flower shorter or hardly longer than others
  B. Flowers yellowish
    C. Leaves sessile, flowers netted with brown .... *D. grandiflora*
    CC. Leaves petioled, flowers not particularly netted............ *D. lutea*
  BB. Flowers red, purple, white; not yellow
    C. Flowers 2–2½" long, strawberry colored, leaves smooth
      above and hairy beneath .... *D. × mertonensis*
    CC. Flowers 1½–2" long, usually purple or white, spotted
      within, leaves wrinkled above and less hairy beneath ... *D. purpurea*

Doronicum (do-ron' i- kum)   Leopard's Bane   Asteraceae

Leopard's bane consists of approximately 25 species with bright yellow daisy flowers and alternate leaves. They range in height from 5" (*D. cordatum*) to 3' (*D. carpetanum*) and flower in the spring. Under warm conditions, a number of species go dormant in the summer and must be replaced with annuals. They are not fussy as to soil type, thrive in full sun or partial shade and may be propagated by seed or division. All species make excellent cut flowers.

Quick Reference to Doronicum Species

	Height (ft)	Flower color
D. carpetanum	3–4	Yellow
D. caucasicum	1–2	Yellow
D. 'Miss Mason'	1–2	Yellow

-carpetanum (kar-pe-tane' um)   Spanish Leopard's Bane   3–4'/2'
Spring   Yellow   Spain   Zones 4–7

A tall coarse species, it is suitable only in larger gardens but the bright yellow flowers wake up the late spring landscape. The 6–8" long heart-shaped leaves are entire and carried on long petioles. Plants are stoloniferous and the tuber-like rhizomes spread rapidly into large clumps. The flowers are 1–2" across and open about 1 week later than other species. Cut flowers are excellent fresh or dried.

Plants can be divided in spring. Seed germinates within 3 weeks if placed in warm (70–75°F), humid conditions.

-caucasicum (kaw-kas-i' cum)		Caucasian Leopard's Bane	1–2'/1'
Spring	Yellow	Europe, Asia	Zones 4–7

This is the most common species in American gardens. It sends up lovely bright yellow daisy flowers over bright green clump-like foliage. The leaves are kidney shaped and deeply toothed but in warm climates, plants go dormant in early summer resulting in gaps in the garden. The flowers are solitary and their bright splash of color is a spectacular addition to the front of the spring border. This is not a particularly good subject in the South as it tends to look limp unless given a good deal of water. Plants are not long-lived even as far north as the Midwest due to warm summer temperatures and humidity. Its summer dormancy is of great survival value but other plants must be used to cover the bare ground.

Cultivars:

'Finesse' has semi-double yellow-orange flowers on 15–18" tall stems.
'Magnificum' grows 2–2½' tall with 1–2" diameter flowers in early spring. An excellent cultivar.
'Spring Beauty' has large double flowers on 12" tall stems. This is one of the better cultivars available.

Propagate similar to *D. carpetanum*.

- × 'Miss Mason'		Miss Mason's Leopard's Bane	1–2'/1'
Spring	Yellow	Hybrid	Zones 4–7

Often listed as a cultivar of *D. caucasicum*, the plant is a hybrid of *D. caucasicum* and *D. austriacum*, a hairy species with canary-yellow spring flowers. The only differences I can determine between this and *D. caucasicum* is that the leaves are less toothed, flowers are produced a little longer and there is less tendency toward summer dormancy.
Propagate by division in spring.

Quick Key to Doronicum Species

A. Tall plants, over 2' tall, roots tuberous .... *D. carpetanum*
AA. Shorter plants, less than 2' tall, roots fibrous
    B. Leaves finely toothed, plant usually goes dormant in summer ....
                                           D. caucasicum
    BB. Leaves scalloped, plant usually does not go dormant in summer ....
                                     D. 'Miss Mason'

E

Echinacea (ek-in-ay' see-a)　　　　Purple Coneflower　　　　Asteraceae

Only 2–3 species occur in the genus and one is a popular and excellent border plant. Because the base of the flower is rather prickly, Konrad Moench of Germany named the genus in the late 1700's after the Greek word for hedgehog, *echinos*. *Echinacea* is closely related to *Rudbeckia*, a genus of yellow and orange coneflowers, and was originally included therein. The leaves are alternate, simple, and dark green. Roots are thick and black and the purple flower petals are usually slightly reflexed.

Propagate by division and seed. The seed of the various species is easy to germinate.

Quick Reference to Echinacea Species

	Height (ft)	Flower Color
E. pallida	3–4	Creamy-white
E. purpurea	2–3	Purple, white

-*pallida* (pal' li-da)　　　　Pale Coneflower　　　　3–4'/2'
Summer　　Creamy-white　　Southcentral United States　　Zones 4–8

This most interesting wild flower is well worth including in the herbaceous garden. The dark green, 3–5" long leaves have 3–5 prominent veins. The lower leaves have long petioles while the upper are sessile. The 4–6" diameter flowers consist of dark central cones surrounded by 8–10 narrow strap-like, drooping petals (ray flowers). The flowers are far more interesting than they are beautiful.

Placed in full sun, plants attain 3–4', however if grown in partial shade, 5' tall, weak-stemmed plants result. Pinching in late spring induces branching and makes support unnecessary. The species tolerates poor soils and additional fer-

187

Echinacea purpurea 'Bright Star'
(58%)

tilizer should not be applied. Plants are not long-lived and 2–3 years can be expected without division, especially in warmer zones.

Propagate by seed or by division every two to three years. Seed germinates in 2–4 weeks if placed in warm (70–75°F), humid conditions. Cover the seed lightly as darkness inhibits germination.

-purpurea (pur-pewr′ ree-a)		Purple Coneflower	2–3′/2′
Summer	Purple	Central United States	Zones 3–8

Although this has been a common garden plant for many years, it is still one of the finest species for today's garden. The 4–8″ long, dark green leaves are coarse, serrated, and have short stiff hairs. The 1½–3″ diameter flowers consist of a brown central cone with bronze tint surrounded by broad, rose to purple petals. These droop slightly although not as much as those of the previous species.

Plants are tough and handle summer heat well, performing as well in zone 8 as in zone 4. They do best in full sun and do not benefit by additional fertilization, particularly if in partial shade. Plants begin to flower in early summer, make a grand display about two weeks later, and continue sporadically until frost. The flower is also useful as a cut flower. Many flower arrangers remove the petals and use the naked cone in bouquets and arrangements. It makes a fascinating and long-lasting specimen.

Cultivars:

'Abendsonne' has lighter, more cerise-pink flowers than the species.
'Alba' has cream-white petals surrounding a greenish disc.
'Bressingham Hybrids' are a seed strain arising from seed of 'Robert Bloom'. Plants vary slightly from light rose to red and are excellent garden performers.
'Bright Star' is a rose-colored, free-flowering cultivar which has performed well throughout the country. Plants are seed propagated and significant variability occurs.
'Magnus' is also rose-colored with petals that don't droop as much as those of the species.
'Robert Bloom' bears 5–8″ diameter purple-rose flowers, upright petals, on 3′ tall stems.
'The King' is 4–5′ tall with 6–8″ diameter rose-red flowers. Its height is a disadvantage in today's smaller gardens and it has been superseded by more compact cultivars such as 'Bright Star' and 'Robert Bloom.'
'White Lustre' differs from 'Alba' by having larger, cleaner white petals and an orange center.

Related Species:

E. angustifolia is the western representative of this species. Plants are only 1–2′ tall and have narrow, entire 4–6″ long leaves. They do not perform as well in the East as *E. purpurea*. Otherwise they are similar in habit and appearance.

E. tennesseensis, Tennessee cornflower, is a southeastern native and on the Federal Endangered Species List. A small number of nurseries now offer nursery propagated plants to the gardener. The foliage is linear and plants grow 1½–2′ tall. Dark mauve flowers with upturned petals and greenish pink centers open from early June until August. In the garden, its lack of vigor compared with other plants may result in being overrun after a year or two.

Quick Key to Echinacea Species

   A. Ray flowers strap-like, off-white, leaves entire .... *E. pallida*
  AA. Ray flowers broad, purple, rose colored, leaves coarsely toothed...........
                                                 E. purpurea

Additional Reading:

Foster, Steven. 1985. Echinaceas, the purple coneflowers. *Horticulture* 63(8):14–16.

Echinops (ek′ in-ops)   Globe Thistle   Asteraceae

    Over 75 species of globe thistle are known, but only one or two are common to gardens in North America. The foliage of the cultivated species appears more prickly than it is, although the flowers are surrounded by bristly bracts. The leaves are alternate and often whitish beneath. The individual flowers are small but are bunched together in a steely-blue globe-like inflorescence.

    All species should be planted in full sun in well-drained soil.

-ritro (rit′ ro)   Globe Thistle   2–4′/3′
Summer   Dark Blue   Europe, Western Asia   Zones 3–8

    This is probably the best of the globe thistles, although considerable confusion exists as to the true identity of many of the plants sold as *E. ritro*. The 6–8″ long leaves have deep wavy margins. The upper surface is smooth while the underside is gray-green and hairy. The stems branch near the top and numerous 1–2″ diameter globose dark blue flowers are formed in early summer (mid-June in zone 8, about 1 week later in zone 6) and persist for 6–8 weeks. The flowers are a beekeeper's delight as they are particularly attractive to bumblebees and nocturnal moths.

    I have grown *Echinops* in southern Ontario, Michigan, and Georgia and found it to be a reliable plant. The cooler nights in the North, however, result in deeper blue flowers compared with plants in the South. Globe thistle produces 4–10 flowers per branced stem which can be used fresh or as long lasting dried flowers. If placed in a dry, warm environment, flowers dry without loss of color. They are becoming more popular with florists and flower designers every year.

Cultivars:

'Blue Cloud' is difficult to locate but has 2″ diameter flowers in soft shades of blue.

'Taplow Blue' is the most popular cultivar and bears 2″ wide steel-blue flowers.

'Taplow Purple' is bluish purple and not as attractive as 'Taplow Blue'.

'Veitchii's Blue' has darker steel-blue flowers than 'Taplow Blue' and is popular in European gardens.

Propagate by seed, divisions, or root cuttings. Seeds germinate within 3 weeks if planted in peat-vermiculite and placed at 70–75°F under high humidity. Division should not be attempted until plants are at least 3 years old. At that time, basal plantlets are visible. Approximately 2–3″ long pieces of roots may be cut in the spring. Treat root cuttings similarly to those of *Anemone* × *hybrida*.

Related Species:

E. exaltatus, Russian globe thistle, is the tallest of the globe thistles and can grow to 5 feet. The stems are unbranched and the leaves are more spiny than the previous species. The flowers are similar to those of *E. ritro* and likely some plants of *E. exaltatus* are sold as *E. ritro*.

E. humilis, Siberian globe thistle, has interconnected hairs on the tops of the leaves which feel like cobwebs while the undersides are white tomentose. An indication of the taxonomic problems in this genus become obvious by reading height descriptions in various texts. *Hortus III* describes this species as 6–12″ tall, while Bailey's *Manual of Cultivated Plants* and the R.H.S. *Encyclopedia of Gardening* list plants as 3–4′ tall. If it is 6–12″ tall, there are many mislabelled plants in botanical gardens around the world, a problem which unfortunately is not uncommon.

Endymion (en-dee′ mee-on)   Bluebell   Liliaceae

This genus consists of ten bulbous species native to western Europe and includes the English and Spanish bluebells. In John Gerard's famous *Herball or Generall Historie of Plantes* (1597), he enlightened his readers with such little-known facts as "the roots being beaten and applied with white wine, hinder or keep back the growth of hairs". At that time, the bulbs were also called sea onions and eaten by sailors.

Bluebells prefer moist, shady areas and are at home near coniferous woodlands where soils are somewhat acid. They should be planted in groups of at least 50 where their strap-like leaves will provide greenery before and after the bell-shaped, blue-purple flowers have opened.

Taxonomically, storm clouds are brewing. People have generally accepted the movement of certain species from *Scilla* and their subsequent placement in *Endymion* and are beginning to understand the botanical differences between the two genera. However, the correct name for *Endymion* on the grounds of priority is *Hyacinthoides*, a name change which I hope will not officially come to pass.

Endymion was removed from *Scilla* because of botanical differences in bulb habit and flower morphology. The following table illustrates a few of the subtle differences.

191

	Endymion	*Scilla*
Bulb morphology	totally renewed each year covered with tubular scales	not renewed each year thin membranous cover
Flower morphology	bracts and bracteoles	bracts only
Height	usually more than 12″ tall	usually less than 12″ tall

The two common species, *E. hispanicus*, Spanish bluebell, and *E. non-scriptus*, English bluebell, readily hybridize when planted near each other and many intermediate forms exist.

Propagate by lifting established clumps in the fall and dividing the bulbs for planting. There will be many more bulblets around the mother bulb than can be lifted. Bluebells reseed prolifically and seed can be sown in containers in the fall. Seeds germinate readily but plants require approximately one year before they form bulbs and are ready for planting. Flowering occurs about 18 months later.

-hispanicus (his-pah′ ni-kus)	Spanish Bluebell	12–15″/12″
Spring Blue	Europe, North Africa	Zones 4–8

(Syn. *Scilla campanulata*, *S. hispanica*, *Hyacinthoides hispanica*)

The foliage consists of 5–6 shiny green linear leaves, approximately 1″ wide and convex on the back sides. Twelve or more, 1″ long, bell-shaped, nodding flowers are borne on each flower stem. They are held in an upright raceme and the petals are slightly flared at the base of the flower.

Plant the bulbs about 2–4″ deep in a well-drained area in the fall. Plants tolerate considerable shade and brighten a woodland garden. Unfortunately, the leaves become weather beaten and shabby before they disappear. These plants are tough enough, however, that if the leaves are an eyesore, the foliage can be removed before it turns yellow and the mess cleaned up. Bulbs should be planted in parts of the garden where leaf unsightliness will not be a problem.

Cultivars:

var. *alba* has creamy white flowers but can vary from clear white to soft pink.
'Blue Giant' has deep blue flowers on 18″ tall stems.
'Blue Queen' bears bell-shaped flowers of porcelain blue.
'Dainty Maid' has rosy pink flowers.
'Excelsior' has 1–2″ diameter flowers of deep purple-blue.
'Queen of the Pinks' has long elegant racemes of soft clear pink.
var. *rosea* has rose-pink flowers which can be quite variable in color and habit.
'White Triumphator' is a beautiful clear white-flowered selection with dark stems. This is one of the best whites.

-non-scriptus (non-skrip' tus)   English Bluebell   12–15"/12"
Spring   Blue   Western Europe   Zones 5–8

(Syn. *Scilla non-scripta, S. nutans, S. festalis, Hyacinthoides non-scripta*)

In England in May and early June, the woodlands and fields are alive with nodding bluebells. Although not so prolific in the United States, large clumps establish quickly. The several strap-shaped leaves are up to 1¼' long and ½" wide. The 6–12 bell-shaped fragrant flowers appear on an arching terminal raceme. The petals are flared and reflexed more than those of the previous species. Plant the bulbs 4–5" deep and by the hundreds if possible, preferably on a wooded hillside or along the edge of a placid pond. They are not plants for the herbaceous border but are magnificent specimens for the woodland garden. They are inexpensive and will not need divsion for years.

The stems and bulbs exude a "slimy, glewish juyce" which was used "to set feathers upon arrows instead of glew, or to paste books with" (Gerard). If removing the flowers, it is important to snap or cut the stems near the base. Do not pull them from the bulb or significant damage and loss of plant vigor will occur.

Cultivars:

'Alba' is a white-flowered form.
'Rosea' bears pink flowers.

Quick Key to Endymion Species

   A. Flowers 6–12, petals strongly reflexed, pedicels (stems of
      individual flowers) not over ½" long .... *E. non-scriptus*
   AA. Flowers usually 12 or more, petals flared but not reflexed,
       lower pedicels to 1½" long................................. *E. hispanicus*

Epimedium (ep-ee-mee' dee-um)   Barrenwort   Berberidaceae

Once established, species of this genus are magnificent evergreen ground covers. Plants do best in soils which have been amended with copious amounts of organic matter such as peat moss. They compete well with roots of trees and tolerate heavy shade, growing in barren areas where many other species perish. Although slow to establish, *Epimedium* forms wonderful clumps of compound foliage, and columbine-like flowers. Flowers consist of four petals and eight sepals. The sepals are arranged in two groups—outer and inner. The outer sepals are usually small and hardly noticeable but the colored inner four often look like petals. The petals may be hooded or spurred (like columbine). In the spring, the leaves are often tinged pink or red and in the fall they usually turn yellow, red, or bronze. If the foliage is clipped low to the ground very early in spring, the flowers can be appreciated. Otherwise they may be lost in the leaves. New

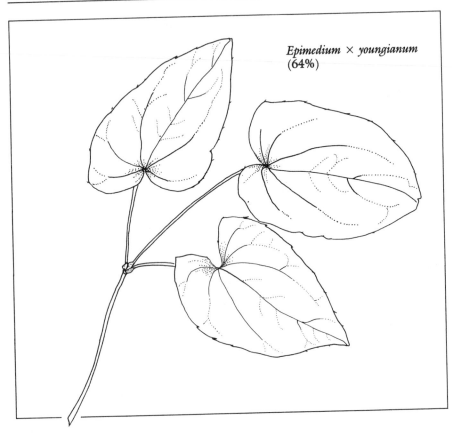

Epimedium × *youngianum*
(64%)

foliage will soon reappear. All plants are excellent groundcovers and persist for many years if provided the proper environment.

Propagate by division in late summer.

Quick Guide to Epimedium Species

	Plant height (in)	Flower color	Flowers with conspicuous spurs (Y/N)
E. alpinum	6–9	dull red	Y
E. grandiflorum	8–15	pale pink	Y
E. perralderianum	10–12	yellow	N
E. pinnatum	8–12	yellow	N
E × rubrum	8–12	bright red	N
E. × youngianum	6–8	white	N

-alpinum (al-pine′ um)   Alpine Barrenwort   6–9″/12″
Spring   Dull red   South and Central Europe   Zones 3–8

194

The leaves are arranged in two groups of three and the 2–3″ long leaflets are pointed at the end. There are 12–20 flowers in a loose raceme above the foliage. The outer sepals are grayish with specks of red; the inner sepals are dark crimson while the petals are yellowish and slipper-shaped.

Cultivars:

'Rubrum' has brighter red inner sepals and brighter yellow petals than the type. It is vigorous and multipies rapidly.

-grandiflorum (grand-i-flo′ rum)	Longspur Barrenwort	8–15″/15″
Spring Pale pink	Japan	Zones 5–8

(Syn. *E. macranthum*)

This is one of the largest species in the genus. The 1′ long leaves are ovate and the margins of the 2–3″ long bright green leaflets are spiny-toothed. The young spring foliage is beige-brown, greening up in early summer. Outer sepals are white, inner ones pale yellow, and the petals are rose or violet colored with a conspicuous ½″ long spur. About a dozen ¾–1½″ diameter flowers are arranged in a tight raceme.

Cultivars:

'Rose Queen' is one of the prettiest cultivars and has crimson leaves. The flowers are rose-pink with long white-tipped spurs. The flowers are larger but borne in smaller numbers than the species.
'White Queen' is similar but with silvery-white flowers.
'Violaceum' has large dark violet flowers.

-perralderianum (pe-ral-de-ree-ah′ num)		10–12″/12″
Spring Yellow	Algeria	Zones 5–8

Each leaf consists of 3 leaflets, about 3″ long, usually tinted red-brown and pointed. The lovely unbranched inflorescence consists of 20–25 yellow flowers. This species is similar to *E. pinnatum* but not as good a garden plant. The small brownish spur is hardly noticeable.

Cultivars:

'Frohnleiten', selected in Germany, is compact and grows 4–6″ tall. The leaves have a reddish tint both when young and in the winter. The flowers are slightly brighter than the type.

-pinnatum (pin-nay′ tum)		8–12″/12″
Late Spring Yellow	Northern Iran	Zones 5–8

The leaves are composed of 5 or more leaflets and the whole plant is hairy, particularly when young. The bright yellow flowers have small petals with short brownish spurs and are arranged in a loose inflorescence of 12–30 flowers. This is one of the few species which has no stem leaves; all the leaves arise directly from the root.

Cultivars:

var. *colchicum* has larger flowers and is more free flowering than the type.

Related Species:

E. × versicolor, bicolor barrenwort, a cross between *E. grandiflorum* and *E. pinnatum* var. *colchicum*, usually has 9 leaflets which are conspicuously red mottled when young. The leaflets turn green in early summer. The sepals are light rose, the petals yellow, and the spur has a red tinge. Variety *sulphureum* has pale yellow sepals and bright yellow petals. The foliage is not as red as the species. This is one of the toughest epimediums available and tolerates dry, shady conditions better than most.

- × rubrum (rew' brum)		Red Barrenwort	8–12"/12"
Spring	Red	Hybrid	Zones 4–8

A hybrid between *E. alpinum* and *E. grandiflorum*, red barrenwort, has the robustness of the latter and the height of the former. Each of the 15–20 flowers are up to 1" across and clustered in a loose inflorescence held slightly above the many leaflets. The heart-shaped leaflets are particularly pretty in the spring and fall when tinged red. The inner sepals are crimson-red and the petals are pale yellow or tinted red.

- × youngianum (yun-gee-aye' num)		Young's Barrenwort	6–8"/8"
Spring	White	Japan	Zones 5–8

This hybrid resulted from crossing *E. diphyllum* and *E. grandiflorum*. The leaves arise from the base of the plant and are usually divided into nine ovate pointed leaflets. The leaflets are sharply serrated, marked with red upon emergence in the spring, and turn a deep shade of crimson in the fall. The 3–8 pendulous flowers are about ¾" across and light pinkish white. Flowers are essentially spurless. The species itself is seldom offered, being superseded by the cultivars.

Cultivars:

'Niveum' is the most common cultivar and bears lovely clear white flowers. 'Roseum' has rose to lilac flowers.

Quick Key to Epimedium Species

    A. Flowers yellow
        B. Flower stems leafless, basal leaves consist of 3 leaflets......*E. pinnatum*
       BB. Flower stems with leaves, leaves consist of 5–11 leaflets................
                                        E. perralderianum

AA. Flowers not yellow
   B. Flowers with conspicuous spurs, nearly as long or longer than inner sepals
      C. Flowers large, 1–2" across........................ *E. grandiflorum*
      CC. Flowers smaller, up to 1" across .... *E. alpinum*
   BB. Flowers with very small spurs, much shorter than inner sepals
      C. Flowers bright red.................................. *E.* × *rubrum*
      CC. Flowers usually white with tinges of pink .... *E* × *youngianum*

Additional Reading:

Lancaster, Roy. 1984. Recent plant introductions. *The Garden* 109(6):244–247.

Stearn, William T. 1979. A new hybrid epimedium (*E.* × *cantabrigiense*). *The Plantsman* 1(3):187–190.

Eranthis (er-anth' is)   Winter Aconite   Ranunculaceae

   The seven species comprising the genus bear solitary bright yellow flowers in late winter and early spring. The petals are modified into small nectaries and the showy part of the flower consists of sepals only. The winter aconites have short stems and are best massed under deciduous trees or along banks where they can be naturalized. Flowers do not show up well when planted in grass. Tubers do better in alkaline soils but will increase if left undisturbed in almost any soil, as they seed prolifically. Plant tubers about 2" deep in late summer or early autumn.
   Propagation is most successful by lifting the tubers after two to three years and breaking them into smaller pieces. The pieces may not flower the first year but will the next. Plants raised from seed require three to four years to flower.

-hyemalis (hye-e-mah' lis)   Winter Aconite   4–6"/4"
Winter, Early Spring   Yellow   Western Europe   Zones 3–7

   The 3–5 lobed palmately cut foliage is carried on long petioles and is most attractive. The 1–2" diameter flowers are made up of 6 sepals and appear before the leaves. Beneath each flower is a large leaf-like collar-shaped bract which appears to support each blossom.
   The tubers are ridiculously inexpensive so there is little excuse not to plant in masses of 50 or more. Within a few years those 50 bulbs will form a golden carpet to welcome the onset of spring. They are particularly beautiful meandering down a slope or naturalized in a wild flower setting. They do not spread as rapidly in zone 7 as in zone 4 but are still excellent colorful plants.

Cultivars:

'Glory' has large lemon-yellow flowers.

'Guinea Gold' has leaves tinged with bronze and deep yellow, fragrant flowers.

It is particularly lovely but, unfortunately, not easy to locate in the trade.

Related Species:

E. × *tubergenii* is a hybrid of *E. hyemalis* and *E. cilicica*. It has 2–2½" wide flowers which, because they are sterile, last longer than those of *E. hyemalis*.

Additional Reading:

Lawrence, George H. M. 1960. *Eranthis hyemalis* and *Eranthis* × *tubergenii*. *Baileya* 8:18–19

Eremurus (air-uh-mure' us)   Foxtail Lily   Liliaceae

Few plants are as impressive as a foxtail lily in flower. The most stately species may be *E. robustus*, which bear 8 to 10' tall spike-like inflorescences of peach-colored flowers. *E. stenophyllus* (*E. bungei*), on the other hand, is only 2 to 3 feet tall with bright yellow flowers but is equally lovely. Of the thirty species, many of which have been hybridized, only one or two are widely available in the United States.

The genus belongs to the same group of plants as the red hot poker (*Kniphofia*), aloes, and yuccas. All the leaves arise from the thick fibrous root and disappear shortly after flowering. In their natural habitat, many species grow in steppe vegetation, often on mountain slopes. They need a thoroughly drained, rich soil and perform poorly in heavy clays. To grow them sucessfully, it is necessary to mulch the plants as soon as the leaves emerge in the spring because spring frosts are deadly. Plant the crowns about 6" deep as soon as received, for they must not be allowed to dry out. Choose a site in full sun away from prevailing winds. Although they are not the easiest plants to grow, they are well worth the effort.

-× *shelford* (shell' ford)   Shelford Foxtail Lily   4–8'/2'
Summer   Various   Hybrid   Zones 5–8

(Syn. *E.* × *isabellinus*)

The Shelford hybrids were raised in Great Shelford, Cambridge, England and have stood the test of time. Plants are variable and 5–6' long racemes in shades of yellow, pink, white, and copper are produced in summer. These free-flowering hybrids are the result of crossing *E. stenophyllus*, a short species with bright yellow flowers, and *E. olgae*, a medium to tall, white-flowered species. The spider-like roots should be spread out carefully in early spring or fall in planting holes 6–8" deep and 18" apart. Do not bury the crown more than 2" below the surface as it may rot if rains occur before the plants are well established. Plants do well in full sun and well-drained soils and generally look best against a green background, such as a hedge of Leyland cypress. Protection from high winds is essential if plants are to look their best. The flowers open from bottom to top and are effective for 2–3 weeks. The leaves decline after flowering and foliage and flowers self-destruct by late summer. Plant annuals or perennials which flop over such as *Boltonia asteroides* or *Clematis heracleifolia* to hide the foliage and fill the gap when the leaves go dormant.

Cultivars:

'Isobel' has pink-orange flowers on 5–6' high plants.
'Moonlight' bears pale yellow flowers.
'Rosalind' has bright pink flowers and is 5–6' tall.
'White Beauty' has clear white blossoms.

Propagate by division after 3–4 years. When the leaves have died back, carefully lift the the crowns and gently separate into individual plants. Plants grown from seed will take four to six years to flower.

Related Species:

E. stenophyllus (syn. *E. bungei*) is a dwarf member of the genus, growing 2–3' tall. The yellow flowers turn burnt orange as they mature providing a two-toned effect. It requires less maintenance because little support is required. 'Magnificus' bears large, bright yellow flowers on a 3' tall flower stalk.

E. elwesii, Elwes foxtail lily, is similar to *E. robustus* in height and may be a hybrid between *E. himalaicus*, a 3' tall white-flowered species, and *E. robustus*, but the parentage has not been verified. The flowers are fragrant and soft pink. 'Albus' is a white-flowered form.

Erigeron (e -rij' er-on)   Fleabane   Asteraceae

Many of the 150 species are native to North America. Although only 2–3 species are useful for the garden, many cultivars have been named and much hybridization and selection have taken place. Flowers of fleabane suggest native asters, but open earlier, and have two or more series of ray flowers compared to one or two in asters. They are attractive for many weeks in the summer, make good cut flowers, and are not fussy as to soil. Unfortunately this genus, like other roadside flowers, is often ignored by gardeners because it is considered a common weed. While many of the species are of little value to the garden, some of the selections are indeed worthy.

Propagation is not difficult by seed, division, or cuttings. Sow the seed when collected or sow purchased seed in late fall. Seed should be covered thinly, and placed at 70–75°F in a humid atmosphere. Seeds germinate in 10–14 days. Divide the plants in the fall every 2–3 years. Two inch long terminal shoot cuttings may be taken any time, but preferably before flower buds have formed.

199

Quick Reference to Erigeron Species

	Height (in.)	Flower color
E. aurantiacus	9–12	Orange
E. pulchellus	18–24	Rose-purple
E. speciosus	20–30	Purple

-aurantiacus (ow-ran-tee' ah-cus)		Orange Fleabane	9–12"/1'
Summer	Orange	Turkestan	Zones 4–8

While most of the fleabanes are rose, violet, or purple, this species has bright orange 1–2" diameter flowers atop 9–12" high plants. The foliage is somewhat velvety and the leaves appear twisted at first glance. The basal leaves are 3–4" long and shaped like a spatula (spatulate) while the upper leaves are ovate and sessile. The solitary flowers have a small green center and open for six to eight weeks in early summer. Plants tolerate partial shade, particularly in the South.

Cultivars:

var. *sulphureus* bears lovely pale yellow flowers and is particularly handsome in the rockery or the front of the border.

Related Species:

E. aureus, gold fleabane, is native to mountainous areas of western North America. It has solitary ½ to ¾" diameter yellow-orange flowers and is only 3–6" tall.

-pulchellus (pul-chel' lus)		Poor Robin's Plantain	18–24"/2'
Early Summer	Rosy purple	Caucasus	Zones 3–7

(Syn. *E. caucasicus*)

This is one of the few stoloniferous fleabanes in cultivation. The 2–6" long, hairy, toothed basal leaves are tufted and attached to the slender stem with a short petiole. The stem leaves are usually sessile and entire. The solitary 1" diameter flowers consist of about 60 ray florets and are lavender with yellow centers. They tolerate poor soils and lose all semblance of tidiness when given too much fertilizer or rich soils. This is a fair garden species, at best.

Related Species:

E. bellidifolius, also known as poor robin's plantain but native to eastern North America, is more weedy and flowers in the spring. Otherwise there is little difference.

-speciosus (spiece-ee-o' sus)		Daisy Fleabane	20–30/24"
Summer	Purple	Western United States	Zones 2–8

This is the most common species of fleabane although the species itself is seldom seen in gardens. The lanceolate stem leaves clasp the stem but the 3–6″ long basal leaves have winged petioles. The numerous flowers usually consist of over 100 ray florets. Each flower is 1–2″ across and occurs in clustered corymbs held well above the foliage. Plants are upright and well branched.

Plants should be grown in full sun and moist soil. Native to western United States, they do poorly south of zone 6, although occasionally worthy specimens are found in zones 7 and 8. Plants may be cut back after flowering to reduce weediness and rejuvenate the foliage.

Cultivars:

Many cultivars are available and while they are usually listed under *E. speciosus*, they are more likely hybrids between *E. speciosus*, *E. s.* var. *macranthus*, *E. aurantiacus*, and *E. glaucus*. The first two are the dominant parents in most cases. The following cultivars are showy, but those taller than 24″ need support.

'Azure Beauty' is one of a series which includes 'Azure Blue' and 'Azure Fairy'. These are usually propagated from seed resulting in a great deal of variation. 'Azure Fairy' and 'Azure Beauty' appear to be the same cultivar but sold under different names by different companies. They have semi-double lavender-blue flowers on 30″ tall stems.

'Azure Blue' is similar to the above but has lighter blue flowers.

'Darkest of All' is a much planted cultivar with violet-blue flowers on 2′ tall stems. It is one of the best.

'Dimity' is only 12–15″ tall and produces orange-tinted flower buds which open to light pink flowers. Dwarfness is an asset as no support is necessary.

'Foerster's Leibling' is a wonderful double pink form, only 18″ tall, and needs little staking.

var. *macranthus* is similar to the type but has ovate rather than lanceolate leaves and slightly larger flowers.

'Pink Jewel' was selected from 'Rose Jewel' and has a variety of pink shades.

'Prosperity' has large single lavender-blue flowers on 18″ tall plants.

'Quakeress' and 'White Quakeress' appear to be hybrids between *E. speciosus* and *E. s.* var. *macranthus*. The former has light mauve-pink flowers while the latter has off-white blooms. Both grow 18–24″ tall.

'Rose Jewel' has lilac-rose flowers and is 30″ tall.

'Rose Triumph' bears semi-double rose-pink blossoms on 24″ tall plants.

Quick Key to Erigeron Species

    A. Flowers orange-yellow, plant 9–12″ tall .... *E. aurantiacus*
  AA. Flowers white, violet, or purple, plant 18–30″ tall
      B. Flowers solitary, not held in an inflorescence .... *E. pulchellus*
    BB. Flowers held in a many-flowered corymb.................. *E. speciosus*

Eryngium (e-rinj-ee-um)   Sea Holly   Apiaceae

Of the 100 or so species, only two or three are used in North America. This is a shame because some of the species in commerce are not particularly ornamental compared with some that are not available. The roots of the European sea holly, *E. maritimum*, were reported to have been given to "old and aged people that are consumed and withered with age, and which want natural moisture" and also "amended the defects of nature in the yonger" (Gerard).

Sea hollies tolerate poor dry soil conditions, including high salt levels, although they also prosper in normal garden soil. They are native to coastal areas, particularly the Mediterranean, although *E. yuccifolium*, rattlesnake master, is native to the eastern United States. The leaves are more or less sheathed at the base and are usually lobed or deeply cut with spiny margins. The individual flowers are small but are held in dense oblong or roundish heads, which turn bright blue under cool temperatures, as do the supporting bracts and upper stems. The terminal flower is first to color but persists long enough that the lateral flowers start to color while the terminals still look fresh. They are particularly striking because the specialized bracts under the flower heads form an involucre which extends beyond the flower head and turns silvery to dark blue. The sea hollies are usually thought of as large plants and while *E. agavifolium* and *E. pandanifolium* can be up to 6' and 10' tall respectively, *E. varifolium* is only about 18" tall. Most of the common species are 2–3' tall.

Full sun is preferable because plants are more open and not as intensely colored in partial shade. Many plantlets are produced at the base of the mother plant. Separating the plantlets is the easiest method of propagation. Buying seed is usually a waste of money because the seed goes into dormancy rather quickly and 1–2 years may be required for germination. A 55% germination rate was obtained with seeds of *E. planum* collected fresh and sown within two weeks but germination plummeted to 5% or less after 3 months. I do not know if this is true of all species but suspect it is a problem with many.

Quick Reference to Eryngium Species

	Height (ft.)	Shape of basal leaves
E. alpinum	1–2	heart-shaped
E. amethystinum	1–1½	pinnately divided
E. bourgatii	1–2	palmate, 3–5 parted
E. giganteum	4–6	heart-shaped
E. planum	2–3	heart-shaped
E. varifolium	1–2	rounded

Eryngium planum
(81%)

-alpinum (al-pine´ um)		Alpine Sea Holly	1–2´/2´
Summer	Blue	Europe	Zones 4–8

The slightly toothed basal leaves are heart-shaped while the upper leaves are 3-lobed or palmately divided. The flower head is oblong like a pineapple and one of the bluest of the sea hollies. The upper part of the stem also turns a dark blue. Twelve to 18 finely divided, rather soft bracts extend from the flower head. The flower and associated involucre look like exploding fireworks. For flower power, this is the best species.

Plant in full sun and well-drained soil. It is a popular cut flower and lasts for at least 2 weeks in water. If the terminal flowers are cut, the side branches continue flowering.

Cultivars:

'Amethyst' is 2½–3´ tall with metallic-blue flowers.

'Opal' is 2´ tall and a shorter form of 'Amethyst'.

'Superbum' has large dark blue flowers on 2–3´ tall stems.

Related Species:

Some magnificent hybrids with *E. alpinum* have been produced but they are difficult to find in the United States.

E. × *oliveranum* is a 3´ tall hybrid whose parentage is confused but is likely the result of crosses between *E. giganteum*, *E. alpinum*, and *E. planum*. It bears light blue, 1½″ long flower heads and stiff involucre bracts.

E. × *zabelii* is a magnificent hybrid and is likely a cross between *E. alpinum* × *E. bourgatii*. It grows 1½´ tall and has 1″ long flower heads. Plants may sometimes be seen in botanical gardens under the name of 'Violetta' and 'Jewel'. I hope that some enterprising nursery person will soon bring this group of hybrids to the United States.

-amethystinum (a-me-thist-eye´ num)		Amethyst Sea Holly	1–1½´/2´
Summer	Blue	Europe	Zones 2–8

This is one of the most cold hardy species and one of the most common in North America. The basal leaves are pinnately parted and differ from those of most other common species. The stems branch near the top, and bear many small (½ –¾″ long) flowers. The 7–8 bracts are much longer than the flower heads and sharply pointed. The color is a steely blue and the flower stem is also deeply colored, adding a good deal of interest to the garden. Its cold hardiness allows plants to be used where others cannot be grown successfully.

-bourgatii (bour-gat´ ee-aye)		Mediterranean Sea Holly	1–2´/2´
Summer	Blue-green	Pyrenees	Zones 5–8

An excellent compact plant, this underused species has palmately cut foliage resembling a hand with 3–5 fingers. The foliage often has white veins and is grayer than most species. The flowers are ovoid and subtended by 12–18, lance-like, spiny bracts which are much longer than the flower head. The ¾" long flowers are silver-blue to blue-green and borne on wiry stems.

-giganteum (gi-gan' tee-um)		Giant Sea Holly	4–6'/4'
Summer	Blue	Caucasus	Zones 4–8

For those gardeners who want a large-flowered, enormous plant, get out your shovels. The oval 3–4" long flowers are subtended by 8 or 9 rigid, long toothed bracts. The spineless basal leaves are deeply heart-shaped and entire. Unfortunately, the species often lasts only 2 years and should be treated as a biennial.

This is a most spectacular plant but looks rather menacing. Provide sufficient room and protect from winds.

Related Species

E. tripartitum is 3½ –4' tall and bears massive numbers of metallic blue flowers. The basal leaves are 3-lobed and coarsely toothed while the bracts are twice as long as the base of the flowers.

-planum (plane' um)		Flat Sea Holly	2–3'/3'
Summer	Blue	Eastern Europe	Zones 5–9

The silver-blue flower heads are small (½–¾"), oval, and numerous. The 6–8 bracts are about the same size or slightly longer than the flower head. The scalloped basal leaves are heart-shaped and not spiny.

This is not as ornamental as *E. alpinum* and less ornamental than most of the species listed. However, it does well under southern conditions and is an excellent long lasting cut or dried flower. Interestingly, it is a more popular export flower in some countries than *E. alpinum*. The small flower heads ship well and more stems may be placed in each shipping box.

Cultivars:

'Blue Dwarf' is similar to the species but grows 15–18" high.

-varifolium (var-ee' fol-ee-um)		Moroccan Sea Holly	1–2'/2'
Summer	Silver-blue	Morocco	Zones 5–8

Another unused, rather unknown species, this is a delightful garden plant. It is one of the few evergreen members of the genus and is also unusual in that the leaves are as striking as the flowers. The small, rounded, spiny leaves have conspicuous white veins and appear variegated. The round flower heads are small but showy. The small size allows it to be used in smaller areas where other species may be too large.

Quick Key to Eryngium Species

    A. Basal leaves heart-shaped or rounded, not deeply cut
        B. Leaves conspicuously white-veined, plants 1–2' tall ...... *E. varifolium*
      BB. Leaves not white-veined, plants 2–6' tall
          C. Plants 5–6' tall, biennial in nature .... *E. giganteum*
        CC. Plants 2–3' tall, perennial in nature
            D. Flower heads small (½–1"), involucre bracts as long
               or slightly longer than flower head .... *E. planum*
          DD. Flower heads large (1–1½"), involucre bracts much
               longer than flower head .... *E. alpinum*
   AA. Basal leaves deeply lobed or divided
        B. Leaves palmately 3–5 parted .... *E. bourgatii*
      BB. Leaves pinnately parted .... *E. amethystinum*

Erysimum (e-ri′ si-mum)	Alpine Erysimum	Brassicaceae

Erysimum is common in the British Isles, continental Europe, and New Zealand, however, it is not often found in American gardens. One or two species are useful for the rock garden or edge of the border. Few differences exist between this genus and *Cheiranthus*, the common wallflower, and the two are often confused. However, *Erysimum* has no nectary glands at the base of the stamens, the fruit (silique) is not as flat, and seeds within the fruit are in a single row compared with two rows in the compressed fruit of *Cheiranthus*. This is not a great deal to go on for those not schooled in the plant sciences. However, for those who like to know "what is it?", the primary garden species, *E. linifolium*, flaxleaf erysimum, has 12" long purple racemes while most of the *Cheiranthus* species have shorter orange-yellow flowers.

Erysimums prefer well-drained soils and benefit from the addition of lime. They should be placed in full sun in the North and partial shade in the South. All should be cut back hard after flowering and should not be expected to persist more than two years. In the South, fall plantings, similar to pansies, are becoming more common. Plants overwinter, flower in spring, and are replaced prior to declining in the summer heat.

Propagate by seed, division, or cuttings.

Quick Reference to Erysimum Species

	Height (in.)	Flower color
E. kotschyanum	3–6	Yellow
E. linifolium	12–15	Purple
E. pumilium	2–4	Yellow

-kotschyanum (kot-shy-aye´ num) Kotschy Erysimum 3–6″/12″
Spring Yellow Asia Minor Zones 6–8

This excellent rock garden plant grows in compact tufts and is covered with bright yellow flowers in the spring. The ½″ long basal leaves are narrow, and finely toothed. The ½″ long flowers are carried in crowded racemes and are not only pretty but also pleasantly fragrant. They grow well in full sun in cracks and crevices in walls and rock gardens. Plants perform well as far south as zone 8 if planted in the fall; however, summer heat and humidity result in decline and plants seldom recover.

Seed sown in a warm (70–75°F) environment begin to germinate within two weeks. Germination is erratic, however, and seedlings may continue to appear over a 4–6 week period. Two inch long terminal cuttings may be taken immediately after flowering or in the fall. Plants should be divided in the fall.

-linifolium (line-i-fo´ lee-um) Alpine Erysimum 12–15″/12″
Spring Purple Spain Zones 5–8

One of the larger species, it can be used as an edging specimen but is equally at home cascading from rock walls. The narrow leaves are gray-green, entire, and evergreen if winters are not too severe. The ¾″ long flowers are held in a dense raceme well above the foliage and the purple color is particularly brilliant early in the spring.

Cultivars:

'Bowles' Beauty' has longer flower heads and is a clearer purple than the type.
'Variegatum' has variegated foliage and lilac flowers. A particularly handsome form.

Propagate similar to *E. kotschyanum*.

-pumilium (pew-mil´ ee-um) Tufted Erysimum 2–4″/6″
Spring Yellow European Alps Zones 4–7
(Syn. *E. helveticum*)

This little-known species bears many pale yellow, fragrant flowers on tufted compact plants. The basal leaves are narrow, gray-green and somewhat toothed. This is more perennial than most other species and should be planted in limey soil in full sun.

Propagate similar to *E. kotschyanum*, however, non-flowering stems may be used for cuttings any time from emergence to midsummer.

Quick Key to Erysimum Species
    A. Flowers yellow or orange-yellow, plant height less than 8″
        B. Flowers large, orange-yellow, 3–6″ tall .... *E. kotschyanum*

BB. Flowers smaller, pale yellow, 2–4″ tall .... *E. pumilium*
AA. Flowers lilac to purple, greater than 8″ tall .... *E. linifolium*

Erythronium (e-rith-roan′ ee-um)　　　Trout Lily　　　Liliaceae

Trout lilies consist of approximately 25 species, most of which are handsome in flower and foliage. Plants are usually used in wild flower areas, and are particularly suitable for naturalizing in shade or near streams where moisture is constantly available. Some of the species are very cold hardy and nearly all have mottled leaves. The name *Erythronium* came from the Greek *erythos*, red, a reference to the leaf mottling. In general, the plant bears 2 leaves, one narrower than the other, although up to four leaves may sometimes be formed. The nodding flowers are borne singly or in twos or threes and the anthers protrude well away from the reflexed petals.

Many common names have been applied to species in the genus. The first species to be named had long, white, shiny tuberous roots resembling canine teeth and was called *denscaninus*, or dog-tooth violet. The term violet was used at the time for many small purple-flowered plants. That particular species is now known as *E. dens-canis*, a native of central Europe. The mottled leaves have given rise to the common names of trout lily, fawn lily and adder's tongue.

Quick Guide to Erythronium Species

	Height (in.)	*Flower color*	*Mottled leaves*
E. albidum	6–12	White	Yes
E. americanum	6–9	Yellow	Yes
E. dens-canis	4–6	Purple	Yes
E. grandiflorum	12–24	Yellow	No
E. revolutum	10–16	Varied	Yes

-albidum (al′ bi-dum)　　　White Trout Lily　　　6–12″/9″
Late Spring　　　White　　　Eastern North America　　　Zones 4–8

One of the latest species to flower, the 1½″ long drooping blossoms are a lovely clear white, with a tinge of yellow at the base. The elliptical 4–6″ long leaves are occasionally mottled with silver-green but under heavy shade, little mottling is apparent. This species recently came into commercial propagation and is more available. Plant in light shade and provide adequate soil moisture. One of the few species to have stoloniferous roots, significant colonies are formed, albeit slowly, within 3–5 years.

Propagation by seed is slow and frustrating, particularly if the seed is not fresh. Keep seed warm (70–75°F) and moist for 2–4 weeks, cool seed to 30–35°F for 4–6 weeks and then raise temperatures again to 75°F. This sequence occurs naturally through the cycles of fall, winter, and spring. Place the seed flats outside in the fall in an area which will not fall below 25°F, such as a cold frame. A covering of snow will do the same thing. Seedlings appear in the spring as temperatures rise. Three to four years are required to obtain flowering plants from seed. Offsets may also be taken from mature plants. Offsets require two years to produce flowering plants.

-americanum (a-me-ri-kay' num)		American Trout Lily	6–9"/9"
Late Spring	Yellow	Eastern North America	Zones 3–8

This common trout lily is found in damp woodlands and pastures from Nova Scotia to Florida. Two dark, glossy green, 3–8" long leaves mottled with brown and purple markings appear in early spring. The 1–2" wide, nodding, pale yellow flowers are occasionally tinged with purple and are borne singly, opening about the same time as *E. albidum*. It is also known as common trout lily, fawn lily and yellow adder's tongue because of the leaf markings. Partial shade and adequate soil moisture must be provided.
Propagate similar to *E. albidum*.

Related Species:
E. tuolumnense is native to California and produces 8–12 golden yellow flowers above unmottled yellow-green foliage. Flowers are up to 3" wide and persist for about 2 weeks.

-dens-canis (dens-kay' nus)		Dog Tooth Violet	4–6"/6"
Spring	Purple	Central Europe	Zones 2–7

This short, early-flowering species has a more limited southern range than the American trout lily but is more winter hardy. The 4–6" long lanceolate leaves are variable but often splotched with dull crimson. The solitary 2" long, nodding rose-purple flowers have sharply reflexed tips and purple stamens.

Cultivars:
'Charmer' has white flowers mottled with crimson on 8–12" tall plants.
'Lilac Wonder' has large muted lilac flowers with a small brown spot at the base of each segment.
'Pink Perfection' is early flowering and has clear pink flowers larger than the species.
'Purple King' is a particularly eye-catching cultivar. Mauve flowers are edged with white and centers are marked with dark brown spots.
'White Splendour' has white flowers larger than the species.

Propagate similar to *E. albidum*. Cultivars must be vegetatively propagated.

-grandiflorum (grand-i-flo' rum)	Lambstongue Trout Lily	12–24"/18"
Spring	Yellow	Western United States	Zones 5–9

This early-flowering species has large golden yellow star-shaped flowers with dark red or maroon anthers. They may be up to 2" long and held in 2–6 flowered racemes. The 4–8" long elliptical leaves are dark green and unmottled. The size of the flowers is arresting but the lack of leaf mottling makes this just another plant when not in flower.

Cultivars:

'Albiflorum' has white flowers tinged with green.

var. *candidum* has greenish to creamy white flowers with white anthers and a yellow interior.

'Parviflorum' has cream-colored anthers instead of the normal crimson color.

-revolutum (re-ve-loo' tum)	Mahogany Trout Lily	10–16"/10"
Spring	Rose-pink	Western North America	Zones 5–8

Although the species is worthy of a place in the garden, several cultivars are much more common than the species. The 6–8" long, deep green leaves are mottled with brown and white, and sport crisped margins. The one or two rose-pink flowers, 3" across and up to 1¾" long, have yellow bands inside the flower and yellow anthers.

Cultivars:

'Pink Beauty' has reflexed petals of clear pink.

'White Beauty' has creamy white flowers with crimson-brown center but the petals are less reflexed.

Related Species:

E. × 'Kondo' has 3–5 large sulphur-yellow flowers shaded brown at the center.

E. × 'Pagoda' has leaves marbled with bronze and pale yellow flowers. These excellent hybrids are the result of crosses between 'White Beauty' and E. *tuolumnense*, a yellow-flowered Western native.

Quick Key to Erythronium Species

    A. Flowers yellow
        B. Flowers borne singly, less than 2" across............... E. *americanum*
    BB. Flowers borne in groups, larger than 2"
        C. Foliage mottled
            D. Flowers sulphur yellow, leaves lightly mottled..... E. × 'Kondo'
            DD. Flowers pale yellow, leaves bronze .... E. × 'Pagoda'
        CC. Foliage not mottled............................... E. *grandiflorum*

AA. Flowers not yellow
    B. Flowers white, leaves mottled silver-green................. *E. albidum*
    BB. Flowers purple to pink
        C. Flowers solitary, less than 2" across, leaves mottled crimson ....
                                                E. dens-canis
        CC. Flowers usually in 2's or 3's, larger than 2" across, leaves
           mottled white and brown .... *E. revolutum*

Eupatorium (yew-pa-tor′ ium)   Boneset   Asteraceae

A half dozen of the 600 species are common wild flowers in the eastern half of the country and excellent garden plants as well. Easily grown in moist well-drained soils and full sun or partial shade, the larger species reach seven feet in height and may require support. A number of roadside weeds such as *E. capillifolium*, dog fennel, and *E. hyssopifolium*, both with small white flowers, have found a place in the wild flower garden. Plants are effective because of their late summer and fall flowering and architectural beauty.

Quick Reference to Eupatorium Species

	Height *(ft.)*	*Flower* *color*
E. coelestinum	2–3	Blue
E. purpureum	4–7	Purple
E. rugosum	3–5	White

-*coelestinum* (sow-les-teen′ um)	Hardy Ageratum	2–3′/36″
Late Summer	Blue	Eastern United States	Zones 6–10

The 2–3" long leaves of hardy ageratum are opposite, triangular, and coarsely toothed. The flower heads consist of up to 70, one-half inch wide flowers clustered in dense corymbs, similar to the annual *Ageratum*, for which they are named. Plants are rhizomatous and can become somewhat of a nuisance.

Plants often look rather weedy. Cut them back once or twice during the summer to force additional lateral shoots. With ample water and a sunny location, an outstanding fall show develops. Supporting the plants is helpful to avoid the weedy look but they flop regardless of supporting technique. Numerous azure blue flowers celebrate the fall season in the garden and should be welcomed. They are handsome combined with *Aster tartaricus*, *Sedum* × 'Autumn Joy' and other fall bloomers.

Cultivars:

'Alba' has white flowers but is otherwise similar to the species.

211

Eupatorium coelestinum
(95%)

Divide plants in the spring every 2–4 years. Seed may require 4–6 weeks of cold moist treatment (35–40°F) if germination does not occur within 3 weeks. Cuttings may also be rooted.

-purpureum (pur-pewr' ree-um)   Joe-Pye Weed   4–7'/3'
Fall   Purple   Eastern North America   Zones 4–9

Although this wild flower occurs from southern Maine to the mountains of north Georgia and as far west as Texas, one must search high and low for its presence in American gardens. On the other hand, it is one of the architectural building blocks of British gardens. People with whom I travel overseas in the fall always wonder why our native plant is so well used and cherished there and so scorned and ignored here. Perhaps just knowing we can find it on meadows and hills of Georgia, Virginia and North Carolina provides reason not to include it in our cultivated areas. Of course, the common name, Joe-pye weed, does nothing to enamour it to gardeners.

The foliage is whorled, generally 3 to 5 leaves to a whorl, each 8–12" leaf coarsely serrated and pointed. The leaves have a distinctive vanilla scent when crushed. The stems are hollow, green with purple nodes and not usually mottled with purple. About 5–7 small purple flowers make up a single flower head but 5–9 flower heads are packed together to make an impressive 12–18" diameter compound inflorescence.

Plants require abundant water and full sun to be at their best. In shady locations, they become excessively tall. This is a large plant and is not for everyone's small urban garden, however, it should not be relegated to the back pasture. Unfortunately, Joe-pye weed does not tolerate the constant high summer temperatures in my Georgia garden. It is a cool season species and is a better plant for areas where night temperatures remain below 70°F.

Cultivars:

var. *album* is an uncommon white-flowered form.
'Atropupureum' is a magnificent plant, eye-catching from a distance and impressive close up. It bears purple flowers, leaves, petioles and upper stems. This is the architectural and color highlight of the fall garden.

Propagate similar to *E. coelestinum*. The divisions have long fibrous roots and a sharp spade is useful when separating the plantlets.

Related Species:

E. maculatum, spotted Joe-pye weed, is also known simply as Joe-pye weed. Plants are similar in height and form but have purple speckled and mottled stems rather than green stems as in *E. purpureum*. The flower heads consist of 9–15 flowers compared with 5–7 in *E. purpureum*. It is more cold hardy than *E. purpureum*, extending as far north as zone 2. Plants offered as Joe-pye weed are often this species.

213

| *-rugosum* (roo-go' sum) | | White Snakeroot | 3–5'/4' |
| Late Summer | White | Eastern North America | Zones 3–7 |

(Syn. *E. ageratoides*)

Although seldom seen in cultivated gardens, plants make an attractive and unusual display when conditions are favorable. The 5–7″ long pointed leaves are opposite, ovate, and sharply toothed. The veins on the underside are often slightly hairy. Mature plants are covered with 3–4″ diameter white inflorescences, consisting of 12–24 one-quarter inch wide flowers arranged in dense corymbs. The flowers are long lasting, persisting well into the fall.

Plants look particularly good at the end of a flower bed where the whole plant may be appreciated, rather than just one side if viewed only from the front. Full sun and well-drained soils are prerequisites for success as well as cool night temperatures. This is not a good plant south of zone 7 because warm nights result in loss of vigor. Plants should be cut to the ground after flowering.

Propagate similar to *E. coelestinum*.

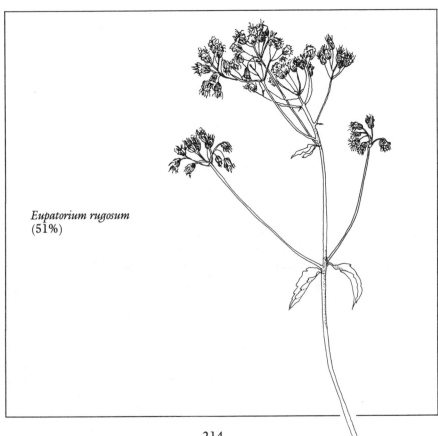

Eupatorium rugosum
(51%)

Related Species:

E. lindleyanum, native to China, is 2–3′ tall and smothered with small creamy-white flowers in late summer. The lance-like foliage is whorled and irregularly toothed.

E. perfoliatum, common boneset, bears stems which appear to grow through the middle of the leathery leaves. The flowers are creamy white and open on 4–6′ high stems in late summer. An excellent overlooked native plant.

E. triplinerve, also smothered in white flowers, has cordate, scalloped leaves and grows 4–5′ tall.

Quick Key to Eupatorium Species

A. Foliage whorled, flowers purple to pink.................... *E. purpureum*
AA. Foliage opposite, flowers blue or white
   B. Flowers blue, height 2–3′............................. *E. coelestinum*
   BB. Flowers white, height 3–5′ .... *E. rugosum*

Euphorbia (yew-for′ bee-a)   Spurge   Euphorbiaceae

This large genus contains well over 1000 species, yet the best known is the greenhouse poinsettia, *E. pulcherrima*, a deciduous shrub reaching heights of 15′ in its native habitat. A number of attractive annual species such as *E. heterophylla*, painted spurge, and the white-flowered *E. marginata*, snow-on-the-mountain, make wonderful conversation pieces. Only about 4 or 5 perennials are available and even these are sometimes difficult to locate.

None of the species has petals or sepals and the "flowers" are actually highly colored bracts. The true flowers are reduced in the male to a single stamen and in the female to a long stalked ovary. Fused together, they are called a cyathium. Most bracts are yellow but those of *E. corollata*, flowering spurge, are white and petal-like. Another characteristic common to all species is the presence of milky sap, which in some species is acrid and poisonous, especially if it comes into contact with open cuts.

Propagate the herbaceous species by terminal cuttings in midsummer, by division, or by seed.

Quick Reference to Euphorbia Species

	Height (in.)	Bract color	Flowering time
E. epithymoides	12–18	Yellow	Early Spring
E. griffithii	24–36	Red	Summer
E. myrsinites	6–9	Yellow	Spring
E. wallichii	24–30	Yellow	Early Summer

215

-epithymoides (e-pi-thi-moi' deez)		Cushion Spurge	12–18"/18"
Early Spring	Yellow	Europe	Zones 4–8

(Syn. *E. polychroma*)

A dazzling plant in early spring, the pale green leaves give way to shiny yellow bracts which light up the early spring garden. When in flower, the clump-forming plants look like yellow cushions. The 2" long, oblong, alternate leaves remain attractive throughout the year if planted in the right conditions, and produce some red fall color.

Cushion spurge tolerates full sun in zones 4 and 5 but even there, protection from afternoon sun is beneficial. Shade is essential in the South. I have grown it in north Georgia in full sun and partial shade—those in full sun performed poorly while plants in shade prospered, spread, and lived up to expectations. The habit, however, becomes a little leggy and the clump opens up as the heat of a southern summer progresses. This is especially true after 2–3 years in the garden, at which time it should be propagated.

Seed germinates irregularly but no special problems are encountered if placed in a warm, humid area. Plants may be carefully divided after 2–3 years. Care must be taken to provide adequate roots on each of the divisions. Two- to four-inch long terminal cuttings may be rooted after flowering is completed. Remove all vestiges of bracts and flowers, insert cutting in equal parts sand:vermiculite, and place in a warm (70–75°F), humid area.

The proper botanical name of this species is constantly in doubt. *E. polychroma*, named by an Austrian, Anton Josef Kerner in 1875, was superseded by *E. epithymoides*, given by Linnaeus, in 1770. The first name takes precedence and thus *E. epithymoides* should be the correct name. However, that name had been given to another species. Because of this confusion, cushion spurge will be listed by both names for many years to come; choose the one you like and stay with it.

Related Species:

E. palustris, grows 2½–3' tall and bears bright yellow-green bracts from late spring through July. Plants are tolerant of dry, sandy soils. Cut back after flowering.

-griffithii (gri-fith' ee-eye)		Griffith's Spurge	2–3'/2'
Summer	Orange-red	Himalayas	Zones 4–8

I am very excited about the future of this species as plants have recently become available in large numbers in the United States. The habit is upright and plants bear many brick-red bracts held above lance-like mid-green leaves with pale pink midribs. A mounded colony is formed, similar to the previous species, and when the bracts fade, an attractive herbaceous shrub remains.

Partial shade is best although full sun can be tolerated in the North. As with other species of this genus, it must not be allowed to dry out.

Cultivars:

'Fireglow' is most common and is similar to the species but has flame-orange bracts, red midveins, and orange-brown stems. It is particularly attractive in combination with yellow-flowering plants such as *Coreopsis*.

'Dixter' arose from the garden of Christopher Lloyd at Great Dixter, Northiam, England, and has red-flushed foliage and orange bracts.

-myrsinites (mur-sin-ee' teez)	Myrtle Euphorbia	6–9"/12"
Spring	Yellow	Southern Europe	Zones 4–9

This evergreen trailing plant produces many gray-green sessile leaves in tight spirals along the prostrate stems. The 2–4" wide flowers are made up of sulphur-yellow bracts at the end of each 8–10" long stem.

The foliage color is an excellent contrast to the bracts. Plants tolerate heat well and have proven excellent for the Southeast.

Propagate by seed and cuttings similar to *E. epithymoides*.

-wallichii (wall-ich' ee-eye)	Wallich Spurge	24–30"/18"
Early Summer	Yellow	Himalayas	Zones 6–9

(Syn. *E. longifolia*)

The 4–6" diameter yellow-green bracts occur in groups of three and encircle the small flowers. Combined with the large eye-catching bracts are lanceolate dark-green leaves with clear white midribs. Although tolerant of full sun, plants do best with some afternoon shade and abundant water. Given these conditions, plants remain attractive all season.

Seed may require a cold treatment (35–40°F) for 4–6 weeks prior to placing in a warm area for germination. Propagate by cuttings similar to *E. epithymoides*.

Related Species:

E. robbiae, Robb's spurge, is a useful evergreen ground cover. The foliage grows about 12" high and the greenish yellow bracts are borne on 2' tall stems. Plants tolerate dry shade and blend well with a wide assortment of plant material.

Quick Key to Euphorbia Species

A. Bracts yellow
　　B. Midribs of leaves white, plants usually taller than 18" ...... *E. wallichii*
　　BB. Midribs of leaves green, plants usually smaller than 18"
　　　　C. Habit erect, forming a clump .... *E. epithymoides*

CC. Habit prostrate, leaves arranged in close spirals around stem . . . .
E. myrsinites

AA. Bracts not yellow . . . . *E. griffithii*

Additional Reading:

Turner, Roger. 1983. A review of spurges for the garden. *The Plantsman* 5(3):129–161.

F

Filipendula (fil-i-pen' dew-la)   Meadowsweet   Rosaceae

This genus of nine or ten species was part of the genus *Spiraea* and is still frequently referred to as false spirea. Plants have alternate, pinnately or palmately lobed foliage and panicles of many small white or pink flowers. The genus name comes from *filum*, thread; and *pendulus*, hanging; and alludes to the root tubers hanging on the fibrous roots of *F. hexapetala*, the species after which the genus is named. Most species are found in moist areas in nature and should be grown where high moisture levels can be maintained. The exception to this is *F. vulgaris* which has more drought tolerance than the others.

Plant in alkaline soil (pH, 7.0–7.5) in full sun to partial shade. Flowers appear in early summer. Propagate by division in fall, or by seed.

Quick Guide to Filipendula Species

	Height (ft.)	Flower color
F. palmata	3–4	Pink
F. rubra	6–8	Pink
F. ulmaria	3–6	White
F. vulgaris	2–3	White

-palmata (pahl-may' ta)   Siberian Meadowsweet   3–4'/3'
Summer   Pink   Siberia   Zones 3–8

(Syn. *Spiraea palmata*)

Each 4–8" wide coarse leaf consists of one large 7–9 palmately lobed terminal leaflet and 3–5 lobed lateral leaflets. All leaflets are white and hairy beneath. A multitude of 6" wide flattened heads (corymbose panicles) of pale pink flowers rise above the foliage in June, and turn white as they mature. Although

219

the flowers only persist for 2–3 weeks, they make a wonderful show. In north Georgia, flowering begins the end of May, about 2 weeks later in zone 6.

This is the finest garden species and lends a bold texture to the garden, remaining attractive all season if moisture is constant. If allowed to dry out, the margins of the leaves turn brown, and if continued, shrivel and fall off. Copious amounts of compost or other moisture-retaining material incorporated in the garden is beneficial. I have grown this for years and have always been rewarded with its graceful habit and excellent performance.

Cultivars:

'Elegans' is a excellent performer and is more compact than the type. It has
   white flowers with red stamens. This is also listed as a cultivar of *F. purpurea*.
'Nana' is similar to the species but only 8–10" tall.

Propagate by division in the fall or by seed. Seed germinates within 3 weeks when lightly covered and placed in warm temperature (70–75°F) and high humidity. Germination is erratic.

Related Species:

F. purpurea, Japanese meadowsweet, has deeper pink flowers and crimson stems and is spectacular in flower. There are few if any lateral leaflets and those present are ovate in shape. Often the two species are used interchangeably.

-rubra (rew' bra)		Queen-of-the-Prairie	6–8'/4'
Summer	Pink	Eastern United States	Zones 3–9

I've never figured out why this native of Pennsylvania to Iowa to Georgia is a Queen-of-the-Prairie. Are there prairies out there I don't know about? Perhaps the common name is the result of its ability to support itself even in high winds. This is a most impressive species, although too large for smaller gardens. The foliage consists of pinnately divided leaflets; the large 5–8" long terminal leaflet has 7–9 lobes and the laterals have 3–5. The lateral leaflets, however, are absent on the upper stem leaves. The pink to peach flowers are arranged in a 6–9" wide panicle and bear exserted, conspicuous stamens. This is a classic accent plant.

Cultivars:

'Albicans' ('Magnificum Album') has white flowers and is shorter than the type
   but difficult to find.
'Venusta' (sometimes offered as *F. venusta*) is the most available cultivar and has
   deep pink to carmine flowers.

Propagate similar to *F. palmata*.

-ulmaria (ul-mah' ree-a)   Queen-of-the-Meadow   3–6'/3'
Summer   White   Asia, Europe   Zones 3–9

This large, stout species is midway in size between *F. vulgaris* and *F. rubra*. The leaves consist of large 3–5 lobed terminal leaflets and toothed lateral leaflets. The leaflets are whitish and hairy beneath. The creamy white flowers are carried above the foliage in a branched, flat 4–6" wide inflorescence similar to *F. vulgaris*.

Cultivars:

'Aurea' is the best cultivar and is grown for the foliage rather than the flowers. The flowers are rather insignificant but the foliage is a lovely golden yellow. The flowers should be removed as they start to develop to encourage foliage vigor. Discourage the growth of seedlings as they will be green-leaved. The foliage holds up better in cooler climates than in the South.
'Flore-plena' is also superior to the species. The flowers are double, more showy, and more persistent.

Divide similar to *F. palmata*. Seed, however, should be placed in a seed flat at room temperature for about 2 weeks, then cooled for 4–6 weeks at 40°F. After the cool treatment, place at 70–75°F under high humidity.

-vulgaris (vul-gah' ris)   Dropwort   2–3'/2'
Summer   White   Europe   Zones 3–8

(Syn. *F. hexapetala*)

The 4–10" long shiny mid-green leaves are pinnately divided into many 1" long leaflets resulting in a somewhat fern-like appearance. The creamy white flowers are borne in many 4–6" diameter branched, flattened inflorescences and are often tinged with pink. The rootstock is tuberous.

Plants prefer constant moisture but tolerate dry soils. Plant in full sun to partial shade.

Cultivars:

'Flore-pleno' is a double-flowered form, usually 1–2' tall and more ornamental than the species.

Propagate similar to *F. palmata*.

Quick Key to Filipendula Species

     A. Leaflets numerous, small, all similar .... *F. vulgaris*
   AA. Leaflets few, terminal the largest
        B. Lateral leaflets 3–5 lobed, flowers usually pink or peach
           C. Leaves hairy beneath, plants usually 3–4' tall .... *F. palmata*

CC. Leaves smooth beneath, plants usually 6–8' tall............ *F. rubra*
BB. Lateral leaflets few or none, not lobed, flowers usually white ....
F. ulmaria

Fritillaria (fri-ti-lah' ree-a)　　　　　Fritillary　　　　　Liliaceae

This genus takes the name from *fritillas*, a chess-board, because the flowers of many species are checkered on the outside. Over 80 species are known but only a small number are available or useful. In my garden in Montreal, the guinea hen flower, *F. meleagris*, was everywhere in the spring and people constantly commented on its unusual appearance. The loveliest species, however, is the crown imperial, *F. imperialis*, which when grown well, is truly impressive. Visiting the tulip fields of Holland in spring is always an enlightening and spectacular time, however, to see a field of crown imperials is a sight never to be forgotten.

They require full sun and well-drained soil. The fleshy bulbs must be handled carefully and planted 4–6" deep as soon as received in the fall.

Propagation from offsets is not difficult. Bulbs should be lifted and offsets potted and grown until ready to replace in the garden. The offsets will bloom in about 12–18 months. Fresh seeds require about four years to reach flowering size.

Quick Guide to Fritillaria Species:

	Height (in.)	Flower mottled
F. imperialis	30–36	No
F. meleagris	12–15	Yes

-*imperialis* (im-pe-ree-ah' lis)　　　Crown Imperial　　　2 ½–3'/1'
Spring　　　　　Orange, Yellow　　　Turkey, Iran　　　Zones 5–8

When the crown imperial is planted in groups of a dozen or more, there are few bulbous species that compare. The alternate, lanceolate leaves are 4–6" long, dark green and have a skunklike odor when crushed. The foliage persists into midsummer and is difficult to hide when senescence begins. The numerous 2–3" long flowers hang down beneath a crown or whorl of leaves which protect the flowers from nature's elements. The stigma protrudes from the flowers like the clapper in a church bell. Large nectar drops reside inside the flowers which defy all laws of gravity by refusing to fall. Gerard compared each drop to a "pearl of the Orient".

Cultivars:

'Aurora' has orange-scarlet flowers.
var. *lutea* bears lemon-yellow flowers.

222

var. *lutea maxima* has flowers which are even larger than the type.
'Orange Brilliant' produces clear orange flowers.
var. *rubra* has red flowers.

Bulbs may be divided after 3–4 years.

-meleagris (mel-ee-ah′ gris)	Guinea Hen Flower	12–15″/12″
Spring Pale Mauve	Western Europe	Zones 3–8

This is more winter hardy but not nearly as magnificent as the previous species. The 1–2″ long solitary, drooping, checkered flowers are borne on 12–15″ tall stems. They are mauve, marked with squares of dark purple "like the board at which men do play at chesse" (Gerard). It is also known as the snake's head daffodil, for before it opens, the broad budded flower resembles the head of a snake. The 3–6″ long foliage is narrow, alternate, and dark green but not as persistent as *F. imperialis*.

Cultivars:

Bulbs are usually offered in an awful assortment of mixed colors but occasionally single colors are available.

'Alba' has creamy white flowers and is much more visible than the dark camouflage colors of the species. It has no markings but is an excellent cultivar.

Bulbs may be divided in 2–3 years.

Related Species:

F. persica is a about 3′ tall with small dark purple fragrant flowers ascending the stem.

Quick Key to Fritillaria Species

    A. Flowers topped with a crown of leaves .... *F. imperialis*
  AA. Flowers at the top of the stems .... *F. meleagris*

G

Gaillardia (gay-lard' ee-a)   Blanket Flower   Asteraceae

The blanket flower is one of the most popular herbaceous plants in gardens today. The reasons for this popularity are ease of culture, tolerance to heat, and long blooming season. Of the approximately 12 species, only two, *G. aristata* and *G. pinnatifida*, western blanket flower, are perennial. Plants of *Gaillardia* need full sun, well-drained soil and occasional removal of spent flowers.

-× *grandiflora* (grand-i-flo' ra)   Blanket Flower   2–3'/2'
Summer   Red, Yellow   Hybrid   Zones 2–10

This hybrid is a cross between *G. aristata*, a 2–3' tall perennial, and *G. pulchella*, a 2' high annual species. Although blanket flowers are often listed under *G. aristata*, that species is seldom seen in gardens today. The resulting tetraploid hybrid is vigorous and easy to grow. The 4–6" long leaves are alternate, coarsely toothed and gray-green. The 2–3" diameter, solitary flower heads are yellow with various amounts of maroon at the base of the petals. The center is often burgundy and the many colors result in a somewhat garish flower of many colors.

One of the decided disadvantages of the above-mentioned cross is that with the addition of genes of the annual species, the hybrid is more short-lived than *G. aristata*. In the Horticulture Gardens at the University of Georgia, plants of *G. aristata* and *G.* × *grandiflora* 'Goblin' were planted side by side. Although 'Goblin' is a better garden plant from the point of view of habit and flowering time, it disappeared after 2 years while *G. aristata* was still prospering. Longevity may not be an important selection criterion but this example points out the fact that desirable characteristics are often lost in breeding in order to gain other qualities. On the other hand, the genes of *G. pulchella* and other annual species have given the hybrid the distinction of having one of the longest flowering periods and most extensive ranges of any perennial.

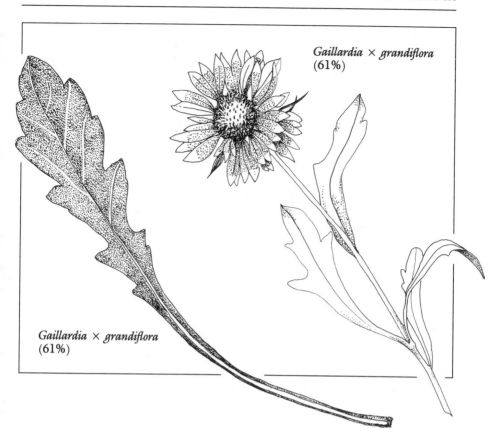

Gaillardia × *grandiflora*
(61%)

Gaillardia × *grandiflora*
(61%)

Cultivars:

'Baby Cole' is an excellent dwarf (6–8") selection with 2–3" diameter yellow,
    red-banded ray flowers.

'Bremen' has coppery-scarlet flowers on 2–3' tall stems.

'Burgundy' bears rich wine-red flowers and grows 2–3' tall.

'Dazzler' produces blooms with crimson-red tips and yellow centers.

'Goblin' is another dwarf selection with 4" diameter flowers wearing red petals
    with yellow edges. It grows only 9–12" tall but is rather variable in height
    and flower color. This is the best cultivar available.

'Lollipop' series is a double-flowered multi-colored group whose extra petals
    and many colors result in particularly loathsome plants.

'Monarch Strain' ('Portula hybrids') is a seed-propagated color mix.

All but 'Baby Cole' and 'Goblin' may be propagated from seed, resulting in a
good deal of variation. Germination is rapid under warm, humid conditions
and seedlings should be ready to place in the garden within eight weeks after
sowing. Flowering occurs the first year from seed.

225

Related Species:
  G. aristata is a fine flowering plant but is much more variable than the hybrid. It grows to 3', often requiring support. Unlike the hybrids, plants raised from seed will not flower the first year.

Additional Reading:
Stoutamire, Warren P. 1960. The history of cultivated gaillardias. *Baileya* 8:13–17.

Galanthus (ga-lanth' us)   Snowdrop   Amaryllidaceae

  Snowdrops never fail to provide pleasure in late winter and early spring as they pop out of the ground, sometimes even before the snow has disappeared. These cool climate plants are known as *pierce neige* ("snow piercing") in France and are totally intolerant of heat. They last longer in the northern parts of the country than in the South but are still a worthwhile addition to the southern garden (at least to zone 7), where they flower in Feburary. A mix of various *Galanthus* species may provide flowers from January to April. In all species, the buds are solitary and erect but the flowers nod on short, wiry stems. They have 3 outer and 3 shorter notched, inner petals held above strap-like leaves. Bulbs should be planted in drifts of 12 or more (preferably in the hundreds), otherwise they make no impact. The spring landscape comes alive when snowdrops are combined with hellebores and winter aconites.
  Plant about 3" deep in well-drained soil in full sun to partial shade. In southern parts of the country, the combination of heavy soils and cold winter rains result in loss of many bulbs. Where conditions are favorable, however, multiplication is rapid. Clumps may be lifted immediately after flowering, separated carefully and replanted as soon as possible.
  Snowdrops are sometimes confused with snowflakes, *Leucojum*, another spring-flowering relative. The flower segments of snowflakes are all equal in size, the plants are usually taller, and they bear 2–3 flowers on each stem.

-elwesii (el-wez' ee-eye)   Giant Snowdrop   9–12"/6"
Winter, Spring   White   Asia Minor   Zones 4–7

  The flowers are up to 2" long and 1" wide. The inner segments have green blotches at the base (point of attachment) and the tip. The two gray-green strap-like leaves are about 1¼" wide, 4" long and deeply channelled. Plants flower about one week later than *G. nivalis*.

Cultivars:
var. *globosus* has broad outer segments resulting in flowers up to 1½" wide.

Related Species:
  G. ikariae, Nikarian snowdrop, is similar but has flared outer segments and broad recurved dark green leaves. The inner segments are almost entirely green.

-nivalis (ni-vaal' is)		Common Snowdrop	6–9"/12"
Winter, Spring	White	Northern Europe	Zones 3–7

One of the earliest species to flower, plants may open as early as January in its southern range and push through the snow by March at the northern end. The foliage consists of 2 narrow (less than ½" wide) strap-like leaves above which the 1" long and ½" wide flowers are borne. They are pure white except for a green crescent at the apex of the inner segments. Bulbs multiply rapidly but must be planted in large numbers to fulfill their potential.

Cultivars:

'Atkinsii' is a vigorous form, growing 9" tall and bearing many 1" wide flowers.
'Flore Pleno' has 1" wide double flowers and is particularly ornamental.
'Ophelia' bears large double flowers filled with green-tipped segments.
'Lutescens' has inner segments marked with yellow rather than green.
'Reginae-Olgae', usually listed as 'Olgae', is similar to the type but flowers in the fall.

Related Species:

G. cilicicus, Cilician snowdrop, is similar to *G. nivalis* and sometimes treated as a sub-species (subsp. *cilicicus*). Flowers open in the fall and do not have the basal green splotch.

Quick Key to Galanthus Species

  A. Leaves up to 1¼" wide, flowers to 2" long, inner segments
    blotched green at base and apex .... *G. elwesii*
  AA. Leaves to ½" wide, flowers to 1" long, inner segments
    blotched green at tips only .... *G. nivalis*

Additional Reading:

Yeo, Peter F. 1975. The hybrid origin of some cultivated snowdrops (*Galanthus*-Amaryllidaceae). *Baileya* 19:157–162.

Galega (gal-ee' ga)   Goat's Rue   Fabaceae

Of the 6–8 species, only *G. officinalis* is of garden value. Plants were once grown for forage and fed to goats to increase milk flow. This was so common that the genus was named after the Greek word *gala*, meaning milk. They have pea-like flowers which are sometimes confused with those of *Baptisia*. In some countries, common goat's rue has become so abundant that it is considered a noxious weed and is under siege of eradication.

-officinalis (o-fi-chi-nah' lis)		Common Goat's Rue	3–4'/3'
Late Spring	Pale blue	Southern Europe, Asia Minor	Zones 3–7

The 1–2' long pinnately compound leaves consist of 11 to 17 entire leaflets held on short petioles (stalk of leaflet). The pale blue to white, 1–1½" long

227

flowers are held in long many-flowered racemes pointing upward like many colored candles.

The species is tolerant of poor soils and if over fertilized, grows too tall and lanky and requires support. Plant in full sun in any well-drained soil. Cut back after the flowers are finished as plants are not particularly attractive after flowering, a problem common to many members of the pea family.

Galega is seldom used in this country, although I am not sure the reason. It is tolerant of cool conditions but does not adapt well to the heat and humidity of the South.

Cultivars:

'Alba' is an excellent form which bears showy white flowers.

Propagate by division every 3–5 years. Seed germinates well in cool or warm conditions.

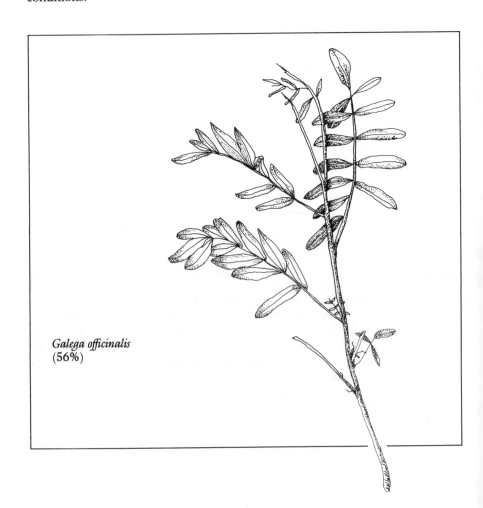

Galega officinalis
(56%)

Related Species:

G. × *hartlandii*, a cross between *G. officinalis* and *G. patula*, is 2–4' tall and has white and blue bicolor flowers. A few cultivars found in European gardens may belong to this hybrid.

'Her Majesty' has clear lilac flowers.
'Lady Wilson' bears blue and white flowers suffused with a tinge of rose.

Galium (gay-lee' um)   Sweet Woodruff, Bedstraw   Rubiaceae

Most species are weeds and have no place in the garden. The exception is *Galium odoratum*, sweet woodruff, a useful and popular ground cover.

-odoratum (o-dor-ah' tum)   Sweet Woodruff   4–9"/12"
Spring   White   Europe   Zones 4–8

(Syn. *Asperula odorata*)

The 1½" long, ½" wide, sessile leaves are borne in a whorl of 6–8 at each node along the length of the square stems. The roots are slender and creeping, making the plants particularly effective ground covers. The white fragrant flowers are only ⅛–¼" long and held in loosely branched cymes. When in flower in the spring, plants look like recently fallen snow.

The whole plant smells like new-mown hay when crushed or dried, thus its other common name, bedstraw. Plants tolerate partial shade in the North but require it in the South. To grow rapidly and cover large areas, a consistent supply of water is necessary. It is particularly pretty in the dappled shade of *Gleditsia* or beneath high canopy trees.

Propagate by division in the spring or fall.

Galtonia (gawl-tone' ee-a)   Summer Hyacinth   Liliaceae

A group of three species of bulbous plants, native to South Africa that are closely related to the garden hyacinth. Only one, *G. candicans*, is worthy of garden space.

-candicans (kan' di-kanz)   Summer Hyacinth   2–4'/3'
Summer   White   South Africa   Zones 6–9

The strap-shaped leaves are 2–3' long, 2" wide and have conspicuous midribs. A leafless scape arises from the basal leaves carrying a loose raceme of 20–30 dangling, bell-shaped flowers on 1–2½" long pedicels. The 1½" long flowers are slightly scented and clear white.

Plants should be grown in full sun and watered and fertilized copiously. If planted in a proper site, staking is not necessary. However, if grown in excessive

229

shade or in lean soil, scapes will not be strong enough to support the heavy flowers. Plant bulbs in early spring about 6″ deep in groups of a dozen or more for the best show.

Cut back foliage after flowering because plants tend to look weedy as leaves decline. Bulbs need to be lifted, similar to gladioli, north of zone 6, although bulbs in zone 5 may overwinter if well protected.

Propagate by lifting bulbs in spring and removing small offsets, which flower after two years. Sow the small seeds in well-drained soil under warm (70–75°F), humid conditions. Approximately 3 years is necessary for flowering plants from seed.

Related Species:

G. princeps has broad gray-green foliage and bears greenish-white flowers 1–2 weeks earlier than *G. candicans*.

Gaura (gaw′ ra)	Gaura	Onagraceae

The genus is a relative newcomer to the American garden scene although most species are native to North America. Plants have proven well suited for the warmer regions of the country. There are only about eight species and *G. lindheimeri* is most available.

-lindheimeri (lind-hay′ mer-eye)	White Gaura	3–4′/3′
Summer	White	Louisiana, Texas	Zones 5–9

Plants are used extensively in the South because plants tolerate heat and humidity well, although problems with legginess and lack of flowering can occur. The 1–3″ long, lanceolate leaves are alternate and sessile. The flowers are carried on a loose open panicle well above the foliage. The 1″ long white flowers are rose-tinged and open up the spike much like a gladiolus but only a few are open at any one time. As they age, the white gives way to pale rose. Plants prefer a rich, well-drained soil in full sun to partial shade.

If spent flower spikes are removed, flowering continues from late spring to fall. Although not the most showy plant in the landscape, gaura is one of the most durable. The thick deep roots help in making plants particularly drought tolerant. If and when breeders produce a fuller inflorescence and brighter flowers, this plant will be used far more extensively. *Gaura* is also highly valued by Mr. Jack Hobbs of the Auckland Botanical Garden in New Zealand, where plants grow three feet tall and flower prolifically throughout the summer and into the fall.

Seed germinates within 14–21 days when sown in a warm, humid area. Division may be accomplished after 2–3 years.

Additional Reading:

Anonymous, 1959. *Gaura lindheimeri* Engelmann and Gray. *Baileya* 7:62.

Geranium (jer-aye' knee-um)   Cranesbill   Geraniaceae

This wonderfully diverse genus, consisting of well over 200 species, is known as cranesbill because of the beak-like fruit. Plants are often referred to as hardy geraniums to separate them from the annual geraniums which belong to the genus *Pelargonium*. Hardy geraniums have been woefully underused in American gardens but a minor renaissance is occurring. As more people travel to fine gardens throughout the world, particularly those of the British Isles, they discover the beauty and variety of these fine plants. Fortunately, additional species are becoming available in North America and the good, the bad, and the ugly are being separated. Alas, we cannot expect equal performance from all species on this continent as in England, but there are many well worth including in the garden. A number of native species such as *G. maculatum*, spotted cranesbill, and *G. robertianum*, herb robert, are common. In fact, spotted cranesbill is an effective garden plant in the southern half of the country, outperforming many of its more sophisticated relatives. A niche may be found in every garden for at least one species as their diversity is extraordinary. A few species such as *G. renardii* appear to have narrow growing ranges (Zones 5 to 7) but most are far more adaptable.

The leaves are usually opposite and palmately lobed or dissected. The flowers have 5 equal and usually overlapping petals, 10 stamens, and seed which is explosively expelled from the fruit. In certain species, so few differences exist that the main distinguishing characteristic is the method of seed expulsion.

In general, most species prefer moist soils and full sun to partial shade although some species are tolerant of heavy shade. In the southern limits of their range, late afternoon shade should be provided. Propagation is by division in spring or fall, terminal cuttings in the spring or after flowering, or by seed.

Most species should be divided every 2–4 years, however, some species have deep taproots making division difficult. Most of these may be raised by root cuttings (see *Anemone* × *hybrida* for details), cuttings or seed. Seed generally requires a ripening period before germinatiom. If seed is collected from garden plants, store it for 2–4 weeks at room temperature prior to sowing in a warm (70–75°F), humid area. Some seed may require a cold treatment of 3–5 weeks but this is not usually necessary.

In the descriptions that follow, I have included a number of species and/or cultivars not widely available in this country. This was not done to frustrate but rather to prepare the reader for introductions making their way to the American marketplace.

Quick Reference to Geranium Species

	Height (in.)	Flower color
G. cinereum	6–12	Red, pink
G. clarkei	15–20	Violet, white

	Height (in.)	Flower color
G. dalmaticum	4–6	Mauve
G. endressii	15–18	Pink
G. himalayense	10–15	Lilac, purple veins
G. 'Johnson's Blue'	15–18	Blue
G. macrorrhizum	15–18	Magenta
G. × magnificum	18–24	Violet-blue
G. phaeum	18–24	Dark maroon
G. platypetalum	18–24	Violet
G. pratense	24–36	Purple
G. psilostemon	24–48	Red, black center
G. sanguineum	9–12	Magenta
G. sylvaticum	30–36	Violet-blue

-cinereum (si-ner' ee-um)		Grayleaf Cranebill	6–12"/12"
Spring	Red, pink	Pyrenees	Zones 5–8

The cultivars of this species are some of the most colorful in the genus. The leaves consist of 5–7 wedge-shaped lobes divided almost to the base. Each division is 3-lobed for about ⅓ the length. The pale, purplish pink flowers have dark veins and are 1" wide. The plant is essentially stemless and its small stature dictates its placement at the front of the garden or in a well-drained rock garden. One of the most demanding as to siteing, plants do poorly below zone 5 or above zone 7. The cultivar 'Ballerina' did wonderfully well in the Horticulture Gardens in Georgia in the spring, but struggled for life during the summer. This is unfortunate as there are some stunning forms available. When placed in partial shade and well-drained soil, it can be a knockout.

Much variation within the species occurs and confusion exists in the classification. Two major varieties have been named, although differences require a taxonomist's eye. Var. cinereum differs from var. subcaulescens in that the latter has darker leaves, magenta colored petals, and blackish stamens and stigmas. Natural hybridization occurs readily, thus making separation even more difficult. From the garden and gardener standpoint, the parentage or history of the garden forms is unimportant as long as the plants perform well.

Cultivars:

'Album' (of var. cinereum) has completely white flowers.

'Ballerina' (G. cinereum var. cinereum × var. subcaulescens), raised by Bloom's Nursery in England, has received numerous awards. Plants stand only 4–6" tall and bear 2" diameter lilac-pink flowers with a dark center and purple veining on the petals. Flowers are largely sterile which accounts for the long blooming time.

'Giuseppii' belongs to var. *subcaulescens*. It has deep magenta flowers with a dark
   spot in the center.
'Lawrence Flatman' is similar to 'Ballerina' but more vigorous. This was also
   raised by Bloom's.
'Splendens' (of var. *subcaulescens*) is 5–6″ tall and covered with vibrant deep red
   flowers with dark centers. It appears to be one of the least vigorous.

Propagate by divisions, stem cuttings or by seed.

Related Species:
   G. argenteum, silverleaf geranium, is almost identical to this species but the
leaves are densely covered with a silvery-gray pubescence.

-clarkei (clar-key′ eye)	Clarke's Geranium	15–20″/18″
Spring	Violet, white	Nepal	Zones 5–8

(Syn. *G. pratense* 'Kashmir Purple' and 'Kashmir White')

   This species has recently been separated from *G. pratense* (which see) by Dr.
Peter Yeo of Cambridge University. Plants are lower growing, leaves are much
more deeply cut, more basal leaves are formed, and a more open inflorescence
is produced than on plants of *G. pratense*.
   The 4–6″ wide basal leaves are deeply divided into seven divisions, each
division deeply pinnately lobed. The ½–¾″ diameter flowers are upward facing
(as are the seed capsules) and purplish violet or white with dark veins. Plants
are completely covered with flowers in late spring and summer and are among
the prettiest geraniums I have seen.

Cultivars:

'Kashmir Purple' bears deep blue flowers and comes relatively true from seed.
'Kashmir White' (syn. *G. rectum* 'Album') has clear white flowers with pale lilac-
   pink veins. When raised from seed, some plants will be purple flowered.

Propagate by division in spring or fall.

-dalmaticum (dal-mat′ i-cum)	Dalmatian Cranesbill	4–6″/6″
Late Spring	Mauve	Balkan Peninsula	Zones 4–8

   This low grower has trailing stems and spreads rapidly by rhizomes but is
not invasive. The smooth foliage is up to 2″ wide and deeply divided. Each of
the 5–7 divisions is 3-lobed for about ¼ its length. The light pink, 1″ diameter
flowers have entire petals (i.e. not notched) and are usually borne 3 to a flower
stem. The foliage has red to orange fall color and persists well into the winter.
   Place in full sun in well-drained soil. Plants tolerate partial shade but will be
taller and not as floriferous.

Geranium clarkei 'Kashmir White'
(48%)

Cultivars:

'Album' is a lovely white-flowered form but not quite as vigorous as the type.

Propagate by division of the rhizome or from seed.

Related Species:

   G. × *cantabrigiense* arose from G. *macrorrhizum* and G. *dalmaticum*. The flowers and leaves are intermediate between the two and plants are sterile. This name was coined by Yeo in 1985 and commemorates the city of Cambridge, England.

-endressii (en-dres' ee-eye)	Endress's Geranium	15–18"/18"
Summer Pink	Pyrenees	Zones 4–8

   This vigorous species bears light pink 1" diameter flowers above 3–5" wide shiny green leaves. Leaves are deeply 5 times divided, each division having 3 lobes cut about halfway down. Plants flower from early summer through the fall in northern gardens but succumb to the heat in the South and stop flowering in mid June. In the North, plant in full sun but provide afternoon shade in the South. Good drainage is essential to plant survival.

Cultivars:

'Wargrave Pink' has superseded the species and is the most popular cultivar. It is a vigorous clone with salmon-pink flowers held well above the foliage. The petals are more distinctly notched than those of the species.

Propagate by division every 2–3 years. Seeds of the species germinate within 3 weeks if placed in warm (70–75°F), humid atmosphere.

Related Species:

G. × *oxonianum*, a hybrid between *G. endressii* and *G. versicolor*, has pink funnel-shaped flowers with darker veins. This name, adopted by Yeo in 1985, commemorates the city of Oxford, England.

'Claridge Dulce', named after its originator, is vigorous with grayish green foliage and lovely purple-pink flowers with dark veins.

var. *thurstonianum* has purple flowers consisting of narrow, strap-shaped petals. It is more interesting than pretty.

G. × *riversleaianum* is a hybrid between *G. endressii* and *G. traversii*, a little-used geranium native to New Zealand. Flowers are pink to magenta and plants grow 12" tall.

'Russell Pritchard' is a well-known cultivar with 1½" diameter magenta flowers and dull gray-green, lobed foliage.

-himalayense (hi-mah-lay-en′ se)		Lilac Geranium	10–15"/15"
Summer	Lilac	Northern Asia	Zones 4–8

(Syn. *G. grandiflorum*, *G. meeboldii*)

Plants are large enough for the border but since they tend to sprawl, are better placed along pathways where their unruly growth can be used to advantage. The 3–6" diameter leaves are deeply cut into seven divisions, each division 3-lobed at the apex. The petioles are up to 6" long, resulting in the sprawling habit. In the fall, the foliage turns bright orange and red before disappearing. The 1½–2" diameter, violet-blue flowers have a warm reddish center and are the largest of any species of geranium. They are saucer shaped with prominent red-purple veins and flowering continues for 4–6 weeks. Plant in full sun in well-drained soil and do not allow to dry out.

Cultivars:

'Birch Double' (syn. 'Plenum') has ½" diameter washed out double lavender flowers. It is less vigorous and less attractive than the species. The flowers are sterile and persist much longer than the singles.

'Gravetye' (syn. 'Alpinum') bears 2″ wide bright blue flowers with reddish centers and dark veins. It is shorter (about 12″ tall) and less unruly than the species. This cultivar is a knockout.

Propagate by division every 2–3 years or from seed.

Related Species:
    G. × 'Johnson's Blue' is an excellent hybrid between G. *himalayense* and G. *pratense* and appeared in English gardens around 1950. The parents are rather different in growth habit, and this hybrid is intermediate between them in leaf characteristics. At 15–18″ tall, it is taller than G. *himalayense* but not as big as a well-grown G. *pratense*. The 1½–2″ diameter clear blue flowers are similar in color to those of G. *himalayense* but without the reddish center. Seed set is minimal so flowering continues for a long time. Plants have done well in zone 8.

-macrorrhizum (mak-ro-rise′ um)	Bigroot Geranium	15–18″/15″
Spring Magenta	Southern Europe	Zones 3–8

    When surrounded by dozens of geranium species, it is nice to know that at least one is easily distinguished from the rest. Crushing a leaf provides the unmistakable medicinal smell of G. *macrorrhizum*. The 6–8″ wide leaves have seven divisions, cut two-thirds the way down, each division shallowly lobed. The 1″ diameter purplish-magenta flowers have entire petals and dark red calyces (the sepals) inflated like tiny balloons. They are held on a slightly hairy peduncle. The plant has thick, fleshy rhizomatous roots and spreads well in areas of full sun to partial shade. The vigorous root system allows it to compete during drought when others falter and thus is an excellent species as a ground cover. Plants are heat tolerant, performing well in zone 8 in partial shade. This is one of the easiest geraniums to grow.

Cultivars:
'Album' bears white petals with pink calyces and is a lovely garden plant.
'Beven's Variety' is 8–10″ tall with 1″ wide flowers consisting of deep red sepals and magenta petals.
'Ingwersen's Variety', named after the noted English horticulturist, Walter Ingwersen, has pale pink flowers with slightly glossier leaves than the type. It is the finest cultivar for the garden.

Propagate by dividing the thick rootstock, using the rosette bearing stems as cuttings, or by seed. Seed should not be covered before placing it in a warm, humid area.

Related Species
    G. *thunbergii* is related only in that plants make an effective ground cover, particularly for southern gardens. It is an almost weedy species, consisting of

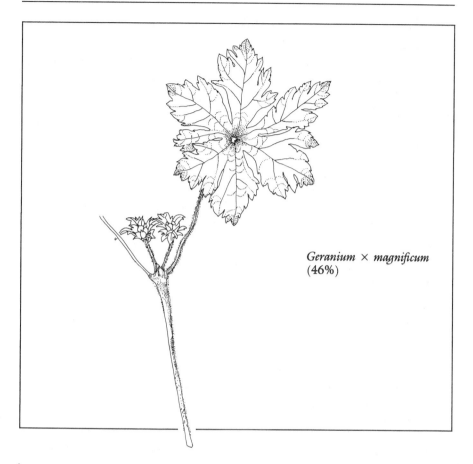

Geranium × *magnificum*
(46%)

light green hairy leaves on sprawling stems and hundreds of ½" diameter white to pink flowers which appear in late summer.

- × *magnificum* (mag-nif' i-cum)	Showy Geranium	18–24"/24"
Summer Violet-blue	Hybrid	Zones 3–8

This sterile hybrid resulted from *G. ibericum* × *G. platypetalum* and bears hairy foliage with 5–7 deeply cut divisions. The flower stems are 4–5" long and the 1½" diameter deep violet-blue flowers are held erect and upright. Plants are large and tend to flop over in rain and wind. They can be cut back after flowering to produce a new set of leaves, however, significant flowering will not occur again. Plants are more vigorous than either of the parents. Grow in full sun to partial shade in well-drained soil.

Propagate by divisions every 2–3 years.

237

-phaeum (fie' um)		Mourning Widow		18–24"/18"
Early Summer	Dark maroon		Europe	Zones 5–7

This distinct species produces very dark, almost black, nodding flowers which suggest "a widow who has ceased to mourn". The petals, which are about as long as broad, are slightly reflexed resulting in the pistil and stamens being totally exserted. The flowers look like a can-can girl raising her purple skirt. The erect stems bear 5–7 deeply divided leaves, each division having small purple spots at their bases. The thick rhizomes allow plants to tolerate some drought although they perform best under moist conditions. Plants are native to damp meadows and shady roadsides and can be grown in shady, moist areas of the garden. This is not a plant which will knock you over with color but one with a quiet charm all its own. I have had little success establishing plants in zone 8, and likely zone 7 is the southern limit for vigorous growth.

Cultivars:
'Album' has white or faintly blushed petals.
var. *lividum* has paler flowers occasionally streaked with lilac spots.

Related Species:
G. *aristatum* is similar to G. *phaeum* but not as upright. The flowers are white to lilac-pink and the reflexed petals have lovely lilac veins. The leaves are also more pubescent.

G. *reflexum* is also similar but the flowers are not as dark purple and are smaller. The petals, which are twice as long as broad, are the most reflexed of any species. The immature fruits are downwardly inclined in this species but upwardly inclined in G. *phaeum*.

-platypetalum (pla-ti-pet-ah' lum)		Broad-petaled Geranium		18–24"/18"
Late Spring	Deep violet		Caucasus	Zones 3–8

The sticky flower stalks carry deep violet 1" diameter flowers with reddish veins. The 4–6" wide rounded leaves have 7–9 divisions, each cut about halfway into the leaf. Partial shade, particularly in the South, is preferable to full sun. Although not as showy as one of its children, G. × *magnificum*, it is heat tolerant and makes a good show in the garden. The foliage persists all season and does not require cutting back as do most other species.

Propagate by divisions or seed.

Related Species:
G. *ibericum*, Caucasus geranium, is similar and often treated as a synonym. Plants differ by having the divisions cut about three-quarters of the way down the leaf. They are also more drought tolerant.

G. *renardii* is a beautiful but temperamental species seldom seen in American gardens. The 5–7 divisions of the dull gray-green foliage are shallowly lobed and the flowers are unmistakable. Each 1" diameter white flower is vividly marked with violet feathered veins. Excellent drainage and a sheltered location are required.

-pratense (prah'ten' see)		Meadow Cranesbill	24–36"/24"
Late Spring	Purple	Northern Europe	Zones 5–8

Meadow cranesbill is widely distributed in the Old World and therefore quite variable. The 3–6" wide leaves are deeply cut into 7–9 divisions, each of which is deeply serrated. The 1½" diameter flowers have reddish, sometimes translucent veins on the dark blue petals. This is one of the tallest and most vigorous of the cranesbills and plants often need support to remain upright. One of the problems with this species is its enthusiasm for seed production, often resulting in rapid and messy shedding of flowers. When grown in zone 8, they tend to look weedy and foliage must be cut back after flowering. The species tolerates limey soils better than many others. Plant in full sun and provide plenty of moisture.

Cultivars:

'Kashmir White' and 'Kashmir Purple' were thought to be cultivars of this species but have been reclassified as cultivars of *G. clarkei* (which see).
'Mrs. Kendall Clarke' has pale blue flowers with rosy-white venation. It is the most common cultivar available.
'Plenum Album', 'Plenum Caeruleum', and 'Plenum Violaceum' have 1" diameter, small double flowers of white, pale blue, and purple, respectively. They persist longer than the single flower types because they do not shed as rapidly.
'Silver Queen' is 3' tall and bears 1–2" diameter silvery-blue flowers.

Propagate by division or seed.

-psilostemon (sye-lo' ste-mon)		Armenian Geranium	24–48"/36"
Summer	Red with black center	Armenia	Zones 5–8

(Syn. *G. armenum*)

The first time I saw this plant was at Sissinghurst Castle and Garden, Kent, England. I observed and studied well over a thousand plant species that trip, but the stateliness and beauty of this one was unforgettable. The 6–8" wide, heart-shaped, basal evergreen foliage is cut nearly ⅘ of the length into 5–7 sections while the stem leaves are triangular. The 1½–2" diameter dark red flowers have a conspicuous black spot in the middle. It is a color one either hates or loves.

This is not a small plant; heights of 3 to 4' are not uncommon and the stems need support. Plants should be placed in broken shade and in rich moist soil to perform their best. They look better planted against a dark background where the luminous flowers will stand out even more. Since the species was almost non-existent in the United States, I obtained seed and now have plants in my Georgia garden. They are not as vigorous in the South as in Europe (but what is?) and stand only 2' tall after 4 years, but I don't have to go across the ocean to see it every year. This magnificent plant is now available and needs to be tested more widely in the United States to determine garden adaptability.

Cultivars:

'Bressingham Flair' is about 2' tall and does not require as much support as the species. The flowers are a little less intense.

Propagate by division of the root stalk or by seed.

Related Species:

'Ann Folkard' is a natural hybrid which occurred in 1973 between *G. procurrens*, a 12" tall ground cover species, and *G. psilostemon*. Raised by an amateur gardener, Rev. O.G. Folkard, it is a testimonial to the ability of amateur gardeners to have a significant impact on horticulture. The 18" tall plants have rich magenta flowers with the expected black center.

G. procurrens has 1" diameter flowers of rich magenta with black centers. Plants provide the color of *G. psilostemon* on a 12–15" tall trailing plant. The red stems trail for long distances and root at the nodes, making them effective ground cover plants for a sunny area.

-sanguineum (sang-guin' ee-um)	Bloody Cranesbill	9–12"/12"
Spring Magenta	Europe, Asia	Zones 3–8

Of the cultivated geraniums, this is the most common garden species in the United States. Plants are adaptable, able to tolerate heat and cold better than other species, and free flowering. Plants generally grow in mounds, consisting of thick shallowly divided basal leaves and thinner, deeply divided stem leaves. The foliage also provides a touch of fall color, turning crimson-red. The 1–1½" diameter flowers are a rich magenta, often too fierce for the tastes of many gardeners. The flowers are solitary and the petals are not notched.

Plants should be placed in full sun or partial shade in the front of the garden. In shade, they are less compact, less floriferous and taller than in the sun. This is the most trouble-free species for southern gardeners as the thick root stalk ferrets out moisture in times of drought and the waxy basal leaves tolerate hot weather.

Cultivars:

'Album' has clear white flowers and grows 10–18" tall. It is an excellent cultivar.

'Alpenglow' grows about 8" tall with vivid rose-red flowers.

'Glenluce' has 1½–2" diameter deep rose flowers.

'Shepherd's Warning' is the most diminutive of the species; only about 4–6" tall with deep rose-pink flowers. Separate from vigorous species or it will be smothered.

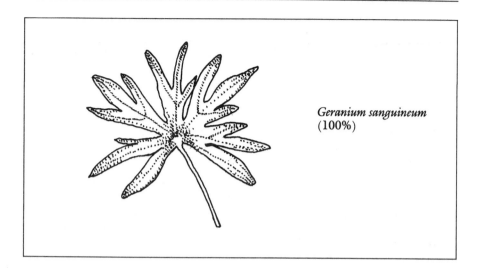

Geranium sanguineum
(100%)

var. *striatum* is probably the best of the lot and is usually sold under the name 'Lancastriense' or 'Prostratum'. It is only 6–8″ tall and although flower color is somewhat variable, light pink flowers with crimson veins are usually produced.

Propagate by division every 3–4 years or from seed.

Related Species:

G. wallichianum, Wallich geranium, is a prostrate species with 2′ long trailing stems making this an excellent geranium for growing over stone walls or in patio pots. The late summer flowers are purple and not outstanding. The cultivar 'Buxton's Variety', however, has small white marbled foliage and saucer-shaped campanula blue flowers with a distinct white center. A planting laden with flowers romping over rocks and walls is a magnificent sight. It may be raised from root cuttings and comes true from seed.

-sylvaticum (sil-va′ ti-kum)		Wood Cranesbill	30–36″/30″
Spring	Violet-blue	Europe	Zones 5–8

One of the earliest flowering geraniums, flowers appear as early as late April in the South and May further north. The 6–7″ wide roundish leaves are deeply cut into 7–9 divisions. The 1″ wide flowers are like tiny chalices open to the sky, being borne neither horizontal or nodding. The seed capsules are thrust in the air like athletes showing the crowd they are number one. The flowers are usually violet-blue with a white center but may be pink or white. The species is not as garden worthy as some of the cultivars but some handsome cultivars exist. Plants are best placed in partial shade and in a moisture retentive soil.

Cultivars:

'Album' has white flowers with light green leaves. It comes true from seed.
'Mayflower', introduced by Bloom's Nursery in 1972, is the best of the group,
   bearing rich violet-blue flowers with a white base.

Propagate by division every 2–3 years or by seed.

Quick Key to the Geranium Species
   A. Plants very low growing, less than 8″ tall
      B. Peduncles (flower stems) bearing solitary flower.......................
                                 G. sanguineum var. *striatum*
   BB. Peduncles usually 2- or 3-flowered
      C. Peduncles usually 2-flowered, flowers erect or upwardly
         inclined ....*G. cinereum*
      CC. Peduncles usually 3-flowered, flowers horizontal or nodding ....
                                    G. dalmaticum
   AA. Plants usually 9″ or taller, may be erect or sprawling
      B. Flowers sterile, no seed produced
         C. Flower petals with obvious notch .... *G.* × *magnificum*
         CC. Flower petals without obvious notch........... *G.* 'Johnson's Blue'
      BB. Flowers not sterile, seed produced
         C. Flowers erect or upwardly inclined
            D. Peduncles 1-flowered .... *G. sanguineum*
         DD. Peduncles 2- to many-flowered
            E. Flowers red to magenta with black central disc................
                                    G. psilostemon
            EE. Flowers white, purple, blue, or pink
               F. Immature fruit erect, flower usually violet-blue............
                                    G. sylvaticum
               FF. Immature fruit nodding, flowers white or
                  purple, or pink
                  G. Flowers white or purple....................... *G. clarkei*
                  GG. Flowers usually pink .... *G. endressii*
         CC. Flowers not erect, directed horizontally or nodding
            D. Leaves not deeply divided, divisions cut only about
               ½ way down leaf, calyx not inflated .... *G. platypetalum*
            DD. Leaves divided so incisions reach more than 2/3 way
               down leaf, calyx may or may not be inflated
               E. Plant usually taller than 24″
                  F. Flowers conspicuously nodding and reflexed,
                     dark maroon to almost black.................. *G. phaeum*
                  FF. Flowers slightly nodding, not reflexed, blue to
                     violet-blue .... *G. pratense*

EE. Plant usually less than 24″ tall
  G. Plants with thickened woody base, flowers
    purple to magenta, foliage strongly aromatic
    when crushed, calyx inflated .... *G. macrorrhizum*
  GG. Plants without thickened woody base,
    flowers lilac to blue, foliage not aromatic
    when crushed, calyx not inflated .... *G. himalayense*

Additional Reading:

Books:

Yeo. Peter F. 1985. *Hardy Geraniums*. Timber Press, Portland, OR: 192 pages. It is impossible to deal with all the potential gems in this genus but for geranium addicts like myself, I highly recommend this book. Dr. Yeo is one of the foremost geranium experts in the world and provides great detail concerning botanical and taxonomic differences between hundreds of species. Although not for the beginner, it is an excellent reference.

Manuscripts:

Forty, Joy. 1980. A survey of hardy geraniums in cultivation. *The Plantsman*, 2(2):67–78. This treatise was further clarified in the form of a Letter to the Editor by Joy Forty, 1981. *The Plantsman* 3(2):127–128.

Harper, Pamela. 1976. True geraniums. *Horticulture* 54(4):56–57.

Hensel, Margaret. 1985. Hardy geraniums. *Horticulture* 63(7):20–23.

Yeo, P.F. 1984. *Geranium candicans* and *G. yunnanense* of gardens. *The Garden* 109(1):36–37.

Geum (jee′ um)   Avens   Rosaceae

Over 50 species are included in this genus known for its bright, showy 5-petaled flowers and dark green leaves. The compound foliage is cut in various ways, depending on the species, but the terminal lobe is always the largest. In some species, their charm is extended by the production of fluffy seed heads, similar to those of *Pulsatilla*. Species such as *G. reptans* are small enough to be included in the rockery while taller ones such as *G. montanum* are sufficiently large for inclusion in the border. All require good drainage, ample moisture and some protection from full afternoon sun. Most geums are easily grown in the northern part of the country but struggle in the South.

Propagate by division in spring or fall or from fresh seed. Multiplication of cultivars should be accomplished vegetatively. Unfortunately, natural hybridization takes place readily between species and the resulting seedlings are often inferior.

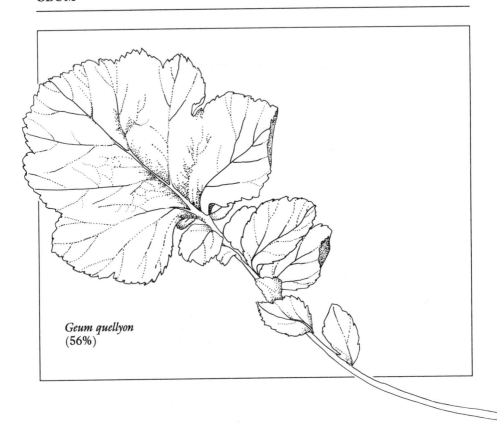

Geum quellyon
(56%)

Quick Reference to Geum Species

	Height (in.)	Flower color	Seed head fluffy
G. × *borisii*	9–12	Orange	Y
G. *montanum*	9–12	Yellow orange	Y
G. *quellyon*	20–24	Yellow, red	Y
G. *reptans*	6–8	Yellow	Y
G. *rivale*	8–12	Red, purple	N

-× *borisii* (bo-ris' ee-eye)	Boris Avens	9–12"/12"
Spring Orange-scarlet	Hybrid	Zones 3–7

This hybrid arose as a result of a cross between *G. bulgaricum*, a 2' tall species with nodding yellow flowers and *G. reptans*, a 6–8" tall yellow stoloniferous species. The trifoliate leaves have rounded lobes and the terminal lobe is twice as large as the laterals. Most of the material labelled as *G.* × *borisii* bears 1–2" wide bright orange, single flowers held well above the foliage on branching stems. Heavy flowering takes place for about 4 weeks in late spring and early summer and intermittently until fall. Plant in partial shade and keep uniformly moist. Flowering was excellent in zone 8 but longevity has not yet been determined.

According to *Hortus III* (but not the *Royal Horticulture Society Dictionary of Gardening*), plants from this cross should have nodding, yellow flowers. Most of the material sold as *G.* × *borisii* in this country bears upright rather than nodding flowers.

Cultivars:

'Georgenburg' is a hybrid with soft, pale yellow flowers that are more appealing than the harsh color of *G.* × *borisii*. It struggles in the South and does not display the vigor necessary to do well in hot summers.

Propagate by division in the spring.

-montanum (mon-tah' num)		Mountain Avens	9–12"/12"
Spring	Golden yellow	Southern Europe	Zones 4–8

The foliage of the species is among the prettiest and long lasting of the genus. The leaves are about 4" long, densely pubescent, and remain fresh well into the summer, unlike many species whose leaves deteriorate soon after flowering. The 1" wide solitary flowers are held well above the foliage and are a lovely golden yellow. The seed heads are feathery and as pretty as the flowers.

Related Species:

G. × *heldreichii* is a hybrid of confused lineage but *G. montanum* is probably one of the parents. Plants are much taller (up to 3') than *G. montanum* and the 1–2" diameter reddish orange flowers are borne in two's and three's. It is well adapted to Georgia heat and has persisted for three years without the deterioration often seen in *G. quellyon* cultivars.

-quellyon (quell-ee' on)		Chilean Avens	20–24"/18"
Spring	Scarlet	Chile	Zones 5–7

(Syn. *G. chiloense*)

This species is the most common of garden avens and, in my opinion, is overrated. The 6–12" long hairy leaves are pinnately divided and the terminal is about twice as large as the other leaflets. The 1–1½" wide scarlet flowers may be single or double. The species doesn't tolerate the excesses of the American climate, struggling a great deal in the summer and often dying out in the winter. Plants are short-lived even under the best of conditions. To be fair, some cultivars can look stunning when grown in a well-drained moist area out of the hot afternoon sun.

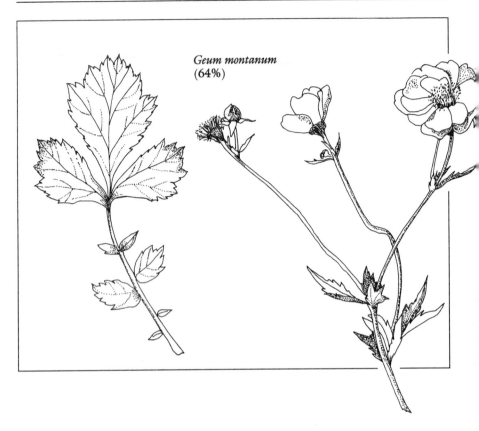

Geum montanum
(64%)

Cultivars:

Cultivars have superseded the species, many of which are hybrids between *G. quellyon* and *G. coccineum*, a species with brick red flowers.

'Dolly North' has golden orange, semi-double flowers.

'Fire Opal' produces many intense red, semi-double flowers

'Lady Stratheden' has deep buttercup-yellow semi-double flowers.

'Mrs. Bradshaw' bears scarlet, semi-double flowers. The last two cultivars can be raised from seed. While both have their admirers, I find they produce too few flowers for the amount of leaf area.

'Princess Juliana' bears soft yellow semi-double flowers that open about one week later than the others.

'Red Wings' is similar to 'Fire Opal' but has more orange in the flower.

-reptans (rep' tanz)		Creeping Avens	6–8"/8"
Spring	Yellow	European Alps	Zones 4–7

If full morning sun, excellent drainage, and somewhat basic soil are provided, this little plant can be a definite asset to the garden. However, if not given

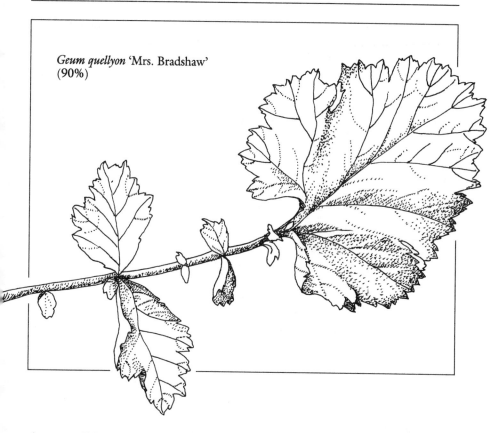

Geum quellyon 'Mrs. Bradshaw'
(90%)

these conditions, it will throw its runners in the air, give up and die. The leaflets are deeply toothed and unlike many others, the terminal leaflet is about the same size as the laterals. As a ground cover, plants multiply by rooting along the nodes of non-flowering runners. Many solitary 1–1½" diameter pale yellow flowers are borne in early summer.

Propagate by cutting the rooted runners and replanting in the final location. Seed germinates within 2–3 weeks under warm (70–75°F), humid conditions.

Related Species:

G. × *rhaeticum*, a hybrid between *G. montanum* and *G. reptans*, has foliar characteristics intermediate between the two. One inch diameter golden-yellow flowers cover 6–8" tall plants.

-rivale (ree-vah' lee)	Water Avens, Indian Chocolate	8–12"/10"
Spring Red, purple	Eurasia, North America	Zones 3–7

While most species bear upright yellowish flowers and require consistent moisture and sharp drainage, this species has nodding, bell-shaped, reddish purple flowers and is for all intents and purposes a bog plant. The foliage consists of 3–6 pairs of leaflets, the terminal twice as large as the lateral ones. The leaflets are hairy and noticeably serrated. This is a good ground cover plant for cool, wet areas where little else does well. However, it may be grown in non-boggy areas but constant moisture must be available. It has performed poorly in the Horticulture Gardens.

The rootstock is thick and brown and if boiled in water, the resultant liquid tastes faintly like chocolate, a tale I have fortunately not had the pleasure of verifying.

Propagate by seed or division.

Cultivars:
'Leonard's Variety' has drooping mahogany-red bell-shaped flowers.

Quick Key to Geum Species
>   A. Flowers upright, petals much longer than sepals
>   B. Plants upright, do not produce runners
>   C. Plants usually taller than 18″ .... *G. quellyon*
>   CC. Plants usually less than 18″ tall
>   D. Flowers usually solitary on flower stem........... *G. montanum*
>   DD. Flowers not solitary............................... *G. × borisii*
>   BB. Plants prostrate, produce many runners .... *G. reptans*
>   AA. Flowers nodding, petals barely longer than sepals .... *G. rivale*

Gillenia (gil-ee′ nee-a)   Physic, Ipecac   Rosaceae

A completely overlooked genus, *Gillenia* contains 2 species native to the United States which are wonderfully ornamental. Moist areas and partial shade are requirements for best performance. Propagate by division in the spring or by seed. Some authorities have changed *Gillenia* to *Porteranthus*.

-trifoliata (tri-fo-lee-ah′ ta)   Bowman's Root   2–4′/3′
Summer   White   Central, Southern United States   Zones 4–8

I was first "turned on" to this species in Aas, Norway, where it shimmered in the late afternoon sun. I was embarassed to learn that it was native from New York to Georgia and that it was seldom commercially available to gardeners in America. The 3-foliate leaves are borne on short leaf stalks and each 2–3″ long ovate leaflet is serrated and pointed. Small insignificant stipules (leaf-like structures) are found at the base of the petiole on the upper nodes.

In the summer, plants bear such masses of 1″ wide white star-shaped flowers that they look like clouds of butterflies. The white petals emerge from small tubular wine-colored sepals which persist long after the petals have fallen. The flowers are held above the foliage on wiry stems terminating in corymbose panicles. Place in partial shade and moist areas or plants will languish. Unfortunately, support is usually required, particularly in the southern zones. A plant or two is well worth trying if you have the space.

Related Species:

G. stipulata, Indian physic, is similar but does not have the persistent red sepals. The leaflets are narrower and the stipules are larger and more leaflike than those of the previous species. It is more difficult to find and not as ornamental as *G. trifoliata*.

Gladiolus (glad-ee' o-lus)   Gladiolus   Iridaceae

The many species and their hybridization can be discussed only superficially in this book. Although over 250 species occur, it is difficult for the home gardener to find anything but the large-flowered hybrids. Recently a number of miniature-flowered hybrids have become available, but one must search to find any of the actual species. Argueably, in point of beauty, the natural species do not compare with today's fine garden hybrids. The modern hybrids evolved from G. × *gandavensis*, G. × *childsii*, G. × *nanceianus*, and G. × *lemoinei*, all of little garden interest today. There has been so much additional hybridization that it is almost impossible to know what parents produced what cultivars. All modern hybrids have been lumped together under G. × *hortulanus*.

Named varieties abound and are usually classified as large-flowered, which have flowers 4–7″ across; butterfly flowers which are half the size as the large-flowered types and have striking throat markings or blotches; miniatures, which evolved from *G. primulinus* and have 2–3″ wide flowers borne on shorter stems; and open face types whose flowers are wide open and point more upright than those in the other classes. For those interested in the history of gladioli and the cultivars available, a number of good books on bulb species and bulb catalogs are available.

Although hybrids abound, there are still a few species available. These cannot compete with the colors and flower size of the hybrids, but they add a touch of class and dignity to the garden.

-byzantinus (bi-zan-teen' us)

-byzantinus (bi-zan-teen' us)	Byzantine Gladiolus	2–3'/2'
Summer Maroon	Mediterranean	Zones 7–10

The leaves are narrower than the hybrid gladioli and the 1–3″ long flowers are loosely arranged on the 6–12 flowered raceme. They are mostly maroon but are sometimes red or copper colored and are borne on one side of the spike only. Corms are hardy in southern areas of the country but must be dug in the North. They are lovely plants, provide long-lasting cut flowers and give the serious gardener a glimpse into the genus before the hybridizers "improved" it.

Plant in a shady area in moist soils. Similar to all gladioli, thrips are a terrible nuisance.

Related Species:

G. callianthus is the name under which some authorities place *Acidanthera bicolor*, a wonderful African species (which see). I have elected to retain the name *Acidanthera*.

Gypsophila (gyp-soff' ill-a)   Baby's Breath   Caryophyllaceae

This genus contains plants that are almost indispensible to the florist as fillers for arrangements. If one thinks of the many bouquets sold each day across the country, the economic importance is quickly realized. Although the commercial production of baby's breath, *G. paniculata*, is big business in many countries, it is also a lovely garden plant. The name gypsophila comes from the Greek word *gypos*, meaning gypsum and *philos*, meaning friendship. This refers to its love of soils with a high pH, a soil condition which must be present if plants are to thrive. *G. elegans* is an excellent, easy to grow annual species for those wishing white baby's breath-type flowers on smaller plants.

Propagation of perennial species may be accomplished by seed or terminal cuttings taken immediately after flowering, or by divisions.

Quick Reference to Gypsophila Species

	Height (in.)	Flower color
G. paniculata	24–36	White, pink
G. repens	4–8	White, pink

-paniculata (pa nik-ew-lay' ta)	Baby's Breath	2–3'/3'
Summer White	Europe, Northern Asia	Zones 3–9

Common baby's breath is a graceful plant covered with wisp-like blooms in midsummer. The narrow, 4" long gray-green leaves are opposite and provide a lovely contrast for the myriad branches of 1/16" wide tiny white flowers. Over 1000 flowers may be produced on a single panicle. The more flowers that are picked, the more will be produced. If the first flowers are cut back immediately upon fading, a second bloom occurs in the fall. Although they are most valued for cutting, the plants make excellent fillers to cover barren areas left by oriental poppies, common bleeding hearts or other plants which go dormant early. They should be grown in basic soil, full sun, and in areas of good drainage. In areas of south Florida (zone 9, 10), it is treated as an annual and replanted from November to January every year. Gypsophila is a long-day plant and flowers faster when daylength is greater than 14 hours long.

Cultivars:

'Bristol Fairy' is the traditional double white-flowered baby's breath and grows about 2' tall. It is one of the best for cut flowers.

'Compacta Plena' is a smaller (18″) form of 'Bristol Fairy' but not as floriferous or as double.

'Flamingo' has double pink flowers and is vigorous, attaining heights of 3–4 feet.

'Perfecta' has larger white double flowers and is more robust than 'Bristol Fairy'.

'Pink Fairy' is a pink version of 'Bristol Fairy' about 18″ tall.

'Pink Star' has bright pink flowers on 18″ tall, compact plants.

'Red Sea' bears double rose-pink flowers on 3–4′ tall stems.

'Rosy Veil' is a paler form of 'Pink Star'.

Many of the double-flowered cultivars have been grafted to single flowered forms. Plants should be planted below the graft union to encourage rooting from the stem of the cultivar. Another means of propagation is by terminal cuttings. In the garden, plants develop large fleshy roots and should be left undisturbed. Tissue culture is becoming the most common means of commercial propagation of large numbers of clonal material.

-repens (ree′ penz)		Creeping Baby's Breath	4–8″/12″
Summer	White	Europe	Zones 3–8

(Syn. *G. dubia*)

This is a wonderful little plant for edging or the front of the border and easy to grow. It tolerates heat but not wet feet. The ½–1″ long leaves are grayer than those of *G. paniculata* and form a large mat in less than 2 years. The white to lilac flowers are not as delicate as those of its larger cousin but still cover the foliage with hundreds of blooms during the summer.

This species is not as fussy about pH as *G. paniculata* and plants have done well in acid soils in zone 8. Plants are excellent wall plants and cascade with abandon. This overlooked species should be used much more in American gardens.

Cultivars:

'Alba' has clear white flowers.

'Bodgeri' produces sprays of double light pink flowers.

'Fratensis' has rich pink flowers.

'Rosea' has pale pink flowers but is not as compact as 'Fratensis'.

Propagate by division in the summer or by seed. Seed is very small and should not be covered. Germination occurs in 3–4 weeks under warm (70–75°F), humid conditions.

Quick Key to Gypsophila Species

    A. Plants creeping, flowers usually single........................... *G. repens*
    AA. Plants upright, flowers single or double.................... *G. paniculata*

H

Helenium (hel-ee' ne-um)   Sneezeweed   Asteraceae

Of the 35–40 species, most are native to the United States. The ornamental species are orange to yellow-flowered and particularly useful for their late blooming time. Most flower in mid- to late-summer and combine well with summer flowering lilies and *Physostegia virginiana*. They are adaptable to many climates and tolerate cold temperatures and moist conditions. In general, snee-zeweeds are large plants and require support to look their best. The leaves are alternate, often sessile, and have few or no serrations. They resemble *Helianthus*, sunflower, but differ by having a naked receptacle (the base of the flower) in-staed of pale bracts, long fruit rather than 4-angled fruit, and alternate basal leaves rather than opposite in *Helianthus*.

Propagation is by division or seed.

Quick Reference to Helenium Species

	Height (*ft.*)	*Flower color*
H. *autumnale*	3–5	Yellow, orange, mahogany
H. *hoopesii*	2–4	Orange

-autumnale (ow-tum-nah' lee)   Common Sneezeweed   3–5'/3'
Late Summer   Yellow, Mahogany   Eastern North America   Zones 3–8

These large plants are best used at the back of the garden or in the center of island beds. The 4–6" long serrated leaves are lance-shaped and the base of each leaf runs down the winged stem (decurrent). The 2–3" wide yellow flowers usually have brown to black centers and are borne in many-flowered corymbs.

252

Flowering starts in summer and continues for 8–10 weeks. Plants should be fertilized sparingly or tall spindly growth results.

Heleniums do well in gardens from zone 3 to zone 8, but as night temperatures rise, plants require additional support and flowers become smaller. Thus, while some cultivars make excellent displays in the South, they soon become weedy and take over large portions of the garden. Regardless of location, the dense foliage should be partially cut back after flowering to keep disease and insect pressure minimized. Plant in full sun and keep well watered.

Cultivars:

The many cultivars, each claiming to be bigger and better than the others, are hybrids between *H. autumnale*, *H. bigelovii*, and *H. hoopesii*. What today's gardeners need, however, is smaller, not larger, cultivars.

'Brilliant' is covered with hundreds of bronze flowers in late summer.

'Bruno' bears bronze-red flowers on 3–4' tall stems in late summer.

'Butterpat' is still one of the best of the yellow heleniums. It stands 4–5' tall and the horizontal petals are attached about ⅔ the way down the central disc.

'Gartensonne' is up to 6' tall and bears primrose yellow flowers with reddish brown centers.

'Moerheim Beauty' bears brownish red petals around a black disk on 3–4' high stems.

'Pumilum Magnificum' is similar to 'Butterpat' but has softer yellow flowers. The name 'Pumilum' means dwarf but this cultivar reaches heights of 5 feet.

'Riverton Beauty' has golden yellow ray flowers around bronze centers. Plants are 3½–4' tall.

'Rubrum' produces beautiful 2–3" wide mahogany flowers on 6' tall plants.

'The Bishop' has clean yellow flowers on 2–2½' tall stems. It is one of the more dwarf cultivars available.

'Wyndley' produces 2–3" diameter handsome coppery brown flowers and is only 2–3' tall.

Propagate by division every 2–3 years or by seed. The seed may be cooled for 3–4 weeks but this is not always necessary. Germination is not particularly uniform but should occur within 4 weeks after cooling.

Related Species:

H. bigelovii, bigelow sneezeweed, is native to the Pacific Northwest and bears solitary 2½" wide yellow daisies with dark brown centers. Plants are 2–4' tall.

-hoopesii (hoop-ess' ee-eye)		Orange Sneezeweed	2–4'/2'
Early Summer	Orange	Rocky Mountains	Zones 3–7

The 3" diameter yellow-orange flowers are held in a 3–8 flowered corymb and are similar to those of the previous species. The basal gray-green leaves are up to one foot long and entire (no teeth). The stem leaves are smaller and sessile and are not decurrent like those of *H. autumnale*. The wingless stems are fuzzy (tomentose) when young but become smooth later. The ray flowers are more strap-like and occur earlier than *H. autumnale*. Although this is a shorter species, support is still required. Plant in full sun and provide sufficient water to keep roots consistently moist. It is not as tolerant of hot summers as the previous species and does not do as well in the South. Both this and *H. autumnale* make excellent cut flowers.

Propagate similar to *H. autumnale*.

Quick Key to Helenium Species

A. Stems and branches winged, leaves decurrent at base, stems
not fuzzy when young . . . . *H. autumnale*

AA. Stems and branches not winged, leaves not decurrent, stems
fuzzy when young . . . . *H. hoopesii*

Helianthemum (hee-lee-an' the-mum) Sun-rose Cistaceae

Of the approximately 120 species, one of them, *H. nummularium*, is finally being recognized as a useful garden plant in the United States. The sun-roses are actually evergreen shrubs with woody stems and persistent foliage. Five-petaled, 1–2″ diameter, single rose-like flowers are produced in numerous colors over green to gray-green foliage. Plants are particularly useful as edgings in gardens or along walkways. They are not winter hardy north of zone 5 but some cultivars can tolerate summers of zone 8. The most important factor in succesful culture is rocky, sandy, or otherwise well-drained soil. Otherwise they will rot before you can say *Helianthemum nummularium*.

-nummularium (num-ew-lah' ree-um) Common Sun-rose 1–2′/2′
Summer Various Mediterranean Zones 5–7

(Syn. *H. chamaecistus*)

When I see plants in England tumbling over rocks, and walls ablaze in pastel pinks or yellows, I want to go home and build a three acre rock garden to accomodate them. However, as rock gardens are not particularly popular in Georgia and my garden is of postage stamp proportions, I accept the fact that I can try but a few. This low-growing subshrub with opposite 1–2″ long evergreen gray-green leaves is the finest of the genus. The mature plant is usually wider than tall and bears many 1–2″ wide flowers in loose 4–12 flowered, 1-sided terminal corymbs. Plant in full sun in the North and partial shade in the South. They have few soil requirements other than excellent drainage. After flowering, shear plants back to encourage new growth.

I grew several in my Georgia garden which has heavy red clay soil, even though it was amended with compost. They were spectacular in the spring and early summer but excessive rain and humidity during the summer killed the plants. Replacement plants ('Mutabile') were placed where drainage was sharper and have done well for three years. There is little doubt, however, that most cultivars do better in cool summers and mild winters.

Cultivars:

'Ben Nevis', one of approximately eight cultivars which start with "Ben", has tawny-gold flowers borne over green foliage.

'Buttercup' is 6–10″ tall and bears clear yellow flowers.

'Cerise Queen' produces double red blooms. Personally, I feel double flowers detract from the charm of the singles.

'Fireball' has deep red double flowers.

'Firedragon' bears coppery-red flowers over gray-green foliage in early summer.

'Jubilee' has double yellow flowers.

'Mutabile' is an interesting cultivar whose flowers open light pink then change to lilac, and finally to white. This variety is difficult to place in a specific color scheme but has proven heat tolerant.

'Orange Sunrise' has golden orange flowers with a dark orange central ring.

'Rose Queen' bears double rose-pink flowers. This and 'Cerise Queen' retain their color in the heat.

'St. Mary's' has large white flowers over green leaves.

'Wisley Pink', a lovely muted pink-flowering plant with gray-green leaves, is one of my favorites. Anyone who has visited Edinburgh Botanical Garden in June will remember this plant draped over rocks at the top of the rock garden like pink icing on a resplendent cake.

'Wisley Primrose' is a light yellow-flowered form similar in habit to 'Wisley Pink'.

'Wisley White' is the white-flowered sister.

Propagate by division every 4–5 years or from 1–2″ long softwood cuttings taken in the spring.

Related Species:

H. apenninum, apennine sun-rose, is closely related but not as winter hardy (to zone 6 with protection). It is taller (18″) than *H. nummularium* and has long, arching branches bearing clusters of 1–2″ diameter white flowers with a yellow blotch at the base of the petals. Cultural requirements are similar to the previous species. Variety *roseum* has clear pink flowers.

Helianthus (hee-lee-an′ thus)   Sunflower   Asteraceae

Not only do ornamental species occur within the 150 species, but also commercially important food and oil crops. The annual sunflower (*H. annuus*) yields seeds with high oil content, and the tuberous roots of *H. tuberosum* (Jerusalem artichoke) are a valuable food crop in many areas of the world. In the

Helianthus salicifolius
(56%)

garden, the perennial species are easy to grow in full sun and tolerate a wide range of soil types. All species are tall and require considerable room. The large flowers are yellow and the leaves are usually rough and coarse. Most flower in late summer and fall.

Propagate by division after flowering or by seed.

Quick Reference to Helianthus Species

	Height (ft.)	Color of disc flowers	Flower time
H. angustifolius	5–7	Brown, purple	Fall
H. × multiflorus	3–5	Yellowish	Late Summer

-angustifolius (an-gus-ti-fo′ lee-us)		Swamp Sunflower	5–7′/4′
Fall	Yellow	Eastern United States	Zones 6–9

This is one of the finest fall-flowering plants for the South. The 5–7″ long narrow, entire leaves are not as coarse as those of other species. In the fall, the plants are smothered with 2–3″ wide bright yellow flowers which light up the garden at a time when other plants are going downhill. Each flower has 10–18 narrow petals surrounding a dark brownish center.

When placed in full sun, plants are well branched and self supporting, however, in partial shade, they are more open, less floriferous and taller. In my partially shaded garden, they grow over 10′ tall and stems break in high winds. The same plants, in the sunny Horticulture Gardens grow no more than 5′ tall and require no support. If planted in partial shade, pinch plants once or twice in early summer to encourage branching. They are heavy feeders, require abundant moisture, and should be well fertilized if grown in full sun.

Propagate by divisions, cuttings, or seeds. Many plantlets are produced around the base of the plants and if not removed, the garden will consist of little else within 2–3 years.

Related Species:

H. salicifolius, willowleaf sunflower, has narrower leaves and smoother stems than *H. angustifolius*, but is otherwise similar in habit and flower color. It is winter hardy to zone 3.

H. tomentosus, hairy sunflower, native throughout the southeastern United States, grows 6–8′ tall with densely hairy stems. Flowers with yellow central disks and golden yellow ray flowers are produced in August and September.

-× *multiflorus* (mul-tee-flo′ rus)	Many-flowered Sunflower		3–5′/3′
Late Summer	Yellow	Hybrid	Zones 4–8

(Syn. *H. decapetalus* var. *multiflorus*)

A hybrid resulting from *H. annuus*, annual sunflower, and *H. decapetalus*, thinleaf sunflower, plants have hairy, coarse leaves up to 10″ long and 4–6″ wide. They are usually 4–5′ tall but may reach heights of 7′ or more. The 5″ diameter flowers may be single or double and are usually yellow or yellow-orange. Flowers persist for 4–6 weeks and continue well into the fall. The oval to heart-shaped leaves degenerate after flowering and plants should be cut back soon thereafter. Place in full sun and provide copious water and fertilizer.

Cultivars:

'Capenoch Star' has single lemon-yellow flowers that are a little cooler to the eye than the others.

'Corona Dorica' produces 5″ diameter double yellow flowers subtended by heart-shaped leaves on five foot stems.

'Flore-plena' is a 5′ tall plant with fully double (little or no center) bright yellow flowers.

'Loddon Gold' bears double, 5–6″ diameter bright yellow flowers and grows 4½–6′ tall.

'Morning Sun' has lovely single yellow flowers with large yellowish brown centers and grows 5′ tall.

Propagate by division or cuttings similar to *H. angustifolius*.

Related Species:

H. decapetalus, thinleaf sunflower, has rough sharply serrated thin leaves above which are borne 3″ diameter single light yellow flowers. The 4–6′ tall plants are covered with flowers in late summer and always make a handsome display.

H. atrorubens, dark-eye sunflower, grows 2–5′ tall with thin opposite leaves and branched stems. Two inch wide flowers consist of deep yellow rays surrounding a dark red disc. A good southern wild flower.

Quick Key to Helianthus Species

    A. Leaves entire, sessile, disc flowers brown or purplish, flowers usually single .... *H. angustifolius*

  AA. Leaves serrated, short-petioled, disc flowers yellow, flowers single or double... *H.* × *multiflorus*

Heliopsis (hee-lee-op′ sis)   Heliopsis   Asteraceae

The genus closely resembles the true sunflower (*Helianthus*) and the literal translation of the name is "sun-like". It has a much smaller habit, however, and flowers in midsummer. There are about 12 species, many of which are rather weedy and seldom used in gardens. The leaves are simple, rough and opposite. Plants should be grown in full sun and fertilized sparingly.

-helianthoides (hee-lee-anth-oi′ deez)   Sunflower Heliopsis   3–6′/4′
Summer   Yellow, orange   North America   Zones 3–9

This short-lived perennial has smooth 4–5″ long serrated leaves and grows 4–5′ tall. The 2–3″ diameter daisy-like flowers consist of pale yellow ray flowers surrounding brownish yellow central discs. The species is weedy, too tall, and is not floriferous enough to be a good garden plant. However, subsp. *scabra*, often referred to as *H. scabra*, rough heliopsis, is much better and more popular in today's gardens.

Plant in full sun in well-drained soil. Support is necessary, particularly if plants are shaded.

Related Species:

Subspecies *scabra* (*H. scabra*) is characterized by sandpapery (scabrous) stems and leaves. Plants grow 2–4′ tall and 2–3′ wide. The upper leaves are often entire while the basal leaves may be toothed. The ray flowers are orange-yellow and the center varies from greenish yellow to brown. Leaves should be cut back in the South after flowering. Division is required every 2–3 years.

'Golden Plume' is a floriferous double-flowered 3–3½' tall cultivar. This is the best of the double-flowered heliopsis.

Goldgreenheart' has interesting, if somewhat gaudy chrome-yellow double flowers surrounding a slightly green center.

'Incomparabilis' bears 3″ wide semi-double flowers with warm orange overlapping petals.

'Karat' is about 3' tall with bright yellow flowers.

'Light of Loddon' is similar to 'Karat' but grows 4' tall. Both may need support, particularly in the South.

'Patula' is 2½–3' tall with golden orange semi-double flowers.

'Summer Sun' is a delightful 2–3' tall plant with 4″ diameter bright yellow flowers. This is the best cultivar for the South as it tolerates heat well and does not get too leggy. It flowers in my Georgia garden for 10–12 weeks and comes fairly true from seed.

All cultivars should be divided every 2–3 years. The species and some cultivars come true from seed and are easily germinated in a warm (70–75°F), humid area.

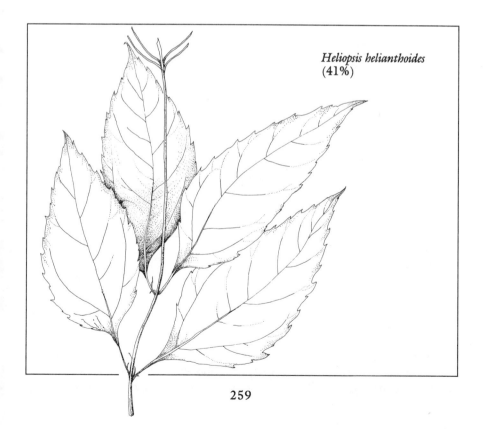

Heliopsis helianthoides
(41%)

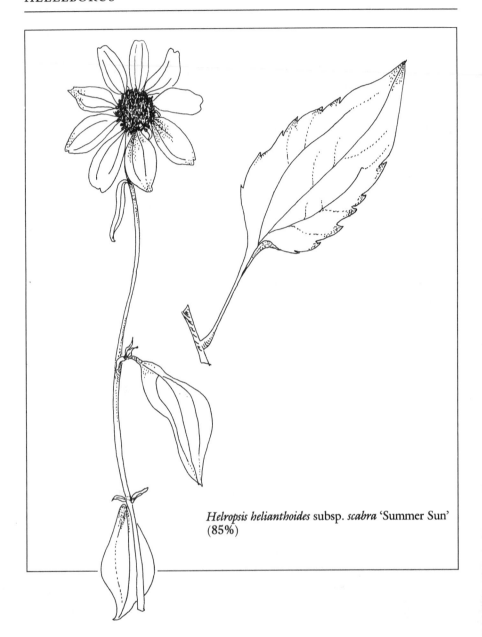

Helropsis helianthoides subsp. *scabra* 'Summer Sun' (85%)

Helleborus (hell-e-bor′ us) Hellebore Ranunculaceae

No garden should be without *Helleborus* to herald the dawn of a new season. Walking by a clump on the edge of a path or on a hillside where the nodding flowers greet me, tells me spring has sprung and all is right with the world. The hellebores consist of 18–20 species, all with some ornamental value. In addition, hybrids have been raised which combine characteristics of the parents. In European gardens, it is not uncommon to find 4 or 5 different species offered by garden centers but in this country, only about 2 species are grown to any extent. All prefer moist soils and shaded conditions. Most species have evergreen, much divided foliage and nodding, white, rose, green, or purple flowers. The sepals are the showy part of the flower; the petals are reduced to inconspicuous nectaries. Part of their charm is the early flowering time resulting in such common names as Christmas Rose and Lenten Rose. Because they flower when the weather is cool, they have an exceptionally long flowering period, often flowering from February to May. Fruit consists of 3–10 sessile follicles containing numerous seeds, which may be collected when follicles are papery and dry.

Garden species may be divided into two categories. The first group includes those with a leafy stem and flowers that are carried at the apex such as *H. argutifolius*, (syn. *H. corsicus*), Corsican hellebore, and *H. foetidus*, bearsfoot hellebore. In the second group are those whose leaves and flowers rise directly from the rootstock, i.e. stemless. This includes *H. niger*, Christmas rose, and *H. orientalis*, Lenten rose.

Propagation from seed is difficult and exacting. Sow seeds in well-drained medium and place at 75–80°F for 7 weeks. Move tray to approximately 32°F for 8 weeks and then raise temperature slowly to 40°F. Germination should commence at 40°F after which soil temperature may be elevated to 50–55°F until germination is complete. This technique is used for many members of the Ranunculaceae such as *Cimicifuga* and *Clematis*. Mother Nature, however, is much more efficient than gardeners. Seedlings of most species may be found under the plant litter at the base of 2–3 year old plants. Gentle removal and subsequent transplanting provide abundant plants for the spring garden. If necessary, roots of mature plants may also be divided in the spring but large showy clumps will result only if plants remain undisturbed.

Quick Reference to Helleborus Species

	Height (in.)	Flower color	Number of leaflets
H. argutifolius	18–24	Light green	3
H. foetidus	18–24	Light green	7–10
H. niger	12–18	White	7–9
H. orientalis	15–18	White, plum	7–9

-*argutifolius* (ar-gew-ti-fo' lee-us)		Corsican Hellebore	18–24"/18"
Early Spring	Greenish	Corsica, Sardinia	Zones 6–8

(Syn. *H. corsicus*, *H. lividus* subsp. *corsicus*)

This stemmed species bears green flowers but should be grown more for the foliage than the flowers. The foliage is unique in that it is gray-green, 3-parted, and the individual leaflets are thick and prickly. The green, cupped flowers have a tinge of white and are held well above the foliage, but are not as decorative as those of *H. niger* or *H. orientalis*. It is a stout, bushy plant with thick stems but should be given winter protection as far south as zone 8. Plants tolerate more sun than others but not the humid conditions found in the Southeast. *H. foetidus*, *H. orientalis*, and *H. niger* are easier to establish.

Many seeds are produced and if a mulch is placed at the base of the plant, seedlings will arise. Division may be accomplished in spring or fall.

Related Species:

H. lividus has similar flowers but is only 12–18" tall, and has smooth-edged dark green leaves with obvious white veins. It is less winter hardy than *H. argutifolius* and difficult to grow in most areas of the country.

-foetidus (foy′ ti-dus)		Bearsfoot Hellebore	18–24″/18″
Winter, Spring	Light green	Western, Southern Europe	Zones 5–9

The evergreen foliage is deeply divided into 4–9 narrow dark green leaflets. In the first year stems and leaves are produced. The second year, several branched stems bear many cup-shaped, light green nodding flowers often rimmed with purple. The specific name, *foetidus*, means fetid or bad smelling and refers to the flowers. It is not a flower one brings in the kitchen to brighten the day. The plant does best in zones 6–8, and struggles with the heat in more southern areas. Partial shade and well-drained soils are the only requirements for establishment. It develops quickly but is not as ornamental as *H. orientalis*. I visited the lovely garden of Mrs. Wheezie Smith in Birmingham, Alabama (zone 8), in late February. Dozens of plants of *H. foetidus* shone beneath her shade trees, *H. niger* was flourishing, and *H. orientalis* welcomed me at every corner. Who says February has no charm?

Propagate from the self-sown seedlings around the base or divide in spring after flowering. Plants resent being disturbed and if lifted for division, the parent plants may take considerable time to re-establish.

Related Species:

H. viridis, green hellebore, is an overlooked species of delicate beauty. It is only 15–18" tall, has 7–11 light green leaflets and about 1" wide drooping green flowers. The leaves differ from most cultivated hellebores in being deciduous, although this is not necessarily true in warmer climates.

-niger (nigh′ ger)		Christmas Rose	12–18″/12″
Winter, Early Spring	White	Europe, West Asia	Zones 3–8

The saucer-shaped, solitary or paired, 2½" wide flowers bear yellow stamens which contrast well with the clear white petal-like sepals. Flowers are held on red-spotted peduncles. Tremendous variation in flower color, size, and earliness to flower occurs, particularly because most of the commercially available plants

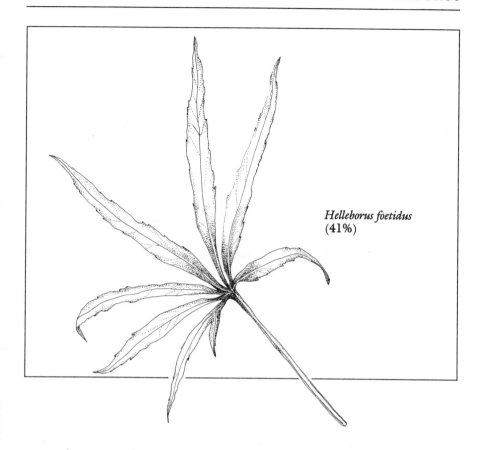

Helleborus foetidus
(41%)

are seed propagated. Although flowering may occur at Christmas in sheltered locations, this seldom occurs and plants are usually at their best in early spring. Plants are more difficult to establish than *H. foetidus* or *H. orientalis*. Consistent moisture, shade and slightly basic soils are necessary.

Cultivars:

var. *altiflorus* has long-stalked, larger and more distinctly toothed leaves than the species. The petioles, peduncles (flower stalks) and the 3–4″ wide flowers are tinged with red spots.

subsp. *macranthus* has small spiny leaves and white flowers tinged with rose held well above the foliage. The peduncle is not purple spotted as in *H. niger*.

'Potter's Wheel' is vegetatively propagated and has been selected for its large rounded white flowers with a distinct green eye. Few nurserymen try to vegetatively maintain clones because they are slow to increase by division.

Related Species:

H. × *nigercors* is a cross between *H. argutifolius* and *H. niger*. It bears serrated foliage and "Christmas rose" type flowers at the end of short stems.

-orientalis (o-ree-en-tah′ lis)		Lenten Rose	15–18″/15″
Early Spring	White, purple	Greece, Asia Minor	Zones 4–9

(Syn. *H* × *hybridus*)

One of the finest low-growing, early-flowering plants in cultivation, no garden should be without several clumps. The 12–16″ wide, leathery dark green leaves are divided into 7–9 segments and remain attractive all year, particularly in the South. The nodding 3–4″ wide flowers last for 8–10 weeks and vary from white to plum-colored and are often spotted inside. Similar to *H. niger*, there is a great deal of variation in color and size of flowers.

This is the easiest species to grow, requiring only shade and occasional water. Fertilizing in early spring as the new leaves emerge results in rapid growth of the clump. Clumps establish quickly and plants can be increased rapidly from the numerous seedlings produced in any rich soil. If the old leaves are damaged from winter winds or snow, cut them back. The new leaves will quickly fill in.

Related Species:

H. atrorubens (sometimes listed as var. *atrorubens*) is much darker than the type and usually bears 9 leaf segments. The rich plum-purple flowers are one of the first to open (early January in my garden). It is winter hardy only to zone 5 or 6.

H. olympicus (sometimes listed as var. *olympicus*) has 5–7 leaflets and many spreading white flowers with a green tinge.

Quick Key to Helleborus Species

    A. Flowers arising at apex of leafy stem
        B. Leaves divided into 3 leaflets, leaflets spiny..............*H. argutifolius*
        BB. Leaves divided into 4–9 leaflets, not spiny.................*H. foetidus*
    AA. Leaves and flowers arising from rootstalk, plants stemless
        B. Flowers usually solitary or in 2's, peduncles red spotted,
            flowers usually white...*H. niger*
        BB. Flowers in 3's or more, peduncles not usually red spotted,
            flower green to dark purple.............................*H. orientalis*

Additional Reading:

Matthew, Brian. 1981. A survey of hellebores. *The Plantsman* 3(1):1–10.

Rackemann, Adelaide C. 1985. Green hellebore. *Horticulture* 63(10):64–66.

Hemerocallis (hem-er-o-kal′ lis)   Daylily   Liliaceae

The modern daylily has undergone such a tremendous facelift in recent years that it is now one of the backbones of many perennial plantings. This is particularly true of commercial installations designed for public buildings, parks, or entrances to malls and condominiums where toughness and long-lasting color

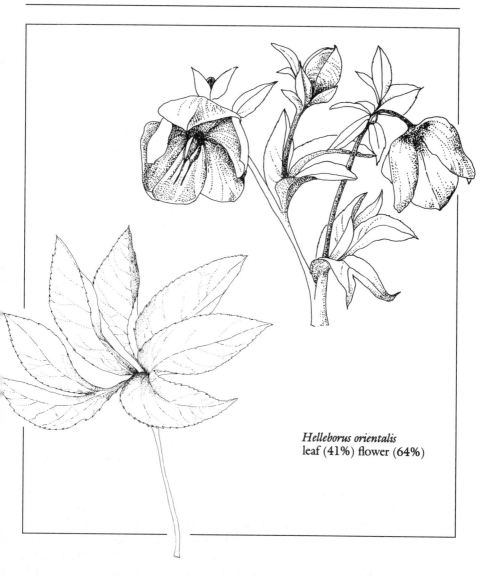

Helleborus orientalis
leaf (41%) flower (64%)

are so important. In few other genera has hybridization proceeded at such a rapid pace. The clamor for larger flowers, more colors, more flowers, and greater vigor has resulted in the introduction of dozens of cultivars every year. This is certainly not all bad and the popularity of the hybrids speak for themselves. The greater use of *H. minor* and *H. nana* to instill genetic dwarfness in hybrids has also opened up a new era of daylily use which is only now being explored. There is little doubt that the breeders have done a tremendous service to horticulture by transforming some of the rather bland species into the wonderful flower colors and excellent garden performers found in today's hybrids.

265

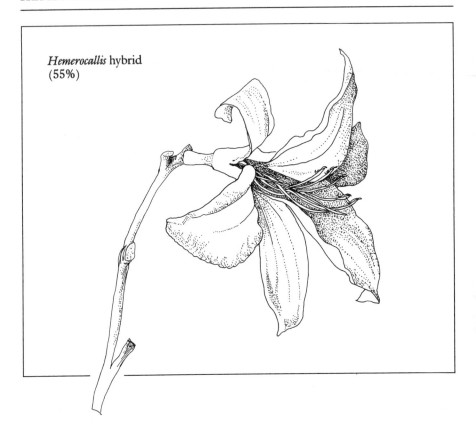

Hemerocallis hybrid
(55%)

Unfortunately, in our pursuit of hybrid grandeur, the old folks got left behind. The parents of the hybrids, i.e. the species, have been forgotten. In garden catalogs, there are pages and pages of descriptions and lovely pictures of daylily hybrids, each seemingly better than the last. It is, in fact, uncommon to see anything but hybrids being offered. The dark brown buds of *H. dumortieri*, the fragrant, dense cluster of *H. middendorffii* flowers and the fragrant old-fashioned lemon-lily, *H. lilio-asphodelus* are becoming more difficult to locate. It is still nice to see the common orange daylily, *H. fulva*, having escaped from old gardens, shining alongside roadways and in wild meadows. Perhaps the relative disdain of the species is a small price to pay for today's garden plants which are tough, reliable, and in colors and sizes enough to suit every taste. However, a few of the better species are included here for those still interested in old fashioned charm for the garden. It is impossible to list even a hundredth of the available hybrids but consulting a plant catalog will yield many excellent choices.

All daylilies thrive in full sun but tolerate partial shade as well. Mites and aphids are troublesome and thrips can be damaging if allowed to proliferate. Diseases are few, particularly if soil is relatively well drained.

Propagate by dividing into plantlets with a single fan of leaves in early spring of fall.

Quick Reference to Hemerocallis Species

	Height (in.)	Leaves longer than flower stalk	Flower color	Flower stalk branched
H. dumortieri	18–24	Y	Yellow	N
H. lilio-asphodelus	30–36	N	Yellow	Y
H. middendorffii	24–30	N	Yellow	N

-dumortieri (dew-mor-tee-ew' ree)		Early Daylily	18–24"/18"
Spring	Yellow	Siberia, Japan	Zones 2–9

The leaves of this light yellow-flowered daylily are about ½" wide and 1½" long. The flower stalks (scapes) are a little shorter than the leaves and thus the flowers are not held high above the foliage as in the hybrids. The scapes are unbranched and carry 2–4 sessile (no pedicel) flowers per stem. The flower buds are tinged brown outside and the 2–3" long flowers are funnel-shaped and fragrant. It is a charming small daylily and the earliest to flower.

-lilio-asphodelus (lil-ee' o-ass-fo-del' us)		Lemon-lily	30–36"/30"
Late Spring	Lemon	Siberia, Japan, China	Zones 3–9

(Syn. *H. flava*)

The foliage is 18–24" long and about ¾" wide. The arching scape is branched and bears 5–9 lemon-yellow 4" long flowers per stem. The flowers are sweetly fragrant and held well above the foliage. Plants are vigorous and spread rapidly. The dried flower buds were a famous aphrodisiac known as gum-jum and were imported from China and Japan. There are few cultivars available but the species provides a pleasing color, lovely fragrance, and strong and sturdy growth. The plant was popular but has since been superseded by the newer hybrids.

-middendorffii (mid-an-dorf' ee-eye)		Middendorf Lily	24–30"/24"
Early Summer	Yellow	Siberia, Japan	Zones 3–9

Plants are similar in habit to *H. dumortieri* and the flowers are also sessile on the scapes. The flower scapes, however, are longer than the 2' long, 1" wide leaves resulting in the flowers being held above the foliage. The tightly clustered 2–3" long flowers open after *H. dumortieri* but before *H. lilio-asphodelus*. They are fragrant, cup shaped and the petals are not as reflexed as those of the hybrids. Beneath each group of 2–4 flowers are conspicuous bracts. Plants are quite tolerant of shade and moisture.

Quick Key to Hemerocallis Species

A. Flowers sessile or nearly so, 2–4 per unbranched scape
   B. Scapes shorter than leaves, leaves narrow (about ½" wide), flower buds tinged brown............................... *H. dumortieri*
   BB. Scapes longer than leaves, leaves about 1" wide, flower buds not obviously tinged .... *H. middendorffii*
AA. Flowers on 1–2" long pedicels, 5–9 flowers on branched scapes ....
   H. lilio-asphodelus

Additional Reading:

Baumgardt, John. 1978. The delirious daylily. *Horticulture* 56(5):41–47.

Eddison, Sydney, 1987. Small-flowered daylilies. *Horticulture* 65(5):56–59.

Kitchingman, R.M, 1985. Some species and cultivars of *Hemerocallis*. *The Plantsman* 7(2):68–89.

Associations

American Hemerocallis Society, Rte. 2, Box 360, De Queen, AR., 71832. Publication: *The Hemerocallis Journal.*

Hesperis (hes' per-is)   Rocket   Brassicaceae

The 15–20 species are characterized by white or purple 4-petaled flowers on long terminal racemes. Most are biennial or perennial; the favorite by far is the old-fashioned biennial, *H. matronalis*, dame's rocket.

-matronalis (mah-tro-nah' lis)   Dame's Rocket   2–3'/3'
Late Spring   White, purple   Central, Southern Asia   Zones 3–8

Although not a true perennial, plants reappear every year from self-sown seed. The ½–¾" wide flowers open in late April and early May in the South (a couple of weeks later in the North) and are wonderfully fragrant, particularly in the evening. The 2–4" long, alternate, hairy, sharp pointed leaves are sessile or borne on short petioles.

In the State Botanical Garden of Georgia, dame's rocket pops up everywhere, providing lovely vigorous showpieces of white and purple that glow in the late afternoon sun. The white-flowered form stands out in the shady garden more than the purple and should be selected whenever possible. The old seed heads should be cut back to the basal foliage by June. Plants require a consistent water supply to continue flowering and prefer partial shade, particularly at the southern end of their range. Annuals should be planted around dame's rocket because large gaps in the garden occur after plants disappear. Although plants die after flowering, seeds emerge readily and plants persist in the garden for years. Plants are not easily found in catalogs, but seeds are available through any seed house.

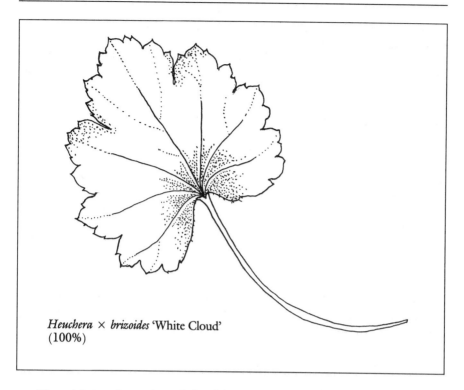

Heuchera × *brizoides* 'White Cloud'
(100%)

Hesperis is handsome in an informal area or in the border itself. It is a charming plant and ease of cultivation makes it well worth growing.

Cultivars:

var. *alba-plena* is one of a number of double-flowered forms. It has white, double flowers and is also fragrant. The double forms must be propagated by divisions or terminal cuttings.

Heuchera (hew′ ker-a)   Alumroot   Saxifragaceae

Fifty to seventy species are native to North America but only *H. sanguinea*, coral bells, and hybrids, have gained popularity in North American gardens. While significant improvements have been made in *H. sanguinea*, unfortunately other lovely species have been ignored. The evergreen leaves are mostly basal and long petioled, and the margins may be lobed, wavy, or entire. The foliage is particularly ornamental in some species. Petals are small or absent and the sepals usually provide the showy part of the bloom. Not all species have showy flowers and some are grown for their ornamental foliage alone.

Many of the improved cultivars are hybrids between *H. sanguinea, H. americana*, and *H. micrantha*. Most species are readily raised from seed but the hybrids must be divided.

269

Heuchera does best in rich, moist well-drained soil in partial shade. They are better adapted to cooler climates and some do poorly in the South. Species grown for their foliage, such as *H. americana* and *H. micrantha* 'Palace Purple', always look better in cooler times of the year and appear rather washed out in the heat of the summer, particularly in the southern end of the growing range.

Quick Reference to Heuchera Species

	Height (in.)	Flower color	Leaves obviously ornamental
H. americana	18–36	Greenish white	Y
H. micrantha	12–24	Yellowish white	Y
H. sanguinea	12–18	Reddish, white	N
H. villosa	12–36	Pinkish	N

-americana (a-mer-i-cah′ na)		American Alumroot	18–36″/18″
Early Summer	Greenish white	Eastern North America	Zones 4–9

This often overlooked species is a tough, steady, reliable performer grown for the handsome evergreen foliage rather than the flowers. The 4–6″ long leaves are rounded to heart shaped with 5–7 lobes. Its charm comes from the

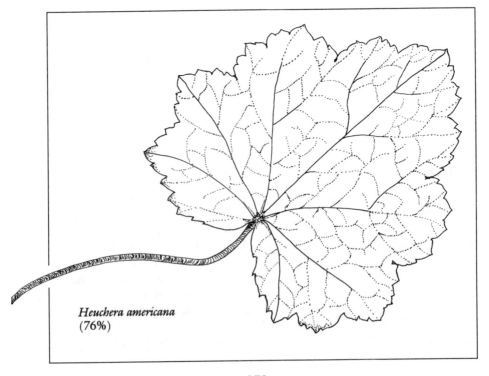

Heuchera americana
(76%)

mottled purple color of the young foliage, which later subsides as the leaves mature. If proper cultural conditions are provided, new leaves are produced all season. The small, ⅛" wide flowers are borne in 15–20" long airy, unbranched panicles. The flowers are not particularly ornamental, but I enjoy them poking through the foliage and swaying in the afternoon breeze.

It is one of the best *Heuchera* for the South and is most attractive in spring and late fall. The dark, healthy, purplish foliage stands out in November, December and January while everything else has succumbed to frost or fatigue.

Plants should be grown in shade and do not tolerate full sun, particularly if moisture is lacking. It is important that the soil remain consistently moist if foliage is to be produced throughout the season.

Cultivars:

'Sunset' is the best cultivar, with conspicuous purple veins radiating from the center of the leaf to the margin of each lobe. The coloration is more persistent than the species.

Alumroot can be propagated easily by division in spring or early fall. The species can also be raised from seed. Cover the small seeds thinly and place seed tray at 68–70°F with high humidity. Grow on at 60°F.

-micrantha (mik-ran' tha)   Small-flowered Alumroot   12–24"/12"
Late Spring   Yellowish white   Western North America   Zones 4–8

The 2–4" long foliage is gray-green and heart-shaped with rounded, shallow lobes. In late spring, loose, airy spires of ⅛" wide yellowish white flowers appear. The petals are twice as long as the sepals (in most species, the petals are shorter or the same size). If well grown, which I have yet to see in this country, sufficient inflorescences are produced to put on a show. Usually, however, they are in the same class as those of *H. americana*. Place in partial shade, provide adequate moisture and mulch well in the winter north of zone 5. A West Coast native, plants do not do well under conditions of fluctuating temperatures common to the rest of the country. It is, however, a parent of several excellent garden hybrids.

Cultivars:

'Palace Purple' ('Powis Purple') is one of the finest introductions in recent years. The ivy-shaped foliage is deep purple but the color is deeper in the spring and fall, fading to bronze green under hot summer conditions. The flowers are of little consequence and should be removed. There is a good deal of variation in depth of color and those with the darkest reds should be propagated vegetatively. A number of southern nurserymen, such as Allen Bush of Holbrook Farms, Fletcher, North Carolina, are actively selecting for richness of color and performance in the South. Opinions differ as to its origin and taxonomic niche. Some argue that it was selected from plants at Powis

Castle in Wales while others claim it to be the result of a chance seedling at Kew Gardens, England. It has been listed under *H. micrantha* var. *versicolor*, *H. m.* var. *diversifolia*, *H. micrantha*, and *H. americana*. Regardless of birthplace or pedigree, it is a eye-catching plant worth trying at the front of the shady garden.

The species may be raised from seed similar to *H. americana*, the cultivar from divisions.

Related Species:

H. cylindrica is native to the West Coast and produces many ¼″ wide cream-colored flowers on 2′ long spike-like racemes (flowers almost sessile on the flower stalk). Plants require the same conditions as *H. micrantha*.

var. *glabella* is similar to the species but the lower part of the stem and leaves are smooth, not hairy. A dwarf form is also available.

'Greenfinch' is a handsome 2–2½′ tall form with greenish white flowers.

'Green Ivory', a selection of 'Greenfinch', is 2½–3′ tall and bears many white flowers with green bases.

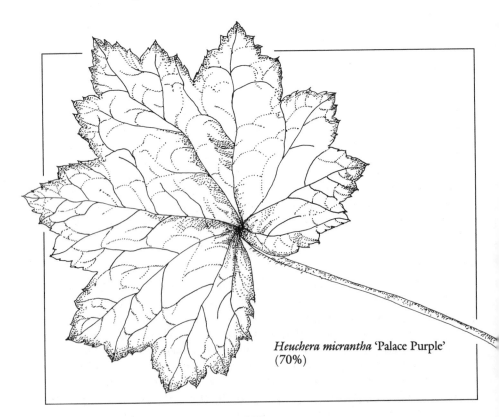

Heuchera micrantha 'Palace Purple'
(70%)

-sanguinea (sang-guin' ee-a)		Coral Bells	12–18"/12"
Late Spring	Red	New Mexico, Arizona	Zones 3–8

The species has undergone intensive breeding and selection and is a common denizen of American gardens. The smallest of the garden *Heuchera*, it is at home as an edging, tucked away in a shady corner or at the front of the border. Although the plant is small, the ½" long, campanulate, red flowers are much larger and showier than the other species. They are held in 10–20" long, loosely branched panicles and persist for 4–8 weeks. Removing spent flower stalks results in extended flowering time. The basal foliage is heart shaped or roundish with 5–7 slightly toothed lobes.

Coral bells require excellent drainage and full sun in the North but partial shade in the South. They perform poorly in heavy acid soils, therefore, coarse sand, manure and dolomitic lime must be added where necessary. Considerable hybridization and selection have been accomplished in the last 50 years and Blooms of Bressingham in Diss, England has been particularly active.

Cultivars:

Most cultivars of *H. sanguinea* average 14–20" tall. Hybridization (see *H. × brizoides*) has resulted in improved forms but the parentage of many cultivars is confused. The following are likely, but not necessarily, cultivars of *H. sanguinea*.

'Bressingham Blaze' has intense salmon-scarlet blooms.
'Chatterbox' is a popular cultivar with large pink flowers.
'June Bride' bears white flowers.
'Matin Bells' has flowers of coral-red.
'Mt. St. Helens' is an excellent garden performer with brick-red flowers.

The species and some cultivars may be raised from seed but division every 2–4 years is the most successful means of propagation.

Related Species:

H. × brizoides claims input from *H. micrantha*, *H. sanguinea* and *H. americana*. It bears profuse numbers of small (⅛" wide) flowers and rounded, lobed foliage. Plants are generally taller than *H. sanguinea* cultivars, averaging 24–30". The insertion of genes of *H. americana* has resulted in significant improvement in garden performance in eastern gardens, particularly in the Southeast. The following are probably cultivars of *H. × brizoides*.

'Bloom's Variety' bears deep coral-red flowers.
'Coral Cloud' produces many flower stalks with coral-salmon flowers.
'Pluie de Feu' ('Rain of Fire') has cherry-red blooms.
'Splendour' produces salmon-scarlet flowers.
'Tattletale' is a lovely clear pink.
'White Cloud' produces dozens of flower stalks upon which hundreds of small

white flowers are carried. This is one of the finest cultivars I have seen in the United States and is truly a "white cloud".

Propagate all cultivars by division.

-villosa (vil-lo′ sa) Hairy Alumroot 1–3′/18″
Summer White Southeastern United States Zones 6–9

The rounded to heart-shaped leaf blades are deeply 5–7 lobed, each lobe somewhat triangular. The leaves and flower stems are hairy and the ¼″ wide, small, whitish pink flowers occur in open, airy panicles up to 3′ long. This species is the latest to flower and among the tallest in the genus. Native to the South, they are at home in the heat and, although not as showy as *H. sanguinea*, are more reliable in the hot, wet summers and make an enjoyable, if not exceptional, border plant.

Quick Key to Heuchera Species

    A. Petals twice as long as sepals
        B. Lobes of leaves triangular, very deeply cut .... *H. villosa*
       BB. Lobes of leaves rounded, not deeply cut................. *H. micrantha*
   AA. Petals shorter than sepals or only slightly longer
        B. Flowers ½–¾″ long, petals red (white and pink in
           cultivars), stamens much shorter than sepals............. *H. sanguinea*
       BB. Flowers ¼″ long, petals greenish white, stamens much
           longer than sepals .... *H. americana*

Heucherella (hew′ ker-ell-a) Foamy Bells Saxifragaceae

Many examples of hybrids between species occur but there are few between genera. × *Heucherella* (the × denotes an intergeneric cross but is not sounded) was produced in 1912 between a *Heuchera* hybrid and *Tiarella cordifolia*.

-tiarelloides (tee-a-rel-loi′ deez) Foamy Bells 15–24″/15″
Spring Pink Hybrid Zones 3–8

The 3–4″ long foliage combines the heart shape of *Tiarella cordifolia*, which is mottled when young and has seven shallow lobes, with the flowering habit of *Heuchera* × *brizoides*. The plant is tufted at the base, stoloniferous, evergreen, and makes a wonderful ground cover. The small flowers bear a marked similarity to *Heuchera* and the tall, airy spires of pinkish flowers, which open in late spring, often rebloom in the fall.

    Plant in a shaded area in the garden where moisture is available. It will not tolerate full sun, particularly in the South.

Related Species:

× *H. alba*, has leaves longer than broad, white flowers, and is not stoloniferous. This was raised at Blooms Nursery and are the result of a cross between *Tiarella cordifolia* var. *collina* (*T. wherryi*) and a *Heuchera* hybrid.

'Bridget Bloom' has lovely shell-pink flowers, mounded habit, and blooms for at least eight weeks.

Both species are easily propagated by division but neither set seed.

Hosta (hos' ta)   Plantain Lily, Funkia   Liliaceae

Daylilies may be kings of the sun but unquestionably hostas are the emperors of the shade. I remember as a child walking down my grandmother's path in Montreal where variegated hostas had long ago been planted on either side. It was a dim, dark pathway but the light airy foliage lit the way. Nothing else would grow there and that path was a living testament to the toughness of these lovely plants.

Hostas have been around for centuries but were "rediscovered" in the last twenty years and an incredible array of cultivars and interspecific hybrids has emerged. The nomenclature is in a state of chaos and seldom is the parentage of plants absolutely certain. Many times hostas are sold with a cultivar name only (i.e. no specific epithet), because there have been so many different species in the pedigree that it is far easier just to call it by a single name.

Hostas are usually grown for their foliage. Leaf texture may be shiny, smooth or puckered, various shades of green, blue-green, white, or edged with gold, yellow or white. They may be narrow, broad and wavy, entire or twisted. When not in flower, plants range from 6″ to 3′ in height. In some species, magnificent 3′ spires (racemes) of lilac, purple, or white flowers rise above the foliage while in others the flowers are best removed less they detract from the foliage. Small hostas (8–12″ tall) include *H. lancifolia*, *H. sieboldii*, and *H. undulata*. Mid-size species (up to 18″ tall) useful for edging or ground covers include *H. crispula*, *H. decorata*, *H. fortunei*, and *H. tardiflora*. For those who prefer a more grandiose scale, *H. montana*, *H. sieboldiana*, *H. tokudama* or *H. ventricosa* grow 2–3′ tall and up to three feet wide when properly grown. Dwarf species such as *H. pulchella*, *H. gracillima* and *H. venusta*, suitable for the rock garden or patio, may also be found.

There are over 400 hybrids, cultivars, and species from which to choose and more become available every year. Perhaps it is time to slow down lest there develop as many cultivars of hosta as there are of petunia. There are so many hostas now that the professional breeder must make serious financial decisions concerning the payback of new cultivars and hybrids which are only marginally different from those already on the market. The amateur breeder will continue to enjoy the results of his hobby, naming clones regardless of existing similarities.

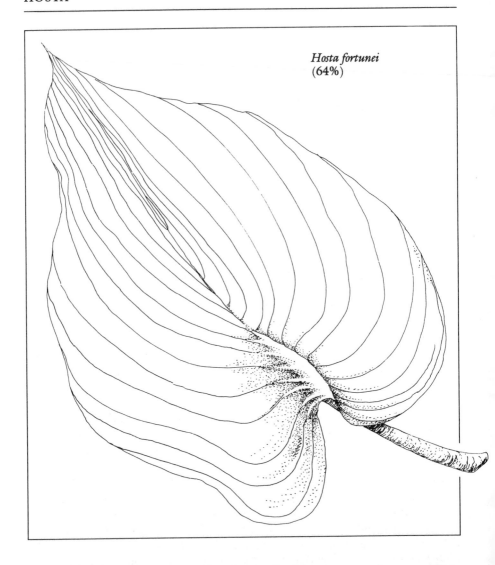

Hosta fortunei
(64%)

Hostas grow best in rich, well-drained soil with constant moisture and light shade. Some species may tolerate full sun in the Northeast and Northwest provided ample moisture is available, but do not tolerate full sun in the South. As a rule of thumb, yellow-leaved and variegated forms need protection from direct sun while blue forms require partial shade. Allowing hostas to dry out is the quickest way to ruin the planting. Under dry conditions, leaves are smaller, turn light brown and papery around the edges and plants never reach their full growth potential.

The amount of puckering on the leaves dictates usefulness under trees. Those heavily puckered catch the drippings from tree leaves complete with gums, saps and other materials. These drippings cause the hostas to look particularly wretched. Glossy or smooth-leaved plants are less prone to tree droppings.

Hostas are tough but not problem free. Slugs and snails devour the newly emerging foliage with gusto. Hostas are to slugs what filet mignon is to people. Early and frequent application of slug pellets is essential to keep them at bay. Beer may also be used but why waste good beer? Black vine weevils have destroyed leaves of my plantings before I even knew they were there. They are about ½–1″ long, black and incredibly hungry. They appear in north Georgia around mid-June and stay about 2–3 weeks. With heavy infestations, they cover the plants and ravage the leaves. Sevin dust is an effective control.

Most hostas do not need dividing for many years and are, in fact, slow growing. It often takes 4–5 years before hostas reach maturity of form and color and should not be judged too harshly if they are not "catalog-perfect" before then. Established clumps (greater than 8 years old) bear little resemblance to the majority of immature hostas grown in the average garden. Plants may be divided after 4–5 years, but only if necessary. Take a wedge-like slice when dividing and the division will not be missed. Divide early in the spring when the tightly curled leaves emerge. The number of crowns are easily visible at that time and damage is minimized. The price of a hosta varies with its availability and ease of propagation. Breakthroughs in tissue culture have occurred in recent years and many hostas offered today had their humble beginnings in a test tube.

Attempts have been made to key hostas into species but with so many common cultivars and hybrids the exercise is difficult and easily defeats all but the most patient plantspeople. There are, however, a number of characteristics which the observant person can use to detect differences between species and hybrids. These include foliage color, leaf texture (amount of puckering), margin, as well as the number of pairs of veins on either side of the leaf midrib. Floral characteristics include the denseness of the inflorescence, flower color, and even the color of the anthers. Since the foliage is most important in hostas, I have listed a few of the popular forms according to foliage color. Further description of the listed species and hybrids follow. A great deal more information on cultivars and their performance may be obtained from the American Hosta Society (see Association at end of Hosta listing).

Quick Reference to Foliage Color and Flowering Season in Hosta

Leaves entirely green, including yellowish green

H. elata	Early Summer
H. fortunei	Summer
H. lancifolia	Late Summer
H. longissima	Late Summer
H. montana	Summer
H. plantaginea, H. p. var. *grandiflora*	Late Summer

277

H. rectifolia, *H. r.* 'Tall Boy'	Summer
H. 'Royal Standard'	Late Summer
H. sieboldii 'Alba'	Summer
H. 'Sea Drift'	Summer
H. 'Snowden'	Late Summer
H. tardiflora	Fall
H. undulata 'Erromena'	Summer
H. ventricosa	Late Summer
H. venusta	Summer

Leaves blue-green or gray-green

H. 'Blue Cadet'	Late Summer
H. 'Blue Skies'	Late Summer
H. 'Blue Umbrellas'	Summer
H. 'Blue Wedgewood'	Summer
H. 'Bold Ruffles'	Summer
H. fortunei 'Aoki', *H. f.* 'Hyacinthina'	Summer
H. 'Hadspen Blue'	Late Summer
H. 'Krossa Regal'	Late Summer
H. 'Love Pat'	Late Summer
H. sieboldiana, *H. s.* 'Elegans'	Summer
H. sieboldiana 'Helen Doriot'	Summer
H. × *tardiana* 'Halcyon'	Late Summer
H. tokudama	Summer

White-edged leaves

H. 'Antioch'	Summer
H. crispula	Early Summer
H. decorata (*H.* 'Thomas Hogg')	Early Summer
H. fortunei 'Albo-marginata'	Summer
H. 'Francee'	Summer
H. 'Fringe Benefit'	Early Summer
H. 'Ginko Craig'	Summer
H. gracillima 'Variegata'	Summer
H. 'Shade Fanfare'	Summer
H. 'Shogun'	Summer
H. sieboldiana 'Northern Halo'	Summer
H. sieboldiana 'May T. Watts'	Summer
H. sieboldii, *H. s.* 'Louisa'	Summer
H. undulata 'Albo-marginata'	Summer

Yellow- or gold-edged leaves

H. 'Aurora Borealis'	Summer
H. fortunei 'Aureo-marginata'	Summer

H. 'Gold Crown'	Summer
H. 'Golden Tiara'	Summer
H. montana 'Aureo-marginata'	Fall
H. sieboldiana 'Frances Williams'	Summer
H. ventricosa 'Aureo-marginata' ('Variegata')	Late Summer

White leaf blades (may be edged in different color)

H. 'Celebration'	Late Summer
H. undulata 'Medio-picta'	Summer
H. undulata 'Univittata'	Summer

Yellow leaf blades (may be edged in different color)

H. 'August Moon'	Summer
H. fortunei 'Albopicta', *H. f.* 'Aurea'	Summer
H. 'Gold Standard'	Summer
H. 'Gold Edger'	Late Summer
H. sieboldiana 'Golden Sunburst'	Summer
H. lancifolia var. *viridis marginata*	Late Summer
H. 'Piedmont Gold'	Late Summer
H. sieboldii 'Kabitan'	Summer
H. 'Sum and Substance'	Summer
H. 'Sun Power'	Late Summer
H. ventricosa 'Aureo-maculata'	Late Summer
H. 'Wogon Gold'	Summer

-crispula (krisp' ew-la)		Curled Leaf Hosta	2–3'/2'
Early Summer	Lilac	Japan	Zones 3–8

A vigorous species, which when protected from wind and sun, is as lovely as any hybrid offered today. The 4–5″ wide dark green leaves are up to 7″ long and have wavy, irregular white margins. They are glossy on the undersides, bear 7–9 pairs of lateral veins and have long-pointed often spirally wound pendant tips. The 2″ long lilac flowers are held loosely on a many-flowered 2–3' tall raceme. This is one of the earliest white-margined hostas to flower. Best grown in partial shade.

-decorata (de-ko-rah' ta)		Blunt Hosta	18–24″/2'
Early Summer	Violet	Japan	Zones 3–8

Similar to *H. sieboldii* in habit and coloration, the leaves are wider and more blunt on the apex. They are broadly oval, 3–8″ long and have 4–5 pairs of lateral veins. Slightly wavy, silvery-white margins surround the matte green leaves. The 2″ long, dark violet flowers are carried on leafless flower stems 1½–2' above the foliage.

Related Species:

H. 'Thomas Hogg' is synonymous with *H. decorata*, at least in this country, but may be a slightly different plant in Europe. In Europe, plants under this name are similar to *H. undulata* 'Albo-marginata'.

-fortunei (for-tewn' ee-eye)		Fortune's Hosta	15–24"/24"
Summer	Lilac	Japan	Zones 3–8

Plants form extensive clumps of somewhat heart-shaped green to gray-green leaves after a few years. Leaves are 9" long, 4" wide, and have 9–11 veins on either side of the midrib. Each leaf is attached to the stem by a deeply furrowed petiole with distinct wings. The flower stem rises well above the foliage and usually has one to several bracts beneath the 1½" long pale lilac flowers. This species provides excellent low maintenance plants for the shade garden.

Cultivars:

'Albopicta' is a popular cultivar with wavy yellow leaf blades ringed with pale green margins. Although the yellow tends to fade in the summer, this outstanding eye-catching plant is one of my favorites.

'Albopicta Aurea' has leaves which are almost totally white but have a thin green central midrib.

'Albo-marginata' (syn. 'Marginato-alba') has a yellow margin in the spring that changes to white in the summer and remains until frost. The margin varies in width. The flowers are pale lavender.

'Aoki' is 1½–2' tall and neat in appearance. It is early flowering with gray-green foliage and lavender purple flowers.

'Aurea' offers shimmering pale yellow leaves in the spring with wavy margins but is less vigorous than many other cultivars. Plants fade badly in full sun.

'Aureo-marginata' (syn. 'Obscura Marginata') has a narrow yellow margin, changing to yellowish green, and then to dark green toward the center. The flowers are light violet.

'Gold Standard' was found as a chance seedling in 1976. It offers vigorous growth, light gold leaves edged with green, and lavender flowers. It may be a hybrid of *H. fortunei*.

'Hyacinthina' (var. *hyacinthina*) is more vigorous, later flowering and has large gray-green leaves with a pencil thin white line at the edge.

-lancifolia (lan-si-fo' lee-a)		Lance Leaf Hosta	1½–2'/18"
Late Summer	Lilac	Japan	Zones 3–8

This is reported to be the oldest known hosta, drawings of which date to 1690. A parent of many modern hybrids, it embodies many fine garden attributes. The 4–7" long, pointed foliage is pure green, glossy on both sides, and only about 1" wide. Each leaf has 3–5 pairs of lateral veins. The flower scape is

12–18″ long and carries 1–1½″ long deep lilac flowers in late summer persisting into autumn.

Although not one of the most decorative hostas, the glossy leaves are pleasant and plants tolerate drier and sunnier conditions better than many other species and hybrids.

Cultivars:

var. *viridis marginata* is a smaller plant (12–15″ tall) with long-lasting yellow leaf blades edged with a narrow green band. Some authorities believe this is the same as *H. fortunei* 'Albopicta'.

-plantaginea (plan-tage′ i-nee-a) Fragrant Hosta 24–30″/2′
Late Summer White China Zones 3–9

The species has been in cultivation since the late eighteenth century and the related hybrids are among the most popular hostas. The large, arching, heart-

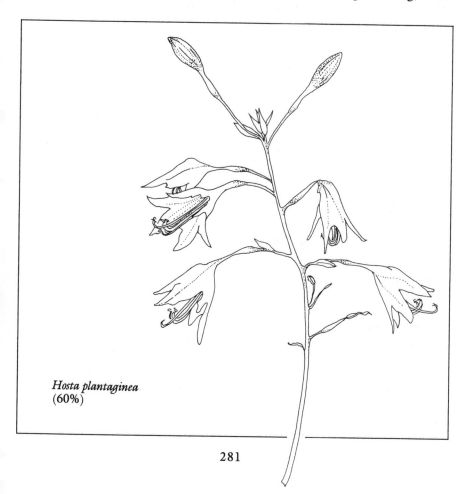

Hosta plantaginea
(60%)

shaped leaves are bright yellowish green with short-pointed tips. They are up to 10″ long with 7–9 veins on each side of the midrib. Although flowers of most hostas are of little interest and often removed before opening, the flowers on this species are most handsome. The fragrant, 3–4″ long, lovely white flowers are held well above the foliage almost at right angles to the stem instead of drooping as in many other species. They are densely arranged near the top of the raceme and the base of each is surrounded by a broad bract.

Cultivars:

var. *grandiflora* has longer, narrower foliage and tends to make a looser clump. The narrow flowers are 5″ long.

Related Species:

Several excellent hybrids, of which *H. plantaginea* is one of the parents, are available. They are taller than *H. plantaginea* and have slightly longer and more yellow leaf blades. *H. plantaginea* and the hybrids tolerate more sun and heat than many others and do poorly in deep shade. They are well suited to southern climes.

'August Moon' has large crinkled yellow blades and white flowers.

'Honeybells' (*H. plantaginea* × *H. lancifolia*) has gorgeous yellow-green wavy leaves, above which rise the pale lilac, fragrant flowers in late summer.

'Piedmont Gold' is an excellent yellow-leaved hybrid which makes a beautiful 18–24″ tall clump with numerous white flowers in the summer.

'Royal Standard' was introduced to the United States by Wayside Gardens, Hodges, S.C. and has green-yellow foliage that is slightly puckered and deeply veined. Leaves are 8″ long, 5″ wide and rather thin. It is taller than *H. plantaginea*, growing to three feet. Foliage is not as yellow as 'Honeybells' but the numerous white flowers have a pleasing fragrance.

'Sweet Susan' is a hybrid between *H. plantaginea* and *H. sieboldii* and has glossy green leaves and large fragrant, lilac flowers.

| *-sieboldiana* (see-bold-ee-ah′ na) | Siebold Hosta | 2½–3′/4′ |
| Summer | Lilac, white | Japan | Zones 3–8 |

Some of the finest garden plants are found in this species. The thick bluish green leaves are heart shaped to almost rounded and have 12–14 pairs of lateral veins. Leaves average 15″ long and 12″ wide. The light lilac flowers seldom rise above the foliage and are often hidden by the leaves. In general, leaves decline by late August in the South and about a month later in the North. Plants may be cut back at that time if foliage becomes too unsightly. The flowers and bracts are densely clustered, and in bud look like an artichoke. They detract from the magnificence of the plant and should be removed prior to opening.

Cultivars:

'Aurora Borealis', a recent sport of 'Frances Williams', is 4–5′ in diameter, taller, more vigorous and has more gold markings on the blue-green leaves. The white flowers rise just above the foliage.

'Elegans' was first offered around 1905 by Georg Arends Nursery (see *Astilbe*) in Germany. It has large leaves of conspicuous steel blue and flowers of light lilac to white. A mature plant grows 3′ tall, 4–5′ wide and is guaranteed to attract attention.

'Frances Williams' is named after Mrs. Frances Williams, an American horticulturist and hosta collector. She spotted a seedling of *H. sieboldiana* var. *elegans* with gold variegated margins in 1936 growing at Bristol Nurseries, Connecticut. Plants have blue-green leaf blades rimmed with golden bands. It is sometimes listed as 'Gold Edge' (distinct from 'Gold Edger', which see) or 'Golden Circles'. This is one of the finest hostas in cultivation today and tops the American Hosta Society's poll as the number one hosta in American gardens.

'Golden Sunburst' consists of 2′ tall clumps of golden yellow foliage prior to flowering. Creamy white flowers are borne in early summer.

'Helen Doriot' has intense blue puckered leaves with white flowers.

'May T. Watts' has heavily puckered leaves with gold centers surrounded by white margins. Introduced by the Planters Palette, Winfield, Ill.

'Northern Halo' is a recent introduction from Walter's Gardens, Michigan, with creamy white margins surrounding blue-green centers.

'Robusta' bears leaves that are not as blue-green as those of 'Elegans' but equally broad. Although sometimes listed as *H. fortunei* 'Robusta', the flower is similar to that of *H. sieboldiana* and it fruits heavily, unlike *H. fortunei*. Lovely specimens can be found at Longwood Gardens.

Related Species:

H. × *tardiana* has been applied to a series of plants resulting from the cross of *H. tardiflora*, a small dark green species, with *H. sieboldiana* 'Elegans'. They were raised in the late 1960's by Eric Smith, an outstanding hosta breeder in England. Plants are usually less than 18″ tall with blue-green leaves.

'Blue Dimples' has thick blue leaves with pale lavender flowers.

'Blue Skies' has small, steely blue, heart-shaped leaves. The plants are 15–18″ tall and bear many lavender flowers.

'Hadspen Blue' grows 12″ tall, has distinctive, 4″ wide, 5″ long blue lanceolate leaves with slight undulations.

'Halcyon' has blue leaves with intense blue lilac flowers rising slightly above them.

H. tokudama is closely related to *H. sieboldiana* and may, in fact, be a variety of *H. sieboldiana*. It is a pretty, diminutive species with deep blue-green, crinkled leaves. Plants are only about 18″ tall, rather slow growing and produce lilac white flowers similar to *H. sieboldiana*.

'Aurea-nebulosa' has leaves with a chartreuse interior surrounded by a glaucous blue margin. Plants grow 24″ tall.

'Buckshaw Blue' has bluer more cup-shaped leaves than the species. The mauve flowers open just above the foliage.

Other Related Hybrids:

Many other hybrids with glaucous blue foliage have resulted from crosses between cultivars of *H. sieboldiana*, *H. tokudama*, *H. fortunei* and others.

'Blue Cadet' is a dwarf form with lavender flowers in late summer. Plants are suitable for the small garden.

'Blue Umbrellas' is 2–4′ tall with blue-green textured foliage. Many white edged lavender flowers are produced in summer. An excellent specimen plant.

'Love Pat' has wide, puckered, gray-green leaves and creamy white flowers tucked into the foliage. Plants are about 2′ tall with lavender flowers in early summer.

'Krossa Regal', a distinctly vase-shaped form, ranges from 2–4′ tall when not in flower. The foliage is silvery blue, leathery, and long-pointed. The lavender flowers, produced in late summer, extend another 2′ above the foliage.

'Snowden', a cross between *H. fortunei* 'Aurea' and *H. sieboldiana* 'Elegans', has long-pointed gray-green leaves in symmetrical 3′ tall mounds. The flowers are pure white with occasional green tinges.

-sieboldii (see-bold'ee-eye)		Seersucker Hosta	12–20″/20″
Summer	Purple	Japan	Zones 3–8

(Syn. *H. albomarginata*)

Known and grown as *H. albomarginata*, it is correctly *H. sieboldii*, named after Philipp Franz von Siebold, in whose Dutch nursery it appeared in the early 1800's. This is one of the smaller hostas but one which quickly fills in due to its creeping rootstock. The 2–2½″ wide lance-shaped foliage has thin pure white margins and 3–4 pairs of lateral veins. Each leaf has a matte-like finish on the upperside but is glossy below. The inflorescence rises well above the foliage and bears a few blunt leaves along its length. Flowers are 2–2½″ long, the outer segments strongly recurved and violet while the inside is marked with violet stripes. Up to 30 flowers are carried on the raceme; they are neither particularly exciting nor do they detract from the foliage. This small, late-flowering hosta is most useful for edging and filling in small shady corners of the garden.

Cultivars:

'Alba' has pure white flowers with plain green leaves.

'Kabitan' has greenish yellow leaf blades rimmed with a narrow band of green.

The margins of the foliage are quite wavy and the light violet flowers appear earlier than other cultivars in the species. Plants are only 8–12″ tall. It is often incorrectly listed as a cultivar of *H. lancifolia*.

'Louisa' combines the wide, white-margined foliage with small (1–2″ long) white flowers. It is an excellent small hosta but a slower grower than the species. Selected in 1965 by Mrs. Williams and named for her daughter.

-undulata (un-dew-lah' ta)		Wavy Hosta	12–18″/18″
Summer	Lilac	Japan	Zones 3–8

This is the common hosta offered by many mail order catalogs as the "variegated hosta". Plant are often listed as 'Variegata' or 'Medio-picta'. The 6″ long leaves are undulated (wavy), thus the specific epithet, and have 8–10 pairs of lateral veins. Leaves typically have green margins and clear white interiors and are often spirally twisted. The winged, red-dotted petiole is deeply furrowed. The 2″ long flowers are light lilac and carried on 2–3′ long flower stems bearing numerous well-developed bracts. This is sometimes offered as *H. undulata* 'Undulata'.

Cultivars:

'Albo-marginata' has thin creamy-white margins surrounding the green center of the leaf blades (i.e., reverse of the species). Plants are 12″ tall and 14–18″ wide.

'Erromena' is a green leaf form with leaves up to 7–9″ long and 4–6″ wide. The 18″ long petioles are channeled with purple dots at the base. Flower stems average 3′ long. This variety probably resulted from a green sport of 'Univittata'.

'Univittata' is more vigorous than the species, growing 2–3′ tall. The foliage has much wider green margins than the species reducing the white coloration to a narrow strip along the midrib.

-ventricosa (ven-tri-ko' sa)		Blue Hosta	2–3′/3′
Late Summer	Violet	Eastern Asia	Zones 3–9

(Syn. *H. caerulea*)

Broad glossy leaves (up to 7″ wide) carried on a short, wide, shallowly furrowed petiole are characteristic of the species. The dark green, 7–9″ long foliage bears 7–9 pairs of lateral veins and unusually distinct cross veins, resulting in a net-like appearance. The flower stem is bractless and carries 20–30 bell-shaped flowers about 3′ above the foliage. The flowers, which are dark purple with darker stripes within, are borne horizontally but become pendent. The petals widen abruptly into campanula-like flowers.

Cultivars:

'Aureo-maculata' has leaf blades of yellowish green surrounded by green margins, although the leaves become mostly green by flowering time.

'Aureo-marginata' ('Variegata') is the reverse of the previous cultivar, having yellow margins that turn white, and green leaf blades. This relatively new introduction was discovered in a bed of seedlings of *H. ventricosa* by Alan Bloom in 1968.

-venusta (ven-ews' ta)		Dwarf Plantain-lily	3–4"/8"
Summer	Lilac	Korea	Zones 3–9

This is one of the dwarfest of hostas, although other hybrids are appearing which are scaled down versions of their predecessors. The green leaf blades are only about 1" long by ¾" wide , with 3–4 pairs of lateral veins. The flower stem rises 8–12" above the foliage and carries 4–8 lilac flowers about 1½" long. Plants are stoloniferous and spread well. Group 6–8 plants in a shady nook or cranny for best effect.

Cultivars:

'Variegata' has foliage with creamy white centers and green margins.

Other Worthy Hybrids:

Although many hybrids have been mentioned with some of the previous species, there are a host of others I have not covered. Numerous nurseries carry new selections every year and it is impossible to see them all and make intelligent comments about them. There are, however, a few additional ones which have proven to be excellent garden performers.

H. 'Antioch' is a medium-sized plant with large leaves, mottled light green with wide, creamy white edges. The lavender flowers are borne well above the foliage.

H. 'Francee' is becoming more popular every year and with good reason. Tidy 2' high mounds of dark green, heart-shaped puckered leaves with a clear white edge of varying width are produced. Lavender flowers open in midsummer.

H. 'Ginko Craig', a dwarf hybrid less than 12" tall, has light green leaves edged with a thin band of white. Plants are free flowering, producing blue-violet flowers well above the flattened clump of leaves.

H. 'Gold Edger' is an attractive small-leaved (3" wide, 4" long) hybrid forming 12" tall clumps of light yellow-green foliage. Plants grow rapidly and are suitable for edging or for the small garden. Pale lilac flowers are produced in late summer.

Quick Key to Hosta Species

Far superior minds than mine have attempted scientific keys to the genus and should be consulted by the hostaphile. It should be painfully obvious by now that a large number of hostas are hybrids or cultivars, and a key to species has limited usefulness. However, in fairness to this great genus, the following key provides horticultural and botanical characteristics of some of the species and a few of the hybrids and cultivars.

  A. Plant less than 6″ tall, leaves green, not exceeding 4″ in length, including petiole, 3–4 pairs of side veins..................... *H. venusta*

 AA. Plant taller, leaves larger

     B. Leaf blade yellowish green, glossy on both sides, flowers fragrant, white, usually opening in evening............ *H. plantaginea*

    BB. Leaf blade green, bluish, or variegated, flowers not fragrant, usually purple to lilac, open during day

       C. Leaf blade with white, yellow, or gold margin

         D. Leaf blade with gold or yellow margin

           E. Leaf blades distinctly puckered on underside, or on both sides

              F. Leaves puckered on both sides, very broad, flower stem barely rising above foliage, flowers pale violet to white ...... *H. sieboldiana* 'Frances Williams'

             FF. Leaves puckered on underside, less broad, flower stem well above foliage, flowers dark violet.........
                    H. fortunei 'Aureo-marginata'

           EE. Leaf blade not puckered, flower stem well above foliage.......
                    H. ventricosa 'Aureo-marginata'

        DD. Leaf blade with white margin

           E. Leaf margin undulated (wavy)

              F. Leaves broad (4–5″ across), long-pointed, flower stem with only one bract-like leaf, broad border....................................... *H. crispula*

             FF. Leaves less broad (2–4″ across), long-pointed, flower stem bearing 3–4 prominent long petioled leaves .... *H. undulata* 'Albo-marginata'

           EE. Leaf margin not conspicuously undulated,

              F. Leaves not puckered on either side, less than 2′ tall when not in flower

                 G. Leaves narrow, elliptical, short pointed...... *H. sieboldii*

               GG. Leaves broader, ovate, ends blunt .... *H. decorata*

              FF. Leaves puckered on underside, more than 2′ long.........
                    H. fortunei 'Albo-marginata'

     CC. Leaf blades without white, yellow, or gold margins

       D. Leaf blades entirely green or blue-green

         E. Leaf blades blue-green or gray-green

           F. Flower stems barely rising above foliage, flowers pale lilac to white

             G. Plant less than 2′tall, leaves 3–4″ wide .... *H. tokudama*

GG. Plant more than 2' tall, leaves up to 1' wide.............
                  H. sieboldiana
FF. Flower stem rising well above foliage, flowers
    dark purple .... *H. fortunei*
EE. Leaf blades entirely green
  F. Plants 2–2½' tall when not in flower
    G. Tube of flower abruptly widening into bell-
      shaped part of flower, dark violet ....*H. ventricosa*
    GG. Tube of flower expanding gradually, flower lilac.........
                  H. undulata 'Erromena'
  FF. Plants less than 2' tall when not in flower
    G. Flower mauve to lilac
      H. Leaves lance-shaped, glossy on both
        sides, about 12–15" tall, summer
        flowering ....*H. lancifolia*
      HH. Leaves ovate, less shiny, 8–12" tall, fall-flowering.....
             H. tardiflora
    GG. Flowers white........................ *H. sieboldii* 'Alba'
DD. Leaves not entirely green or blue-green, leaf blades
white or yellow sometimes with a green margin
  E. Interior of leaf blades white
    F. Margin very wide, white reduced to broad
      stripe along midrib, leaf not conspicuously undulated......
          H. undulata 'Univittata'
    FF. White and green both heavily splashed on leaf
      blade, leaf conspicuously undulated .... *H. undulata*
  EE. Interior of leaf blade yellowish
    G. Leaves all the same color
      H. Flowers white, height 12–18"... *H.* 'Piedmont Gold'
      HH. Flowers lilac, height 10–12" ..... *H. fortunei* 'Aurea'
    GG. Leaves with greenish margin
      H. Height 10–12", leaves ovate .. *H. fortunei* 'Albopicta'
      HH. Height 8–12", leaves lance-shaped ....
         H. sieboldii 'Kabitan'

Additional Reading:
Books:

Aden, Paul. 1988. The Hosta Book. Timber Press, OR. 133 p. The best book
by far on hostas for the American gardener. A must.

Manuscripts:

Aden, Paul. 1986. The cultivation of hostas. *The Garden* 111(5):222–225.

Busse, A., Viette, A., Schmid, G., and W. Pollock. 1988. A Hosta by any other name may be something else. *Perennial Plant Newsletter* 15:10–18.

Greenfell, Diana. 1981. A survey of the genus *Hosta* and its availability in commerce. *The Plantsman* 3(1):20–44.

Hansen, Karel, J.W. 1985. A study of the taxonomy of cultivated hostas. *The Plantsman* 7(1):1–35.

Ingram, John. 1967. Notes on the cultivated Liliaceae. 5. *Hosta sieboldii* and *H. sieboldiana. Baileya* 15:27–32.

Lacy, Allen. 1986. Hosta revival. *Horticulture* 64(1):28–34.

Maekawa, F. 1940. The genus *Hosta. Journal of the Faculty of Agriculture of Tokyo University*, Sect. 3 (Botany) 5:317–425. Reprinted in *Am. Hosta Soc. Bull.* 1972(4):12–64 and 1973(5):12–59.

Associations:

American Hosta Society, 3103 Heather Hill, S.E., Huntsville, AL. 35802. Publication: *American Hosta Society Bulletin.*

Houttuynia (hoo-tie' nee-a) Chameleon Plant Sauraceae

The genus contains several species but only *H. cordata* has gained favor in recent years, particularly the many-colored ground cover form, 'Chameleon' ('Cameleon'). I have seen a number of plantings in this country and don't yet understand why people get excited about it. Plants require abundant moisture and are, in fact, classified as water plants. If given moist, cool conditions and rich soil, it prospers to the point of becoming invasive. Place where plants may roam freely because once established, they are difficult to eradicate. Where moisture is constant, full sun to partial shade is ideal. Leaves deteriorate by late midsummer, particularly if allowed to dry out. Other ground covers such as, *Ajuga reptans* 'Burgundy Glow' or 'Gaiety' provide multicolored leaves but are not as invasive nor do they deteriorate as rapidly.

The green alternate leaves of the species are approximately 2–3″ long, heart shaped, and malodorous when crushed. Hardy in zones 3–8, it reaches a height of 18–24″. However, the species is seldom seen.

Cultivars:

'Chameleon' ('Cameleon') has leaves splashed with white, pink and red. The ½″ long, white flowers are secondary in interest and appear on 1–2″ long spikes in May and June. The plant is an effective ground cover due to its underground stems which result in rapid multiplication where conditions are ideal. It is not quite as invasive as the species.

'Flore-plena' bears purple tinged green leaves and double white flowers.

Propagate by division to multiply as needed or root 2–3″ long terminal cuttings in spring and summer.

Hyacinthus (hy-a sin' thus) Hyacinth Liliaceae

If one was to read major bulb catalogs, he would surely believe the definition of floral perfection was the florist's hyacinth, *H. orientalis*. There is a love-hate relationship between people and hyacinths. As a forced flower, its sweet scent and bright colors elicit responses of beauty, fragrance, and love. On the other hand, some bulb connoisseurs such as Louise Beebe Wilder in her delightful book *Adventures with Hardy Bulbs* look at them as "obese, fat-stalked, over-stuffed, overscented Levantines." The sentiments of most people fall somewhere in between. They are plants which prefer cool climates (to zone 3), performing poorly south of zone 7 where they can be used effectively only as annuals. They may be left in the ground for many years but are slow to multiply. Best results occur if replaced every 2–3 years, regardless of location. Bulbs are expensive and some industrious gardeners lift and dry them every spring and replant in the fall. Although this results in greater longevity of the bulbs, I have never felt that energetic. It is not necessary to plant great drifts, regardless of the advertisements, as 6–12 plants nestled in a protected area or beside a pond can make

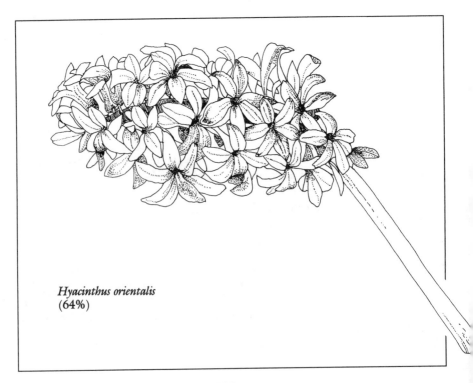

Hyacinthus orientalis
(64%)

a most effective display. Plant enough, however, to be able to bring some inside to savor the fragrance. Bury about 6″ deep and bulb to bulb for best display.

Hundreds of cultivars are available and it is a wonderful exercise in indecision to look through the gorgeous photos in the catalogs. There is, however, nothing better than browsing through those catalogs to bring a little spring into long winter months.

Related Genera:

All previously recognized species of *Hyacinthus*, except *H. orientalis*, have been shuffled off to other genera. *H. amethystinus*, Spanish hyacinth, has become *Brimeura amethystinus*; *H. azureus*, azure hyacinth, has been relegated to *Muscari azureus*; and *H. candicans*, summer hyacinth, is now *Galtonia candicans*.

Muscari azureus (*H. azureus*) is a scaled-down version of the common grape hyacinth, *Muscari armeniacum*, but is easily distinguished by its open flowers compared with the closed mouths of the latter *Muscari*. Plants are 4–6″ tall and flowers appear in late winter. Full sun and good drainage are required.

Hypericum (hy-per′ i-cum)   St. John's-wort   Hypericaceae

Although not used extensively in this country, the genus contains over 200 species, many of them ornamental. Shrubs, sub-shrubs (partly woody) and herbaceous perennials are included. Flowers are bright yellow, vary from ⅛″ to 3″ in diameter and may be solitary or clustered. They have 5 petals, 5 sepals and many stamens that form a bushy center. Some species, such as *H. inodorum* and *H. androsaemum*, produce ornamental fruit (capsules) used in bouquets and arrangements. The most common species are less than 2′ tall and are suited for low borders or ground covers, such as *H. calycinum* which spreads rapidly by underground stems. However, *H. hookerianum* may reach 4–5′ in height with 2″ wide, somewhat pendent flowers. Leaves are opposite or whorled and most species do best in partially shaded locations and moisture retentive soil.

Plants of St John's-wort were used in combination with "white wine two pintes, oile olive foure pounds, oile of turpentine two pounds . . . , set in the sun eight or ten daies . . ." to heal wounds, particularly those "made with a venomed weapon" (Gerard).

Quick Guide to Hypericum Species

	Height (in.)	Flower diameter (in.)	Use	Flowering Wood
H. buckleyi	9–12	¾–1½	Small sub-shrub	Old
H. calycinum	15–18	2½–3	Ground cover	Old
H. olympicum	9–12	1½–2	Ground cover	New
H. patulum	18–36	1½–2	Medium sub-shrub	New
H. polyphyllum	6–12	1½–2	Small sub-shrub	New

291

| *-buckleyi* (buk-lee′ eye) | Blue Ridge St. John's-wort | 9–12″/24″ |
| Summer | Yellow | North Carolina to Georgia | Zones 5–8 |

This little-known species should be used more often, particularly in southern gardens. The plant forms rounded low-growing mats which make an effective ground cover. The stems do not root readily and plants do not spread rapidly. Some fall color is provided as the ¾″ long, blunt, gray-green leaves turn a lovely red in September and October. The ¾–1½″ diameter flowers have 3 styles, distinct exserted stamens and occur in groups of three at the end of the stems.

Although not as flamboyant as *H. calycinum*, it is more adaptable to conditions in the eastern and southeastern states and may be counted on to grow and flower in those areas. This species is native to the Appalachian Mountains and not commonly cultivated.

Propagate by seed or from soft basal cuttings in the summer.

| *-calycinum* (kal-i-sigh′ num) | Aaron's Beard | 15–18″/24″ |
| Summer | Yellow | Southeast Europe, Turkey | Zones 5–9 |

The many protruding stamens suggest the name Aaron's beard and when in flower, this is one of the finest ground covers available. I have seen it cover areas under trees, crawl over hillocks and berms, and change barren hillsides into seas of green and yellow. One of the finest plantings may be seen at Butchart Gardens on Vancouver Island, Canada. The leaves are 3–4″ long, blue green and conspicuously fine netted beneath. The 2–3″ wide flowers are usually solitary, consisting of hundreds of stamens with reddish anthers, and five styles. The many stamens are in five bundles giving the flower a rose-like appearance. The 4-angled stems grow upright as well as along the ground.

Plants perform better in the northern end of their hardiness zone than in the southern end. In the South, they grow well and are evergreen under normal winters but flower sporadically if at all. In cold winters, the leaves may fall off or turn brown from desiccating winds, particularly when followed by bright sun. It is a vigorous grower and can be invasive if placed in a small garden area. Plants should be sheared back every few years to keep them in bounds.

Propagate by cuttings, division or seed. Cuttings should be taken from vegetative shoots in late spring or early summer. A rooting hormone is useful but not essential. Seeds germinate readily but not uniformly.

Related Species:

H. androsaemum, known as tutsan, has leaves similar in size to *H. calycinum* but bears 1″ wide bright yellow flowers with 3 styles. It produces colorful fruits which change from yellowish to deep red and finally to black. Although this species is hardy only as far north as zone 5, its southern limit is probably zone 7. Plants are not as heat tolerant as *H. calycinum* and have melted out every year in my garden (zone 8), regardless of planting site.

-olympicum (o-lim' pi-kum) Olympic St. John's-wort 9–12"/12"
Late Spring Yellow Southeast Europe, Asia Minor Zones 6–8

With delicate ½"–1" long sessile, pointed, grayish green leaves attached to trailing stems, plants are useful at the front of the garden, tucked in and around rocks and as a ground cover. The 1½–2" wide flowers are large relative to the size of the plants and occur in 2–5-flowered cymes at the end of the stems. The many stamens are arranged in three bundles and the sepals are rigidly pointed, almost sharp. Flowers are produced mid-May to early June in zone 8. The species tolerates partial shade but also grows well in full sun.

Cultivars:

var. *citrinum* bears pretty pale yellow flowers but is otherwise similar to the species.

Propagate by fresh seed or by soft basal cuttings in early summer or terminal cuttings in fall.

Related Species:

H. polyphyllum differs by having grayer leaves, less pointed sepals often speckled with a few black dots, and the absence of a woody base. The golden yellow flowers are 1½–2" across and occur in 4–10 flowered clusters at the end of the stems. It is likely that many plants sold under this name are actually *H. olympicum*. 'Sulphureum' has sulphur yellow flowers, as does 'Citrinum', which is probably the same thing.

H. reptans is only 6–9" tall with narrow leaves which form dense tufts. Plants are heat tolerant to zone 8 and bear 1" wide yellow flowers.

-patulum (pat-ew' lum) Golden Cup St. John's-wort 18–36"/24"
Summer Yellow China, Japan Zones 5–7

This evergreen shrub bears shoots which are somewhat purplish, spreading, and drooping. The 1½–2½" long leaves are gray-green beneath. The flowers are held in clusters of 2–4 and bloom profusely in June and July and sporadically until frost. The rounded petals overlap on the 1½–2" diameter flowers.

Cultivars:

'Hidcote' originated in Hidcote Gardens in England and grows 18" to 3' tall with 2–3" diameter yellow flowers. In colder climates, it dies down in winter to reemerge next spring. In warmer areas, leaves remain evergreen and plants reach heights of three feet. It is particularly susceptible to root rot and wilt and severe losses occur in warm, humid climates. May be a hybrid with *H. forestii*.

'Sungold' is a handsome, arching 18–24" tall sub-shrub with slightly larger flowers and greater cold hardiness than 'Hidcote'.

var. *henryi* has flowers up to 3" across and 2–3" long leaves. It is vigorous and well worth searching out.

All varieties and cultivars of *H. patulum* flower on new wood, therefore, plants which don't die to the ground in winter should have the previous years' stems cut to a few buds of old wood in the spring.

Only the species can be propagated from fresh seed but all may be propagated by taking 4–5″ long cuttings of non-flowering shoots, preferably with a piece from the parent plant in the summer. Insert the cuttings in a well-drained medium, keep moist and warm and rooting should take place in 3–4 weeks.

Related Species:

H. × *moseranum* (*H. calycinum* × *H. patulum*) is 2–3′ tall with the 3″ wide flowers of *H. calycinum* and the overlapping petals of *H. patulum*. Flowers appear over several months and plants have reportedly performed well in zone 6.

Quick Key to Hypericum Species

    A. Plants greater than 2′ tall, shrubby.......................... *H. patulum*
  AA. Plants less than 2′ tall, sub-shrubs or herbaceous perennials
        B. Styles 5, flowers 2–3″ across, stoloniferous.............. *H. calycinum*
      BB. Styles 3, flowers 1–2″ across, plants not stoloniferous
            C. No part of plant woody, sepals often with black dots................
                                           H. polyphyllum
          CC. Base of plant woody, sepals without dots
            D. Leaves pointed at end, conspicuously gray-green,
                stamens in 3 bundles............................. *H. olympicum*
          DD. Leaves blunt at end, mostly green, stamens not
                arranged in bundles................................ *H. buckleyi*

Additional Reading

Robson, N. K. B. 1980. *Hypericum olympicum*—wild and cultivated. *The Plantsman* 1(4):193–200.

I

Iberis (eye-beer' is)   Candytuft   Brassicaceae

Many gardens sport this popular genus in the form of *I. sempervirens*, the perennial matted candytuft. Approximately 40 species are known, many of which were discovered in Spain (originally known as Iberia). Although superseded by more colorful bedding plants, a number of annual species exist such as the delightful *I. amara*, rocket or hyacinth-flowered candytuft. Only one perennial species, *I. sempervirens*, is grown to any extent although others are occasionally offered. The perennial species are actually sub-shrubs whose stems are woody at the base. The leaves are alternate and usually entire while the flowers are often white or pink. Plants are tufted and well adapted to the front of the garden or cascading over rock walls. Full sun and well-drained soils are necessities. All perennial forms should be cut back after flowering every year to reduce fruit set and maintain quality foliage.

Quick Key to Iberis Species

	Height (in.)	Flower color
I. gibraltarica	9–12	outer pink, inner white
I. saxatilis	3–6	white, tinged purple
I. sempervirens	9–12	white

-gibraltarica (ji-brawl-tah' ri-ca)   Gibraltar Candytuft   9–12"/12"
Spring   Pink and white   Gibraltar   Zones 7–9

Not reliably hardy in most of the country, plants are seldom seen in American gardens. The 1" long evergreen leaves are toothed, particularly near the ends, and produced in basal rosettes. The flowers are arranged in 1½–2" long flattened umbel-like inflorescences. The outside flowers are pink to red while those inside the inflorescence are white or slightly tinged pink. They are worth trying as a self-sowing annual north of zone 7.

Seeds germinate readily and softwood cuttings of non-flowering shoots root within 14–21 days.

-saxatilis (saks-ah′ ti-lis)	Rock Candytuft	3–6″/6″
Spring	White	Southern Europe	Zones 2–7

The word *saxatilis* means "growing on rocks" and this compact plant is perfect in and around rocks. The evergreen, entire leaves are only about ⅛″ wide and ¾″ long. Flowering and non-flowering stems occur. At the end of the former appear umbel-like inflorescences of ½″ long white flowers often tinged with purple, especially as they fade. Plants are very cold hardy, unusual for a species native to Southern Europe.

Propagate similar to *I. gibraltarica.*

-sempervirens (sem-per-vi′ renz)	Evergreen Candytuft	9–12″/18″
Spring	White	Southern Europe	Zones 3–9

This is certainly the most popular of the candytufts. It has been used for centuries as an edging plant to bridge lawns with taller plantings in the garden. The evergreen foliage consists of numerous ¾″ wide and 1–1½″ long, entire leaves. Plants are woody at the base and should be cut back severely at least every other year to insure they do not get leggy. The flowers are invariably white although there may be some variation in seed propagated material in clearness of color. The 1½–2″ wide inflorescence is borne in the lateral axils rather than terminal as in *I. saxatilis.* Flowers open in early March in zone 8 gardens and persist for ten weeks.

Cultivars:
The numerous selections offer improvements in flower color and habit.

'Alexander's White' is 10–12″ tall and very floriferous.
'Autumn Snow' is 8–10″ tall and has clear white flowers larger than those of the type. It blooms profusely in the spring and again in the fall.
'Little Gem' is only 5–8″ tall and has small, clear white flowers.
'October Glory' is about 8″ tall and reblooms in the fall.
'Purity' is another white-flowered form with lustrous, deep green leaves and an abundance of flowers. It is slightly taller than 'Little Gem' and smaller than 'Snowflake'.
'Pygmaea' is a prostrate form which hugs the ground and sends up small white blossoms in early spring.
'Snowflake' is 8–10″ tall and bears 2–3″ wide inflorescences of pure white flowers which shine on sunny spring days.
'Snowmantle' is more compact than 'Snowflake'.

All cultivars may be propagated by cuttings while the species is readily raised from seed.

Quick Key to Iberis Species

    A. Plants less than 6″ tall, prostrate habit......................... *I. saxatilis*
   AA. Plants more than 6″ tall, flower stems ascending
        B. Flowers conspicuously pink to red, at least outer flowers of
           inflorescence, leaves toothed near apex .... *I. gibraltarica*
       BB. Flowers white, leaves entire .... *I. sempervirens*

Incarvillea (in-car-vill′ ee-a)   Hardy Gloxinia   Bignoniaceae

The genus is not often grown in the United States although I would like to see more people try it. Because plants grow from a long taproot, they are usually available through bulb supply catalogs. It is not hardy in many areas of the country but when grown in the right location, plants are magnificent. The flowers resemble gloxinia and the leaves are similar to Jacob's Ladder (*Polemonium*). Of the six species, only *I. delavayi* is readily available in the United States.

-delavayi (del-a-vay′ eye)   Delavay Incarvillea   18–24″/18″
Spring   Rose purple   China   Zones 5–7

The 12″ long basal leaves consist of 15–20 pinnately compound leaflets, each 3–4″ long, which form a handsome mound of foliage. Five to twelve flowers are carried on stems which rise 1–2′ above the foliage. The trumpet-shaped rose-purple flowers are 2–3″ long and wide and have yellow throats. Remove blossoms after flowering to extend bloom time. Although often listed as being hardy in zones 5–8, I have had little success in over-summering plants in zone 8. Well-drained, sandy soils and partial shade are recommended. In zones 5 and 6, mulching the plants in the fall is good practice.

Related Species:
I. compacta is 8–12″ tall and more compact than the previous species. The flowers are purple and carried on one-foot-tall racemes.

I. mairei (*I. grandiflora* var. *brevipes*) has 2–3 flowers but each may be up to 4″ across.

It is difficult to divide the long taproot. Division should be accomplished in spring immediately after flowering. Seed propagation is the easiest means to increase the various species. Fresh seed sown and placed under heat and high humidity result in seedlings in 10–20 days.

Inula (in′ yew-la)   Inula   Asteraceae

Although consisting of about 60 species, only one or two have outstanding ornamental properties not found in other yellow daisy flowers abundant in the summer garden. Most species are hairy and coarse, and bear alternate leaves. Two to four inch diameter bright yellow flowers are borne solitary or in twos. They are easily grown when placed in full sun and moist, well-drained soil, although most tolerate somewhat boggy conditions. *I. ensifolia* and *I. royleana* are the primary species for the formal garden while *I. helenium* and *I. magnifica* are bigger, coarser and more suitable for larger, less formal areas. The genus is similar to *Buphthalmum* except for minor differences in the flower and fruit morphology (the receptacle and the achene are slightly different).

All may be propagated by seed or division.

Quick Key to Inula Species

	Height (ft.)	Flowers solitary	Leaves very hairy
I. ensifolia	1–2	Y	N
I. helenium	4–6	Y	Y
I. royleana	1½–2	Y	Y

Inula ensifolia
(64%)

| *-ensifolia* (en-si-fo′ lee-a) | | Swordleaf Inula | 1–2′/2′ |
| Late Spring | Yellow | Europe, Asia | Zones 3–8 |

This is the best of the small inulas as it is self-branching, compact and produces many long-petaled, bright yellow to orange daisy-like flowers. The 1–2″ wide flowers are borne singly at the end of the stems and persist for about 6 weeks. The sessile leaves are linear and slender-pointed with numerous parallel veins. The species name means "sword-like" and refers to the shape of the leaves.

Plants are heat tolerant to zone 8 and are good alternatives to *Doronicum caucasicum*, another small yellow daisy. Unlike *Doronicum*, they do not go dormant in the summer. Plants are short lived in the Southeast, persisting for about 3 years.

Cultivars:

'Golden Beauty' forms 18–24″ tall bushes covered with 2″ wide yellow daisies.

Propagate by seed or division in the fall.

| *-helenium* (he-len′ ee-um) | | Elecampane | 4–6′/4′ |
| Summer | Yellow | Europe, Northern Asia | Zones 3–8 |

Although native elsewhere, plants have been naturalized in eastern North America. Dried roots yield a white, starchy powder called inuline which has long been valued for medicinal uses. In fact, elecampane is a living drugstore, also yielding a volatile oil, a resin, and a bitter extract, all of which were employed by apothecaries of old. If you grow this plant and don't like it, grind it up to cure your sick dog. It enjoys full sun but tolerates limited shade. The 12–16″ long basal leaves are held on petioles up to one foot long but become much reduced in size, and sessile as they ascend the brownish furrowed stem. They are velvety beneath but rough-hairy above. The 3–4″ wide flowers are usually solitary but occasionally occur in groups of two or three.

Plant in well-drained moist soil in full sun. They are coarsely magnificent in flower but decline rapidly in the fall, particularly if abundant water cannot be supplied. Plants require a good deal of room to grow and should be spaced at least 3′ from other specimens.

Propagate by seed or divide in the fall or early spring.

Related Species:

I. magnifica grows 6′ tall and bears 5–6″ wide flowers in a many-flowered inflorescence (corymb). The center of each flower (disk flowers) is deep yellow with orange tips, while the ray flowers are golden yellow and 2–3″ long. The stem has purple striations. Plants are hardy in zones 3–8.

| *-royleana* (royl-ee-ah′ na) | | Himalayan Elecampane | 1½–2′/3′ |
| Late Summer | Orange | Himalayas | Zones 3–7 |

The flowers are handsome but the unbranched habit does not make it an especially good garden plant. The 6–10″ long leaves are oval, slightly toothed, and densely fuzzy underneath (tomentose). The upper leaves are clasping; the lower are 3–4″ wide on long winged petioles. The solitary orange-yellow flowers are about 4″ across and emerge from black buds in late summer and fall.

This is a better plant for northern climates than southern. It tolerates moist conditions and needs cool nights for best performance.

Propagate from divisions in early spring or from seed.

Related Species:

I. orientalis grows 2–2½′ tall and bears 4–6″ long entire leaves with marginal glands. The orange-yellow solitary flowers are up to 3″ wide.

Quick Key to Inula Species

A. Plants 4–6′ tall, flower usually solitary or at most in 3's, disk flowers yellow	*I. helenium*
AA. Plants less than 2′ tall	
B. Stems unbranched, leaves tomentose, oval with netted veins, buds black.	*I. royleana*
BB. Stems branched, leaves not tomentose or hairy, linear with parallel veins, buds not black.	*I. ensifolia*

Ipheion (if′ ee-on)   Starflower   Amaryllidaceae

The genus contains 10–20 species but only *I. uniflorum*, spring starflower, is cultivated to any extent. It is a species that no genus seems to want. At one time or another, *I. uniflorum* has been classified under *Brodiaea* (where it is still often called *B. uniflora*), *Milla*, *Triteleia*, or *Tristagma*. Pertinent differences among three of these closely related genera are given below.

	Brodiaea	*Ipheion*	*Triteleia*
Origin	North America	South America	North America
Root	Corm	Bulb	Corm
Leaves	Rounded	Flat	Keeled beneath
Fertile Stamens	3	6	6
Inflorescence	Umbel	1–2 flowers	Umbel

-uniflorum (ew-ni-flo′ rum)   Spring Starflower   4–6″/8″
Early Spring   White, pale blue   Argentina, Uruguay   Zones 5–9

The leaves, when crushed, smell like garlic, although not as pungent. They are nearly flat, ¼ to ⅜″ wide, 6 to 9″ long, and often pale green. The flowering stem rises about 6″ above the foliage and usually bears one but sometimes two pleasantly fragrant flowers. The 1″ wide star-shaped flowers are about 1″ long and have a whitish, porcelain blue hue. They are lovely along paths, at the front of borders, or in rockeries where they should be planted in generous drifts. They enjoy well-drained soils in full sun where colonies increase rapidly. In some gardens, particularly in the South, plants can become invasive. In my garden, they are at their peak in mid- to late March.

Cultivars:

'Wisley Blue' is most popular and has larger (up to 2″ wide) flowers of rich, deep blue.

var. *violacea* has pale blue flowers the same size as the species.

Offsets are readily produced and if new colonies are wanted, simply lift existing plantings after flowering, separate bulbs and offsets, and replant immediately where desired. Plants need to be divided every 2–4 years to maintain vigor.

Iris (eye′ ris)   Iris   Iridaceae

The age-old misconception that iris is a summer flowering plant should at once be dispelled. Few other genera provide flowers as long and as often as the iris. With reasonable selection and care, it is possible to have one kind of iris or another in flower for seven or eight months of the year.

The genus took its name from the Greek goddess Iris, who was the messenger of Juno, the goddess of marriage. Iris walked between heaven and earth over

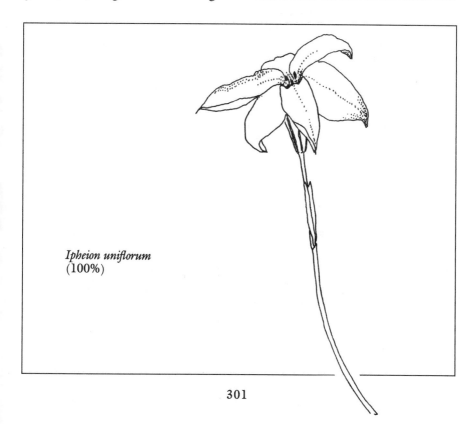

Ipheion uniflorum
(100%)

301

a bridge made by the rainbow. Legend says that wherever she walked on earth, her footprints bore flowers with as many colors as the rainbow.

The iris was said to have first been adopted as an emblem in the sixth century by King Clovis of the Franks, after a clump of yellow flag iris had shown him where he could ford a stream and escape a superior force of Goths. It was revived as an emblem, the Fleur-de-Louis, in 1147 when Louis VII of France set off on the ill-fated second crusade. The emblem, used since 1180 as a badge of the kings of France and referred to as the "Lily of France", was probably *Iris pseudacorus*. The iris has been adopted by many kings since and has represented the birth of Christ in numerous classical paintings. Not to be outdone, even the Canadian Province of Quebec uses the Fleur-de-lis on her provincial flag. Countries of the world seem unabashedly attached to the beauty of the iris and in any one garden, English, Spanish, Dutch, Persian, German, Californian, Japanese, Louisiana, Pacific Coast, and Siberian iris may be found.

Plants range from the tiny *I. danfordiae*, Danford iris, to large water irises such as *I. pseudacorus*, yellow flag iris. Many species such as *I. sibirica* are easily grown while others such as the exotic *I. susiana*, *I. haynei* and *I. samariae* require truly religious experiences to insure continued success.

Bearded iris are most common and so many cultivars have been produced that they have been divided into miniature dwarf, standard dwarf, intermediate, miniature tall, border, and standard tall bearded groupings. The standard tall bearded iris are the most common but many cultivars are available in all the bearded groups. Plenty of species, however, exist for the the hard-core taxonomic gardeners. The genus has been divided into 10 sub-genera which subdivide into 19 sections, 24 sub-sections, and 59 groups or series. Each series may have 5 to 25 species and each species may be subdivided into numerous cultivars. It would take many years to visit enough gardens around the world to see all the species and much longer to collect them for your own garden. Although interesting to see obscure species in botanical gardens, less than twenty are readily available in this country. However, there is enough choice of color, habit, and environmental needs within that group to satisfy all but the greediest of iris lovers.

The floral parts are in sets of three. Flowers consist of 6 segments: 3 inner (standards) which generally are upright and 3 outer (falls) which are reflexed and are often bearded at the base. The standards are large and showy in most species but reduced in *I. kaempferi*, Japanese iris and nothing but short bristles in *I. setosa*, bristly iris. Three style branches arch over the anthers and the stigma is found on the underside of the branches near the end. This combination of style, anther, and stigma lies on the inner part of the fall and essentially makes a tunnel through which insects must enter to feed on the nectar, insuring that said insect collects lots of pollen to further impregnate other unsuspecting flowers.

Some species require constantly moist soil and perform best along sides of ponds or pools, thus the ability to maintain soil moisture is an important consideration in selecting iris species. Many others, such as the bearded types, will be at home under "normal" conditions, that is, rich well-drained soils and full sun to partial shade. Although some species are bulbous (all of these are un-bearded), most iris have underground rhizomes, a horizontally creeping stem, and may or may not be crested or bearded.

Propagation of all the rhizomatous iris can be accomplished by dividing with a sharp spade or by pulling apart tangled rhizomes with garden forks. Although the latter takes more time and effort, healthier and faster flowering plants result.

The flowering times listed below illustrate the long seasonal interest (adapted from "The World of Iris", AIS, 1978). Not all species included in this list are described. The American Iris Society is a must for enthusiasts (see associations after *Iris*).

Mid to Southern states	Mid to Northern states	Group	Species
L.Nov–L.Jan	Nov.–Mar.	Unguicularis	*I. unguicularis*
M.Feb—M.Mar	M.Mar—M.Apr	Reticulatas	*I. bakeriana*
			I. danfordiae
			I. histrio
			I. histrioides
			I. reticulata
L.Feb—E.Apr	E.Apr—E.May	Min. Dw.	*I. chamaeiris*
		Bearded	*I. pumila*
M.Mar—M.May	L.Apr—L.May	Medians	St. Dw. Bearded
			Int. Bearded
			Border Bearded
			Min. Tall Bearded
M.Mar—M.Apr	L.Apr—M.May	Junos	*I. bucharica*
			I. willmottiana
E.Apr—E.May	L.Apr—E.Jun	Arils	*I. hoogiana*
			I. korolkowii
			I. hookeriana
			I. susiana
E.Apr—L.May	L.Apr—M.Jun	Xiphiums	*I. xiphium*
			I. xiphioides
			Dutch hybrids
L.Apr—E.May	E.May—L.May	Vernae	*I. verna*
L.Apr—L.May	E.May—E.Jun	Evansias	*I. cristata*
			I. tectorum
L.Apr—L.May	M.May—M.Jun	Tall Bearded	*I. pallida*
E.May—E.Jun	M.May—L.Jun	Louisianas	*I. fulva*
			I. nelsonii
M.May—M.Jun	E.Jun—L.Jun	Siberians	*I. sibirica*
			I. sanguinea

Mid to Southern states	Mid to Northern states	Group	Species
M.May—M.Jun	M.Jun—M.Jul	Spurias	*I. graminea*
			I. spuria
E.Jun—L.Jun	L.Jun—L.Jul	Apogon	*I. kaempferi*
			I. laevigata
			I. pseudacorus
			I. setosa
			I. versicolor
M.Sep—M.Nov	E.Sep—E.Oct	Rebloomers	Many species

Abbreviations
E = early, M = mid, L = late
Dw = dwarf, Min = miniature, Int = intermediate, St = standard

Quick Reference to Iris Species

	Height (in.)	Color of flowers	Bearded, crested or beardless	Bulbous or rhizome
I. "Bearded hybrids"	8–36	Various	Bearded	Rhizome
I. cristata	6–9	Lavender	Crested	Rhizome
I. danfordiae	4–6	Yellow	Beardless	Bulbous
I. foetidissima	18–24	Lilac	Beardless	Rhizome
I. kaempferi	24–30	Various	Beardless	Rhizome
I. pallida	24–36	Violet	Bearded	Rhizome
I. pseudacorus	24–36	Yellow	Beardless	Rhizome
I. reticulata	4–6	Violet	Beardless	Bulbous
I. sibirica	24–36	Blue	Beardless	Rhizome
I. tectorum	12–18	Lilac	Crested	Rhizome
I. verna	4–6	Blue	Beardless	Rhizome
I. "Xiphium hybrids"	12–18	Various	Beardless	Bulbous

-"Bearded hybrids"   Bearded Iris   8–36"/10–24"
Early Summer   Various   Hybrid   Zones 3–10

The majority of people who first use iris in the garden try one of the bearded hybrids. It is estimated that well over 90% of all iris used in this country are in this group and that 90% of these are the tall bearded types. Market research, however, has not determined whether there was such a high demand because breeders turned out so many hybrids and cultivars, or there were so many available that it became difficult to buy anything else. Regardless of the reasons for their popularity, new cultivars continue to be produced and demand is unabated.

Plants may be classified into dwarf (less than 15"), intermediate (15–28"), and tall bearded iris (28″ or taller). The American Iris Society has further divided the dwarfs into miniature (4–10″) and standard categories (10–15″) while the intermediates have been classified into intermediate, table and border iris.

Dwarf Bearded: This group of bearded iris is often sold under *I. pumila*, dwarf iris, and although the species is sometimes available, its main contribution to gardening is as the dominant parent of the miniature dwarf hybrids. *I. chamaeiris*, Crimean iris, has also been used in this group. Both are native to southern Europe and exist in many colors. *I. pumila* differs from *I. chamaeiris* by having a shorter stem and longer flower. Other parents of lesser importance include *I. attica*, *I. griffithii*, and *I. flavescens*.

The miniature dwarf forms (4–10″ tall) are the earliest to flower and stems are usually unbranched, bearing a few 2–3″ wide flowers with spotted falls. All irises in this class require good drainage and are often grown in rockeries or on stone walls where drainage is excellent.

Cultivars:

'Already'	Wine-red flowers
'Angel Eyes'	White with blue spots on falls
'Banberry Ruffles'	Purple flowers
'Blue Frost'	Light blue flowers
'Cherry Spot'	White with cherry red falls
'Commencement'	White, spotted yellow on falls
'Curtsy'	White with lavender falls
'Fashion Lady'	Orange-yellow flowers
'Little Sapphire'	Light blue flowers
'Pixie Princess'	Blue flowers
'Red Gem'	Deep red flowers
'Sky Baby'	Ruffled blue flowers
'Watercolor'	Light yellow with brown spot on falls

The standard dwarf forms, sometimes called Lilliputs, are more robust than the miniatures. They arose from crossing *I. pumila* with standard tall species and hybrids. The 3–4″ wide flowers open about a week later than the miniatures. Good drainage is beneficial although not as absolute a requirement as with the miniatures. The Lilliputs are quite at home in a small grouping at the front of a sunny border.

Cultivars:

'Baby Snowflake'	White flowers
'Bingo'	Deep velvet-purple flowers
'Dark Fairy'	Purple flowers
'Early Sunshine'	Yellow flowers
'Lemon Flare'	Creamy white flowers
'Red Dandy'	Wine-red flowers

| 'Small Sky' | Light blue flowers |
| 'Sunlight Trail' | Yellow flowers |

Intermediate Bearded: In general, flowering time is between the dwarf and the tall bearded iris as plants resulted from crosses between the two. Other species which fit into this class or have been used in hybridization are *I. pumila*, *I. chamaeiris*, *I. melitta*, and *I. balkana*. They are handsome garden plants and attain respectable height and flower size without staking. The main difference between intermediate, table, and border bearded iris is their parentage and flowering time.

Cultivars:

'Blue Fragrance'	Blue flowers
'Butterbit'	Yellow flowers
'Lemonade'	Yellow with white falls
'Little Angel'	White flowers
'Sweet Allegro'	Pink flowers

Tall Bearded: The tall bearded iris are still the most popular iris in gardens today. Many have escaped from cultivation and "blue flags" can be found around old farmsteads and meadows. Plants enjoy soil with a basic pH (as do the other bearded types) and full sun. The dazzling array of colors is the result of their complex parentage. The first tall bearded irises introduced commercially were selections from natural hybrids of *I. variegata* and *I. pallida*. Many selections were made between 1822 and the 1880's by French, Dutch and English hybridizers, but few breakthroughs occurred until the large-flowered species *I. trojana*, *I. cypriana*, and *I. mesopatamica* were discovered and introduced from the Near East. They resulted in "magical" crosses, for unbeknownst to the hybridizers, these species had twice the number of chromosomes (i.e. tetraploid) as those used previously.

In the crosses that followed, fertile tetraploids with larger flowers and much improved vigor occasionally appeared and were used in further breeding. From this point on, hybridization knew no bounds and the thousands of cultivars available today do not even closely resemble the parents from which they sprang.

Tall bearded irises have been further classified into flower colors and shapes but these are of interest only to those afflicted with irisitis, an incurable compulsion to grow every different tall bearded iris ever developed. Those so affected have been known to babble incomprehensibly about amoenas, plicatas and selfs, but they can be safely approached.

Several pests plague bearded iris and are particularly troublesome in heavy, poorly drained soils. Soft rot turns healthy rhizomes into mush. As leaves begin to yellow and die, they should be removed without delay or the fungus will infect the rhizome. Various leaf spots can be disfiguring such as the ailment known as scorch. Leaves turn red to brown all at once resulting in death of the plant. The cause and cure are unknown. The iris borer is the most serious insect and is best controlled by removing dead debris in which they overwinter, particularly the spent iris leaves themselves.

There are simply too many cultivars of tall bearded iris to produce a useful list. Consult growers or specialists to keep abreast of the current cultivars. The American Iris Society can be helpful in choosing the best cultivars for different areas of the country.

| *-cristata* (kris-tah′ ta) | Crested Iris | 6–9″/15″ |
| Spring   Pale blue, yellow crest | Eastern North America | Zones 3–9 |

Numerous iris are native to the United States and this is one of the finest available. A shallow rhizome creeps along the surface resulting in rapid multiplication of the clump. The leaves are about 4″ long and arise from the rhizome. One to two flowers are produced on each 6″ tall stem; the standards are shorter and narrower than the falls and the crest is a lovely deep yellow. Plants tolerate partial to heavy shade and look magnificent in great drifts in the woodland garden. The woodland floor awash in pale blue is a sight to savor. Plants combine well with Canadian columbine, *Aquilegia canadensis*.

Cultivars:

var. *alba* is a white-flowered variety not as common or as vigorous as the type. The handsome flowers contrast more with the woodland floor than the type.
'Shenandoah Sky' has light blue flowers
'Summer Storm' bears deeper blue flowers than the species

Related Species:

I. lacustris, dwarf lake iris, is similar but only about 3″ tall, and has narrower leaves and a more slender rhizome. The flowers are slate blue with a whitish patch and yellow crest on the falls. It is native to the shores of the Great Lakes. *I. cristata* is a better garden plant.

Additional Reading:

Brearley, Christopher. 1985. The crested irises of North America. *The Plantsman* 7(2):114–115.

| *-danfordiae* (dan-ford′ ee-eye) | Danford Iris | 4–6″/3″ |
| Early Spring   Bright yellow | Eastern Turkey | Zones 5–9 |

The bulbs have a netted or reticulated cover with brownish fibers, thus belonging to the group known as reticulated iris. Brilliant primrose-yellow flowers open in early spring or late winter (as early as late January in my garden) depending on soil temperature. Plants are short and should be planted where they can be enjoyed close up. The leaves are square, hollow, and barely developed at time of flowering, although they grow 12″ long after flowering. The standards are less than ¾″ long and the falls have small brown or black spots.

Plants like hot, dry conditions during their long summer dormancy but tend to break into masses of small bulbs after the first couple of years. These bulblets require 2–3 more years to flower. They should be treated as annuals or biennials if consistent flowering is the goal.

-foetidissima (foy-ti-dis′ i-ma)		Stinking Gladwin	18–24″/18″
Summer	Lilac	Europe	Zones 6–9

This unusual species is the only iris grown for the fruit rather than flowers. The leaves are evergreen, about 18″ long and are characterized by their foul odor

Iris foetidissima
(64%)

when broken or crushed. The purplish gray flowers are 2–2½" across and rather unexciting. Not until autumn is the beauty of this plant appreciated. Then, the seed capsules split open and reveal rows of scarlet seeds which remain attached throughout the winter. The fruiting stem may be hung upside down to dry and used for indoor decoration.

Plants do well in partial shade and are among the most shade tolerant of iris species. Two to three years are necessary to establish a clump of stinking gladwin. The first year in the Horticulture Gardens yielded few seed capsules but 6–8 appeared the following year. Propagate by seed, or lift and divide in the fall.

Cultivars:

var *lutea* has yellow flowers.
'Variegata' has variegated leaves which add foliar appeal to an otherwise drab flowered plant.

Additional Reading:

White, Anne Blanco. 1985. An iris for all seasons. *The Garden* 110(12):573–576.

-kaempferi (kemp' fa-ree)		Japanese Iris	24–30"/24"
Summer	Various	Northern China, Japan	Zones 4–9

(Syn. *I. ensata*)

This woodland iris adapts well to partial shade and moist soils. In its native form, plants are rather unimpressive, with ordinary red-purple flowers, small standards and floppy falls. However, over the centuries the Japanese have developed large-flowered plants characterized by the virtual elimination of the standards and subsequent increase in size of the falls. The flowers may be up to 10" across and due to lack of standards, the overall appearance is that of a flattened flower head. Cultivars include singles (with 3 broad, overlapping falls), doubles (with 6 falls but are actually standards and falls lying together), and peony-style flowers with up to 12 flower parts.

Plants perform well in any organic-rich soil where moisture can be consistently provided; they do not need to be planted in a bog. Acidic conditions are necessary and lime must not be added to the soil. Plant in full sun or partial shade.

Cultivars:

Cultivars which have been developed are truly magnificent and are becoming less expensive and more available every year. The one drawback is that the flowers are so large they must be removed as soon as they fade. As with other popular species of iris, catalogs provide the most vivid descriptions of cultivars. The pictures are also prettier.

'Aichi' has pink flowers with darker pink veining.
'Aka-fukurin' has white flowers with red trim.

'Cry of Rejoice' produces purple flowers with yellow centers.

'Emotion' bears large white flowers with purple-edged petals.

'Higo' strain from Japan consists of 24–30″ tall cultivars with 6–9″ wide, heavily veined blooms.

'Ise' has pale blue to almost white, single flowers.

'Nara' bears double violet flowers which bloom about one week later than the other cultivars.

'Nikko' is 18–24″ tall and produces single pale blue flowers with deep purple veining. The last three cultivars are part of the Higo strain.

'Over the Waves' bears pure white highly ruffled flowers with a light purple border.

'Pink Frost' has double, 8″ wide pink flowers which are lighter and more ruffled than those of 'Pink Lady'.

'Pink Lady' has large, single, light pink flowers.

'Purple and Gold' has a name totally lacking in imagination but the single purple flowers with golden stripes on the falls have been lovely in the Georgia gardens in recent years.

Plants may be divided in spring and fall.

Related Species:

I. laevigata, rabbit-ear iris, is a most magnificent species. The 2–3″ wide flowers are flattened and lavender blue. The blue-green leaves have visible black "watermarks" along the veins. Plants are more lime tolerant than *I. kaempferi*. They are difficult to find in this country because of the narrow limits of adaptability. Roots must be constantly moist and best grown on streambanks, bogs, or other areas high in moist organic matter. The finest examples I have seen are at Longstock Water Gardens near Longstock, England. 'Alba' has pure white flowers and is prettier than the species. 'Variegata' has sharp white leaf variegations which contrast well with the blue flowers.

I. spuria, seashore iris, requires plenty of water in spring and fall but prefers to be hot and dry during the summer. Hybrid forms grow 4′ tall and almost as wide. Flowers of the species are lavender purple but cultivars occur in an assortment of colors. Flowers open in June and July. Plants resent disturbance and should not be moved unless absolutely necessary.

Additional Reading:

Mackintosh, Esther. 1983. The Americanization of Japanese iris. *Horticulture* 61(2):23–25.

-pallida (pa′ li-da)		Sweet Iris	24–36″/24″
Summer	Violet	Northern Italy	Zones 4–8

This species is an important building block in the development of the bearded iris, however, it has some lovely attributes of its own. Although the flowers are fragrant, they are an unremarkable lavender-blue bearded type, and much more statuesque flowers may be found in any number of bearded hybrids.

The foliage, however, is an excellent soft gray-green which is retained throughout the year and is a good foil for dark green plants in the garden.

Like other bearded species, *I. pallida* grows best in well-drained soils and is not particularly tolerant of wet feet. Full sun is preferred but partial shade is tolerated.

Cultivars:

'Albo-variegata' ('Zebra') has white and cream streaking on blue-green leaves. An exceptional garden plant with all-season appeal.

var. *dalmatica* is the best of the glaucous foliage plants with larger leaves and handsome foliage.

-pseudacorus (sood-a′ ko-rus)   Yellow Flag Iris   24–36″/24″
Early Summer   Yellow   Europe   Zones 5–9

Yellow flag iris has been grown for centuries and all parts of the plant have been found useful in one way or another. The rhizome acts as a powerful cathartic; the powdered roots were used as snuff and contain antidotal properties for poisons. The seeds were roasted for a coffee-like beverage while the flowers produced a yellow dye.

This is a most adaptable species. To be sure, plants are at their best where the roots are submerged in water or at least constantly moist. Heights of three to four feet are not uncommon in such situations. However, they also grow well in drier areas as long as irrigation is provided. *I. pseudacorus* has grown well in my garden, tucked away in a corner (as well as one can tuck a plant of this size), through two major droughts. When grown under less than ideal conditions, plants are shorter and less vigorous. This is not usually a problem as plants grown in streams and ponds are often too big for most gardens.

The 2–3′ long leaves are sword-shaped, bright green and rather coarse. The 2″ wide yellow flowers are not particularly large but often have brown veins with a brown blotch on the falls. The fruit capsules of all varieties are large and sought after for dried arrangements. I grow this species through plants of *Sedum* × 'Autumn Joy'. The sedum grows around the foliage throughout the summer and the sword-like leaves of the iris provide additional architectural interest.

Propagate by division of the rhizome every 2–4 years or raise from seeds. Seed propagated plants are variable and take two years to flower.

Cultivars:

var. *bastardii* bears pale primrose flowers without the markings on the falls.

var. *variegatus* has yellow stripes on the leaves and is the finest of all the water irises for foliage effect. The flowers are lost in the variegated effect but the leaves are so outstanding that the flowers are not missed.

Related Species:

I. versicolor, blueflag iris, native to North America, is similar to *I. pseudacorus* in size, habit, and tolerance to moisture. This is the common blue flag iris found in moist soils from eastern Canada to Pennsylvania. The flowers occur in shades of reddish or blueish purple. It is adaptable to most climates but not common in the trade.

-reticulata (re-tik-ew′ lah-ta)		Reticulated Iris	4–6″/4″
Winter, Early Spring	Violet	Turkey	Zones 5–9

The little bulbs emerge in the spring or even in late winter. In my garden in north Georgia, flowers appear by February 15 and are finished by the fourth of March. Few plants surpass the richness of the purple and gold flowers which also possess the delightful fragrance of violets. Bulbs have netted veins similar to *I. danfordiae* and should be planted 2–3″ deep. The pointed leaves are acutely four-angled and 3–6″ tall at flowering time, then elongate to 12–18″ tall after the flowers have finished. Because of their diminutive size at flowering time, bulbs must be planted in large numbers to make any kind of show. Leaves disappear by late spring or early summer and annuals may be used to fill in the gaps. All species in the reticulated iris group require dry summers for the bulbs to ripen and set buds for the next year. In areas with heavy summer rains, plantings decline in the first three years but those that adapt continue to flower in

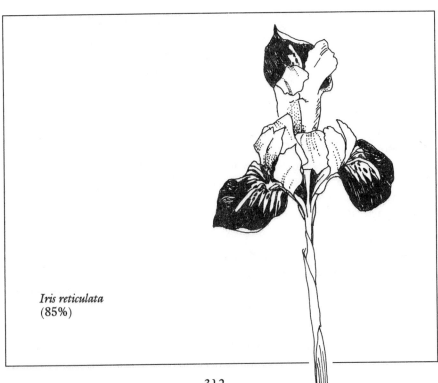

Iris reticulata
(85%)

312

larger clumps each year. Many of my original bulbs had disappeared but those remaining are magnificent and produce six to seven flowers on each clump.

The offsets may be divided immediately after flowering.

Cultivars:

'Cantab' has pale blue flowers and shows up well in the spring.

'Harmony' has royal blue flowers with a yellow and white blotch on the falls. The flowers do not show up well against dried leaf mulch, a common mulch in the Southeast.

'Joyce' has handsome sky blue blossoms.

'J.S. Dyt' has purplish red flcwers.

Related Species:

I. histrio, Syrian iris, is distinctly bluer than *I. reticulata* with a hint of red in its makeup.

I. histrioides, harput iris, is larger (6–9″) and flowers 1–2 weeks later than *I. histrio*. Both have a creamy white area on the falls, flower earlier and produce many more smaller offsets than *I. reticulata*.

-sibirica (si-bi′ ri-ka)	Siberian Iris	24–36″/24″
Spring Blue	Central Europe, Russia	Zones 3–9

Native to moist meadows, Siberian iris does well in a moist or bog garden. However, they perform admirably in normal garden situations as long as moisture can be provided throughout the season. They are smaller than when grown in their favorite bog. Dwarfing due to lack of water also occurs with *I. sanguinea*, an unexciting blue-flowered species, *I. pseudacorus* and *I. versicolor*.

Siberian iris has 2–5 blue-purple flowers per stem, but may occasionally be lavender or white. The 1–2″ wide flowers are held well above the narrow lance-like foliage. Many cultivars are available, including vigorous tetraploids (twice as many chromosomes as usual), which make the species pale in comparison. One of my favorite plantings, however, is the 6 to 8 plants of the species which line a sunny path in my garden. The many flowers (each plant produces 12–20 flowers) unfurl in mid-May and provide that certain touch of class that is the hallmark of the Siberian iris. I prefer them to tall bearded types not only because of their smaller, more delicate flowers, but because they are less prone to soft rot and iris borer.

Unlike the bearded iris, they should not be disturbed until the clump is obviously producing fewer flowers than normal. Use two spading forks to divide and do not allow the divisions to dry. They resent being disturbed and may take a year or more to look their best.

Cultivars:

Many fine cultivars of Siberian iris are available and I must give way to those ubiquitous iris catalogs for a proper overview of available colors and range of

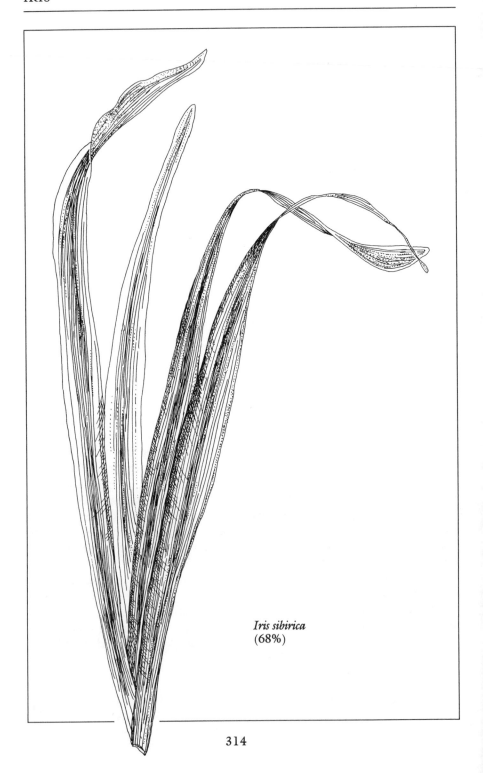

Iris sibirica
(68%)

vigor. Busse Gardens of Cokato, MN. for example, lists over 200 cultivars. However, here are a few I think are outstanding.

'Blue Brilliant' has proven well adapted to many locales and bears clear blue standards and lighter blue falls. It flowers on 2–3′ tall stems.
'Caesar's Brother' is about 3′ tall with dark velvety violet-blue flowers.
'Fourfold White' has clear white flowers with yellow at the base of the falls. This tetraploid is particularly vigorous.
'Mildred Peck' has lovely lavender-pink flowers borne on 3′ tall stems.
'Perry's Blue' has handsome sky blue flowers.
'Persimmon' is 3′ tall with rich blue flowers.
'Tycoon' has large violet-blue flowers with long drooping falls.
'White Swirl' produces clear white flowers which carry a touch of yellow. A superb cultivar.

Related Species:
I. chrysographes, goldvein iris, has dark maroon flowers with gold markings on the falls. An outstanding but little-known species. Consistently moist soil is required.

I. orientalis is native to Japan and similar to *I. sibirica*. It has larger but fewer flowers which barely extend above the foliage. Plants are not as decorative as *I. sibirica*. 'Snow Queen' (often offered under *I. sibirica*) is about 2½′ tall with milky white flowers.

-tectorum (tek-tor′ um)		Roof Iris	12–18″/18″
Summer	Lilac	China, Japan	Zones 4–9

Because of the interesting shape of the flowers, the evergreen foliage and the increased availability, this species is gaining popularity every year. Its specific name, *tectorum*, means "growing on roofs" from the custom of being grown on the edges of thatched roofs in Japan. The powdered roots were also used by ladies in China for whitening skin.

The large 6″ wide lilac flowers are mottled with dark blue to black blotches. Plants belong to the crested iris group (as does *I. cristata*), because of the conspicuous whitish brown jagged crest (rather than a beard) on the flowers. The standards lie almost level with the falls, resulting in an open, wide flower. Each flower stem usually bears two flowers and the evergreen leaves are 3–4″ wide, yellow-green and somewhat floppy.

Partial shade is tolerated but roof iris prefers full sun and well-drained soils. A number of reports on culture, particularly from England, suggest that plants are heavy feeders and must be moved from site to site every other year. The reports state that without heavy fertilization, the plant quickly depletes the soil and flowering is sparse. I have not found this to be true in the United States. Plants should be fed 1–2 tablespoons of a complete fertilizer such as 8-8-8

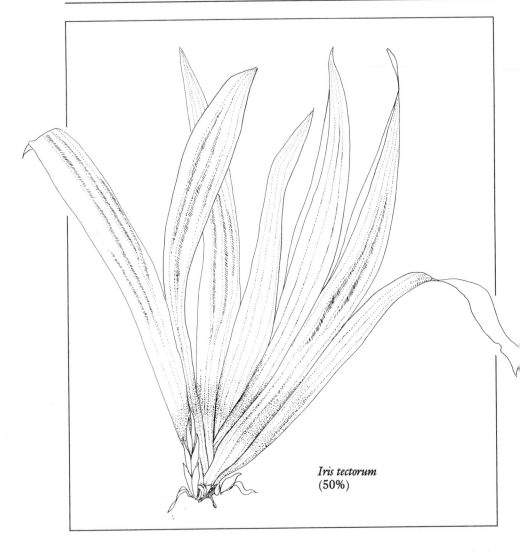

Iris tectorum
(50%)

around the base of the plant (take care not to allow the granules to touch the leaves or the crown) in the spring.

Cultivars:

var. *alba* is harder to find and more expensive but is no longer rare. The flowers are white with a yellow crest on the falls.

'Variegata' has lavender-blue flowers and variegated foliage.

Propagate by division of the rhizomes immediately after flowering, just as the last flower has faded. Plants can be moved at any time of year, providing they are irrigated well.

Related Species:

I. gracilipes, slender iris, is another graceful species of the Crested Iris group. It is shade tolerant, 8–10″ tall, and bears beautiful lilac-pink flowers with an orange crest over narrow, arching foliage.

-verna (ver′ na)		Vernal Iris	4–6″/12″
Spring	Blue	Eastern United States	Zones 6–10

This dwarf native plant has a creeping rootstock similar to *I. cristata*. The 1½″ long flowers are dark blue with a large orange blotch on the falls. They are similar in habit to the dwarf bearded irises, but much smaller. This species is taxonomically very close to the bearded irises and some people refer to the flower as semi-bearded. Upon inspection, the pubescence on the falls is noticeable. The shortened stems are no longer than six inches long. The narrow foliage is approximately 6″ long during flowering but elongates to 9–12″ after flowering.

Plants prefer shady, dry areas but do not do particularly well in woodland settings. They are most at home in a raised bed where good drainage can be provided.

Propagate by division of the rhizome after flowering.

'Xiphium hybrids' (zi′ fee-um)		English, Spanish, Dutch Iris	12–18″/12″
Spring	Various	Southern Europe, Northern Africa	Zones 6–9

English (*I. xiphioides*), Spanish (*I. xiphium*) and hybrid Dutch iris are bulbous plants belonging to the subgenus *Xiphium*. In American gardens, the Dutch iris are the most popular of the group. They are more tolerant of inclement weather than the others and are widely available in many colors. All irises from this group now offered by bulb houses, however, are hybrids.

The English irises are the last of the group to flower and do so in June-July. They are predominantly *I. xiphioides* but other species have undoubtedly played a role in their development. Growing 1–2′ tall, they have the largest flowers (5″ across) of the group. Although no yellow flowers are available, white, blue, pink, or purple occur and all have a gold blotch on the falls. They are native to the French and Spanish Pyrenees but are called English iris because they reached the Low Countries from England, most probably without notice of their true habitat. They grow well in English gardens but are difficult in America because of the requirement for constantly moist soil. Copious amounts of water and rich soils are necessary.

Spanish iris is smaller in all respects than the English iris. It is a hybrid of *I. xiphium*, *I. tangitana*, and others. Plants are 12–18″ tall with 3–4″ diameter flowers in a wide range of colors. Bright sunshine and warm, dry exposures are preferred.

The Dutch iris was produced by the Tubergen Nurseries in Haarlem, Holland and is best described as a large and earlier-flowering strain of Spanish iris.

They are the first to flower, starting in mid-May and continuing through June. The foliage appears in the winter and although the leaves may be killed back by frosts, little damage to the flower bud occurs (unless the petal color is visible at time of frost). They are hardier than the others and may be overwintered to zone 6. Plants are 15–24″ in height and flowers are 4–5″ in diameter. They are particularly popular as cut flowers and may be forced in greenhouses year round. When planted in groups of a dozen or so, they make lovely garden plants requiring little room, and can be enjoyed inside and out. There are dozens of cultivars in a varied range of colors from bright yellow to the darkest blue.

In general, bulbs should be planted about 6″ deep and once planted, need not be disturbed. However, all species and hybrids in the *Xiphium* group can be split into bulblets after the foliage has died down. Many naturally split into two large bulbs as well as many smaller offsets. The large bulbs may be replanted and will flower the following year, the smaller ones should be set aside and allowed to mature in a propagation bed until large enough to flower.

Related Species:
I. bucharica, Bokhara iris, bears creamy standards and yellow falls on 12–18″ tall stems in April. Leaves are 8–12″ long, 2″ wide, glossy above and whitish underneath. Foliage disappears by midsummer.

Quick Key to Iris Species
- A. Rootstock bulbous
  - B. Standards minute, spreading, flowers yellow, stemless .... *I. danfordiae*
  - BB. Standards conspicuous, erect, flowers variously colored, may be stemless
    - C. Plants stemless or nearly so, less than 1′ tall, flowers purple, leaves 4-sided .... *I. reticulata*
    - CC. Plants with stems more than 1′ tall, flowers variously colored, leaves linear and furrowed........... *I.* 'Xiphium hybrids'
- AA. Rootstock a rhizome
  - B. Falls with a crest or beard
    - C. Falls with fringed crest on lower part of fall
      - D. Stem none or very short, leaves less than 6″ long, sword-shaped........................... *I. cristata*
      - DD. Stem 1–2′ long, leaves more than 1′ long, arching, broad........ *I. tectorum*
    - CC. Falls with colored hairs (beard) along midrib
      - D. Height 2–3′, flowers violet, bracts surrounding buds quite dry when flowers open, silvery-white, leaves blue-green .... *I. pallida*
      - DD. Height 8–36″, flowers variously colored, bracts

surrounding bud often flushed purple, usually dry
when flowers open, leaves green to gray-green ....

I. 'Bearded hybrids'

BB. Falls without conspicuous crest or beard
   C. Plants more than 1' tall
      D. Leaves linear, usually less than ½" wide .... *I. sibirica*
    DD. Leaves sword-like, usually more than ½" wide
        E. Flowers yellow............................... *I. pseudacorus*
      EE. Flowers not yellow
          F. Flowers not showy, foliage emitting
            disagreeable odor when crushed, seeds scarlet
            and persistent in capsule .... *I. foetidissima*
         FF. Flowers large and showy, foliage odor not
            disagreeable, seeds not scarlet or persistent.... *I. kaempferi*
  CC. Plants less than 1' tall .... *I. verna*

Additional Reading:

The scope of this book does not lend itself to a thorough enough discussion for the serious iris enthusiast. Some of the better publications include:

Books:

American Iris Society. 1978. *The World of Irises*. B. Warburton (ed.).

Caillet, M. and J. K. Mertzweiller. 1988. *The Louisiana Iris: the history and culture of five native American species and their hybrids*. Texas Gardener Press, Waco, TX. An excellent treatise on the past, present and future of Louisiana Iris. Excellent color plates bring many of today's cultivars to life.

Cassidy, G. E. and S. Linnegar. 1982. *Growing Irises*. Timber Press, Portland, OR., 160 p.

Dykes, W. R. 1912. *Irises*. Present Day Gardening Series (out of print). 110 p.

Dykes, W. R. 1913. *The Genus Iris*. Dover Books (1975, reduced facsimile from 1913 publication).

Manuscripts:

Hoog, M.H. 1980. Bulbous irises. *The Plantsman* 2(3):141–164.

Hudak, Joseph. 1976. The iris of May. *Horticulture* 54(5):37–39.

Ingram, John and William J. Dress. 1968. The Louisiana irises and Hortus Third. *Baileya* 16(2):92–97.

Lloyd, Christopher. 1986. A pride of Iris. *Horticulture* 64(12):21–25.

Weiler, John. 1986. The saga of remontant SDB. *The Garden* 111(10):475–477.

White, Ann Blanco. 1984. Trial of *Iris spuria* cutivars. 1984. *The Garden* 109(12):519–521.

Associations:

Society for Siberian Irises, 631 G24 Highway, Norwalk, IA, 50211.

The American Iris Society, 6518 Beachy Ave, Wichita, KS, 67206.
Publication: *Bulletin of the American Iris Society.*

Ixia (iks-ee′ a)   Corn-lily   Iridaceae

The corn-lilies are native to South Africa and rather uncommon in American gardens. Flowers arise from corms planted 2–3″ deep after the last frost. They are winter hardy from zone 8 south but, with winter protection, may survive in zone 7. Soils with a basic pH are preferable and lime should be incorporated in acid soils prior to planting.

Corms offered in catalogs are hybrids developed by Dutch nurserymen. The plants have 8–12″ high wiry stems and narrow, grass-like leaves. The cup-shaped flowers are composed of six brightly colored segments, and a spike of 9–12 blooms is produced from each corm. The colors range from white with a blue, red, or purple center to yellow and red forms usually with an eye of a different color.

Corms are inexpensive and the resulting flowers are gorgeous. They are worth trying, even as annuals, to add brightness to the late spring and early summer garden. Alternatively, they may be treated as gladioli and removed in fall, stored in a cool place and replanted in the spring. At this time, the small cormels may be removed.

Cultivars:

'Afterglow' has orange flowers.
'Bridesmaid' bears white flowers with a red eye.
'Wonder' produces pink double flowers.

Related Species:

I. maculata has yellow flowers with black spots on the throat.

I. paniculata bears 6–12 large (1–1½″ wide) creamy white to yellow flowers.

I. viridiflora, green ixia, is one of the more interesting species. Plants have 1–2″ wide flowers consisting of extraordinary blue-green petals with a purple-black eye.

Ixiolirion (iks-io-lir′ ee-on)   Siberian Lily   Amaryllidaceae

Three species of bulbous plants occur and only *I. tataricum* is generally available.

| *-tataricum* (tar-tar' i-kum) | | Siberian Lily | 12–20"/18" |
| Spring | Blue | Central Asia | Zones 7–9 |

(Syn. *I. montanum*)

The 3–8 linear leaves give rise to a spreading inflorescence (umbel) of 4–6 sky blue, lily-like blossoms on slender rounded stems. The flowers bear segments with 3–5 dark lilac ribs. They should be lifted (like gladioli) when planted north of zone 7. In the South, winter drainage is most important because bulbs rot if soil does not drain rapidly.

Similar to other half-hardy minor bulbs, *Ixiolirion* is inexpensive and can be used even as an annual. Many of the minor bulbs are hidden treasures which will be discovered only with a little plant exploration of our own.

K

Kirengeshoma (ki-reng-ge-show' ma)   Yellow Waxbells   Saxifragaceae

A monotypic genus, *K. palmata* has recently been introduced to gardeners in America. Reports on garden performance have been mixed, but as additional plant material becomes available, it will likely enjoy greater popularity.

-palmata (pahl-may' ta)   Yellow Waxbells   3–4'/4'
Summer   Yellow   Japan   Zone 5–8

The opposite, 7 to 10-palmately lobed foliage is hairy and toothed around the margins and is possibly the best part of this plant. The basal leaves are 6–7" wide while those near the top are smaller and sessile. The leaves are carried on thinly branched stems, the tops of which often have a purplish cast when sunlight falls upon them. The 1½" long, waxy, bell-shaped flowers may be found nodding from the axils of the topmost leaves in late summer and fall. Unfortunately, individual flowers start to turn brown at the edges in a matter of days. There are usually three flowers in each inflorescence (cyme) and the weight of the flowers and subsequent fruit causes stems to bow to the ground. Waxbells produce the "Stephen King" of fruit. Three long pointed horns protrude from a brownish green swollen capsule; the effect is enough to cause a nightmare!

Plants are cold hardy to zone 5 but have not been grown enough in the South to determine heat tolerance. I have tried it in my garden and it quickly surrendered to the elements. Native to cool woodland areas, good performance is questionable south of zone 7. Great care must be taken in choosing a site. One in semi-shade, sheltered from strong winds, in a constantly moist but not boggy area, with an abundant source of organic matter and an absence of lime should be chosen.

Kirengeshoma has been called a "rarity for the connoisseur". This is a plant for those interested in experimentation, and with a willingness to fail several times before being successful. An unusual plant from its bowed gracefulness to its horned fruit, it adds a touch of grace to the shade garden.

Propagate by division after 3–5 years only if necessary. Allow it to remain undisturbed for as long as possible.

Additional Reading:

Chatto, Beth. 1986. Kirengeshoma. *Horticulture* 64(9):34–35.

Kniphofia (nee-fof′ ee-a)   Red Hot Poker, Torchlily   Liliaceae

(Syn. *Tritoma*)

The 60–70 species are characterized by basal tufts of long, coarse, sword-like leaves and spike-like inflorescences of bright, shortly stalked flowers. Although best known for orange-red flowers, species and cultivars occur with green, coral, yellow, red, scarlet, and bicolor blooms. Torchlilies may be as small as 18″ (*K. macowanii*, Macowan torchlily), to the 8′ tall giant hybrids. Many of the plants in today's gardens are *K. uvaria*, common torchlily, whose red flowers become yellowish green as they mature. Flowers on the upper half of the spike are still opening and bright red, while the lower ones are finished and yellow green. The spike is often described as two-tone. Many cultivars have been raised from seed, resulting in a much variation. New Zealand is one of the finest areas in the world to see torch lilies. There, the bold magnificent deep orange spires of *K. praecox* dominate roadsides and gardens in June and July.

-uvaria (oo-vah′ ree-a)   Common Torchlily   3–5′/4′
Late Spring   Red   South Africa   Zones 5–9

The gray-green evergreen foliage is 18–36″ long and sharply pointed. After the flowers senesce, the leaves decline and plants are an eyesore. Cut the foliage about halfway back to improve appearance without injury. The flower stems should also be removed after flowering. In the Horticulture Gardens at the University of Georgia, 20 flower stems, which emerge from our original clump of 3 seed propagated plants, dominate the late spring garden. Flowers open as early as May 10 in the garden, but late May and early June are more common in zone 8. Plants require full sun, and do not tolerate wet feet. In zones 4 and 5, the foliage can be tied over the crown of the plant in the fall to exclude water, which may subsequently freeze and kill the plant.

Cultivars:

Although few other species are offered, a number of fine hybrids are presently available to extend the choice of flowering season, height, and color. The parentage is confused but *K. uvaria*, *K. galpinii*, *K. praecox* and *K. macowanii* appear to have taken some liberties with each other. Most flower in late spring and early summer.

'Maid of Orleans' has ivory flowers on 2' tall stems. Against a dark background, it stands out without being as garish as are some of the screaming scarlet-flowered forms.

'Primrose Beauty' grows 3' tall with primrose-yellow flowers.

'Rosea Superba' has rose-red flowers on 2½–3' tall plants.

'Royal Castle' grows 2–3' tall with vibrant yellow-orange flowers.

'Royal Standard' bears scarlet buds which open to bright yellow flowers.

'Springtime' has upper flowers of coral red tipped yellow and muted yellow basal flowers. 'Royal Standard' and 'Springtime' are 3–4' tall.

'Underway' produces apricot-orange flowers in midsummer.

'Wayside Flame' has flaming orange-red flowers in late summer and fall.

Seed of *K. uvaria* should be placed at 40°F for at about 6 weeks. Germination will be erratic but seedlings should begin to emerge within 3 weeks. Keep soil moist and out of direct sunlight. Retain the seed tray for 3 months before discarding. Plants flower the second year. Cultivars and hybrids may also be divided in the fall.

Additional Reading:

Taylor, Jane. 1985. *Kniphofia*, a survey. *The Plantsman* 7(3):129–160.

L

Lamiastrum (lay-mee′ ay-strum)   Yellow Archangel   Lamiaceae

The genus consists of a single species, *L. galeobdolon*. It is often included in *Lamium*, but differs by having yellow flowers whose lower lips bear side lobes slightly shorter than the middle lobe. It is a good ground cover for shady areas.

-galeobdolon (ga-lee-ob′ do-lon)   Yellow Archangel   9–15″/18″
Spring   Yellow   Europe, Western Asia   Zones 4–9

(Syn. *Lamium galeobdolon*)

Plants spread by short underground stolons and are best used where allowed to roam freely as they are difficult to keep under control. The 1–3″ long leaves are oval, slender-pointed and serrated. During late spring, spikes with whorls of 5–6 yellow flowers, each about ¾″ long, arise from the leaf axils. Heavy to partial shade is best in the southern end of its range but some direct sun is tolerated further north. Plants are useful for filling in heavily shaded areas where little else grows. If plants become too leggy, cut back to 6–8″.

Cultivars:

var. *compacta* is much more compact than the species, does not grow as rapidly, and is useful for small areas.

'Herman's Pride' has smaller flowers, is less aggressive than the species and the silver markings on the foliage are more striking.

'Variegata' is the most common form with silver variegation running through the leaf blade while the midrib and margins remain green. 'Variegata' and Herman's Pride' are more handsome than the species and should be used whenever possible.

Propagate by divisions or terminal cuttings.

325

Lamium (lay-mee′ um)   Dead Nettle   Lamiaceae

Most of the approximately 40 species are considered weeds. Related to stinging nettle, *Urtica dioica*, but lacking the stinging hairs, they are known as dead nettles. The only species used to any extent is *L. maculatum*, an excellent ground cover for semi-shaded locations.

-maculatum (mak-ew-lah′ tum)   Spotted Nettle   8–12″/18″
Spring   Red to Purple   Europe, West Asia   Zones 3–8

The oppositely arranged, 1–2″ long leaves usually have white stripes or blotches beside the midrib. The purplish red flowers bloom at the end of the

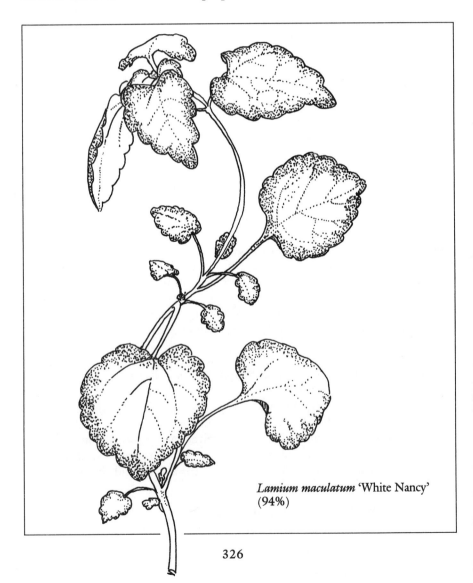

Lamium maculatum 'White Nancy' (94%)

326

the stem all summer and are partially lost in the leaves. Although some cultivars grow well as far south as zone 9, the species performs best in areas of cooler nights which keep growth more compact. In the summer in zones 7 to 9, plants become straggly and must be cut back to maintain some semblance of order. Provide an evenly moist, well-drained soil in partial shade. If plants repeatedly dry out, bare patches appear.

Cultivars:

The species is seldom used in the United States, having been replaced by a number of selections with superior foliage.

var. *aureum* has the same white midvein area as the species but the rest of the leaf is a soft yellow. It is not as aggressive and will not do well in full sun, particularly in zones 7 or south.

'Beacon Silver', one of the most popular cultivars, has silver leaves surrounded by green margins. The foliage stands out well and catches the eye even in a shaded area. Performance has been excellent in zone 8.

'Chequers' has silver variegated leaves and amethyst-violet flowers. It is similar to 'Beacon Silver' with broader green margins. Plants are 9–12″ tall when in flower.

'White Nancy' is 6–8″ tall and fills in rapidly. It has often been described as a white-flowering 'Beacon Silver'. The additional white of the flowers in the spring is particularly appealing. The evergreen foliage remains fresh all year in my garden and has proven to be one of the best ground covers I have tested.

Lamium is easily propagated by division at any time of year as long as adequate moisture is provided to the plantlets. Cuttings may be rooted at any time during the season.

Lathyrus (lath' i-rus)   Sweet Pea   Fabaceae

The sweet pea is best known as a vigorous climbing vine whose tendrils provide support, allowing plants to grow 10′ tall. The common sweet pea, *L. odoratus*, is an annual but a number of perennial species occur. *L. grandiflorus*, two-flowered sweet pea, has spectacular 1½″ long rose-red flowers and *L. latifolius*, everlasting sweet pea, bears flowers in many colors. Most members are climbing species but a few non-viney members are available. One of these bears the wretched name of spring vetchling, *L. vernus*.

-vernus (ver′ nus)		Spring Vetchling	9–12″/18″
Spring	Red to violet	Europe	Zones 4–7

Two to three pairs of 1½–3″ long light green leaflets are produced on sparsely branched stems. In early spring, 5–8, ¾″ long, reddish violet flowers are borne on short axillary racemes. The racemes are shorter than the leaves and may be lost in the foliage without a thorough search. Plants are deep rooted and thus able to tolerate drought. It is not a rapid spreader and the foliage dies down after flowering.

Although cold tolerant to zone 4, plants have not performed well in zone 8. In partial shade, plants did little more than survive and, in full sun, death was swift.

Cultivars:

var. *albiflorus* has creamy white flowers.
var. *cyanus* bears light blue flowers.
var. *roseus* produces pink blossoms.

Carefully divide the rootstock about two weeks after flowering. Use a sharp knife and allow at least one eye to remain on each piece of separated root. Seeds should be soaked in warm water overnight prior to sowing. Transplant when seedlings reach the 3–5 leaf stage. If sown in the spring, flowering occurs one year later.

Related Species;

 L. luteus var. *aureus*, golden yellow vetchling, grows 18″ tall and bears light green leaves topped with erect heads of fawn or yellowish brown flowers. It was absolutely stunning in Edinburgh Botanic Garden. The quality of the foliage declines later in the season in all but the coolest areas of the United States.

| *Lavandula* (lav-an′ dew-lah) | Lavender | Lamiaceae |

Lavender is an indispensible herb and a surprisingly useful ornamental plant. All parts of common lavender, *L. angustifolia*, are fragrant and provide oils for the perfume industry. Lavender was recognized as a useful herb by Gerard who explained that flowers when "mixed with Cinnamon, Nutmegs, and Cloves, made into pouder, and given to drinke in the distilled water thereof, doth helpe the panting and passion of the heart, prevaileth against giddinesse, turning, or swimming of the braine, amd members subject to the palsie." (Gerard's Herbal). Lavender farms still operate in England, France, and New Zealand for perfumes and potpourri.

| *-angustifolia* (an-gust-i-fo′ lee-a) | Common Lavender | 2–3′/3′ |
| Summer | Blue | Mediterranean Region | Zones 5–9 |

(Syn. *L. spica*, *L. officinalis*)

 Two and one-half inch long, ¼″ wide opposite gray-green evergreen leaves occur on square stems. The 3–4″ long terminal flower spikes consist of 6–8 whorls of lavender flowers subtended by gray-green bracts. The fragrant flowers are often dried and used in potpourri. The plants are pretty enough to be included in the mainstream garden and need not be shunted off to languish in obscurity, admired only when flowers are to be sacrificed. They are superb for edgings, and the gray-green foliage calms even the harshest leaf and flower colors.

Plants require full sun and well-drained soil. Pruning to 6–8″ in the spring results in vigorous new growth. For drying, pick flowers when showing color but before fully open. Hang them in a cool, dry spot.

Cultivars:

Selections have been based on improvements in flower color and habit. Some may be selections of lavandin, *L.* × *intermedia*, a hybrid between *L. angustifolia* and *L. latifolia*.

'Hidcote' grows about 18″ tall and has deep purple flowers.
'Jean Davis' has pinkish white flowers, blue-green foliage and is 10–15″ tall.
   Cultivars sold as 'Hidcote Pink', 'Loddon Pink' and 'Rosea' are essentially identical.
'Munstead Dwarf', which bears early lavender flowers, grows only 12″ tall.

Related Species:

L. latifolia, spike lavender, is similar to common lavender but has silver green foliage. Plants are fuller, grow 1–1½′ tall and are cold hardy to zone 6.

L. stoechas, French lavender, has purple flowers crowned with a cluster of ¾–1″ long, petal-like veined bracts. The bracts are the chief attraction of this unique flower. Plants are cold hardy to zone 6.

Propagate by taking 3–4″ long cuttings of non-flowering shoots in the fall. Roots will appear in 14 days if placed in sand and misted. Remove cuttings from mist as soon as roots appear. Seed sown and placed in 70–75°F and humid conditions will germinate rapidly, although erratically. More uniformity will result by cooling the seed flat at 40°F for 2–4 weeks prior to placing in warm temperatures.

Additional Reading:

De Wolf, Gordon P. 1955. Notes on cultivated Labiates. 5. Lavandula. *Baileya* 3:47–57.

Tucker, Arthur O. 1981. The correct name of lavandin and its cultivars (Labiatae). *Baileya* 21:131–133.

Tucker, Arthur O. and Karel J.W. Hensen. 1985. The cultivars of lavender and lavandin (Labiatae). *Baileya* 22:168–177.

Leucojum (lew-ko′ jum)   Snowflake   Amaryllidaceae

The snowflakes consist of 9–10 low-growing bulbous species with nodding white flowers. They are divided into two distinct groups based on the appearance of the leaves. The hardy, robust and larger-flowered species have shiny

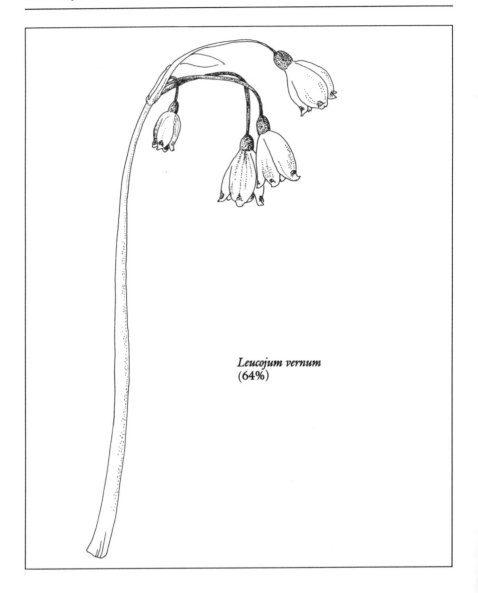

Leucojum vernum
(64%)

strap-like leaves and include the popular spring and summer snowflakes, *L. vernum* and *L. aestivum*, respectively. The second group was a separate genus, *Acis*, but now shares the same roof. This group has thread-like leaves and is more difficult to establish. The only thread-leaf species cultivated to any extent is the autumn snowflake, *L. autumnale*.

The flowers of all species consist of 6 segments; 3 outer and 3 inner of approximately equal size. They are white and tipped with green, yellow, or a tinge of red. Bulbs should be planted in the fall in large drifts, 3–5″ deep. Flowering begins the next spring, immediately after the snowdrops (*Galanthus*) and continues into early summer.

Leucojum is often confused with *Galanthus* but a number of recognizable differences separate the genera.

	Leucojum	*Galanthus*
Flower stalk	hollow	solid
Number of leaves	numerous	2–3
Number of flowers	2–5	1
Flower segments	2 equal groups	2 unequal groups

Leucojum are better plants for the South than *Galanthus*. They tolerate partial shade but prefer a sunny location with adequate moisture. The bulbs should be left undisturbed for at least three years while they slowly increase. They can be moved when overcrowded.

Plants propagated from seed take 3–4 years to attain flowering size. The bulbs are inexpensive enough that seed propagation can be left to the breeders.

Quick Reference to Leucojum Species

	Number of flowers per flower stem	Flowering time
L. aestivum	2–8	Mid Spring
L. autumnale	1–3	Late Summer
L. vernum	1–2	Early Spring

-aestivum (ies' ti-vum)		Summer Snowflake	12–18"/10"
Mid Spring	White	Central, Southern Europe	Zones 4–9

The name summer snowflake is a misnomer, for the species flowers only several weeks after *L. vernum*, spring snowflake. Three to five flowers usually occur on the hollow scape, each about 1" across, bell shaped and drooping. The pure white segments are tipped inside and out with jade green. The dark green leaves are about ½" wide and 1–1½' long.

Cultivars:

'Gravetye Giant' is a large-flowered cultivar useful when planting only a few bulbs in a small corner. It produces 1–1½" long flowers on taller stems and is worth the extra expense.

var. *pulchellum* blooms earlier and has smaller flowers than the species, but otherwise is almost identical.

-autumnale (ow-tum-nah' lee)		Autumn Snowflake	4–6"/6"
Late Summer	White	Southern Europe, Mediterranean	Zones 5–9

Autumn snowflake does not have a large following because it is not as easily established as other species, not as easily found in garden catalogs and more expensive. On the other hand, the flowers, described as "delicately flushed lilies-of-the-valley", open when small bulbs are most welcome. Other characteristics separate the species from the common snowflakes. The nodding ½–¾" long flowers are tinged with red and open in late summer in the South or early fall in the North. The thread-like leaves appear after the flowers and remain green until early summer, and bulbs may then be divided and moved. Bulbs are planted in the spring or early summer and are not usually available for fall planting.

Some gardeners throw their hands up in frustration trying to establish this bulb while others would not have a garden without it. Plants are native to dry, sandy soils and require excellent drainage. Size precludes it from areas other than the rock garden or small containers where it can be enjoyed on the patio or deck.

Related Species:

L. nicaeense (Syn. *L. hiemale*), Mentone snowflake, named after the town in France to which it is native, has drooping rosy white bells appearing in April in the South. They are not hardy north of zone 7, and even there require protection.

L. roseum is 4–6" tall and bears rose-colored flowers in the fall. The above two species are in the "I love a challenge" class. I am confident there are many gardeners who welcome such plants.

-vernum (ver' num)		Spring Snowflake	10–12"/10"
Early Spring	White	Central Europe	Zones 3–9

This most accommodating snowflake seems to thrive in virtually all conditions. It overlaps the flowering time of snowdrops (*Galanthus*) in the South and flowers about two weeks later in the North. The plant is not as tall but the leaves are a little broader (up to ¾" wide) than those of the summer snowflake. The flowers are white, drooping, and usually borne one to two per flower stalk. The white segments are tipped with green similar to *L. aestivum*.

Unfortunately in the past, there have been a number of instances where plants ordered as *L. vernum* turned out to be *L. aestivum*. There seems to be enough stock of both species and there need be no problem when dealing with an established bulb supplier.

Cultivars:

var. *carpathicum* usually bears two flowers per stem. Each flower is tipped with yellow rather than green.

Quick Key to Leucojum Species

    A. Leaves strap-like, flower in spring
        B. Flowers 2–8 (usually 2–5), open late spring, tipped green . . . .
                                     L. aestivum

BB. Flowers 1–2, bloom early spring, tipped green or yellow
    C. Flowers tipped green .... *L. vernum*
    CC. Flowers tipped yellow................... *L. vernum* var. *carpathicum*
AA. Leaves thread-like, flower in late summer or fall............ *L. autumnale*

Liatris (lie' a-tris)   Gayfeather, Blazing Star   Asteraceae

Liatris sends up tall stems, at the end of which is an inflorescence of 15–45 oblong, usually purple flowers. Although belonging to the daisy family, the flowers consist of disc flowers only, and are very undaisy-like. Flowers provide architectural as well as botanical interest. They are one of the few cultivated flowers with the unusual habit of opening from the top of the inflorescence to the base (basipetally). The straight, strong stems carry narrow, entire, alternate foliage.

Liatris has experienced a meteoric rise as a cut flower in recent years. Few florists do not include gayfeather in bouquets and arrangements today, yet five years ago, this was not the case. Dutch flower exporters included it in the "Dutch Mix" sent to American florists and liatris soon became popular as a "Dutch" flower. The irony is that *Liatris* is native to North America, in fact, is

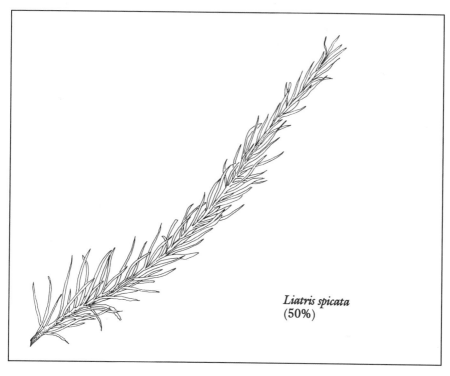

Liatris spicata
(50%)

a wild flower in much of this country! Growers in the United States are now paying more attention to this plant as a viable crop for cut flower production.

Tuberous roots should be planted 4–6" deep in well-drained soil in full sun. Plants associate well with *Rudbeckia*, *Monarda*, and *Echinacea*. All species are easily raised from seed and flower the following year. The tuberous roots may be lifted, cut with a sharp knife allowing at least one eye to remain, and replanted. Dust the cut ends with a fungicidal powder.

Quick Reference to Liatris Species

	Height (ft)	Color
L. pycnostachya	3–5	Mauve
L. spicata	2–3	Mauve

-pycnostachya (pik-no-stak' ee-a)	Kansas Gayfeather	3–5'/2'
Summer Mauve	Wisconsin to Louisiana and Texas	Zones 3–9

Largest of the cultivated species, this is the least useful for the garden. The 10–15" long lower leaves are lance-like and about ½" wide and become reduced in size as they ascend the stem. The flower spike is 15–18" long and consists of numerous ½–¾" wide flowers along the length. Leafy bracts, often longer than the individual flowers, are produced under the flowers.

L. pycnostachya is too tall for most gardens and the spikes become so heavy they fall over, resulting in the growing end of the spike twisting upwards. Support is necessary, particularly in the second year. Plants should be treated as biennials, at least in the South. Experiments in Georgia indicate that two years of good performance was the norm, three years if conditions were perfect. Although problems exist, it flowers heavily and 12 flower stems per plant are not uncommon in the second year.

The species is found in moist soils of the Great Plains but does not tolerate wet feet in winter. A well-drained, moisture retentive soil in full sun is necessary for best results.

Cultivars:

var. *alba* has creamy white flowers.

Related Species:

L. aspera, rough gayfeather, grows 4–6' tall and bears 15–40 one inch wide rounded lavender flowers, each spaced well apart. It occurs from North Dakota to Ontario and Ohio in the north to Texas and Florida in the south.

L. scariosa, tall gayfeather, is similar with dense flower spikes but grows only 3' tall. Much of the material sold as *L. scariosa* is probably *L. aspera*. 'September Glory' bears purple flowers which open almost simultaneously. 'White Spire' is similar to 'September Glory' but has white flowers.

Both are better garden plants than *L. pycnostachya*.

1.
Acanthus spinosus

2.
Achillea
× 'Coronation Gold'

COLOR PLATES
page 335

3.
Acidanthera bicolor
'Muralis'

4.
Actaea alba

5.
Agapanthus ×
'Loch Hope'

6.
Alchemilla mollis

7.
Allium aflatunense

8.
Amsonia tabernaemontana

9.
Anaphalis cinnamomea

10.
Anemone coronaria
'Mona Lisa'

COLOR PLATES
page 337

11.
Anemone × *hybrida*
'Max Vogel'

12.
Anthemis tinctoria

13.
Aquilegia canadensis

14.
Artemesia absinthium
'Lambrook Silver'

15.
Arum italicum
'Pictum'

16.
Aruncus dioicus

17.
Asclepias tuberosa

18.
Aster × frikartii

COLOR PLATES
page 339

19.
Aster novae-angliae
'Lyle End Beauty'

20.
Astilbe × arendsii
'Emden'

21.
Baptisia australis

22.
Boltonia asteroides
'Snowbank'

23.
Bergenia cordifolia
'Perfecta'

24.
Campanula portenschlagiana

25.
Centaurea hypoleuca
'John Coutts'

26.
Chrysanthemum coccineum
'Brenda'

COLOR PLATES
page 341

27.
Cimicifuga racemosa

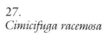

28.
Coreopsis verticillata
'Moonbeam'

29.
Crocosmia ×
'Lucifer'

30.
Cyclamen hederifolium

31.
Dianthus gratianapolitanus
'Bath's Pink'

32.
Dicentra ×
'Luxuriant'

33.
Dictamnus albus
var. *purpureus*

34.
Digitalis purpurea

COLOR PLATES
page 343

35.
Endymion hispanicus

36.
Epimedium × *youngianum*
'Niveum'

37.
Euphorbia epithymoides

38.
Geranium sanguineum

39.
Geranium × magnificum

40.
Geum borisii

41.
Helenium autumnale
'Riverton Beauty'

42.
Helleborus orientalis

COLOR PLATES
page 345

43.
Heuchera × brizoides
'Coral Cloud'

44.
Heuchera micrantha
'Purple Palace'

45.
Hosta × tardiana
'Halcyon' (top)
Hosta fortunei
'Albo-marginata' (bottom)

46.
Hypericum polyphyllum
'Sulphureum'

47.
Incarvillea delavayi

48.
Iris pseudacorus
var. *variegatus*

49.
Iris reticulata
'Harmony'

50.
Kirengeshoma palmata

COLOR PLATES
page 347

51.
Lamiastrum galeobdolon

52.
Lavendula angustifolia
'Hidcote'

53.
Leucojum vernum

54.
Liatris spicata
'Kobold'

55.
Ligularia stenocephala
'The Rocket'

56.
Lilium ×
Mid-Century hybrid

57.
Linum perenne
var. *album*

58.
Lobelia fulgens

COLOR PLATES
page 349

59.
Lupinus ×
'Russell Hybrids'

60.
Lychnis coronaria
'Abbotswood Rose'

61.
Lythrum virgatum
'Morden Pink'

62.
Mertensia virginica

63.
Nepeta gigantea
'Six Hills Giant'

64.
Oenothera tetragona
'Yellow River'

65.
Papaver orientale
'Turkish Delight'

66.
Penstemon ×
'Garnet'

COLOR PLATES
page 351

67.
Perovskia atriplicifolia

68.
Phlomis russelliana

69.
Physostegia virginiana

70.
Platycodon grandiflorus

71.
Polemonium caeruleum

72.
Polygonatum × hybridum

73.
Polygonum bistorta
'Superbum'

74.
Primula × polyantha

COLOR PLATES
page 353

75.
Pulmonaria saccharata
'Margery Fish'

76.
Rheum palmatum

77.
Rodgersia podophylla

78.
Rudbeckia fulgida var.
sullivantii 'Goldstrum'

79.
Ruta graveolens

80.
Sanguinaria canadensis

81.
Saxifraga × *urbium*
'Chambers Pink Pride'

82.
Sedum ×
'Autumn Joy'

COLOR PLATES
page 355

83.
Silene polypetala

84.
Sisyrinchium striatum

85.
Smilacena racemosa

86.
Spigelia marilandica

87.
Stylophorum diphyllum

88.
Thalictrum aquilegifolium
'White Cloud'

89.
Thermopsis caroliniana

90.
Tradescantia × andersoniana
'J.C. Weguelin'

COLOR PLATES
page 357

91.
Trillium grandiflorum

92.
Trollius pumilus

93.
Verbascum olympicum

94.
Verbena canadensis
'Gene Cline'

95.
Veronicastrum virginicum

96.
Zauschneria californica

-spicata (spi-kah' ta)		Spike Gayfeather	2–3'/2'
Summer	Mauve	Maine to Florida and Louisiana	Zone 3–9

(Syn. *L. callilepis*)

This is the best species for the garden, particularly some of the cultivars. The basal leaves are usually 10–12" long and ½" wide, progressively reduced in size up the stem. The inflorescence is 6–15" long and individual flower heads are sessile and mauve.

Plants were trialed in the cut flower program at the University of Georgia. Roots arrived under the name of *L. callilepis*, which most authorities treat as a synonym of *L. spicata*, although some European taxonomists still treat it as a separate species. In the first year, plants were 2' tall and no support was necessary. The flowers were dark purple, and growth and yield were excellent. In the second year, however, plants grew 3–4' tall and required support to maintain straight spikes. Yield and quality of flowers were still excellent. It is a fine cut flower and should be produced by more commercial growers in this country.

Cultivars:

'August Glory' has purple-blue flowers on 3–4' tall plants.

'Floristan White' is 3' tall and bears many creamy flowers. It has performed well and has shown no signs of decline after four years in Georgia tests.

'Kobold' ('Gnome') is one of the finest selections for the garden. Plants are seldom taller than 2½' and multiple spikes of lilac-mauve flowers are produced in early summer.

var. *montana*, native to the mountains of Virginia and North Carolina, is only 10–20" tall and bears ¾" wide flowers on compact spikes. It can be located through wild flower specialists.

Related Species:

L. elegans performs well in dry soils and full sun. Plants are 2–4' tall with 3–6 purplish flowers on 1–2' tall narrow spikes.

L. mucronatum, native to central and south Texas, bears 3–5' tall stems with lilac-mauve flowers. Superb specimens may be seen at the San Antonio Botanical Garden.

Additional Reading:

Dress, William J. 1959. Notes on the cultivated Compositae. 3. *Liatris*. *Baileya* 7:23–32.

Gaiser, L.O. 1946. The genus *Liatris*. *Rhodora* 48:163–183, 216–263, 273–326, 331–362, 393–412.

Libertia (lee-bert' ee-a)	Libertia	Iridaceae

Libertia have short creeping rhizomes (similar to *Iris*), long fibrous roots and evergreen foliage. Unfortunately, it is difficult to locate these plants, perhaps because they are so tender, being cold hardy only to zone 8. Of the eight species, only *L. formosa* is offered.

| *-formosa* (for-mo' sa) | | Showy Libertia | 15–20″/12″ |
| Spring | White | Chile | Zones 8–10 |

The ¾″ long white flowers are held in tapering one foot long inflorescences and remain effective for 3–4 weeks. The flowers are densely clustered, unlike other species whose flowers are loosely arranged. The 6–12″ long sword-like leaves are about ½″ wide and produced in a fan-like arrangement similar to leaves of *Iris*. Plants should be placed in full sun or partial shade in groups of at least a half dozen. I have admired this species in Europe but have not been successful with it in North Georgia. It simply does not tolerate the heat and humidity during the summer, and the lack of summer vigor inhibits subsequent flowering the next spring. Plants are more tolerant of West Coast conditions.

Division of the rhizome is the easiest method of propagation but seed may also be used. Plants require two years to flower from seed.

Related Species:

L. ixioides is native to New Zealand and bears three to eight 1″ wide white flowers often tinged green on the outside. The flowers are less densely arranged and have longer pedicels than *L. formosa*. It is difficult to establish in United States but is probably the loveliest species.

| *Ligularia* (lig-yew-layer' ee-a) | Ligularia | Asteraceae |

These large plants may be 6′ tall in flower and equally broad. Some, such as *L. dentata*, bigleaf ligularia, are grown for their attractive foliage while *L. stenocephala*, narrow spiked ligularia, also has attractive flowers. All species and cultivars must be grown in moist, cool areas. I have seldom seen well-grown plants south of zone 6; in fact, except for parts of New England, I have seldom seen plants of this genus look good for longer than a month anywhere east of the Rocky Mountains. In Michigan, if plants survived the cold winters, the hot summers were not to their liking. In North Georgia, plants look lovely in the spring but wilt every day during the summer and beg to be put out of their misery. To be fair, I have seen spectacular ligularia in proper sites, but those sites are not easy for the average gardener to provide. Around ponds, along stream banks, or wherever their roots can stay constantly moist and afternoon shade can be provided are potential locations.

Only a small number of the approximately 80 species are garden worthy. All have bright yellow daisy flowers held in a spike or in a branched inflorescence just above the long-petioled leaves. Large alternately arranged leaves arise from the base and ascend the stem.

The petioles of the basal leaves completely encircle the stem with a short sheath. This encircling sheath separates *Ligularia* from the closely related genus

360

Senecio. Propagation is primarily by division although seed may be sown when fresh.

Quick Key to Ligularia Species

	Height (ft)	*Leaf* shape	*Inflorescence* shape
L. dentata	3–4	Kidney	Branched
L. przewalskii	5–6	Triangular	Spike
L. stenocephala	3–4	Triangular	Spike

-dentata (den-tah' ta)	Bigleaf Ligularia	3–4'/4'
Summer Bright Orange	China	Zones 5–8

(Syn. *L. clivorum*)

The long-stalked leaves are the best part of the plant. They are kidney-shaped, up to 20" wide, and coarsely toothed. Large clumps of established plants are particularly impressive. The 2–5" diameter, bright orange flowers are held in branched corymbs. The 10–14 ray flowers are long and strap-like and appear to be wilting even in moist growing areas. Personally, I think the flowers detract from the plant. Allow flowers to develop the first year to become familiar with the bloom, then remove the developing flower stalks in subsequent years. Grow in cool, moist conditions or not at all. Although plants recover from constant wilting, too many other lovely plants are available to allow these to tie up garden space unless the correct site is available.

Cultivars:

'Desdemona' has large, deep purple foliage and is more compact than the species. Leaves are beet-red upon emergence in the spring, become green on top but remain purple on the undersides as they mature. It is more heat tolerant than other cultivars.

'Othello' is similar to 'Desdemona' but not as compact and with smaller flowers. There is not, however, a great deal of difference between them.

'Greynog Gold' (*L. dentata* × *L. veitchiana*) has bright orange flowers held on an upright, conical inflorescence over richly veined heart-shaped leaves. Plants can reach 6' tall. Developed in Wales, it is seldom seen in commercial catalogs in this country.

Related Species:

L. hodgsonii, Hodgson's ligularia, is similar to *L. dentata* but grows only 2–3' tall.

-stenocephala (sten-o-seph' a-la)	Narrow-spiked Ligularia	3–4'/5'
Summer Yellow	Japan, North China	Zones 5–8

Unlike *L. dentata,* this species is better known for flowers than foliage. The purplish flower stems end in spike-like 12–18" long racemes bearing many 1–

1½" wide bright yellow flowers. The light green leaves are triangular to heart-shaped with coarse triangular teeth around the margin. The large leaves (up to a foot long and as wide) lose excessive amounts of water on warm days resulting in wilted foliage. It is one of the earliest flowering *Ligularia*. Moist soil conditions and afternoon shade are necessary. They do not require dividing but if additional plant material is needed, division should be accomplished in early spring or late fall. Copious amounts of water must be provided for plantlets to become established.

Cultivars:

'The Rocket' is more compact and has 18–24" long upright racemes of smaller lemon-yellow flowers. The long spikes are useful design components in the garden. It may also be listed as a cultivar of *L. przewalskii*.

Related Species:

L. przewalskii (sha-val' skee-eye), Shavalski's ligularia, is named after the Russian explorer, Nicolai Przewalski. Plants are similar and the two species are often confused. Both are native to northern China, bear spike-like yellow flowers and dark flower stems. However, the stems of *L. przewalskii* are blacker and the leaves are palmately cut, not heart shaped. The plant is taller and usually has five ray florets in each flower compared with three in *L. stenocephala*. Plants are used like 'The Rocket' and equally effective.

Quick Key to Ligularia Species

    A. Inflorescence cylindrical and spike-like
      B. Leaves palmately cut, stems black .... *L. przewalskii*
      BB. Leaves not palmately cut, stems purple................. *L. stenocephala*
    AA. Inflorescence branched, not spike-like......................... *L. dentata*

Additional Reading:

Dress, W. J. 1962. Notes on cultivated Compositae. 7. *Ligularia*. *Baileya* 10:63–87.

Loewer, Peter. 1983. The late blooming ligularia. *Horticulture* 61:12–13.

Lilium (lil' ee-um)   Lily   Liliaceae

Few gardeners can scour garden catalogs and then show sufficient self-discipline to refrain from ordering at least a dozen lily bulbs for the garden. They grow from 12" to 7' in height, bloom from early summer to late fall, are exceptionally hardy and long lived, are relatively inexpensive, and the flowers cover the entire spectrum of the rainbow (except blue). Many of the 80–90 species are still available to the gardener, but with the recent interest in commercial hybridization, the hybrids are often touted with more fanfare than the species. Magnificent additions to the genus have occurred with the work of American and European plant breeders and gardeners are the ultimate winners.

Lilies are native to three main areas of the world and their provenance somewhat determines their position in the garden. European species (*L. bulbiferum, L. candidum, L. martagon, L. pyrenaicum, L. monodelphum*) and their hybrids require rich soils well amended with organic matter. Many Asiatic species (*L. auratum, L. henryi, L. regale, L. rubellum, L. speciosum, L. tigrinum*) and their hybrids produce roots not only at the base of the bulb but also at the stem just above the bulb. These should be planted 8–10" deep to allow for stem-rooting. North American species (*L. canadense, L. pardalinium, L. philadelphicum, L. superbum*) and their hybrids are not stem rooted but often have stoloniferous or rhizomatous bulbs. Well-drained soils amended with leaf mold and peat moss provide the greatest success.

General statements about the ease of lily culture in this country are impossible due to the diversity of climate. While it is enjoyable to read about the ease of growing lilies in England, the cultural information must be applied to eastern gardens most cautiously. However, a broad rule, provided by Alan and Ester Macneil in "Garden Lilies", (see additional reading), states that most Asiatic types do well in areas east of the Rocky Mountains, while those native to the Pacific coast (*L. pardalinum, L. parryi, L. washingtonianum*) and to Europe often struggle there. European species do well on the west coast, and western species do better on the other side of the ocean than on the other side of the mountains.

Lilies usually arrive packed in moist peat moss and should not be removed until planting time. They dry out quickly if exposed to the air because they have no natural protection around the bulb to prevent desiccation. Planting depth varies with species but in general they should be planted 2–3 times deeper than their diameter. However, *L. davidii* should be planted 8" deep while *L. candidum* requires shallow planting. All lilies look better when planted 12–18" apart in groups of three to five. Organic matter should be spread around the emerging stems in early spring, especially those which are stem rooters. The taller lilies, particularly those with large trumpet flowers, should be staked. Insert bamboo stakes close to the stems (without piercing the bulbs) when they are about one foot tall and tie securely as they grow.

Remove flowers when they fade to reduce seed set. If flowers are to be brought inside, cut as little stem as possible. The leaves and stem manufacture food for next year's flowers and if too much is removed, performance declines in subsequent years. The stems can be removed in the fall after they have died back, although I like to leave some of the stem around all winter so bulbs can be located in spring. Most are sun-loving plants but many tolerate partial shade. The most important cultural requirement is good drainage; although abundant water is required in the summer, bulbs abhor poorly drained soils in the winter.

A number of diseases have plagued lilies from the beginning of their cultivation and still persist today. *Botrytis*, a fungal disease, is known as gray mold because of the grayish residue that occurs on leaves and stems particularly after prolonged rain. Bottom leaves usually fall off and although plants are disfigured, little permanent damage occurs. Basal rot is caused by *Fusarium oxysporum* and occurs on infected bulbs. Symptoms are yellow foliage and total disintegration of the bulb. It occurs more often in warm climates than in areas with cooler summer conditions. Most lily propagators dip their bulbs in fungicide after harvesting from the field, and basal rot is not as serious today as in the past. However, it will not go away. The most serious disease is lily mosaic virus which is carried from plant to plant by aphids. Symptoms vary but, in general, irregular yellow streaks or mottling appear on the leaves and many become twisted and distorted. The most susceptible species are *L. formosanum* and *L. auratum*, although *L. canadense*, *L. japonicum* and *L. superbum* are often infected and act as carriers. It is advisable to plant these some distance from other lily species. The virus can also be spread from tulips, particularly Rembrandt types, and tulips and lilies should not be planted side by side. On the other hand, *L. davidii* is one of the most virus tolerant species. It has been used in lily breeding programs to reduce sensitivity to virus in many hybrids.

Lilies are propagated vegetatively or sexually. Vegetative propagules include scales, stem bulbils, or division. The advantage of vegetative propagation is to multiply hybrids or cultivars which will not come true from seed. The biggest disadvantage is the transmittance of viral or fungal pathogens from mother to daughter plant. Scale propagation may be done on most species in June and July in the United States. Discard the outer scales and peel the inner scales of the bulb. Dip the cut end in a fungicide (available at a garden center) and place into clean coarse vermiculite or a mixture of sand and peat moss. Tie a polyethylene bag over the container and place in a warm area. Small scales such as those of *L. superbum* or *pumilum* should be almost covered while bigger ones such as those of *L. henryi* may be left protruding above the surface. Bulbils will form on the scales in 4–10 weeks and some top growth will occur. At that time place the container in a cooler for at least 6 weeks of cold temperatures (less than 40°F). Pot up in the spring and allow for additional growth or place in the garden at this time.

Stem bulbils occur on *L. henryi*, *L. tigrinum*, many of the Backhouse hybrids, and occasionally on *L. bulbiferum*. Simply remove the bulbils when ripe (usually in midsummer) and plant them in peat medium in a propagation frame. Overwinter to provide the necessary chilling and place container and plantlet in the garden the next spring. For those so inclined, breaking off the top of the plant just when flower buds are visible will force many plants to form adventitious stem bulbils. Some species such as *L. speciosum* have rhizomatous bulbs and careful removal of the daughter bulbils is a useful method of propagation.

Reproduction by seed is time-consuming for some species but surprisingly fast for others. The main advantage of seed propagation is freedom from disease. Many species germinate rapidly and top growth occurs in 2–3 weeks. Others form a bulbil prior to top growth development, and in these species, it appears as if nothing is happening and seeds are often discarded too soon. Germination responses of some of the species are shown below. Some such as *L. candidum*, *L. henryi*, and *L. philadelphicum* are variable in their response and could be placed in either category. Those in the slow germination category may be accelerated by providing 40°F for 6 weeks.

Fast germination	Slow germination
L. amabile	*L. auratum*
L. candidum	*L. bulbiferium*
L. formosanum	*L. canadense*
L. longiflorum	*L. henryi*
L. philadelphicum	*L. martagon*
L. pumilum	*L. pardalinum*
L. regale	*L. speciosum*
L. tigrinum	*L. superbum*

Most lilies require a minimum of 6 weeks cold to develop good flowering stems. Lilies raised from seed may take 4 years to flower. Others such as *L. formosanum*, Formosa lily, flower the first year after the cold treatment.

Hybrids: Hybrids can be found under names such as Mid-Century and Preston hybrids and numerous cultivars may occur within each hybrid group. They have been placed in 8 divisions by the North American Lily Society and the Royal Horticultural Society for ease of classification. The divisions are based on the parentage of the hybrids, the position (nodding, upright) and shape of the flower (trumpet, star, bowl).

Quick Guide to the Hybrids—A Sampling Only

	Flower color (inside/outside)	Height (ft.)	Flower shape	Flower time*
African Queen Strain	Gold apricot	5–6	Trumpet	J, A
Aurelian Hybrids	Mix	4–6	Trumpet	J, A
-*Backhouse Hybrids*	Orange to yellow	5–6	Nodding	J, J
-*Mrs R.O. Backhouse*	Yellow, purple spots	5–6	Nodding	July
-*Sutton House*	Yellow/purple spots	5–6	Nodding	July
Bellingham Hybrids	Mix	4–7	Nodding	J, J
Shuksan	Yellow orange, red dots	4–5	Nodding	July
Black Dragon Strain	White/purple brown	5–8	Trumpet	J, A
Byam's Ruby	Ruby red	1–2	Erect	June
Bright Star	Orange/ivory	3–4	Trumpet	J, J
Connecticut Yankee	Apricot-orange	3–4	Outward	J, J
Copper King Strain	Deep apricot/maroon red	4–6	Trumpet	J, A
Corsage	Ivory pink	2–3	Outward	J, J
Fiesta Hybrids	Mix	3–5	Nodding	J, J

	Flower color (inside/outside)	Height (ft.)	Flower shape	Flower time*
-Burgundy Strain	Cherry red	3–5	Nodding	J, J
-Citronella Strain	Golden yellow	3–4	Nodding	J, J
Golden Splendor Strain	Deep yellow/maroon stripe	3–6	Trumpet	J, A
Golden Sunburst Strain	Clear yellow	5–7	Nodding	J, A
Green Mt. Hybrids	White with green throat	5–7	Trumpet	J, A
Harlequin Hybrids	Pink to tangerine	4–5	Nodding	J, J
-Minuet	Soft yellow	4–5	Nodding	July
Imperial Strain	Crimson, gold, pink	5–6	Outward	J, A
Mid Century Hybrid	Mix	3–5	Erect,Out	J, J
-Bounty	Yellow	3–5	Outward	July
-Cinnabar	Maroon red	2–3	Erect	July
-Enchantment	Red	2–3	Erect	July
-Prosperity	Lemon yellow	3–4	Outward	July
-Tabasco	Dark red, black spots	3–4	Outward	July
Olympic Hybrids	Ivory to sulphur/purple	5–6	Trumpet	July
Paisley Strain	Ivory to mahogany	4–5	Nodding	June
Pink Perfection Hybs.	Orchid purple	4–6	Trumpet	J, A
Preston Hybrids	Mix	2–5	Erect,Out	J, J
-Brenda Watts	Deep red, purple dots	3–4	Outward	June
-Spitfire	Deep apricot, brown spots	2–5	Erect	July
Thunderbolt	Tangerine orange	6–7	Trumpet	J, A

* J, J = June, July
J,A = July, August

Specialists list many more hybrids, all of which have unique characteristics slightly different from others.

Species: The proliferation of hybrids has left some of the species out in the cold from the viewpoint of garden appeal. The species, however, possess a charm of their own and although some are uncommon, others such as tiger lily and regal lily will always occupy a space in the summer garden.

Quick Guide to Lily Species

	Ease of growth	Flower color	Height (ft.)	Flower shape	Flower time
L. auratum	ME	White, yellow band	2–4	Bowl	A, S

	Ease of growth	Flower color	Height (ft.)	Flower shape	Flower time
L. bulbiferum	MD	Red-orange	3–4	Cup	J, J
L. candidum	E	White	2–4	Trumpet	June
L. formosanum	ME	White	4–6	Trumpet	Oct.
L. henryi	E	Light orange	4–6	Nodding	J, A
L. martagon	MD	Purple-red	3–4	Nodding	J, J
L. philadelphicum	D	Orange-red	2–4	Erect	J, J
L. pumilum	E	Coral-red	1–2	Nodding	J, J
L. regale	E	White	4–6	Trumpet	J, A
L. speciosum	E	White, red spots	4–5	Nodding	J, A
L. superbum	E	Orange	4–7	Nodding	J, A
L. tigrinum	E	Orange, spotted	4–5	Nodding	A, S

Ease of growth: E = easy, ME = moderately easy, MD = moderately difficult,
D = difficult (for gardens east of Rocky Mountains).

Flw. time: A, S = August, September

J, A = July, August

J, J = June, July

-auratum (ow-rah' tum)　　　　Goldband Lily　　　　2–4'/1½'
Summer　　　　White　　　　Japan　　　　Zones 4–9

L. *auratum* has often been described as "the queen of the lilies" and is well deserving of the name. The large flowers have prominent gold bands down the center of each white petal and are heavily spotted with gold and crimson. The wonderfully fragrant blooms are borne horizontally and each of the 5–15 blossoms is 6–10" in diameter. The flowers are funnel shaped, the petals are slightly reflexed, but a long flower tube is not produced as in the trumpet lilies. The red anthers contrast prominently with the white petals.

The introduction of L. *auratum* bulbs to England and North America in 1862 created a groundswell of interest in this and other lilies. Unfortunately, the wholesale propagation of bulbs in Japan was handled poorly and basal rot and lily mosaic decimated plantings. Few old established plantings remain. This species and L. *formosanum*, Formosa lily, are the two most susceptible to lily mosaic and complete destruction of the entire plant, including the bulb, can occur within one year. Propagation and cultural techniques have greatly improved and although there is far less incidence of disease, the reputation still lingers.

This species is more frost tender than many others and should be mulched well in zones 4 and 5. Bulbs require a well-drained soil and do not tolerate lime. They are also particularly sensitive to winter moisture. Bulbs grow on volcanic ash and lava debris in Japan, indicating their dislike of moisture around the bulbs. The bulbs are not stem rooters and should be planted about 6″ deep. Although not a long-lived species, often disappearing in a year or two, it is lovely enough that frequent renewal is justified.

Cultivars:

var. *platyphyllum* is better than the type with larger less heavily spotted flowers. It is a vigorous grower and can reach heights of 6–8′.

var. *rubro-vittatum* has a crimson rather than a yellow band through the petals.

var. *virginale* is an albino form of the species, with pale yellow banding and few or no spots.

Hybrids:

   L. × *parkmanii*, raised in Boston in 1869 by Francis Parkman, an amateur gardener, is a cross between *L. auratum* and *L. speciosum*. The segments are crimson inside with white margins and the flat flowers are up to 12″ across. The original hybrids were lost but subsequent crosses have been made. This is considered to be one of the finest hybrids ever produced.

'Empress of China' (*L.* 'Jilian Wallace' × *L. auratum* 'Crimson Queen') has a pale green stripe in the center of the petals, and maroon spots.

'Empress of Japan' (*L. auratum* × *L. speciosum*) bears white flowers with a golden band and purple spotting on the petals. The 'Empress' forms were raised at the Oregon Bulb Farm.

'Excelsior' (*L. auratum* var. *platyphyllum* × *L.* 'Jilian Wallace') has rose petals with narrow white margins.

Others with *L. auratum* and *L. speciosum* parentage include the Imperial Strain, the Potomac hybrids, and the Jamboree Strain.

-bulbiferum (bul-bi′ fe-rum)		Fire Lily	3–4′/1½′
Summer	Orange-red	Eastern and Central Europe	Zones 2–8

   The species is occasionally offered but is often outclassed by many of the hybrids. It is, however, hardy, vigorous and one of the easiest lilies to grow. The orange-red, cup-shaped flowers are erect or outward facing and have yellow blotching at the base. If the flowers are disbudded or if the stem is damaged, many bulbils appear in the axils of the leaves. For large scale production, plants are topped to induce bulbil formation from the leaf axils.

   Bulbs should be planted 6–8″ deep and are not particular as to soil type. They are tolerant of shade and should be placed where they remain undisturbed.

Cultivars:

var. *chaixii* is a dwarf plant seldom over 2′ tall with orange flowers.

var. *croceum* has brilliant, deep orange flowers. In Northern Ireland, it is the symbol of the Order of the Ulster Orangemen, who celebrate the victory of William of Orange in 1691. This variety is also one of the parents of the hybrid 'Redbird', a purple-stemmed plant bearing red flowers with mahogany spots.

Hybrids:

L. bulbiferum has been used extensively in hybridization resulting in erect-flowered hybrids known as *L.* × *hollandicum* or *L.* × *maculatum*.

-candidum (kan' di-dum)   Madonna Lily   2–4'/1½'
Summer   White   Eastern Mediterranean   Zones 4–9

This may be the earliest lily in cultivation, grown circa 1500 BC in Crete. The Madonna lily has always represented the good and beautiful to artists and poets. The Madonna flower is depicted in paintings and frescoes by Boticelli and Titan and is still considered by many to be the "lily of the valleys" mentioned in Song of Solomon 2:1–2. The 10–20 funnel-shaped flowers are pure white (the name *candidum* means not just white but "of dazzling white"), 3–4" long and equally wide. They are delicately fragrant and each waxy flower faces outward to allow full view of the lovely yellow stamens.

This is one of the few bulbs which must be planted near the surface; only 1" of soil should cover the bulb. Basal evergreen leaves form soon after bulbs are planted in the fall. It is best placed in the company of other low-growing plants which shade the bulb but not the stem leaves. For this reason, Madonna lily does well in the mixed border where it persists for many years.

Hybrids:

L. × *testaceum* (*L. candidum* × *L. chalcedonicum*) bears pendent ivory flowers flushed with pink and scarlet anthers.

'Apollo' (*L.* × *testaceum* × *L. chalcedonicum* var. *maculatum*) has tan flowers with apricot shading.

'Zeus' (*L.* × *testaceum* × *L. chalcedonicum*) has deep red flowers. All hybrids bear pendulous flowers.

Related Species:

L. longiflorum, Easter lily, is a beautiful garden plant. If potted lilies are received as gifts, plant immediately after flowering. The pure white flowers are 4–5" long and 1–1½" broad. Unfortunately, bulbs are only winter hardy to zone 8 (zone 7 if well mulched).

-formosanum (for-mo-say' num)   Formosa Lily   4–6'/1½'
Late Summer   White   Taiwan   Zones 5–8

The outward-facing flowers are funnel-shaped with reflexed petals. The 2–4" long white blooms often have purplish brown markings on the outside to match the purplish hue of the stem. Five to six fragrant flowers are borne in the stem axils in late summer in the South and autumn in the North. The late flowering characteristic is sufficient to recommend the species but in the North, insufficient time may be available for the bulb to ripen after flowering and bulbs may only persist a year or two. In the South, this is not a problem.

Unfortunately, bulbs are susceptible to virus diseases, particularly lily mosaic. The virus causes rapid decline of the bulb and increases the potential of infection to other bulb species in the garden. To avoid infection, it is not advisable to plant Formosa lilies among other lilies. (Also see *L. auratum*).

Cultivars:

var. *pricei* is only 18–24″ tall and a definite improvement on the species. Plants are suitable for the front of the garden and should be planted like *L. candidum*, using other plants to provide shade for the base. Flowers open earlier, and bulbs are more cold hardy than the species.

This is one of the fastest species to flower from seed, flowering the first year ʲʰᵉr cold. Germination occurs in 3–4 weeks in warm (70–75°F), humid areas. Variety *pricei* also comes true from seed.

-henryi (hen′ ree-eye)		Henry Lily	4–6′/2′
Late Summer	Orange	Central China	Zones 4–8

One of the building blocks of the hybridizer, it has been a parent of many a grateful hybrid as well as an excellent long-lived species, flowering prolifically in mid- to late summer. The bulbs are exceptionally large (8–10″ in diameter), and relatively resistant to fungi and virus. The length and width of the leaves vary considerably but become smaller near the top of the stem. The stem itself varies from green to dark purple. The 2″ wide nodding, light orange flowers have strongly reflexed petals and the centers have numerous raised projections called papillae.

This stem-rooting species should be planted 6–8″ deep. The major disadvantage is the inherent inability of the stems to stand upright. They start to bend long before the flower buds have reached appreciable size and touch the ground as the flowers open. Support early in the growing season or allow to grow through shrubs in the mixed border. It is native to limestone cliff faces in China and is therefore tolerant of high pH soils.

Under favorable conditions, large amounts of seed form and seedlings reach flowering size in about three years. Multitudes of small bulbs forming at the base of the stem may also be detached and grown on.

Hybrids:

The Aurelian hybrids (*L.* × *aurelianense*) are the most important hybrids associated with *L. henryi*. They arose from crosses with *L. sargentiae*, Sargent's lily, a trumpet lily with white flowers with a brown tint. The resulting crosses produced hybrids whose flowers vary in shape from trumpet, bowl-shaped, pendant to sunburst types.

370

Cultivars:

Many clones from various strains of the Aurelian hybrids have occurred over the years, all benefited from the added vigor and stronger garden constitution of their parents.

'Black Beauty' is a relatively new hybrid resulting from the cross between *L. henryi* and *L. speciosum*. Flowers are deep crimson with recurved petals. These normally incompatible species were united by embryo culture, a powerful technique for the development of future hybrids.

'Bright Star' is a sunburst type lily (star-shaped flowers which open flat) with white flowers and an orange-gold center.

'Eureka', a bowl-shaped, outward facing, pale orange lily also resulted through embryo culture (*L. henryi* × 'Wiltig', and Asiatic hybrid.)

'First Love' has 6–8″ wide gold flowers with pink edges. The flowers are clearly bowl shaped and outward facing.

Golden Clarion Strain consists of trumpet-shaped flowers ranging from yellow to gold, usually with maroon or deep crimson on the outside.

Golden Shower hybrids bear long pendant type flowers on long pedicels. They are bright yellow with maroon tinges on the outside.

'Heart's Desire' has bowl-shaped flowers in shades of white, cream, yellow, or orange.

'Honeydew', a trumpet form, has long, pendulous greenish yellow flowers outside; deep yellow inside.

'Limelight' bears funnel-shaped trumpets of chartreuse yellow. Unfortunately, it is rather sensitive to virus.

'Pink Perfection' has 6–8″ long, deep pink trumpet flowers. Plants grow 7′ high in my garden.

'Thunderbolt' bears deep apricot starburst flowers with tinges of green and purple on the outside of the petals.

-martagon (mar′ ta-gon)	Martagon Lily, Turk's-cap	3–4′/1½′
Summer	Purple-red	Europe, Asia	Zones 3–8

This lily has an extremely wide distribution, ranging from Portugal to northern Mongolia and from Britain to Siberia. As would be expected, it is variable in habit and adaptable to a wide range of climates and garden environments. Plants tolerate heavy shade as well as full sun, a plus for many gardens.

The word "martagon" may be derived from a Turkish word denoting a special form of turban used by sultans. This rather loose translation has evolved into the common name of this plant, the Turk's-cap lily. Many other species with the same nodding flower orientation are referred to as turk's-cap flowers. Alchemists in the 15th century held the martagon in high regard for its ability to change metals into gold, perhaps because of the gold roots.

Plants are distinguished by 3–4 whorls of leaves consisting of 6–9 leaves per node. The nodding flowers are dull purplish red and spotted dark purple throughout. The petals are strongly recurved and each stem bears 20–30 small flowers. The 1–2" wide flowers are fragrant but the fragrance is in the nose of the smeller; I find the odor rather unpleasant. There are even those who claim it "stinks".

Cultivars:

var. *album* is an albino form with creamy white unspotted flowers and pale green leaves. It is particularly outstanding in front of a solid green background in the garden and, unlike other albino forms, grows vigorously.

var. *cattaniae* is similar to the species but has dark maroon unspotted flowers and hairy buds and stems. I find the unspotted nature of the flowers more pleasant than the type. Crosses made in Scotland between these two varieties yielded cherry-colored flowers sold as 'Gleam' and 'Glisten' but I am not aware of any commercial source in the United States.

Hybrids:

Backhouse hybrids resulted from *L. martagon* and its varieties, particularly var. *cattaniae*, and *L. hansonii*, a nodding orange-yellow species. They were developed at the end of the last century and are still widely grown. Named clones include 'Mrs. R.O. Backhouse', with orange-yellow flowers flushed with pink, and 'Brocade' with pale buff-yellow recurved flowers. They are vigorous, excellent garden plants.

Paisley hybrids (*L. martagon* var. *album* × *L. hansonii*) contain nodding flowers of clear white, orange and mahogany. No named cultivars have yet been developed.

-philadelphicum (fil-a-delf' i-cum)		Wood Lily	2–4'/1½'
Summer	Orange-red	Eastern North America	Zones 4–8

This North American native ranges from Nova Scotia to Ontario and from southern Quebec as far south as North Carolina. Fiery orange-red erect flowers with dark maroon spots contrast with the dark green whorled leaves. Open wooded areas and areas with partial afternoon shade are common locales to find this native. The flowers are sufficiently showy that mass plantings are not necessary, and if provided ample space, are visible from one end of the garden to the other.

Unfortunately, this is not one of the easier lilies to establish and only a small percentage persist more than two years. However, those that do become established are long-lived. The rock garden serves the needs of this diminutive lily better than the mixed border, particularly when the soil is sandy and highly acidic. Given the wide distribution, it is surprising that establishment is so difficult. Sowing seed in the cold frame in fall, with subsequent planting of the seedlings next spring helps establish the plants.

-pumilum (pew mi-lum)		Coral Lily	1–2'/1½'
Summer	Coral-Red	Eastern China, Siberia	Zones 3–7

(Syn. *L. tenuifolium*)

The exceptionally waxy, coral-red, nodding flowers are unlike any others. The petals are highly reflexed and practically unspotted. Each stem may bear up to twenty, 2″ wide flowers in early summer, although 10 is more common. The numerous leaves are narrow and grass-like. As coral lily is a stem-rooting species, bulbs should be planted about 4–5″ deep.

Plants are not long-lived and accepting this fact makes them much less frustrating to grow. They persist 2–4 years in full sun. Prolific amounts of seed are produced which provide new seedlings to perpetuate the species for many years. Four years is about the maximum length of time bulbs persist, however, removing spent flowers keeps plants in place a little longer but eliminates the source of fresh seed for new plantings.

Cultivars:

'Golden Gleam' is a golden form of the species.
'Red Star' bears star-shaped scarlet flowers about a week later than the type.
'Yellow Bunting' is a pure yellow form which comes true from seed.

-regale (re-gah' lee)		Regal Lily	4–6'/2'
Summer	White	China	Zones 3–8

The regal lily was discovered by the great plant explorer E.H. Wilson in western Szechwan in 1903. Imagine his thrill of gazing upon drifts of pure white lilies "not in twos and threes but in hundreds, in thousands, aye, in tens of thousands. The air in the cool of the morning and in the evening is laden with delicious purfume exhaled from each bloom." (*The Lilies of Eastern Asia*, 1925, E.H. Wilson). While we cannot duplicate this sight, a half dozen bulbs can provide almost as much pleasure. The trumpet-shaped flowers are white with a canary yellow inner funnel and usually wine colored on the outside. The stigmas are green and the anthers golden yellow. There may be up to twenty 5″ wide and 6″ long flowers per stem, although 10–15 is more common. When in flower, this is the dominant plant in the garden. Other plants should be chosen to complement and not compete.

Bulbs should be planted 6″ deep in well-drained soil in partial shade or full sun. One problem with regal lilies is that they emerge in early spring and may be nipped by late spring frosts. Planting through low growing plants such as *Campanula carpatica* protects the new shoots while providing color at the base. Bulbs are long-lived and multiply rapidly, however, once planted, they resent disturbance.

Seeds are produced prolifically and flowering plants can be produced in as little as two years.

-speciosum (spece-ee-o' sum)		Speciosum Lily	4–5'/2'
Summer	White with red	Japan	Zones 4–8

Once grown in large numbers for the cut flower trade, the species has been superseded by the hybrids. It is still, however, a popular late-flowering lily for gardens with full sun and lime-free soil. The 6" wide, white, fragrant flowers have reflexed petals flushed with pink and heavily spotted with pink or crimson. They have red fleshy bumps (papillae) in the center of the blossom, similar to *L. henryi*. A well-grown plant may have as many as 30 blossoms per stem although 15–20 is more realistic. Plant bulbs about 6" deep. Due to their susceptibility to virus and disease, keep them away from *L. auratum* and *L. formosanum*.

Cultivars:

var. *album* (*album novum*) has white flowers with a pale green band radiating from the center.

var. *roseum* bears 8" wide soft pinkish red flowers with a white margin around the petals.

var. *rubrum* produces large, 8" wide ruby-red flowers with a broad white margin. These are commonly known as rubrum lilies.

'Uchida' may be a cultivar of var. *rubrum* or a hybrid with *L. auratum*. Nevertheless, the vigorous plants perform well and bear rich carmine-pink, spotted flowers. 'Uchida' is more virus resistant than the species.

Hybrids:

'Allegra' [(*L. auratum* × *L. speciosum* var. *rubrum*) × *L. speciosum* var. *album*] has beautiful white recurved flowers with a central green star.

Other hybrids such as *L.* × *parkmanii* have been listed under *L. auratum*.

-superbum (soo-perb' um)		American Turk's Cap Lily	4–7'/2'
Late Summer	Orange	Eastern United States	Zones 4–9

The variable American turk's cap lily used to be far more abundant in the eastern United States than it is today. Peter Hanson of Brooklyn, after whom *L. hansonii* was named, "once found a spot in New Jersey where there were at least 5000 plants of this noble lily in flower at once, ranging up to 2m high and bearing as many as 30 flowers to a stem, but out of the whole number it was difficult to find three exactly alike." (*Monograph of the Genus Lilium*, 1877–1880, by H.J. Elwes). *L. superbum* is a martagon-type lily (see *L. martagon*), with orange-red, heavily spotted reflexed flowers often with a green center at the base. The stems are usually flushed with dark purple and may bear up to 40 flowers although 20 is more common. Plants prefer damp conditions and perform better if they do not dry out during the summer, although bulbs are more tolerant of drought than many other species. The leaves are whorled like *L. martagon* and the bulbs are rhizomatous resulting in the establishment of large colonies.

Cultivars:

A number of cultivars was raised by Mrs. J.N. Henry, an amateur lily enthusiast from Gladwyne, PA. She also discovered *L. iridollae*.

'Norman Henry' has fine unspotted butter-yellow flowers.

'Port Henry' bears clear pale orange flowers with only faint spotting. Other cultivars were also selected which bear the Henry name but unfortunately are most difficult to locate.

Seeds sown in the fall reach flowering size in two years.

Related Species:

L. canadense, Canada lily, has a similar growth habit but is distinguished from *L. superbum* by dark-spotted yellowish flowers rather than orange, by less reflexed petals, and by the absence of a green spot at the base of the flower.

L. iridollae, pot of gold lily, was found by Mrs. J. N. Henry (see cultivars above) in southern Alabama. Native to Alabama and Florida, it bears nodding pure yellow flowers on 3' tall stems. Unfortunately, this little gem is difficult to find but if a source is discovered, it should definitely be used in southern gardens.

L. michauxii, is a similar but more southerly species of *L. superbum* and was thought to be a variety (*L. superbum* var. *carolinianum*). Native to the southeastern United States, plants are tolerant of summer heat and humidity. It is not as floriferous as *L. superbum* but bears 3–5 fragrant, nodding light orange or crimson turk's-cap flowers. The species is well worth growing in zones 8–10.

-tigrinum (ti-gri' num)	Tiger Lily	4–5'/2'
Summer, Fall Orange, spotted	China, Korea, Japan	Zones 3–9

(Syn. *L. lancifolium*)

The few demands as to soil type, sun or shade or irrigation make the tiger lily one of the easiest to grow. The 2–4" long flowers have strongly recurved petals and may be up to 9" wide. Each stem bears 8–20 deep orange flowers with purplish black spots. Bulbs are stem rooters and should be planted 6" deep and mulched around the base to allow full development of stem roots. The purplish green stem has white cobweb-like hairs and numerous black bulbils which are formed in the leaf axils.

L. tigrinum was used as a food plant for more than a thousand years by the Chinese, the bulbs being quite edible and said to taste like artichoke. It is interesting that *L. candidum*, Madonna lily, has been grown for an equal length of time for beauty, not the food value. Debates still rage in lily circles as to which species was first cultivated.

Unfortunately, *L. tigrinum* has a history of being infected with lily mosaic virus and has been called a "Typhoid Mary." In this species, however, the symptoms are almost entirely masked. Aphids spread it to other species quite readily and thus the tiger lily is seldom found in the gardens of lily enthusiasts. Established plants, however, may live for years and multiply rapidly.

Vigorous efforts have been made to raise virus-free stock and it is better to pay the extra price for this material than to infect the rest of the garden.

Plants multiply readily from bulbils formed at the base of the bulbs. Abundant seed is also produced which is scattered randomly by birds and plants to germinate along roadsides and streams.

Cultivars:

Many seed-propagated cultivars are available as White, Yellow, Pink, Red, Cream, Orange, and Gold tiger lilies. All are variable and flowers are heavily sprinkled with black dots.

var. *flaviflorum* has yellow flowers but is particularly susceptible to virus and has not proven to be a good selection.

var. *flore-plena* has double flowers but, in my opinion, is rather coarse. The style and grace of a lily flower lies in its clean lines and simple architecture. Double-flowered lilies destroy such grace.

var. *fortunei* has bright salmon-orange flowers and is distinguished by the dense woolly hairs which coat the stem. It is later flowering than the species and is particularly useful in the South where frost doesn't occur until November or December.

var. *splendens* has larger, brighter reddish orange flowers than the type and is one of the best varieties for the late garden.

Hybrids:

'Cardinal' (*L. tigrinum* × *L. amabile*) has nodding, orange-red flowers which bloom late in the season.

The Mid-Century hybrids were developed by the Oregon Bulb Farm during and after World War II and include some of the best known lilies. They resulted from crosses between *L. tigrinum*, *L. dauricum*, *L wilsonii*, *L. davidii* and *L. bulbiferum*. They were a major breakthrough in lily breeding and provided the backbone of many of today's hybrids. There are many named clones of Mid-Century hybrids. Consult lily catalogs for additional selections.

'Enchantment' bears bright orange, outward facing flowers on 2' tall stems. An excellent cut flower species.

'Cinnabar' is only 1½–2' tall and bears bright maroon-red, erect flowers.

Related Species:

L. pardalinum, leopard lily, has 9–20 whorled leaves and 2–4" wide nodding flowers. They are yellow at the base, orange-scarlet above and spotted maroon. Native to California, they are magnificent for western gardens but perform poorly in the East.

Quick Key to the Species

(The majority of lilies encountered will be hybrids and this key will be of little use. However, for gardeners with a fascination for species, it may be of value.

- A. Flowers erect or nearly so
    - B. Leaves whorled about stem, stem smooth .... *L. philadelphicum*
    - BB. Leaves scattered about stem, top part of stem somewhat hairy ....
      L. bulbiferum
- AA. Flowers horizontal or pendulous
    - B. Flowers trumpet shaped with distinct tube, ends of petals may be spreading but not reflexed
        - C. Tube hardly widening from base of tube to middle, petals tinged purple on outside, flowers 5–6″ long .. *L. formosanum*
        - CC. Tube widening from its base upward, flowers 2–7″ long
            - D. Flowers 2–3″ long, petals pure white................ *L. candidum*
            - DD. Flowers 4–7″ long, petals white with purple tinge on outside or inside of flower .... *L. regale*
    - BB. Flowers not trumpet shaped, petals recurved near tips, flowers horizontal or pendulous
        - C. Flowers horizontal, bowl shaped, white with yellow band on petals .... *L. auratum*
        - CC. Flowers pendulous
            - D. Leaves arranged in whorls
                - E. Color of flowers white to rose to purple.......... *L. martagon*
                - EE. Color of flowers yellow to orange-red............ *L. superbum*
            - DD. Leaves scattered, not in whorls
                - E. Flower color white, or rose with red or rose spots.............
                  L. speciosum
                - EE. Flower color scarlet to orange or yellow
                    - F. Plants usually less than 2′ tall, leaf veins 1 ..... *L. pumilum*
                    - FF. Plants usually 3–7′ tall, leaf veins more than 1
                        - G. Leaves with 5–7 veins, upper leaf axils with bulbils .....
                          L. tigrinum
                        - GG. Leaves many-veined, few if any bulbils in upper axils .... *L. henryi*

Additional Reading:

Books:

Anonymous. Yearly. *The North American Lily Society Yearbooks*. These are excellent sources of information written by amateur and professional plantsmen.

Elwes, H. J. 1880. *A Monograph of the Genus Lilium*. This was the most ambitious work on lilies ever undertaken. Information was compiled on species and hybrids known at the time and excellent botanical drawings were included. Unfortunately, the work was well beyond the reach of almost all who wished to own it or even refer to it (see Synge, Patrick).

Macneil, Alan and Esther Macneil. 1946. *Garden Lilies*. Oxford University Press. The Macneils provide good listings of the species and although not particularly useful for the hybrids, the book is well written and informative.

Slate, George, L. 1939. *Lilies for the American Garden*. A source of good information on lilies for the United States.

Synge, Patrick M. 1980. *Lilies*. Batsford Ltd., London. This recent revision of Elwes monograph and its supplements make that fine work available to gardeners. Although most suitable for British readers, the information on species and hybrids is superior to any other I have found. A must for lily enthusiasts.

Manuscripts:

Baxter, Felicity. 1986. *Lilium albanicum. The Garden* 111(7):324–326.

Blake, Felice. 1987. The loveliest species of all, *L. mackliniae*. Bulletin of the North American Lily Society 41(2):19–20.

Gibson, R. J. 1986. The aurelians of Leslie Woodriff. Bulletin of the North American Lily Society 40(3):2–3.

Hermes, Alfred R. 1986. Lilies that last. *Horticulture* 64(6):26–31.

Hermes, Alfred R. 1989. The coral lily. *Horticulture* 67(4):72.

Ingram, John. 1967. Notes on the cultivated Liliaceae. 6. *Lilium pensylvanicum* Ker (*L. dauricum* Ker). *Baileya* 15:109–111.

Synge, Patrick M. 1980. Some newer hybrid lilies. *The Plantsman* 1(4):250–252.

Associations:

North American Lily Society, Box 476. Waukee, IA, 50263. Publication: *North American Lily Society Quarterly Bulletin*.

Limonium (li-mon' ee-um)   Statice, Sea Lavender   Plumbaginaceae

Well over 150 species of statice have been characterized and a number have become well established in the garden and florist trade. The common annual statice, *L. sinuatum*, is available in many colors from seed. Another annual grown by commercial plantsmen for cut flowers is rat-tail statice, *L. suworowii* (soo-vo-rov' ee-eye) (syn. *Psylliostachys suworowii*), with its unique spiked inflorescence of small dark purple flowers. For statice enthusiasts, many species are available as cut flowers. Most prefer well-drained, slightly acidic soils, and full sun. Some of the better ones include *L. sinense*, an annual with small yellow flowers; *L. perezii*, Perez statice, a 3–4' tall stout plant with 12–15" wide, flat, dark blue flowers with white centers; *L. roseum* (*L. perigrinum*), rosy statice, a tender perennial with fleshy leaves and unique rose flowers. The best forms are available from tissue culture only. Other statice for cut flowers are *L.* × 'Misty Blue', *L.* × 'Misty Pink', and *L.* × *caesium*. Unfortunately, they are seldom available to the gardener. Common perennials such as *L. latifolium* and *L. tataricum* bear large airy heads of tiny flowers in shades of lavender and blue and are useful fresh or dried. The flowers are composed of outer sepals (calyx) and inner petals (corolla) and may be different colors. In some species, the corolla falls early, leaving the calyx in full color.

Statice prefers partial shade in the southern part of the range (zones 7,8) but will tolerate full sun further north. Good drainage is essential as they are susceptible to various fungal diseases prevalent in moist soils. This is particularly true of *L. sinuatum*.

To dry the cut flowers, harvest before they fully open. Tie the stems in bundles and hang upside down in a shady, dry, airy shed.

Propagate by root cuttings (see *Anemone* × *hybrida*) and division in early spring or by seed. Seeds are small and should be barely covered. Germination occurs in 2–3 weeks under warm (70–75°F) humid conditions.

Quick Reference to Limonium Species

	Height (in)	Hairy leaves (Yes, No)	Color of corolla
L. latifolium	24–30	Yes	Blue
L. tataricum	10–15	No	Ruby-red

-*latifolium* (lah-tee-fo' lee-um)		Sea Lavender	24–30"/30"
Summer	Lavender-blue	Bulgaria, Southern Russia	Zones 3–9

Plants may be 3' tall and 3' wide with over a dozen flowering stems when well established. The flower stalk is slender and multi-branched, creating a flower head 18–24" across. The 6–10" long leaves are produced in rosettes and are often just as wide (*latifolium* means wide leaf). Small branched hairs cover the leaves which taper at the base into petioles nearly as long as the blades. Plants are susceptible to crown and root rot and should be spaced 18" or more, otherwise air circulation is restricted and disease increases.

Cultivars:

'Blue Cloud' has lighter blue flowers than the type.
'Violetta' bears dark violet flowers and is an outstanding garden plant.

Propagate from seed in late fall or from division. Seed is the easiest and least disruptive form of propagation. The roots are long and division is difficult. Established clumps should not be disturbed.

Related Species:

L. bellidifolium is only 4–10″ tall at flowering, and bears sprays of lilac flowers over handsome lanceolate foliage (*bellidifolium* means beautiful-leafed).

L. gmelinii, Siberian statice, produces 2–3′ tall spires of smoky lilac flowers in late summer. This is an extremely vigorous grower, particularly when provided with deep, rich soil and plenty of moisture.

-tataricum (ta-tah′ ri-kum)	German Statice	10–15″/15″
Summer Red/white	Southeastern Europe	Zones 4–9

(Syn. *Goniolimon tataricum*)

Similar to *L. latifolium*, but the habit and flowers are smaller. The flowers appear whitish to light blue but upon close inspection, ruby-red inner petals are evident. The rosette leaves are smooth and about 4–6″ long. This species is grown commercially as a dried cut flower and the flower stalks are stiffer than common sea lavender.

The genus of this species is in doubt and has been split off to *Goniolimon* by some taxonomists. *Goniolimon* differs from *Limonium* in having hairy styles and capitate stigmas (compact cluster of stigmas).

Cultivars:

var. *angustifolium* has narrow lance-like leaves.
var. *nanum* is only about 9″ tall and bears pinkish flowers.

Propagate by seed, root cuttings or division.

Quick Key to Limonium Species

A. Plant 10–15″ tall, corolla reddish, leaves smooth, not hairy,
4–6″ long.. *L. tataricum*
AA. Plant 24–30″ tall, corolla lavender, leaves hairy, 6–10″ long .. *L. latifolium*

Linum (ly′ num)	Flax	Linaceae

Flax has been grown for centuries for oil, fiber and ornament. The perennial *L. perenne* and the annual *L. usitatissimum*, common flax, were grown for fiber to make linen, cordage and rope. During Tudor times in England, when linen tableclothes adorned the tables of abbots and kings, a royal proclamation was issued that a better source of cordage was necessary to properly equip the newly established Royal Navy. *Linum* was replaced by *Cannabis sativa* as the source of royal rope. Little did they know about the other mind-bending properties of this now infamous plant! Linseed oil is produced from the seeds of *L. usitatissimum*.

Three or four species out of the approximately 150 are used for ornamental purposes. The red-flowered *L. grandiflorum*, flowering flax, is an excellent annual but most others are perennial. In general, they are short-lived plants but reseed prolifically. Named cultivars may be propagated vegetatively. The flowers are 5-petaled and are blue, white, yellow, or occasionally red. Although the individual flowers last only a day, so many flowers are produced that the plant is in flower over a 4–6 week period. The leaves are alternate, narrow, and usually entire.

Linum is easily grown in a light, well-drained soil in full sun. Propagate by divisions or stem cuttings, or from seed sown in a cool area where soil temperature is 50–60°F.

Quick Reference to Linum Species

	Height (in.)	Flower color
L. flavum	15–18	Yellow
L. narbonense	18–24	Blue
L. perenne	12–18	Blue

-flavum (flay' vum)		Golden Flax	15–18'/12"
Summer	Yellow	Europe	Zones 5–8

The fact that this species is not offered by more nurserymen is a shame, especially as some cultivars and varieties are of exceptional garden merit. The 1" diameter golden yellow flowers consist of petals much larger than the sepals. Up to fifty flowers may be carried in a single inflorescence (cyme). The narrow, lanceolate leaves have 3–5 veins and small glands on each side of the leaf base. Plants benefit from a loose mulch of pine straw, leaves, or wheat straw over the winter.

Cultivars:

var. *compactum* is superior to the type, stands 6–9" tall, and is covered with yellow flowers.

'Gemmel's Hybrid' is closely related to *L. flavum* and is either a cultivar or a hybrid with *L. flavum* as a parent. I saw this plant when wandering through Harlow Car Gardens near Harrogate, England. A compact plant (only 9–12" tall), it was smothered in exceptionally bright golden flowers. Perhaps it will be offered in the United States in the near future.

Related Species:

L. capitatum, purging flax, is similar to golden flax but the leaves are in basal rosettes and the flowers occur in a dense inflorescence. Much of the material sold under this name is *L. flavum*.

-narbonense (nar-bon-en' see)		Narbonne Flax	18–24"/18"
Summer	Blue	Southern Europe	Zones 5–9

This long-lived blue-flowered species is one of the best for the garden. Winter protection must be provided in zone 5 and north. The 2" wide funnel-shaped flowers are blue with a clear white center. The stamens are also white, contributing to the bicolor effect. The ¾" long, narrow leaves have three veins. After flowering, cut back stems to eight inches. Similar to the other *Linum* species, well-drained soils are necessary, and plants flower well in full sun or partial shade.

Cultivars:

'Heavenly Blue' has ultramarine flowers on 12–18" tall stems. More compact than the species, it does not fall over with rain and wind. Greater compactness, however, is still required and would be most welcome.

Related Species:

L. salsaloides, Russian thistle flax, has 1" diameter white flowers with purple veins. The foliage is needle-like. Plants are more useful for gardens west of the Rocky Mountains. Variety *nanum* is only 2–4" tall and prostrate. It is excellent where low-growing white-flowered plants are needed.

-perenne (pe-ren' ee)		Perennial Flax	12–18"/12"
Spring	Blue	Europe	Zones 4–9

The flowers are more open than those of *L. narbonense*, smaller, and without a white eye. The ¾" wide, azure blue flowers open for up to 12 weeks when planted in partial shade. In the Horticulture Gardens at the University of Georgia, the first flowers open in early April and continue into early July. The narrow 1" long leaves transpire little water and tolerate the heat of southern summers. As with other flax species, it abhors wet feet and will not return next spring if winter drainage is poor. When planted in a group of six or more, the plants provide a lovely display. The stems become long and leggy in the heat of the summer and require pruning after flowering.

Cultivars:

var. *album* is widely available with white flowers on upright stems. It is not a clear white, however, and appears washed out in full sun.

var. *alpinum* (syn. *L. alpinum*), alpine flax, grows 8–12" tall with slender, wiry stems which carry ¾" wide, clear blue flowers. It is not as floriferous as the species, but if given well-drained soil in full sun, lovely drifts of blue result.

var. *nanum* is a shorter (6–12" tall) version of the species.

'Saphyr' has blue flowers and is more compact than the species. It is an excellent garden plant.

Seed-grown plants often flower the first year. Divide in spring or early fall.

Quick Key to Linum Species
> A. Flowers yellow... *L. flavum*
> AA. Flowers blue or white, not yellow

B. Flowers blue with white eye, funnel shaped, 1½–2″ in diameter........
  L. narbonense

BB. Flowers blue without eye, saucer shaped, 1″ or less in diameter.........
  L. perenne

Liriope (lear'ree-ope, le-rye'o-pee) Lily-turf Liliaceae

In the *Standard Cyclopedia of Horticuture* by L. H. Bailey (written 1900, revised until 1943), *Liriope* received a minimum of space because it was "little cultivated". Today, it is one the premier and predominant landscape ground-cover plants in the South. Of the five species, only *L. muscari* is commonly cultivated.

-muscari (mus-cah' ree)		Blue Lily-turf	12–18″/12″
Late Summer	Lilac	Eastern Asia	Zones 6–9

A healthy disregard for heat, humidity, and drought, and a built-in resistance to insects and diseases make this an excellent ground cover. The strap-like, dark

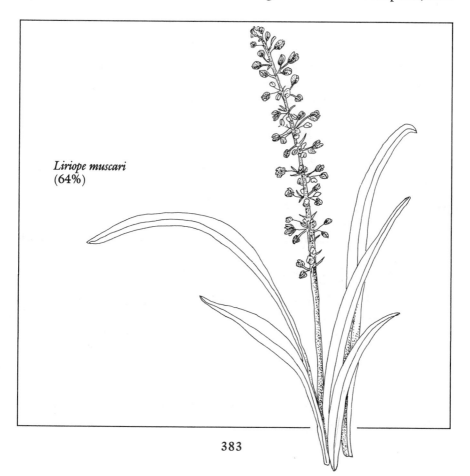

Liriope muscari
(64%)

383

green 1–1½″ wide evergreen leaves emerge from the crown of the plant. The lilac-purple flowers are borne on dense spike-like flower stalks in August. Dark black berries ripen in the fall and persist into the winter. Plants are not particular concerning soils, if drainage is adequate. Large clumps are formed by means of the short, thickened stoloniferous roots.

When planted 8–12″ apart, *Liriope* provides an effective ground cover which can substitute for grass. Plants tolerate heavy shade although they will take longer to spread and the flower stems are more elongated compared with plants grown in full sun. In late winter, plantings may be mowed to the ground to eliminate old foliage and allow a new flush of growth in the spring. The true pinnacle of success of a plant is when it does so well as to be taken for granted. This is true for this plant in the South.

Liriope is closely related to *Ophiopogon*, mondo grass, but is hardier, has broader leaves, and flowers above the foliage while the flowers of mondo grass often occur deep within the foliage.

Cultivars:

Green-leaved forms:

'Christmas Tree' (Munroe #2) has unique lilac flowers on spikes which are much wider at the base and taper towards the tip, resembling a Christmas tree.

'Lilac Beauty' bears showy, stiff, lilac flower clusters held well above the foliage.

'Majestic' has larger, deep lilac flowers.

'Munroe's White' (Munroe #1) is an excellent white-flowered cultivar but is slower growing than the lilac types. The flowers stand out and provide an additional dimension to the species.

Variegated forms:

The variegation pattern does not stand out as well in heavy shade as in full sun.

'Gold Banded' has wide arching leaves with a narrow gold band down the middle and bears lavender flowers.

'John Burch' produces attractive variegated foliage and cockscomb-shaped lilac flower spikes.

'Silvery Midget' grows about 8″ tall, and bears short green leaves with narrow white bands.

'Silvery Sunproof' has almost white leaves in full sun but more green or yellow-green in partial shade. Flowers are lavender.

var. *variegata*, the prettiest and most common of all the lily-turfs, bears creamy margins which brighten up any landscape. Flowers appear about 2 weeks later than the species. This variety does not spread as rapidly as the type so it is more expensive to purchase. Seeds yield about 65% variegated plants.

Propagation by division results in many plantlets which can be replanted or handed over the fence to a new neighbor. The seed coat contains a water soluble inhibitor and soaking seeds in warm water results in more uniform and faster germination. Tissue culture has also been successfully used to multiply slower cultivars.

Related Species:

Liriope spicata, creeping liriope, is cold hardy to zone 4 and used as a rapidly spreading ground cover. It is only 12–18″ tall and has narrower leaves (only about ¼″ wide) than *L. muscari*. Plants, in effect, resemble tall grass. Foliage tends to be more yellow-green during the winter than *L. muscari*. The pale lavender flowers are not as showy as those of *L. muscari*.

Additional Reading:

Fagan, Ann E., M.A. Dirr, and F.A. Pokorny. 1981. Effects of depulping, stratification, and growth regulators on seed germination of *Liriope muscari*. *HortScience* 16(2):208–209.

Hume, Harold H. 1961. The Ophiopogon-Liriope Complex. *Baileya* 9:135–158.

Rackeman, Adelaide. 1987. Lilyturf. *Horticulture* 65(8):42–43.

Smith, Gerald and Henry Clay. 1982. Liriope culture in Georgia. Co-operative Extension Service, *University of Georgia, Bulletin 755*, 10 pp.

Lithodora (lith-o-do′ ra)   Lithodora   Boraginaceae

L. diffusa, acidsoil lithodora, is a common European plant, and grown there as *Lithospermum diffusum*. I greatly admire the lovely blue flowers and creeping habit. However, there is only one mention of lithodora in the dozen or so American garden catalogs I have piled around me. Of the approximately seven species, *L. diffusa* is the best garden species. Athough best suited to the climate of the Pacific Northwest, with adequate protection and a proper site, it can also be a valuable plant in the Northeast.

-diffusa (di-few′ sa)		Acidsoil Lithodora	8–12″/12″
Summer	Blue	Southern Europe	Zones 6–8

(Syn. *Lithospermum diffusum*)

This low-growing plant has ¼–1″ long, alternate, narrow, sessile leaves, hairy on both surfaces. The ½″ long flowers occur at the end of lateral stems which emerge from each leaf axil. They are deep blue with reddish violet stripes and appear from midsummer to fall. Plants are not particularly tolerant of weather extremes and suffer in the South, particularly if placed in full sun or allowed to dry out. In the North, mulching is beneficial in zones 5 and 6. The common name results from the intolerance to lime, and like *Iris kaempferi*, Japanese iris, requires acid soils for optimum performance. This is not true of other species of *Lithodora* or *Lithospermum*.

Cultivars:

var. *alba* has white flowers but is not as showy as the species or the following
   cultivars. Who wants a white lithodora?
'Grace Ward' consists of silvery green mats with dark blue flowers.
'Heavenly Blue' is the best cultivar and bears numerous clear blue flowers.

If propagated by soft stem cuttings in humid, warm conditions, rooting takes
place in 14 to 21 days. Seeds may also be used but the seed coat is hard and
germination takes a long time unless seeds are soaked in warm water for at least
two days, or the seed coat is scarified with light sandpaper or other abrasive
material.

Lobelia (lo-bee' lia)   Lobelia   Campanulaceae

Lobelia consists of over 250 species of annual and perennial herbaceous
plants. One of the most popular bedding plants is the blue-flowered annual
lobelia, *L. erinus*, used for edging or in hanging baskets. The perennial species,
however, provide a brilliant splash of summer color and range from the deepest
scarlet to the darkest blue. All have alternate leaves and tubular or star-shaped
flowers on racemose inflorescences held well above the leaves.

The perennial lobelias are somewhat short-lived and must be replaced or
divided at least every three years. Many are native to stream banks and other
areas of moist soil and prefer a rich, moist, but well-drained location in the
shaded garden. In the Northeast and Northwest, plants tolerate full sun or partial shade, but in the Midwest and South, shade is essential. Regardless of where
they are grown, a light (½–1″ deep) winter mulch is beneficial. If mulched
heavily, plants die. Remove mulch early in the spring.

Considerable breeding has produced hybrid strains with dark stems and brilliant scarlet or purple flowers. They are excellent additions to the lobelias and
without doubt, will be offered by more perennial specialists.

The species may be propagated from seed or division; the hybrids and
named cultivars should only be divided. Seed is tiny and should be lightly covered to insure it does not dry out. Sow under warm (70–75°F), moist conditions.

Quick Reference to Lobelia Species

	Height (ft.)	Flower color
L. cardinalis	2–4	Red
L. × gerardii	3–5	Purple
L. syphilitica	2–3	Blue

-cardinalis (kar-di-nah′ lis)   Cardinal Flower   2–4′/2′
Summer   Red   North America   Zones 2–9

This species has an extensive natural range; occurring as far north as New Brunswick, south to Florida, and west to Texas. The plant is usually unbranched with 3–4″ long, dark green, irregularly toothed leaves attached either directly to the stem or by a short petiole. Each 1½″ long flower is brilliant cardinal and the lower lip, consisting of 3 distinct lobes, is bent downwards. Up to 50 flowers may be produced on a single 2′ long inflorescence. In my garden, flowering begins in early August and continues for about three weeks. Flowers open from

Lobelia cardinalis
(64%)

387

the base to the apex (acropetally) but by the end of three weeks, the inflorescence looks "tired".

Soil amended with copious amounts of aged manure or peat moss, and one which will retain moisture during dry weather is essential for good garden performance and longevity. Growth and flowering occur in dry areas but flowers are not as persistent or dramatic. In most parts of the country, shade should be provided for most of the day, and certainly during late afternoon. Abundant seed is produced which may be sown in a greenhouse, cold frame, or allowed to self-sow.

Related Species:

L. splendens (syn. *L. fulgens*), Mexican lobelia, is closely related to *L. cardinalis*. Plants have larger bracts beneath the flowers, are more pubescent, and usually have bronze stems and leaves. Bronze-leaf cardinal flowers, particularly if grown from seed, are likely *L. splendens*. Although spectacular in flower, they are less cold hardy (to zone 7 or 8), shorter lived, and not as tolerant of dry soils as *L. cardinalis*.

Hybrids:

Numerous hybrids have been developed from *L. splendens*, *L. cardinalis*, and *L. syphilitica* and grouped under the catchall name of *L. × hybrida* (or sometimes *L. splendens* var. *hybrida*). The addition of the other two species to *L. splendens* results in hybrids which are longer-lived and more tolerant of garden conditions. If a perennial bronze-foliaged cardinal flower is necessary, it will be well to stay away from *L. splendens* and consider the hybrids.

'Bees' Flame' bears vermillion-red flowers and beet-red foliage and can reach heights of five feet. This is an absolutely magnificent plant in moist, partially shaded conditions.

'Queen Victoria' is the most popular cardinal flower with brilliant red flowers over bronze foliage. In flower, plants grow to 5' tall.

Propagate from offshoots in late summer and fall. Stem cuttings in midsummer or seed may also be used.

Related Species:

L. tupa, blood lobelia, has unique wrinkled, gray-green, soft downy leaves. Plants are more branched and usually not as tall as *L. cardinalis*. The 2–4" long tubular scarlet-red flowers are held in terminal racemes, and while not as spectacular as cardinal flower, provide a lovely display in late summer and early fall. Plants are cold hardy to zone 8 and do moderately well in the South.

-× *gerardii* (ger-ard-ee' eye)	Hybrid Purple Lobelia	3–5'/2'
Summer	Purple	Hybrid	Zones 4–8

(Syn. *L. × vedariensis*)

The result of a cross between *L.* × *hybrida* 'Queen Victoria' and *L. syphili-tica*, plants are sometimes included under *L.* × *hybrida*. The habit of the plant is similar to *L. cardinalis*, with unbranched stems bearing many star-shaped purple flowers on spike-like racemes. The 4–6″ long clasping leaves are dark green and elliptical. Stems are strong and seldom need staking.

This hybrid appears longer-lived than the species. Moist soil, partial shade and a light winter mulch are recommended.

Terminal cuttings or division are the common methods of propagation but *L.* × *gerardii* comes fairly true from seed.

-syphilitica (si-fi-li′ ti-ka)	Big Blue Lobelia	2–3′/1½′
Late Summer	Blue	Eastern United States	Zones 4–8

The specific name arose from the supposed medicinal properties but plants are now grown for ornamental value only. The one inch long blue flowers are surrounded by leafy bracts and look weedier than *L. cardinalis*. The flowers, which tend to fade into the bracts, are held in dense terminal racemes above the unbranched plants. They appear later than cardinal flower and persist for about four weeks. The 3–5″ long leaves are narrowed at both ends and attached directly to the flower stem (the bottom leaves have short petioles). Constant moisture and partial shade are necessary for optimum performance but, unfortunately, plants are short-lived and should be divided and moved every 2–3 years.

Cultivars:

'Blue Peter', developed by Blooms Nursery in England, has light blue flowers on a three-foot plant and may prove more perennial than others.

Propagate the species by seed and cultivars by division.

Hybrids:

L. × *speciosa* is a tetraploid (double the usual number of chromosomes, see *Hemerocallis*) recently developed by Wray Bowden at Ottawa, Canada. Parents include *L. siphilitica*, *L. cardinalis*, 'Queen Victoria' and 'Illumination'. The plants have large flowers, thick, stiffly erect stems, thick leaf blades, and well-developed fibrous roots. The stems usually have a bronze cast and although still somewhat short-lived, are winter hardy to zone 3 and appear to be excellent garden plants. Numerous cultivars have been developed and six of the best are listed.

'Brightness' is 3–4′ tall with bright cherry-red flowers atop dark bronze foliage.
'Hamilton Dwarf' is only 2′ tall with 6″ long blood-red racemes maturing to crimson.
'Oakes Ames' bears deep scarlet flowers and bronze stems and leaves.
'Robert Landon' produces large cherry-red flowers and has proven exceptional in tests in Ottawa.
'Simcoe' also has scarlet flowers on 2′ long racemes.
'Wisley' has lighter red flowers and stem color than 'Oakes Ames'.

Quick Key to Lobelia Species

    A. Flowers red to scarlet
        B. Stems green, or mostly so, flowers obviously lipped .... *L. cardinalis*
        BB. Stems bronze or tinged red, flowers star-shaped or lipped ....
                                                                                   L. × *hybrida*
    AA. Flowers blue to purple
        B. Flowers clear blue, obviously lipped, hairy .... *L. syphilitica*
        BB. Flowers purple, star shaped, not hairy .... *L.* × *gerardii*

Additional Reading:

Bowden, Wray. 1984. Perennial tetraploid lobelia hybrids. *The Garden* 109(2):55–57.

Lunaria (loon-air' ee-a)   Honesty, Money Plant   Brassicaceae

    Honesty has been a popular garden plant since Victorian times when it was first grown for the round papery-thin fruit (silicles). The most common species is the biennial dollar plant, *L. annua*, and the only one listed in most garden catalogs. However, *L. rediviva*, perennial honesty, is more persistent. The fruit is more elongated than those of *L. annua* and not as ornamental. This probably accounts for its almost total absence in the United States.

    Lunaria is not difficult to grow and does well in almost any garden soil if some afternoon shade is provided. The leaves are opposite, toothed and heart-shaped. The purple or white flowers are held above the foliage and fruit is present while the uppermost flowers are still opening.

Quick Reference to Lunaria Species

	Height *(ft.)*	*Flower* *color*	*Fruit* *shape*
L. annua	2–3	Purple, white	Round
L. rediviva	3–4	Purple	Oblong

-*annua* (an-ew' a)		Honesty, Dollar Plant	2–3'/2'
Spring	Purple	Europe	Zones 4–8

(Syn. *L. biennis*)

    While technically a biennial species, it self sows so readily that it is always somewhere in the garden, although probably not where originally planted. An April visit to my friend, Mrs. Laura Ann Segrest, is always a delight when *Lunaria* is in flower and fruit throughout her garden. A great deal of variation occurs in the species and the heart-shaped leaves may be opposite or alternate. They are coarsely toothed and the upper leaves are sessile. The flowers of the species are purple but the var. *alba*, with white flowers, is just as common. When seed or plants are purchased, there is a good chance that both colors will be present.

The fruit is the most ornamental part of the plant and is 2″ wide, round, and papery thin. If brought inside, the stems must be cut just as the green color disappears from the fruit. Hang upside down in a cool, well ventilated place for 3–5 weeks. They dry exceptionally well and make wonderful additions to winter bouquets.

Plants should be placed in full sun in the North and away from afternoon sun in the South. The white-flowered forms are handsome in the spring shade garden as light reflects off the flowers and brightens the surrounding greenery. Flowering occurs in late April in north Georgia (zone 8), and mid-May in Iowa (zone 5).

Cultivars:

var. *alba* has white flowers (see text).
var. *atrococcinea* has deep red flowers.
'Munstead Purple' has flowers of rich purple.
var. *variegata* bears leaves with irregular white margins resulting in a plant with
   interesting foliage, good-looking flowers and desirable fruit.

All varieties can be raised from seed (although var. *variegata* yields variegated and green leaf forms). Seed germinates irregularly over time; placing seed at 35–40°F for 4 weeks enhances uniformity.

-rediviva (re-di-veev′ a)	Perennial Honesty		3–4′/2½′
Spring	White	Europe	Zones 4–8

This plant's existence is a well kept secret, for I can find no offering of perennial honesty in the United States. Plants are larger than *L. annua*, have finely toothed, petioled leaves and smaller, lighter purple, more fragrant flowers. The main difference, however, is the 2–3″ long, 1″ broad elliptical fruit compared to the round fruit of *L. annua*. They may be dried similar to those of *L. annua*. Although not as well known as money plant, this species is worth seeking. Well-drained soil in partial shade provides optimum growing conditions. Do not allow soil to dry out. Propagate from division in spring or by seed. Seed must be kept warm and moist for the first two weeks, then placed at freezing or just above for 4–6 weeks. Finally, expose seeds to 70–75°F until germination occurs. This system of germination is best accomplished by sowing seed in the fall and burying the seed trays in soil for the winter. Seed germinates in the spring.

Quick Key to Lunaria Species

   A. Upper leaves sessile, silicles round.............................. *L. annua*
   AA. Upper leaves with long petioles, silicles elliptical .... *L. rediviva*

Additional Reading:

Brandies, Monica. 1986. *Lunaria. Horticulture* 64(8):26–27.

Lupinus (loo-py' nus)   Lupine   Fabaceae

Flowers more perfect than those of the lupine hybrids are difficult to imagine. One of my most vivid memories is the Lupine Garden at Chatsworth House, England. Great drifts of orange, blue, white and purple assailed my senses as I neared the walled garden. As each flower took shape, nowhere could I look without sucking in my breath in utter delight. The scene was simply too perfect to be true.

One does not have to go to England, however, to see beautiful lupines. They are, in fact, relatively easy to grow and if soils are rich and conditions are cool, flowers persist for weeks in the spring garden. Few flowers withstand close scrutiny as well as the lupine; they look even more perfect from 3 inches than from 3 feet. The multicolored spires add an aristocratic aura to the garden available from few other species. Many of the over 300 species are native to western North America, but the hybrids, particularly the Russell hybrids, are the overwhelming favorites of North American gardeners.

Numerous handsome annuals occur such as *L. hartwegii*, Hartweg lupine, a 2–3' tall plant with blue and rose spikes and *L. luteus*, European yellow lupine, with yellow, fragrant flowers on 1½ –2' tall stems. A lovely perennial species is *L. arborescens*, the tree lupine, native to California and growing well on the West Coast. This sub-shrub bears many stems with lemon-yellow flowers although occasionally violet or white are seen. The best known of the perennial species, however, is the Washington lupine, *L. polyphyllus*, also native to the west coast. Unlike other West Coast natives, plants are tolerant of cold, heat and humidity (zones 3–6). Leaves consist of 10–16 finger-like leaflets and flowers are normally deep blue although var. *albus* has white flowers and var. *roseus* has rose blooms.

Hybrids:

James Kelway of Langport, England crossed *L. polyphyllus* with *L. arborescens* in the late 1890's and other English pioneers such as Downer and Harkness continued the early development of lupines by developing hybrids with many different flower colors. One of the first breakthroughs was the red 'Downer's Delight' raised about 1917 and honored by the Royal Horticultural Society in 1918.

In 1911, the flowers of the various cultivars, forms and hybrids of *L. polyphyllus* caught the attention of a hobby gardener from Yorkshire, England by the name of George Russell. He continued to cross various forms of *L. polyphyllus* with *L. arborescens* as well as with species such as *L. mutabilis* (a five-foot plant with white and blue flowers) from South America, and *L. nanus* (a lovely 1' tall annual with blue flowers) from California. By 1937, Russell had perfected

392

flowers of blue, purple, yellow, intense reds, deep pinks, and numerous combinations of bicolors. Many of these original breakthroughs are still available today as Russell hybrids. Development of the herbaceous lupines has continued since Russell's time and new cultivars appear every year.

Unfortunately, few of the hybrid lupines tolerate the heat and humidity of warm summers and are best treated as annuals in zones 6 and south. This is not as bad as it seems as they look terrific in March and April if planted in November. Even in the Northeast, lupines tend to be short-lived and should routinely be replaced in the fall. Plant in full sun in well-drained, acidic soil. Often self-sown seedlings emerge, and although the progeny will not be the same as the parents, half the fun is guessing just what is coming next.

Cultivars:

'Gallery Hybrids' are 15–18″ tall and occur in shades of blue, pink, red and white.

'Minarette' consists of dwarf (18–20″) plants in mixed colors.

'My Castle' is 2–3′ tall with brick red flowers.

'Noble Maiden' bears white flowers atop 2′ tall plants.

'The Governor' produces perfect blue and purple flowers on 2–3′ tall stems.

Seeds of some of the species are difficult to germinate and should be soaked in warm water overnight or placed in containers and provided with 4–6 weeks of cold, moist stratification between 30 and 40°F. Seeds of the hybrids are available as complete mixes or as single colors.

Additional Reading:

Foster, Catherine Osgood. 1984. Lupines. *Horticulture* 62(5):32–35.

Lychnis (lick′ nis)   Campion   Caryophyllaceae

Lychnis comes from the Greek *lychnos*, meaning lamp, and provides an apt description of the flame-colored flowers of certain species. There was so much variation in species originally placed in the genus that many have been transferred to other genera such as *Silene* and *Agrostemma*. Such is the imperfection of plant classification. For the garden taxonomists (these are people who derive special pleasures from tearing apart flowers), a few of the differences between the three genera are presented below. Next month, they may be different.

Some differences between Agrostemma, Lychnis, and Silene

    A. Number of styles (female part of the flower), 3.................... *Silene*
  AA. Number of styles, 4 or 5
      B. Styles opposite the petals .... *Agrostemma*
    BB. Styles alternate with the petals .... *Lychnis*

To add to the confusion, a carmine-red-flowered intergeneric hybrid arose between *Lychnis* and *Silene*; × *Lychsilene grandiflora*.

Of the ten species, many are brilliantly colored but short-lived garden plants. Most have simple, opposite leaves and bright orange, rose, or red flowers produced singly, in twos or in many-flowered clusters. In many areas of the South, they are like shooting stars, brilliant during their time but quickly disappearing. Further north, they persist longer but still must be replaced every few years.

All species are easily propagated from seed which may be sown directly in the garden or in containers for subsequent transplanting.

Quick Reference to Lychnis Species

	Height (in.)	Flower color	Inflorescence few- or many-flowered
L. × arkwrightii	18–24	Orange-scarlet	Few
L. chalcedonica	24–36	Scarlet	Many
L. coronaria	24–36	Rose	Few
L. flos-cuculi	12–24	Deep rose	Few
L. × haageana	10–18	Orange-scarlet	Few
L. viscaria	12–18	Red	Many

-× *arkwrightii* (ark-right' ee-eye)	Arkwright's Campion	18–24"/12"
Early Summer Orange-scarlet	Hybrid origin	Zones 6–8

This hybrid, between *L. chalcedonica*, Maltese cross and *L. × haageana*, Haage campion, is gaining popularity due to the brilliant orange-scarlet flowers. The 1½" wide flowers are carried in a 3–10 flowered cyme and contrast well with the dark bronze foliage. They have notched petals and are often borne singly the first year. Garden longevity is a little better than *L. × haageana* but not as permanent as *L. chalcedonica*. In the South, longevity is 2–3 years; in the North, one or more additional seasons may be possible. Plants should be pinched early in the season to force additional shoots and reduce the potential legginess. In their first year in the Horticulture Gardens at Georgia, plants flowered from April 27 to June 25. After flowering, the swollen seed pods turned from green to brown providing additional interest in the season.

Shade should be provided in zones 7 and 8 but full sun is acceptable further north. Unfortunately, insufficient information is available to accurately determine the northern limits when mulched in the winter.

Cultivars:

'Vesuvius' is similar but has vermillion flowers, a color one either loves or hates.

Propagate by division or stem cuttings. Little variation occurs with seed grown plants.

-*chalcedonica* (chal-ce-don' i-ka)	Maltese Cross	24–36"/18"
Summer Scarlet	Eastern Russia	Zones 3–9

Maltese cross was a favorite in every grandmother's garden (it was in mine) and perhaps for that reason, is often referred to as an old-fashioned flower. Ease of cultivation and rich flower color keep this species popular today. The ¾–1" wide flowers are deep scarlet and held in dense rounded clusters of twenty to fifty. The individual, 4-petaled flowers are shaped like a cross, thus the common name. The opposite, 2–4" long dark green leaves often clasp the stem.

This is the most persistent species of the genus. Plants perform best in well-drained soil with consistent moisture and full sun.

Cultivars:

var. *rubra-plena*, a double red form, is even more brilliantly colored than the type. Plants are difficult to produce commercially thus difficult to locate. White, salmon, and rose forms are available but none is equal to the scarlet.

They are easily raised from seed and divisions.

-coronaria (ko-ro-nah' ree-a)	Rose Campion	24–36"/18"
Spring	Rose	Southern Europe	Zones 4–8

Rose campion is probably the showiest species when well grown. The woolly, 2–4" oblong leaves are grayish green and contrast with the 1–2" wide, single, rose to red flowers profusely produced during the summer. The flowers almost glow, making them difficult to coordinate with other plants.

There are, however, other problems associated with this species. It is not a true perennial and although plants may survive a number of seasons, should be treated as biennials or annuals. In the South, flowering is magnificent and decline rapid. Second year plants are often better than first year and may bloom profusely on 3' high and equally wide bushy, gray-green specimens. The heat and summer rains of the second season result in loss of much of the foliage and plants that return to life the next spring are tired from their struggle to survive. However, they seed themselves prolifically and never disappear. The same is true in the North, although flower colors are brighter due to cooler night temperatures in the summer. The plants are also short-lived there.

For best results, place in full sun, or provide shade from afternoon sun, in well-drained soil. To overwinter plants in areas of little snow cover, plant in raised beds or place a liberal addition of gravel around the roots.

Cultivars:

'Abbotswood Rose' is a compact, floriferous plant covered with soft pink flowers in late spring.
var. *alba* has white flowers.
var. *atrosanguinea* bears carmine-red flowers.

All preceding cultivars have silver-green leaves like the type.

Related Species:

L. flos-jovis, Flower-of-Jove (Jupiter), is similar, also bearing white-woolly foliage. The plants are only 1–2' tall with muted scarlet flowers about ¾" wide. The lobed flowers are carried in a loose inflorescence somewhat similar to the flower head of primrose. Plants are longer lived than those of rose campion and should be used more in this country. 'Hort's Variety' bears clear rose-pink flowers.

L. × *walkeri*, a hybrid between *L. coronaria* and *L. flos-jovis*, has carmine-red flowers on short flower stems.

Propagation of all species can be accomplished from seed or basal cuttings taken in the spring.

-flos-cuculi (flos-kew-kew' lee)		Ragged Robin	12–24"/12"
Summer	Deep Rose	Europe	Zones 3–8

From the rosette of narrow, grass-like, gray-green leaves emerge many stems bearing 1–3 rose to red flowers. The petals are deeply cut into four segments thus resembling a "ragged robin". Flowering persists for 6–8 weeks. Plants are adapted to sunny, moist areas and do well in the garden only if sufficient moisture can be provided.

Cultivars:

var. *albiflora* has clear white flowers but is otherwise similar to the species.
var. *pleniflora* is an excellent selection, bearing double flowers of deep rose. This
double campion was known as bachelor's buttons during Elizabethan times.

Seed is the best means of propagation. Seed placed in warm (70–75°F), humid conditions germinates within 21 days.

- × haageana (hah'gee -ah' na)		Haage Campion	10–18"/12"
Summer	Orange-scarlet	Hybrid origin	Zones 3–9

It is interesting that this plant, which is fast becoming established in American gardens, is a hybrid between two species seldom used as ornamental plants. The cross occurred between *L. fulgens*, brilliant campion, a 2–3' tall plant with bright scarlet flowers and *L. coronata* var. *sieboldii*, crown campion, a 10–12" tall plant with white, slightly notched petals. The result is a good garden plant with large, 2" wide, orange-scarlet flowers. The flowers are distinctive, having two-lobed petals, each having small teeth on the margin.

Full sun and consistent moisture are keys to growing this hybrid, although partial shade is beneficial in the South. Although often placed at the front of the garden because of size, the bright flowers are noticeable even in the shadow of taller neighbors. Plants may go dormant in late summer in the southern half of the country but reappear the following spring. As with other species of *Lychnis*, two to four years is the normal life span, after which replacement is necessary.

Slugs enjoy dining on this delicacy and suitable slug deterrents should be used in early spring.

Although a hybrid, plants come fairly true from seed.

-viscaria (vis-cah' ree-a)	German Catchfly	12–18"/10"
Early Summer	Magenta	Europe	Zones 3–8

(Syn. *Viscaria vulgaris*)

This plant is sometimes included in a separate genus, *Viscaria*, however, similarities with other *Lychnis* species indicate it should be included here. The foliage is grass-like and grows in tufts. The 1" wide magenta flowers appear in early summer and are sometimes difficult to weave into the overall color scheme. The flower stalk is sticky (viscous) just below the 3 to 5-flowered panicle, as are the internodes, thus accounting for the specific and common name.

Plants tolerate full sun in the North but partial shade is required in the South. They are more tolerant of dry conditions than many other members of the genus.

Cultivars:

var. *alba* bears white flowers.

var. *splendens flore-plena* has double rose-pink flowers and is the best form of the species.

Propagate by seed or division.

Quick Key to Lychnis Species

    A. Foliage gray-white, woolly throughout
        B. Flowers borne singly or in 2–3's, magenta, plants 2–3' tall............
                                                                         L. coronaria
      BB. Flowers borne in clusters, pink, plants 1–2' tall .... *L. flos-jovis*
  AA. Foliage predominantly green or bronze, but may be hairy
        B. Inflorescence a dense head, terminal
           C. Flowers orange-scarlet, 5–15 flowers in head, foliage bronze, plants 18–24" tall........................ *L.* × *arkwrightii*
          CC. Flowers red-scarlet, 20–40 flowers in head, foliage green, plants 24–36" tall............................ *L. chalcedonica*
      BB. Inflorescence open, panicle, raceme or cyme
        C. Petals deeply 4-lobed................................. *L. flos-cuculi*
        CC. Petals notched, toothed, or entire
           D. Petals slightly notched, flower stalks sticky .... *L. viscaria*
          DD. Petals toothed, flower stalks not sticky .... *L.* × *haageana*

Additional Reading:

Lawrence, G.H.M. 1953. The cultivated species of *Lychnis*. *Baileya* 1:105–114.

Lycoris (lie' core-is)   Resurrection Flower   Amaryllidaceae

This bulbous genus consists of about eleven species with interesting, eye-catching flowers. The leaves arise in fall, winter or early spring and persist until early summer. The unwary gardener might believe that the bulbs have died and should be removed. In late summer and fall, however, smooth straight flower stalks arise from seemingly barren ground (thus its common name) to produce umbels of small trumpet-like flowers of pink, red, yellow or white. The flowers and plant habit are remarkably similar to *Nerine sarniensis*, an excellent cut flower species native to south Africa also exhibiting summer dormancy. In some

Lycoris radiata
(64%)

species, the stamens are extended far beyond the petals, resulting in the common name, spider flower.

Bulbs should be planted about 6″ deep in the fall in full sun or partial shade and overplanted with annuals or low-growing perennials. Only *L. squamigera*, autumn lycoris, is reliably cold hardy north of zone 7. All species spread by bulb offsets. Divide and replant after flowering. Offsets flower in 1–2 years.

Quick Reference to Lycoris Species

	Height (in.)	Flower color	Flowering time
L. africana	12–24	Yellow	Summer
L. radiata	12–18	Red	Fall
L. squamigera	18–24	Pink	Late summer

-africana (af-ri-kah′ na)		Golden Lycoris	1–2′/2′
Summer	Yellow, gold	China	Zones 7–10

(Syn. *L. aurea*)

In the fall, bulbs produce ¾″ wide, glaucous, sword-shaped foliage, which dies back in late spring. The 3″ long funnel-shaped golden-yellow flowers appear on 18″ long scapes in summer. The stamens and style protrude slightly from the flower (exserted).

Bulbs should be planted so the neck is just below the soil surface. Since flower buds are formed during winter and spring, beds must be well drained during those seasons or flowers will not develop.

-radiata (raid-ee-ah′ ta)		Short Tube Lycoris	12–18″/12″
Fall	Red	China, Japan	Zones 8–10

L. radiata has the shortest flower tube, thus the common name, and the smallest flower among the common garden species. The 1½–2″ long flowers, however, provide brilliant splashes of deep red in September and October. The leaves, which emerge in fall and persist through the winter, are only 4–6″ long and ¼″ wide making them much less of a nuisance than those of the other species. Unfortunately, flowers persist for less than two weeks. Plant in full sun—fewer flowers occur in partial shade.

Cultivars:

var. *alba* has white flowers with yellow tinges at the base of the segments. It is pretty but cannot compare to the species.

Related Species:

L. albiflora is similar to the species buts bears smaller white flowers and narrower leaves. Bulbs are marginally hardy in zone 8.

L. incarnata, native to Japan, has magnificent white flowers with pink stripes. The flower stems are 15–20″ long.

L. sanguinea, red heart lycoris, bears four to six 2″ long dull red flowers in August and September. The stamens are not as exserted as *L. radiata*. Plants are 12–20″ tall.

-squamigera (skwah-mi′ ge-ra)   Autumn Lycoris   18–24″/24″
Late Summer   Rose-pink   Japan   Zones 5–9

Autumn lycoris is the most common because of its greater growing range. Cold hardy to zone 5, the lovely rose pink flowers may be enjoyed by many more gardeners. Approximately four to seven, 3″ long fragrant flowers appear on 2′ tall scapes in late summer. Although the flowers are wonderful, the spring foliage is messy as it dies down. The 9–12″ long and 1″ wide leaves are fresh in the early spring, but look terrible in late spring and summer. The size and density of the foliage make it difficult to interplant annuals. Bulbs spread rapidly, however, and make wonderful gifts to neighbors.

Cultivars:

var. *purpurea* bears lilac to purple flowers.

Quick Key to Lycoris Species

    A. Flowers pink or red, not yellow,
        B. Flowers rose-pink, up to 3″ long, foliage greater than ¾″ wide ....
                            L. squamigera
       BB. Flowers red, about 1½″ long, foliage about ¼″ wide .... *L. radiata*
    AA. Flowers gold to yellow...................................... *L. africana*

Lysimachia (lie-sim-ak′ ia)   Loosestrife   Primulaceae

Lysimachia was named in honor of King Lysimachus of Thrace. It was believed that the plant was used to pacify angry oxen by " appeasing the strife and unrulinesse which falleth out among oxen at the plough, if it be put about their yokes". (Gerard's Herball). The origin of the legend began with King Lysimachus who, as a last resort, waved a plant of *Lysimachia* before a pursuing, maddened beast, thus tranquilizing it. Loosestrife is a literal translation of the Greek word *Lysimachia*.

Approximately 165 species occur with opposite or whorled leaves and small rounded or bell-shaped flowers borne either singly or in narrow racemes. In general, plants establish easily in rich, moist soil and some species travel through the garden at the speed of light. Most loosestrifes thrive in the northern part of the United States and Canada but few make good garden plants for the South.

Quick Reference to Lysimachia Species

	Height (in.)	Flower color	Habit
L. clethroides	24–36	White	Upright
L. nummularia	4–8	Yellow	Creeping
L. punctata	12–24	Yellow	Upright

-clethroides (kleth-roi' deez)	Gooseneck Loosestrife	2–3'/3'
Late Summer White	China, Japan	Zones 3–8

This was one of my favorite plants when I lived in Montreal. The fine foliage and the handsome white, arching flower spikes were not only appreciated in the garden but could also be enjoyed inside as a cut flower. Growth was vigorous but its wandering nature was not difficult to control. In Michigan, although plants were still enjoyable, I found myself spending much time wondering how plants appeared in areas where I knew they had not been planted. In Georgia, this beautiful northern plant liked conditions so much that it began to explore every square inch of my garden and was seriously thinking about trying out the neighbor's. Unfortunately, the flower heads were small and the plants rather weedy, and it was relegated to a local plant sale. This may well become the next kudzu of the South.

Numerous ½″ wide white flowers are held in a 12–18″ long, narrow, curved raceme which resembles a goose's neck, thus the common name. The inflorescence straightens as the fruits mature. The slightly pubescent, 3–6″ long leaves are opposite and narrowed at each end. Moist, but not waterlogged soils, and full sun result in optimum growth. Due to the large size, sufficient room must be provided. Gooseneck loosestrife is grown commercially as a cut flower in northern Europe and is finding its way into florist bouquets in the United States.

Propagation is not difficult by division or seed.

Related Species:
L. ephemerum produces narrow, branching 12–15″ long spires of starry white flowers over several weeks. The opposite foliage is gray-green, sessile, and joined at the base around the stem. The most important characteristic is the lack of invasiveness. Unfortunately, few nurseries carry this species.

-nummularia (num-ew-lah' ree-a)	Creeping Jenny	4–8″/24″
Early Summer Yellow	Europe	Zones 3–8

This European native has become naturalized in the eastern United States and is often found at the edge of wooded areas. The fragrant 1″ diameter, bright yellow flowers are borne singly in the axils of the opposite, rounded 1″ long leaves. Plants are prostrate and each long stem produces roots along the length

401

resulting in rapid multiplication. Large patches of creeping Jenny quickly appear in shady areas where soil is moist. Plants are best used as ground covers by streams, pools, or other wet areas.

Propagate by division in spring or fall.

Cultivars:

'Aurea' is popular and with good reason. The lime green to yellowish leaves brighten up any shady area in which it is planted. The yellow flowers, however, are not as noticeable.

Related Species:

L. congestiflora, dense-flowered loosestrife, forms dense mats of dark green stems and terminal ½–¾" wide yellow flowers. Native to China, it is cold hardy to about zone 6 if winter mulch is provided. Introduced recently by Dr. Don Jacobs of Eco Gardens in Georgia, plants are presently being offered by southern nurseries.

Cutivars:

'Eco Dark Satin' bears yellow flowers with a red throat.

-punctata (punk-tah′ ta)		Yellow Loosestrife	1–2′/1′
Summer	Yellow	Europe, Western Asia	Zones 4–8

This species has also found the United States to its liking and is found growing in moist areas throughout the country. Particularly fond of moist, shady places, the plant is often known as the "ditch-witch" of the countryside. The 1–3" long whorled leaves occur in groups of 3's or 4's. The ¾–1" wide flowers are also whorled and borne in the upper leaf axils from May to September. They are lemon yellow with a small brownish circle in the throat. Plants are much better for zones 4 and 5 than for 7 and 8 where they become more weedy and flowers lose their sparkle.

Propagate by cuttings or seed.

Quick Key to Lysimachia Species

    A. Leaves whorled, flowers whorled............................ *L. punctata*
   AA. Leaves opposite
      B. Flowers white, arching, terminal racemes, plants upright.. *L. clethroides*
     BB. Flowers yellow, borne singly in leaf axils, plants prostrate ....
                                    L. nummularia

Additional Reading:

Chatto, Beth. 1986. *Lysimachia. Horticulture* 64(7):22–23.

Ingram, John. 1960. Notes on the cultivated *Primulaceae* 1. *Lysimachia. Baileya* 8:85–97.

Lythrum (li' thrum)   Lythrum   Lythraceae

Lythrum is naturalized in North America and can be seen along highways and byways in the northern United States and Canada during the summer. Upper New York state and southern Ontario, among other places, are ablaze with this "weed" in July through September. However, excellent breeding work has produced some fine garden cultivars.

The entire leaves are opposite and bear small pink or purple flowers on leafy spike-like racemes along the length of the four-angled flower stem. In general, moist soils are preferred but plants grow well in well-drained garden soils if not allowed to dry out. Of the 25 or 30 species, only 2 or 3 closely related ones are cultivated.

Quick Reference to Lythrum Species

	Height (ft.)	Flowers distinctly stalked
L. salicaria	3–5	No
L. virgatum	2–3	Yes

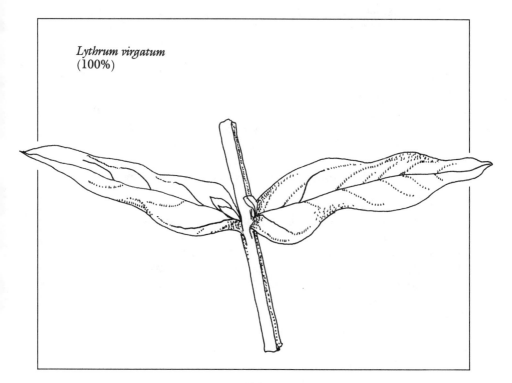

Lythrum virgatum
(100%)

-salicaria (sal-i-kah′ ree-a)		Purple Lythrum	3–5′/2′
Summer	Purple-rose	Europe, Australia	Zones 3–9

The species has naturalized in cooler areas of the United States and in Canada and is particularly abundant in marshes and wet meadows, often crowding out native wetland species. Plants are tolerant of heat and humidity and do well in southern gardens as long as adequate moisture is supplied. Full sun and moist, well-drained soils insure vigorous growth and abundant flowers. The willowy, lanceolate, 4–6″ long leaves are slightly hairy, heart shaped at the base and often clasp the stem. The ¾″ wide flowers, borne in almost sessile whorls in dense terminal leafy racemes, persist from early summer to early fall. Japanese beetles, however, have a particular fondness for purple lythrum.

Cultvars:

'Firecandle' bears intense rose-red pointed racemes.

'Robert' has deep pink flowers, is only 2′ tall and has excellent fall color.

'Roseum Superbum' bears rosy-purple flowers up to 1″ wide and is the most vigorous.

'The Beacon' has bright rose-red spires borne on 3½′ tall plants. The brightness of the flowers act as a beacon in the garden. An excellent cultivar.

The species may be propagated by seed, and self seeds prolifically. Every spring, dozens of seedlings are culled from the Horticulture Gardens. Cultivars must be multiplied by division or stem cuttings in the spring.

-virgatum (vir-gah′ tum)		Purple Loosestrife	2–3′/2′
Summer	Purple	Europe, Asia	Zones 3–9

There is little difference between this and the previous species. The base of the leaf is narrower and seldom clasps the stem. Each ½″ wide flower is borne on a small flower stalk (pedicel) while those of *L. salicaria* are nearly sessile. The stems are more twiggy but this characteristic is not easy to discern. It is an excellent plant for the garden and responds well to moisture and full sun.

Cultivars:

'Dropmore Purple' is one of the best cultivars. It has rosy-purple flowers on 2½′ tall stems.

'Morden's Gleam' has rose flowers on 2–3′ tall stems.

'Morden Pink' bears bright pink flowers. Both are more compact than the type. The Morden series emerged from the excellent breeding program at Morden, Manitoba, Canada and is cold hardy to zone 2.

'Pink Spires' bears deep pink flowers and stands about 3′ tall.

'Purple Spires' is similar to 'Pink Spires' but has rose-purple flowers.

'Rose Queen' is only 18″ tall and has light pink flowers.

'The Rocket' has deeper pink flowers and stands around 2½′ tall.

The species self sows prolifically. Seeds of cultivars do not come true. Propagate similar to *L. salicaria*.

Quick Key to Lythrum Species

A. Flowers sessile or almost so, leaves rounded or heart shaped at base.. *L. salicaria*

AA. Flowers borne on distinct pedicels, leaves narrowed at base .. *L. virgatum*

M

Macleaya (mack-lay′ ya)   Plume Poppy   Papaveraceae

The genus consists of two species although hybridization has resulted in at least one intermediate form. Few people looking at the five to eight foot tall plants would guess they are part of the poppy family. The main species in American gardens is *M. cordata*, long known as *Bocconia cordata*.

-cordata (kor-dah′ ta)	Plume Poppy	6–10′/6′
Summer Cream	China, Japan	Zones 3–8

(Syn. *Bocconia cordata*)

This most impressive plant, towering 6–10′, is topped by 10–12″ long plumes (panicles) of numerous cream-colored flowers. Each flower is apetalous (no petals), has only two sepals, but bears 25–30 ornamental stamens. The 8″ wide heart-shaped leaves are pubescent beneath and consist of about seven lobes. Its stature relegates it to the back of the border or the middle of the island bed but it is also most impressive as a specimen plant where nothing detracts from the pleasant foliage.

Seldom is sufficient room provided and plants often outgrow their welcome. They spread aggressively, which detracts from, rather than adds to, the beauty of the garden. Most people who have planted this poppy are constantly trying to find unwary people to take divisions.

Related Species:

M. × kewensis is a hybrid between *M. cordata* and *M. microcarpa* and has been reported growing at Kew Gardens, England.

M. microcarpa, small-fruited plume poppy, is similar in habit to *M. cordata* but bears bronze flowers consisting of 8–12 stamens. The nondescript flowers open in early summer and the fruit contains a single seed compared with the 4–6 seeded capsule of *M. cordata*. The roots are even more rhizomatous.

406

Propagate *Macleaya* by divisions in the spring or from seed. The small seed should be barely covered and placed in a warm (70–75°F), moist environment. Germination occurs within 2 weeks but is not particularly uniform.

Malva (mal′ va)   Mallow   Malvaceae

Closely related to *Hibiscus*, plants are equally beautiful in flower, but subject to attack by a host of insects and diseases. Of the approximately 30 species, only two or three are particularly useful for the garden.

-alcea (al-see′ a)   Hollyhock Mallow   2–3′/18″
Summer   Rose, white   Europe   Zones 4–8

The 5-parted light green stem leaves contrast with the 2″ wide deep rose to white flowers that appear in the axils. Flowering begins in early summer and continues for 6–8 weeks. All mallows enjoy full sun, well-drained soils and moderate to high pH. Garden performance is superior in the North compared with zones 7–9 where spider mites, thrips, Japanese beetles, and a potpourri of foliar diseases find the plants particularly appealing.

Cultivars:

'Fastigiata' has essentially superseded the species and is offered by most perennial specialists. Plants are more upright, well branched and carry 2″ diameter rose-pink flowers.

Propagate by seed, terminal cuttings in spring, or division. Seeds should be placed at 40°F in moist medium for six weeks. Germination is non-uniform and seedlings emerge over a 2 to 3 month period.

Related Species:

M. moschata, musk mallow, grows 3′ tall and is naturalized in the northeastern United States. Although the showy rose-colored flowers are up to 2½″ wide, garden performance is fair at best, particularly in the South. Plants are summer hardy to zone 8 but perform consistently well only in zones 3–5. Variety *alba* has white flowers, var. *rosea* bears pink flowers.

Mertensia (mer-ten′ see-a)   Bluebells   Boraginaceae

Few plants exist that are necessary for a garden to be complete. This is one of them. *Mertensia* is so easy and unpretentious and provides so much pleasure that it should be part of every spring garden. Of the 40–45 species, the most popular is *M. virginica*, Virginia bluebell. I look forward with anticipation to its appearance in my garden every March and April.

407

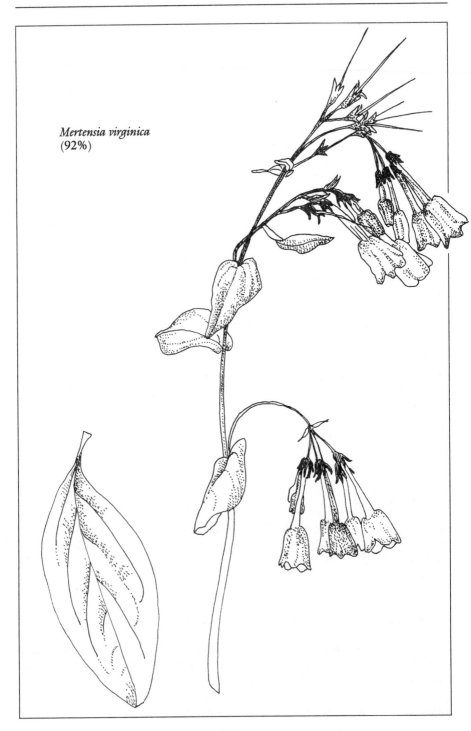

Mertensia virginica
(92%)

-virginica (vir-jin' i-ka)		Virginia Bluebells	1–2'/1'
Spring	Blue	Eastern United States	Zones 3–9

From the moment the blue-green mouse-ear shaped leaves break the soil in the spring until they disappear in summer, these plants provide immense plea-sure. The 4" long, 3–4" wide alternate leaves are smooth with prominent veins. Clusters of 5–20 one inch long tubular flowers are borne in nodding racemes at the end of the stems. The buds and young flowers are pink, but turn a bluish purple as they mature.

The leaves yellow as summer progresses and completely disappear by mid-summer in most parts of the country. This creates a problem if planted in large numbers or in a prominent place, however, annuals may be used to cover the empty spaces. Moist shady areas and partial shade are necessary for Virginia bluebells, particularly in zones 7–9. If plantings are not disturbed, they will slowly colonize the area.

Cultivars:

'Alba' has white flowers.
'Rubra' has pink flowers but is no great improvement on the species.

Propagate by fresh seed, or by spring division.

Related Species:

M. sibirica, Siberian bluebells, is also a lovely garden plant. Plants grow to 18" tall, are fuller and less coarse in appearance than *M. virginica*. The foliage does not go dormant in the summer. Why it is so difficult to find remains a mystery. More plants must be grown in the United States to provide additional information on garden tolerances.

Monarda (mo-nard' a)　　　　Bee-balm　　　　Lamiaceae

Monarda consists of about 12 species, one of which (*M. didyma*) is loved and hated with equal degrees of intensity. The leaves are toothed, aromatic and usually opposite. The flowers are terminal and often surrounded by brightly colored bracts. Only two species are cultivated to any extent, although others have potential as fillers in the wild flower garden.

Quick Guide to Monarda Species

	Height (ft.)	Flower color
M. didyma	2–4	Red
M. fistulosa	2–5	Purple

-didyma (di' di-ma)   Bee-balm, Oswego Tea   2–4'/3'
Summer   Red   Eastern North America   Zones 4–9

John Bartram, the American botanist, first collected bee-balm near Oswego, N.Y. on Lake Ontario. The leaves were used to make tea and plants were routinely included in kitchen gardens for their herbal properties. Its natural provenance along stream banks with overhanging trees suggests its rightful place in the garden is an area where moisture can be freely provided.

The four-sided stems bear 4–6″ long, thin, scented, pointed leaves. The bright scarlet flowers are surrounded with red-tinged bracts and carried in globular terminal, whorled clusters. Removing the faded flower heads results in 8

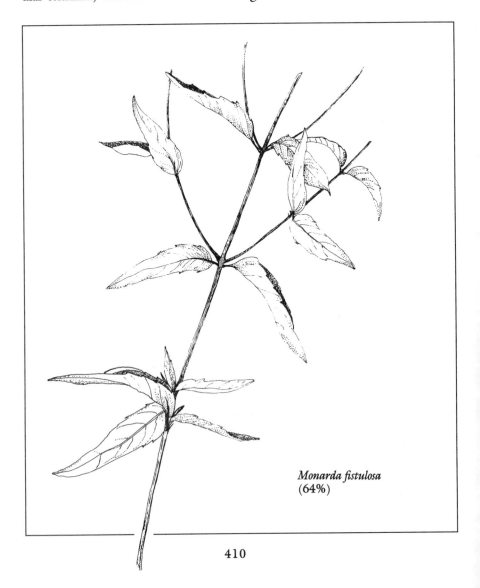

Monarda fistulosa
(64%)

weeks or more of flowering. If grown well and properly cared for, a planting of bee-balm is a magnificent sight. Unfortunately, this is seldom the case. If plants dry out, the stress results in greater susceptibility to foliar diseases such as powdery mildew. While powdery mildew is present even in native plantings, it can be much worse in the garden, particularly if plants are crowded, or the soil is not consistently moist. Spray with a fungicide starting in early June through frost. Bee-balm multiplies by underground stems and can be quite invasive, taking over large areas of the garden. Clumps tend to die out in the center and must be divided every two to three years for aesthetic purposes.

As garden plants, they are lovely in the North; but in the South, are more trouble than they are worth. However, if placed in a rather wild, moist area where large clumps can form and mildew is not objectionable, they make wonderful plants attractive to bees, butterflies, and hummingbirds.

Cultivars:

A good number of cultivars have been raised and all are superior to the type for garden culture. Some may be hybrids between this and *M. fistulosa*, wild bergamot.

'Adam' bears cerise flowers, is more compact, and withstands dry conditions
    better than other cultivars.
'Blue Stocking' carries violet-blue blossoms.
'Cambridge Scarlet' has flaming scarlet flowers and is very vigorous.
'Croftway Pink' bears soft pink flowers and blends into the garden more easily.
'Mahogany' probably has the darkest red flowers of any cultivar and grows 3'
    tall.
'Panorama' is a seed-propagated strain of 3' tall plants of mixed colors.
'Prairie Night' sports lilac-blue blooms.
'Snow White' provides creamy white flowers on 3' high stems and blends well
    with other plants in the border.
'Violet Queen' has deep purple flowers. I have trouble seeing any difference
    between violet-blue ('Blue Stocking'), lilac-blue ('Prairie Night'), and purple
    ('Violet Queen') flowers.

-fistulosa (fist-ew-low' sa)		Wild Bergamot	2–5'/3'
Late Summer	Lavender	North America	Zones 3–9

The stem is less noticeably four-angled than *M. didyma* and the 4" long leaves are slightly more hairy and less toothed. The flowers are also borne in tight whorls surrounded by bracts and range from light lavender to whitish pink. The throat of the sepals on each flower is densely hairy, a totally useless piece of information for gardeners, however, this characteristic helps distinguish this species from the previous. The stems grow out of the previous flower head, creating a candelabra effect. Because the flowers are not as brilliantly colored as *M. didyma*, little interest has been shown in developing this as a garden plant.

However, plants are more tolerant of dry conditions and less susceptible to mildew. Heights of 5′ are not uncommon. Plants are better suited to a wild area rather than the cultivated garden.

Division every 2–3 years will maintain plant vigor. Seed is also available. Germination takes place in 2–3 weeks if seed is lightly covered and placed in a warm (70–75°F), moist environment.

Related Species:

M. punctata, spotted bee-balm, bears lovely whorled yellow flowers which are spotted purple. The bracts beneath the flowers range from pink to lavender. Plants are tolerant of dry soils, relatively tolerant to mildew and perform well in zones 4–9.

Quick Key to Monarda Species

- A. Stems acutely 4-sided, sepal throat slightly hairy, flowers bright red... *M. didyma*
- AA. Stems bluntly 4-sided, sepal throat densely hairy, flowers lavender to pale pink... *M. fistulosa*

Additional Reading:

Hayward, Gordon. 1983. Bee Balm. *Horticulture* 61(7):16–19.

Muscari (mus-car′ ri)　　　　　　Grape Hyacinth　　　　　　Liliaceae

Grape hyacinths have graced gardens for centuries and are well known for the bright many-flowered cone of urn-shaped blue flowers in the spring. However, flowers are also shades of pink, white and yellow. The musky odor of the yellow-brown-flowered *M. racemosum*, musk hyacinth, is responsible for the name *Muscari*. It is interesting that this species, after which the genus was named, has now been placed in a totally different genus (*Muscarimia moschatum*) by some authorities. Nothing is sacred!

All species are sun lovers and need little more than well-drained soil to look their best. The two most common in the garden are *M. armeniacum* and *M. botryoides* and differences are difficult for anyone but the taxonomist to unravel. Fortunately, there are no differences in garden requirements. Regardless of the name on the package, enjoy their beauty.

Quick Reference to the Muscari Species

	Height (in.)	*Flower color*	*Flower shape*
M. armeniacum	6–8	Pale blue	Cone
M. botryoides	6–8	Pale blue	Cone
M. comosum var. *monstrosum*	6–12	Mauve	Plume

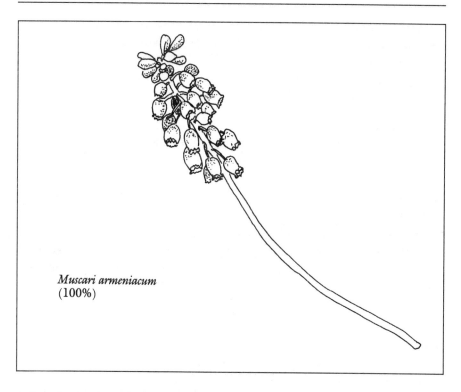

Muscari armeniacum
(100%)

-*armeniacum* (ar-men-ee-ah′ cum)   Armenian Grape Hyacinth   6–8″/6″
Spring   Pale Blue   Turkey   Zones 4–8

Depending on the source of bulbs, this or *M. botryoides* is the common grape hyacinth. The 6–8 leaves are about ¼″ wide and appear in the fall. In areas without significant snowfall, they are rather messy throughout the winter and early spring but do serve a useful function. Edith Edelman, the curator of the perennial border at the North Carolina State University Arboretum, suggests using *Muscari* as a marker for other spring-flowering bulbs whose leaves have not emerged at time of spring cleaning. Having a bulb or two of grape hyacinths reminds you that other bulbs are still sleeping and to keep the trowel away. The leaves soon fade into the background as the blue conical flower spikes begin their annual emergence. Each mature bulb will send up 1–3 flower spikes with 20–40 densely packed, ¼″ long, pale blue urn-shaped flowers.

Cultivars:

'Blue Spike' is one of the fullest of the grape hyacinths due to the double, soft
    blue flowers.
'Cantab' bears flowers of soft blue on 6″ tall stems.
'Early Giant' has cobalt blue flowers with a white rim at the mouth of each
    flower.

'Heavenly Blue' bears gentian-blue flowers and multiplies rapidly. This may be a cultivar of *M. conicum*, the conical grape hyacinth, but is similar enough to be included here.

All cultivars may be propagated by bulbils. Separate and replant in the fall. Seed is produced but offspring may not be the same as the parent.

Related Species:

M. tubergenianum, Tubergen's grape hyacinth, bears many densely arranged deep blue and pale blue flowers on the same spike. Plants grow 4–8" tall.

-botryoides (bot-ree-oi′ deez)		Common Grape Hyacinth	6–8"/6"
Early Spring	Blue	Italy, France	Zones 2–8

The common name for the genus was based on this species because the flowers looked like a miniature bunch of blue grapes. Bulbs are common in the garden trade not only for the lovely blue flowers but because of the white and pink varieties available. The 2–4 leaves are usually shorter than the inflorescence and about ⅓" wide. *M. botryoides* is more cold hardy than the previous species and flowers earlier. Otherwise, there is little difference.

Cultivars:

var. *album* bears clean white flowers. This makes a good garden plant and is the white grape hyacinth of catalogs.

var. *carneum*, a pink-flowered form, fades quickly to flesh-colored flowers and is not particularly attractive.

Propagate by bulbils although the species will self sow.

Related Species:

M. latifolium, broad-leaved grape hyacinth, has loose clusters of dark blue flowers above a solitary strap-like leaf. No problem of messy foliage with this species.

-comosum (ko-mow′ sum)		Tassel Grape Hyacinth	6–12"/6"
Spring	Mauve	Western Asia, North Africa	Zones 4–8

This species and common variety *monstrosum*, have the dubious distinction of being "conversation-piece" plants. In describing this plant, Louise Wilder (*Adventures with Hardy Bulbs*) states that "the fact that the uppermost flowers . . . are gathered into a bunch, and stand wildly on end on long pedicels, while the lower flowers, that are cylindrical, droop dismally, does give the plant a somewhat distraught appearance". The 3–4 thick leaves are up to 1½′ long. The species is different enough to have been renamed *Leopoldia comosa* by some authorities although I have never seen it listed as such in any trade catalogs.

Cultivars:

var. *monstrosum* (syn. *plumosum*) is even more atypical for a grape hyacinth and well described by its varietal name. All the flowers of the inflorescence are sterile and look like slender filaments. This altogether curious plant is most attractive under sunny, pleasant skies but after a rain, looks like a half-drowned puppy dog in need of a home. It is the kind of plant one orders based on the glowing commentary of a bulb catalog in a weak moment. It is seldom ordered again.

Propagate by bulbils.

Quick Key to Muscari Species

```
    A.  Flowers in cone-like inflorescence
        B.  Plant bears solitary leaf.................................. M. latifolium
       BB.  Plant bears more than one leaf
            C.  Leaves 4–8, equal or longer than scape ............ M. armeniacum
           CC.  Leaves 2–3, usually shorter than scape ................ M. botryoides
   AA.  Flowers in tassel- or plume-like inflorescence
        B.  Top of inflorescence only bears slender sterile flowers,
            inflorescence tassel-like.................................. M. comosum
       BB.  All flowers slender, sterile, inflorescence plume-like.....................
                                                    M. comosum var. monstrosum
```

Myosotis (my-o-so′ tis)   Forget-me-not   Boraginaceae

The forget-me-nots have always had a special appeal to gardeners of all ages. There are many stories as to the derivation of the common name but most agree that the tale of the young man collecting these flowers for his lady by the bank of the river sounds the best. He slipped and fell into the fast-moving stream and as he was being swept away, he clenched the flowers in his hand and cried "forget me not!" to his lover on the shore.

None of the 40–50 species is particularly long-lived but most are self-sowers and appear to be perennial. They grow less than a foot tall and produce inflorescences coiled like the tail of a scorpion (scorpioid cymes). All do well in partial shade but full sun may be tolerated in the North if ample water is supplied.

Quick Reference to Myosotis Species

	Height (in.)	*Habit*
M. scorpioides	6–8	Prostrate
M. sylvatica	6–8	Upright

415

-scorpioides (skor-pee-oi' deez)   True Forget-me-not   6–8"/8"
Spring   Blue   Europe, Asia   Zones 3–8

(Syn. *M. palustris*)

    Often referred to as the water forget-me-not because it grows naturally in water, constant moisture is required if plants are to perform well in a "normal" garden. Because of the stoloniferous nature and prostrate growth habit, stems may grow to 18" long. The lovely ¼" wide flowers are bright blue with a small

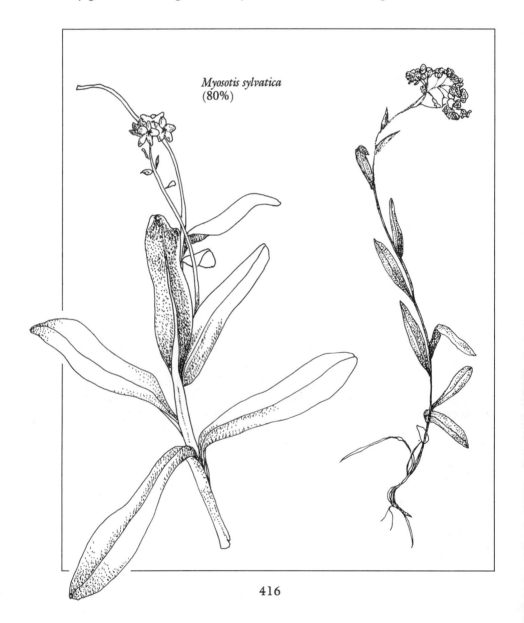

Myosotis sylvatica
(80%)

yellow eye. Plants look particularly beautiful in a partially shaded woodland growing near the banks of a stream.

Cultivars:

var. *semperflorens* is much more compact than the type and more floriferous.

Propagate by division in spring or fall and by seed.

-sylvatica (sil-va' ti-ka)		Woodland Forget-me-not	6–8"/6"
Spring	Blue	Europe	Zones 3–8

Dense cymes of fragrant, ⅜" wide azure-blue flowers with distinctive yellow eyes are produced in April and May. The 2–3" long hairy leaves are lance shaped, somewhat pointed and have 3 faint veins. In the North, flowers are produced prolifically in late spring and sporadically through the late summer. In the South, the dense leaves must be thinned in June to reduce the incidence of leaf rot which occurs due to afternoon thunderstorms and hot humid weather. If not thinned, the hairy leaves hold water, creating perfect conditions for diseases. Plants seldom last more than two years in the South or three in the North. However, they self-sow abundantly and many additional plantlets emerge in the spring.

Cultivars:

var. *alba* has white flowers but why anyone would want to grow a pink or white forget-me-not is beyond me.
'Blue Ball' bears indigo blue flowers over compact, ball-shaped plants.
'Victoria Blue' is an early flowering cultivar with gentian blue flowers.
'Victoria Rose' also flowers earlier than the type and bears pink blossoms.

Propagate by seed or by division in the spring or fall.

Related Species:

M. alpestris is similar to *M. sylvestris* and the differences are in the length of the pedicel relative to the calyx (much longer in *M. sylvatica*, about equal in *M. alpestris*). Most plants sold as *M. alpestris* are probably *M. sylvatica*. Both are fine species and the only importance to the gardener in distinguishing between the two is the satisfaction of knowing what one is growing.

Quick Key to Myosotis Species

    A. Plant stoloniferous, prostrate habit.........................*M. scorpioides*
   AA. Plant not stoloniferous, upright..............................*M. sylvatica*

N

Narcissus (nar-sis' us)   Jonquil, Daffodil   Amaryllidaceae

The bright yellow, white and orange flowers splash across the dreary early spring landscape and bring the world to life. Such is the role of *Narcissus*, the first of the major bulbs to welcome spring. The attributes of the daffodil have been praised for centuries. Homer spoke of "The *Narcissus* wonderously glittering, a noble sight for all, whether immortal gods or mortal men . . .". Centuries before Homer, the flowers were used by the Egyptians in funeral wreaths and have been found in crypts and tombs, preserved after 3000 years.

The origin of the word *Narcissus* has two main schools of thought. It was believed to have been named for the golden-haired youth, Narcissus, who was changed by the gods into a flower after he gazed so longingly at his own image in a stream, believing the image was that of his long-lost sister. Others believe that *Narcissus* was derived from Narce, a narcotic thought to be present in the flower's scent. Accounts of the dulling properties of *Narcissus* flowers stemmed from the time of Sophocles. Few people in those days brought cut narcissus in the home because they believed that the scent of *Narcissus* was most harmful. This belief persisted at least until the nineteenth century. Personally, I prefer the first explanation.

All daffodils and jonquils belong to the genus *Narcissus*. The common name, jonquil, popular in the South and in England, comes from the Latin word *juncus* meaning rush, and refers to the round leaves on *N. juncifolius*, rush-leaf daffodil. The term has since been accepted to describe dwarf, small-cupped daffodils with rush-like leaves. The common name, daffodil, may be used to describe all others. Although the large-flowered hybrid daffodils are best known, there are many smaller species which are greatly overlooked. Some of the species flower as early as January in Southern areas and as late as June in Northern gardens. For instance, *N. minimus* (syn. *N. asturiensis*), least daffodil, flowers in late February in Bronxville, New York, in early February in Tidewater, Virginia, and as early the first day of the new year in Charlotte, North Carolina. Vast beauty and charm reside in these relatively undiscovered species, although finding them can be an altogether frustrating experience. However, half the fun of gardening is the hunt for something different and the discovery of something new.

A well-drained soil, deeply worked and containing humus is ideal for narcissus. Bulbs prefer neutral to slightly acid soil and lime should be incorporated in highly acid soils. Bulbs flower abundantly in woodland soils with natural leaf mold, but should be planted away from hungry tree roots. Narcissus can be naturalized wherever bulbs may be left undisturbed, however, if naturalizing in lawns, the grass cannot be cut until the narcissi leaves have yellowed. Removal of leaves too early results in poor performance in subsequent years.

About 60 species of narcissus are known, many available to gardeners, although the greatest breakthroughs in garden daffodils have resulted from interspecific hybridization. Some marvelous breeding has created today's large-flowered hybrids, often resulting from an embarassing number of parents.

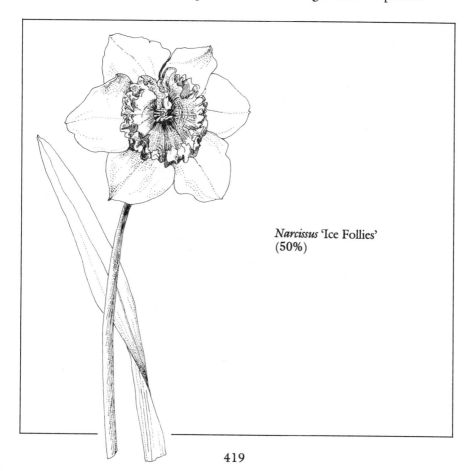

Narcissus 'Ice Follies'
(50%)

So much work in *Narcissus* breeding has occurred that eleven categories, based on flower morphology, have been developed to classify the species and hybrids. In the daffodil flower, the cup is known as the corona and the outer flared segments are collectively called the perianth. Following is a table of classification and a few cultivars of each type. This is but a smattering of the cultivars available.

I. *Classification:* TRUMPET NARCISSUS
   Distinguishing Characteristics: One flower to a stem, corona as long as, or longer than perianth segments
   a. Yellow
      Distinguishing Characteristics: Perianth colored, corona colored, not paler than the perianth.
      Cultivars: 'Dutch Master', 'Explorer', 'Golden Harvest', 'King Alfred', 'Rembrandt', 'Standard Value', 'Unsurpassable', 'Yellow Triumphator'.
   b. Bicolor
      Distinguishing Characteristics: Perianth white, corona colored.
      Cultivars: 'Foresight', 'Magnet', 'Trousseau', 'World's Favorite.'
   c. White
      Distinguishing Characteristics: Perianth white, corona white, not paler than the perianth.
      Cultivars: 'Beersheba', 'Cantatrice', 'Matterhorn', 'Mount Hood', 'W.P. Milner.'
   d. Other combination
      Cultivars: 'Spellbinder', (perianth sulphur yellow, corona sulphur yellow outside, white inside); 'Rushlight', (lemon yellow perianth, white corona edged in yellow).

II. *Classification:* LARGE-CUPPED NARCISSUS
   Distinguishing Characteristics: One flower to a stem, corona more than one-third, but not equal to the length of the perianth segments.
   a. Yellow
      Distinguishing Characteristics: As in Ia.
      Cultivars: 'Bermuda', 'Carbineer', 'Carlton', 'Fortissimo', 'Fortune', 'Galway', 'Nimrod', 'Rustom Pasha', 'Scarlet Elegance', 'Yellow Sun'.
   b. Bicolor
      Distinguishing Characteristics: As in Ib.
      Cultivars: 'Duke of Windsor', 'Kilworth', 'Mrs. R.O. Backhouse', 'Pink Beauty', 'Professor Einstein', 'Roseworthy', 'Salmon Trout'.
   c. White
      Distinguishing Characteristics: As in Ic.

Cultivars: 'Amor', 'Dr. Alex Fleming', 'Ice Follies', 'Milk and Cream', 'Orange Bride'.

    d. Other combinations
    Distinguishing Characteristics: As in Id.
    Cultivars: 'Binkie', (perianth sulphur yellow, corona sulphur yellow turning to white); 'Charter', (perianth primrose yellow with white base, corona cream tinged yellow); 'Daydream', (perianth yellow, corona white); 'Handcross', (perianth dresden yellow, corona pale yellow).

III. *Classification:* SMALL-CUPPED NARCISSUS
Distinguishing Characteristics: One flower to a stem, corona not more than one-third the length of the perianth segments.

    a. Yellow
    Distinguishing Characteristics: As in Ia.
    Cultivars: 'Apricot Distinction', 'Dinkie', 'Jezabel', 'Lemonade'.

    b. Bicolor
    Distinguishing Characteristics: As in Ib.
    Cultivars: 'Barrett Browning', 'Blarney', 'Dreamlight', 'Limerick', 'Merlin'.

    c. White
    Distinguishing Characteristics: As in Ic.
    Cultivars: 'Chinese White', 'Dallas', 'Foggy Dew', 'Frigid', 'Veronica'.

    d. Other combinations
    Cultivars: 'Birma', deep yellow petals, small orange-red trumpet.

IV. *Classification:* DOUBLE NARCISSUS
Distinguishing Characteristics: Flowers double.
Cultivars: 'Cheerfulness', (white); 'Cheerfulness Primrose', (primrose-yellow); 'Golden Ducat', (yellow); 'Mary Copeland', (white with orange-red cup); 'Tahiti', (yellow interspersed with segments of saturn-red); 'Texas', (yellow interspersed with yellow and red); 'White Lion', (white with straw yellow segments); 'White Marvel', (white).

V. *Classification:* TRIANDUS NARCISSUS
Distinguishing Characteristics: Obvious characteristics of *N. triandus*, the dominant parent of the hybrids. Slender round leaves, drooping white flowers borne in clusters, perianth segments bent back to reveal a globular corona, like teardrops. Often called the angel's tears daffodil. Usually 9–12″ tall. Also available as var. *alba*. Hardy in zones 4–9.

    a. Large corona
    Distinguishing Characteristics: Corona not less than two-thirds the length of perianth segments.

Cultivars: 'Liberty Bells', (yellow); 'Thalia', (white); 'Tradition', (yellow), 'Tresamble', (cream-white).

b. Small corona

Distinguishing Characteristics: Corona less than two-thirds the length of the perianth segments.

Cultivars: 'April Tears', (yellow); 'Arish Mell', (white); 'Hawera', (yellow); 'Silver Chimes', (white).

VI. *Classification:* CYCLAMINEUS NARCISSUS

Distinguishing Characteristics: Obvious characteristics of *N. cyclamineus,* the dominant parent. Perianth segments turned back, long cylindrical corona, serrated at the edge, early blooming, usually 6–10″ tall. Hardy in zones 6–9.

Cultivars: 'February Gold', (yellow); 'February Silver', (white with yellow cup); 'Jack Snipe', (white with yellow cup); 'Jenny', (white); 'Little Witch', (deep yellow); 'Peeping Tom', (golden yellow); 'Tete-a-Tete', (yellow).

VII. *Classification:* JONQUILLA NARCISSUS

Distinguishing Characteristics: Obvious characteristics of *N. jonquilla,* the dominant parent. Rush-like channelled leaves, fragrant golden-yellow flowers borne in clusters of 3–6, with a cup-shaped corona. Usually 6–12″ tall. Hardy in zones 4–9.

Cultivars: 'Baby Moon', (pale yellow); 'Lintie', (yellow with orange cup, 6″); 'Sugarbush', (white with chartreuse cup); 'Sundial', (sulphur-yellow); 'Suzy', (yellow with dark orange cup); 'Trevithian', (lemon-yellow).

VIII. *Classification:* TAZETTA NARCISSUS

Distinguishing Characteristics: Obvious characteristics of *N. tazetta,* the dominant parent of the hybrids. Four to 6 narrow leaves, flowers almost flat with a shallow corona, very fragrant. Flowers borne 4–8 to a 12″ tall stem, often referred to as paperwhites or bunch-flowered narcissus. Usually 12–15″ tall. Hardy in zones 6–10.

Cultivars: Those hardy in zones 5 (4 with mulch) to 9: 'Cragford', (white with orange-red cup); 'Geranium', (white with orange cup); 'Scarlet Gem', (white with orange-red cup) Those tender (zones 8–10): 'Nazareth', (pale yellow with lemon-yellow cup); 'Paperwhite', (white).

IX. *Classification:* POETICUS NARCISSUS

Distinguishing Characteristics: Obvious characteristics of *N. poeticus,* the dominant parent. Narrow blue-green leaves. Flowers are solitary, white with small saucer-shaped corona of pale yellow, edged red and often referred to as Pheasant-Eyes. Sweetly fragrant and late flowering. Hardy in zones 4–9.

Cultivars: 'Actaea', (white with yellow cup edged red); 'Cantabile', (white with green cup edged red).

X. *Classification:* SPECIES OTHER THAN THOSE PREVIOUSLY LISTED

-*bulbocodium* (bul-bow-ko' dee-um)   Hoop Petticoat Daffodil   8–12"/6"
Early Spring   Yellow   Southern France, Morocco   Zones 6–9

The petticoat daffodils always elicit interest and conversation because of their unique flower shape. Three to four rush-like leaves, up to 15" long, emerge early in the spring. Unique solitary bright yellow flowers on eight-inch stems rise through the foliage. The perianth is made up of narrow segments but the cup is widely expanded to resemble a petticoat. Excellent drainage is necessary to overwinter the bulbs. Plant in containers or protected areas because inclement weather in January and February can spoil emerging blossoms.

Cultivars:

var. *citrinis* has lemon-yellow blossoms.
var. *conspicuous* is the latest to bloom and produces deep golden-yellow flowers.
'Tenuifolius' bears a 6-lobed, wide yellow corona above thin thread-like leaves.

Related Species:

N. *cantabricus*, Cantabrian daffodil, bears fragrant white "petticoat" flowers in early spring. Only one leaf is formed and flowering occurs as early as January or February in North Carolina. This is sometimes offered as *N. bulbocodium* var. *monophyllus*.

N. × *romieuxii* is a tetraploid, probably the result of *N. bulbocodium* × *N. cantabricus*. The sulphur yellow "petticoat" flowers are the first yellow daffodils to emerge in the spring.

-*canaliculatus* (kan-al-ick' u-lah' tus)   Chinese Lily Narcissus   6–9"/6"
Spring   White with yellow cup   Southern France   Zones 6–9

This may be a subspecies of the paperwhite group of narcissus, *N. tazetta*, which it closely resembles in a miniature form. Bulbs must be well established before sufficient flowers are produced; plants are best in their second or third year. Four to six flowers are produced per stem.

Related Species:

N. *nanus*, dwarf daffodil, (sometimes sold as *N. lobularis*) is 6–8" tall and bears small, fragrant white flowers with a rich yellow cup.

N. *obvallaris*, tenby daffodil, has 12" long stems topped with golden yellow flowers with a long yellow, green-tinged cup.

423

XI. *Classification:* MISCELLANEOUS NARCISSUS:
Distinguishing Characteristics: Daffodils which do not fit in any of the above categories.

a. Split corona daffodils
Distinguishing Characteristics: Distinguished by the corona being split for at least one-third its length. They are also referred to as collar and papillion daffodils.
Cultivars: 'Cassata', 'Dolly Mollinger', 'Firestreak', 'Orangery', 'Mol's Hobby', 'Papillion Blanc', 'Pink Supreme'

b. Pink-flowered hybrids.
Distinguishing Characteristics: Pink coloration in corona, perianth white or yellow.
Cultivars: 'Mrs R. O. Backhouse', 'Rose Caprice', 'Salome', 'Satin Pink'

Additional Reading:

Books:

There are many sources of information concerning daffodils. Any book on flowering bulbs is sure to have a section on the genus. The better catalogs attempt to properly classify the species and hybrids.

Gray, Alec. 1955. *Miniature Daffodils.* Transatlantic Arts, New York.

Lawrence, Elizabeth. 1957. *The Little Bulbs, A Tale of Two Gardens.* Criterion Books. In this most charming book, she discusses experiences with the small bulbs in her gardens in Raleigh and Charlotte, NC, and those of her friend Mr. Krippendorf in his garden in Ohio. This was recently reprinted by Duke University Press in 1986.

Wilder, Louise Beebe. 1936. *Experiences with Hardy Bulbs.* Macmillan Co. New York. I highly recommend this book for information about many garden bulbs.

Wister, J. C. 1930. *Bulbs for American Gardens.* The Stratford Co. Boston.

Manuscripts:

Davis, Rosalie. 1986. Planting daffodils. *Horticulture* 64(10):54–55.

Donald, Kate. 1984. *Narcissus cyclamineus. The Garden* 109(7):285–287.

Willis, David. 1981. The origins of pink daffodil cultivars. *The Plantsman* 3(1):51–59.

Associations:

American Daffodil Society, Tyner N.C. 27980. Publication: *Daffodil Journal.*

Nepeta (nep′ e-ta)　　　　　　　Nepeta　　　　　　　Lamiaceae

One of the better known representatives of this genus is the old-fashioned light blue-flowered plant, *N. cataria* or catnip. There is nothing particularly special about it except its perverse ability to make cats crazier than they already are. The famous French botanist and plant explorer, J. P. de Tournefort wrote in the early 1700's about the effect of this magical plant on the feline race. "... when a Cat has smelt it (even before she has well seen it) hugg'd it and kiss'd it, wantonly running upon it and scouring away from it by turns, and has rub'd herself against it very much and long, using strange Postures and playing with it, she at last eats it up and devours it entirely." This is not a pretty picture! Apparently cats don't bother seedlings as much as mature plants.

Nepeta has square stems, opposite leaves and white to blue flowers. *N. govaniana*, Kashmir nepeta, however, has yellow flowers, is 3′ tall and unappealing to cats. Most nepeta are best grown as edging plants but tend to cascade over the area they are designed to edge, either a charming sight or a terrible nuisance depending on one's degree of patience. The gray-green leaves help blend other plants together when used in the garden. They perform best in full sun and well-drained soil and tolerate partial shade in zones 5 and 6. Afternoon shade is necessary further south. Plants prefer full sun to partial shade. Shear foliage 8″ to the ground in early summer.

There is confusion as to the identity of species sold under the name *Nepeta* and the two principal ones are closely related.

-mussinii (mu-sin′ ee-eye)　　　Persian Nepeta　　　　12–18″/24″
Spring　　　　　　Blue　　　　　　Caucasus　　　　　　Zones 3–8

The gray, hairy, cordate-ovate leaves (leaves heart-shaped with a rounded apex) are about 1″ long and highly scented. The pale blue flowers consist of numerous ½″ long, lipped flowers held in loose terminal racemes. They make a pleasant, if not outstanding plant for the garden. The species and cultivars set seed profusely. In my Georgia garden, plants did well but the flowers faded in the sun and never attained the sparkle I have seen overseas. Plants persisted for about three years before succumbing to heat, cats, dogs, and children.

Cultivars:

'Blue Dwarf' produces many pale blue flowers on compact plants.
'Blue Wonder' is 12–15″ tall, compact, and bears dark blue flowers on 6″ tall
　spikes. Cut back after flowering for repeat bloom in the fall.
'Snowflake' bears creamy white flowers.
'White Wonder' is a white-flowering form of 'Blue Wonder'.

Propagate by seed, terminal cuttings in spring, or by division.

Related Species:

N. × *faassenii* (fah-sen′ ee-eye), Faassen's nepeta, is a sterile hybrid between *N. mussinii* and the rather nondescript white-flowered *N. nepetella*. The stems are about the same length as those of *N. mussinii* but are more upright (which makes plants appear taller). The 1½″ long leaves are considerably narrower with a triangular base. Since plants are sterile, no seed is formed, therefore plants raised from seed cannot be *N.* × *faassenii*. Flowers appear about a week later than those of *N. mussinii* but are more persistent. This hybrid is a better garden plant, although cold hardy only to zone 4. Propagate by spring division or by terminal cuttings. Take 3″ long cuttings in summer and root in sand or peat-perlite mix. Rooting occurs within 2 weeks.

N. gigantea (of gardens) is a species name coined by Graham Stuart Thomas (*Perennial Garden Plants*) for a cultivar listed as 'Six Hills Giant', although others claim it is a cultivar of *N.* × *faassenii*. One of the finest plants I have seen, it is used extensively in the British Isles for edging pathways and for mass plantings. The 9–12″ tall racemes consist of dark violet flowers borne in axils and terminals atop 3′ tall erect plants. Unfortunately, I have not seen this listed in the United States.

Additional Reading:

De Wolf Jr., Gordon. 1955. Notes on cultivated Labiates. 6. *Nepeta*. *Baileya* 3:98–107.

Haywood, G. 1988. The attraction of catmints. *Horticulture* 66(8): 22–25.

O

Oenothera (ee-no-the' ra)   Evening Primrose, Sundrop   Onagraceae

Of the 150–200 species of annuals, biennials, and perennials, about a half dozen are well-known garden plants. Many are native to the United States and Canada and have become well established in gardens. The leaves are alternate, and stems are often woody at the base. The 4-petaled flowers are usually yellow, although white and rose flowers occur on a number of lesser-known species. Height ranges from 4–6" for the diminutive *O. acaulis*, dandelion sundrop, to the 4' tall Lamarck's sundrop, *O. lamarckiana*.

A number of species have vespartine flowers, which means they open in the evening, and accounts for one of their common names. For example, the flowering habit of the common evening primrose, *O. biennis*, now more of a roadside weed than a garden plant, fascinated the English poet Keats who was "startled by the leap of buds into ripe flowers" and for "shutting again with a loud popping noise about sunrise". However, many species do not exhibit this nocturnal manner and are referred to as sundrops. Japanese beetles find *O. biennis* particularly tasty and Harry Phillips (*Growing and Propagating Wild Flowers*) reports that their presence spares neighbouring plants from attack.

Quick Reference to Oenothera Species

	Height (in.)	*Flower color*	*Flowers nocturnal*
O. caespitosa	4–8	white, pink	Yes
O. fruticosa	18–24	yellow	No
O. missouriensis	6–12	yellow	No
O. odorata	18–24	yellow	Yes
O. perennis	12–24	yellow	No
O. speciosa	12–24	white, pink	No
O. tetragona	12–36	yellow	No

427

-caespitosa (say-spi-to' sa)		Tufted Evening Primrose	4–8"/12"
Early Summer	White, pink	Western North America	Zones 4–7

This little-known prostrate species is most suitable for the front of the border or in the rock garden. Plants are stemless and the 4" long narrow, hairy leaves are clustered together. The 2–3" wide fragrant flowers almost dwarf the plant as they open white and fade to pink. Flowering persists for 4–6 weeks but one must be present in late afternoon and evening to enjoy them as they seldom open at midday.

Cultivars:

var. *eximea* is similar in flower habit but has stems, resulting in a somewhat taller plant (8–12").

Propagate by seed or division in the spring. Seeds should be lightly covered and sown in a well-drained medium. Place seed tray in warm (70–75°F), humid conditions.

-fruticosa (froo-ti-ko' sa)		Common Sundrops	18–24"/2'
Summer	Yellow	Eastern North America	Zones 4–8

The reddish, slender, hairy stems bear 1–3" long, entire, lance-shaped sessile leaves. Erect flower buds open to a terminal cluster of 1–2" wide, bright yellow flowers resulting in one of the prettiest species of the genus. Full sun is necessary for best performance. Dry soils are tolerated.

Propagate by seed or division in summer.

-missouriensis (mi-sur-ree-en' sis)		Ozark Sundrops	6–12"/12"
Summer	Yellow	Southcentral United States	Zones 4–8

When plants are well grown, their beauty is unrivaled. Although plants may be small in stature, the paper thin flowers are up to 5" across. Solitary, bright yellow, funnel-shaped flowers persist for many days. The sepals are often spotted red in the bud stage and remain so even while the flowers are open. The spreading plants bear reddish upright growing tips (decumbent). The 1–4" long leaves are petioled and entire.

Plants struggle in the summer heat in the South while in the North, the addition of a winter mulch is beneficial. Plant in full sun to partial shade and allow soil to occasionally dry out.

Propagate by seed or by division after flowering.

-odorata (o-do-rah' ta)		Twisted Evening Primrose	18–24"/2'
Early Summer	Yellow	Southern South America	Zones 4–8

The fragrant, solitary yellow flowers have a red tinge, are 1–2" wide, and open in late afternoon. The base of the plant is somewhat woody and the sessile, 4–6" long stem leaves have conspicuous wavy edges.

This is a fair garden performer at best but other yellow-flowered species are available which are hardier, more floriferous, and provide open flowers during the day and evening.

Propagate by seed or division.

-perennis (pe-ren' is)		Nodding Sundrops	12–24"/18"
Summer	Yellow	Eastern North America	Zones 3–8

(Syn. *O. pumila*)

This common sundrop occurs over much of eastern North America and may be treated as a biennial or perennial. The 1–2" long leaves are lance-like, slightly hairy, and entire. The plant often begins to flower when 3–5" tall but the flower stalk continues to expand to 1½ to 2' in height. The flower buds are nodding, thus the common name, and reveal handsome 1" wide yellow flowers. The leafy flower stalk is often branched and diurnal flowers (open during the day, closed at night) are carried in loose panicles or racemes. This species is commonly offered by nurserymen but is not nearly as showy as *O. fruticosa* or *O. tetragona*. Perhaps it is so popular because people look at the botanical name and believe they are purchasing a long-lasting perennial plant.

Propagate by seed any time or by division in the spring or fall.

-speciosa (spee-see-o' sa)		Showy Evening Primrose	12–24"/18"
Summer	White, Pink	Southcentral United States	Zones 5–8

Due to the stoloniferous rootstock, plants tend to be more spreading than many other species. The 1–3" long linear leaves are pinnately lobed and bear a soft pubescence. The 1–2" diameter diurnal flowers, which appear in the axils of the upper leaves, are white then mature to rose. If grown in full sun and moderately good soil, handsome, compact plants result. However, in rich soils or when heavily fertilized, plants become a rampant nuisance. Plants are naturalized along roadsides in Texas and may be found in dry fields and prairies. High humidity is tolerated and plants do well in the plains states in addition to the East and South.

Related Species:

O. berlandieri, Mexican evening primrose, is usually listed as *O. speciosa* var. *childsii*. Plants bear slender prostrate branches about 6–12" tall, upon which are produced 1–2" diameter rose-colored flowers. Plants offered as *O. speciosa* 'Rosea' are similar and probably the same. Performance has been excellent in zone 8.

O. rosea, rosy evening primrose, has rose-colored flowers but the buds are erect, not nodding. The flowers open pale pink and mature to rich rose. This species is not difficult to locate and seed can also be found from specialists.

Propagate from seed or division.

-tetragona (tet-ra-go' na)	Four Angled Sundrop	1–3'/1'
Late Spring	Yellow	Eastern North America	Zones 3–8

(Syn. *O. youngii*)

Native north to Nova Scotia, south to South Carolina and west to Louisiana, plants are common along woodsides and open places. Due to lack of persistence in the garden, the well-branched plants are treated as biennials or short-lived perennials. The erect buds are tinged red and the pubescent stems are reddish brown. One to three, 1–1½" wide yellow flowers are produced on each flowering branch. The species is not an outstanding garden plant, however, selection has resulted in a number of improved cultivars.

Cultivars:

'Fireworks' grows about 18" tall with red stems and buds which open to 2–3" wide bright yellow flowers. In the trials at the University of Georgia, flowering occurred from May 20 to mid-June.

'Highlights' grows 12" tall with 2" wide yellow flowers.

'Yellow River' is about 18" tall and has 2–2½" wide deep yellow flowers.

Propagate the species from seed or division; the cultivars by division.

Quick Key to Oenothera Species

A. Flowers yellow
　　B. Plants more than 1' tall
　　　　C. Flowers open in late afternoon and evening, not on
　　　　　　bright days... *O. odorata*
　　　　CC. Flowers open on bright days
　　　　　　D. Buds and tip of flower head nodding................ *O. perennis*
　　　　　　DD. Buds and tip of flower head erect
　　　　　　　　E. Leaves usually shorter than 2½", stem often reddish ....
　　　　　　　　　　　　　　　　　　　　　　　　　　　　　O. fruticosa
　　　　　　　　EE. Leaves usually longer than 2½", stem without
　　　　　　　　　　reddish tinge................................... *O. tetragona*
　　B B. Plants less than 1' tall............................... *O. missouriensis*
　AA. Flowers rose, pink, or white
　　B. Flowers open in late afternoon and evening, not on bright
　　　　days, plants less than 1' tall .... *O. caespitosa*
　　BB. Flowers open during day, open white, age to rose, plants
　　　　more than 1' tall.. *O. speciosa*

Omphaloides (om-fa-loi deez)　　　　Navel-Seed　　　　Boraginaceae

A number of species of *Omphaloides* are occasionally grown in the United States, and like all the members of the Boraginaceae, have blue flowers, alternate leaves and bear hard fruits (nutlets). The common name, navel-seed, comes from the deep groove in the nutlet, a characteristic which separates *Omphaloides* from the other members of the family. It is sometimes confused with *Myosotis* and *Cynoglossum* because of their similar size, foliage, and blue flowers. Some of the more visible differences include:

	Omphaloides	*Cynoglossum*	*Myosotis*
Habit	creeping(*)	upright	upright
Leaves	petioled	petioled	sessile
Pubescence	sparsely	stiff	slightly
Flowers	blue	dark blue	blue with eye
Nutlet	slightly hairy	prickly	smooth, shiny

(*) *O. verna*, the most common in cultivation.

An annual species, *O. linifolia*, flaxleaf navel-seed, about one foot tall with fresh white flowers, is occasionally grown but the only perennial commonly offered is *O. verna*, blue-eyed Mary.

-verna (ver' na)		Blue-eyed Mary	2–8"/12"
Spring	Blue	Southern Europe	Zones 6–9

O. *verna* is well established in European gardens but only beginning to be appreciated in the United States. Spreading rapidly by underground stems, it makes a useful ground cover for partially shaded locations. The 1–3" long oval leaves are long-petioled, and have a short, abrupt point at the end. They are entire, conspicuously veined and remain evergreen in the South. The long flower stems bear 2–4 deep blue, ½" wide flowers with white throats which cover the foliage in spring and early summer. The blue-eyed flowers were a favorite of Queen Marie Antoinette, thus accounting for the popular name. Although tolerant of poor soils and dry shade, garden performance is enhanced in moist areas and partial shade. Full sun results in stunted plants which never attain the graceful habit seen in partial shade. Slugs tend to dine on it, as they do on many other stoloniferous species, and slug repellent should be applied in early spring.

Cultivars:

var. *alba* is similar, but has white flowers.

Propagate from seed or division in spring immediately after flowering.

Ophiopogon (o-fee-o-po' gon)   Mondo Grass   Liliaceae

The 5–10 species of edging and ground cover plants are often confused with *Liriope muscari*, common lily-turf. Both genera are tufted, have basal leaves, and bear bluish purple flowers in summer. However, the leaves of mondo grass are more narrow than those of lily-turf, the smaller flowers are hidden by the leaves,

431

the fruits are metallic blue compared to the lustrous black fruits of *Liriope*, and the species are less cold hardy. These differences, however, do not make mondo grass any less useful or ornamental.

Ophiopogon is an excellent edging plant and ground cover which tolerates full sun but prefers area of moist soils and partial shade. The most common species is *O. japonicus*, dwarf mondo grass.

-japonicus (ja-pon' i-kus)		Dwarf Mondo Grass	8–15"/12"
Summer	Lilac	Japan, Korea	Zones 7–9

The numerous dark green grass-like leaves are 15" long and ¼" wide. Light lilac flowers are held in short terminal racemes, almost hidden by the foliage. The long underground stolons and tuberous roots result in spreading, drought tolerant plants useful as edging or ground covers.

Cultivars:
'Nana' may be the same as 'Nippon' and is common in commerce.
'Nippon' is about 2–4" tall and has whitish flowers in the summer.
var. *variegatus* has white-margined foliage.

Related Species:
O. jaburan is coarser than *O. japonicus*, with light purple to white flowers. Plants grow 15–18" tall but are not as good a ground cover as the previous species. Cold hardy to zone 9, var. *aurea* bears yellow-striped leaves which provide additional foliar interest. Variety *variegatus* has white-striped leaves and is also more effective than the species. Both look particularly good in groups of 6 or more.

O. planiscapus 'Nigrescens', black mondo grass, is an interesting recent introduction from England. The dark purple leaves appear almost black and plants are about 6" tall. The flowers are light lilac to pink and followed by black berries in the fall. Growth is slow, but the foliage provides a wonderful contrast to light colored foliage such as the light green species of *Hosta*. It is listed as being cold hardy as far north as zone 5 but zone 7 is more realistic.

The most common method of propagation is by division, although seeds germinate in 6 weeks if the berries are soaked for 24 hours to facilitate removal of the pulp.

Additional Reading
Hume, H. Harold. 1961. The *Ophiopogon-Liriope* complex. *Baileya* 9:134–158.

Rackemann, Adelaide. 1987. Lilyturf. *Horticulture* 65:42–43.

Ornithogalum (or-nith-og' al-um)   Ornithogalum   Liliaceae

Many decorative species are available as border plants or cut flowers. The most common species, *O. umbellatum*, star-of-Bethlehem, has been grown for weed. Others such as *O. thyrsoides*, chincherinchee, and *O. arabicum*, Arabian star flower, are better behaved and found in florist shops and flower markets as cut flowers. All do well in strong light and loose soil, although few situations exist that deter *O. umbellatum* from colonizing the world.

Quick Reference to Ornithogalum Species

	Height (in.)	*Flower color*	*Flower number*
O. arabicum	18–24	White, black center	6–12
O. nutans	12–15	Greenish white	3–12
O. thyrsoides	12–15	White	12–30
O. umbellatum	6–9	White	10–20

-arabicum (a-ra' bi-kum)   Arabian Star Flower   18–24"/18"
Summer   White   Mediterranean   Zones 8–10

Due to lack of winter hardiness in most parts of the country, this species is not as popular as other members of the genus. The 12–18" long leaves emerge early and generally lie on the ground. In North Georgia, leaves emerge in December and are invariably damaged by frosts. The clusters of fragrant white flowers rise 1–2' high in early summer and have conspicuous yellow anthers and a jet black ovary. Flowers do not open all at once, but there are always enough to provide a nice show. They tend to close just before nightfall when they appear like "immense pearls clustered in some sumptuous ornament" (Wilder, *Adventures with Hardy Bulbs*). The flower heads are also popular as a cut flower because of their excellent shelf life. If the stems are waxed, the flowers will last for several months.

Plant bulbs about 6" deep in a well-drained area of the garden in full sun. Lift in the fall prior to the first hard frost. Store the bulbs in peat moss in a cool, dry place and replant after the last frost date in the spring. In zones 8–10, they can remain in the ground and flowers appear in late spring to early summer, although the flower heads require staking to prevent twisting of the flower stem. They are best suited to west coast gardens of northern California and the Pacific Northwest.

Propagate by removing offsets when the bulbs are lifted. The offsets usually require 2–3 years before flowering. Bulbs raised from seed will be plantable size in 18–24 months.

-nutans (new-tanz)   Drooping Star-of-Bethlehem   12–15"/12"
Early Summer   Greenish white   Southern Europe   Zones 5–9

This species has naturalized in the Northeast but remains little grown in America. The narrow ⅜" wide leaves are about 12–18" long, and often have a white line running lengthwise down their middle. The 2″ wide greenish white flowers are star-shaped, somewhat drooping, and have lovely white margins in front and green markings in the rear. They are loosely borne on a 12–15″ tall stem in late spring and early summer, then shortly after flowering, the plant withers away.

O. *nutans* tolerates partial shade and is often planted on the edge of wood-lots or in partially shaded areas. It also may be naturalized through grass and because the leaves disappear quickly, the grass may be cut before it gets knee high, a common problem when naturalizing other bulbs such as daffodils in grassy areas.

Cultivars:

var. *boucheanum* has larger, whiter flowers than the type but is difficult to locate.

Propagate similar to O. *arabicum*.

| *-thyrsoides* (thur-soi′ deez) | Chincherinchee | 12–15″/12″ |
| Summer | White | South Africa | Zones 7–9 |

Like O. *arabicum*, chincherinchee is known mainly as a cut flower in the florist shop. In most areas of the country, it is not cold hardy, however, bulbs are inexpensive and can economically be treated as annuals. Alternatively, bulbs may be lifted, similar to gladiolus and tuberous begonias. Bulbs produce 5–6 broad leaves above which emerge 12–30 pure white, ¾″ long flowers with brown centers on 12″ tall flower stems in early summer. Similar to O. *arabicum*, plants are best adapted to west coast gardens.

The common name, chincherinchee, is an onomatopoeic word used to describe the sound of the south winds as they blew through the stalks and flowers in the hedgerows in Cape Province of South Africa. The shelf life of the flowers is legendary and they will last for months in water or on the plant. If you can't grow them in the garden, pick some up at the florist and enjoy them at home.

Cultivars:

var. *album* has dark-centered pure white flowers that are more densely arranged on the stem.
var. *aureum* bears golden yellow flowers.

Propagate similarly to O. *arabicum*.

| *-umbellatum* (um-bel-ah′ tum) | Star-of-Bethlehem | 6–9″/6″ |
| Late Spring | White | Mediterranean | Zones 4–9 |

This is the best known species due to its ability to survive where most others can not. Although native to the Mediterranean, it has become naturalized in many areas of the northeastern United States and as far south as Mississippi. Plants have been grown and enjoyed for hundreds of years; Linnaeus believed that this plant was the "Dove's dung" mentioned in the Bible (2 Kings 6:25) and eaten by the Samarians during the great famine. Other accounts of the edibility of these bulbs abound through folk literature, however, in *Plants of the Bible*, H. and A. Moldenke showed the bulbs to be poisonous unless cooked. Regardless of culinary properties, this species has been and will continue to be grown for some time.

Bulbs produce a mound of narrow, smooth leaves, each about 12″ in length, followed by a flower stem carrying 10–20, star-shaped white flowers. Each flower is about 1–2″ across and striped green on the outside of the three outer segments. The flowers are also remarkable for their consistency in opening just before noon and closing again before sunset. It is so punctual that plants are known as the eleven o'clock lady in English, French, and Italian languages. Other common names include six o'clock flower, wake-at-noon and sleepy dick.

This species is not fastidious as to planting site. Deep shade should be avoided but partial shade to full sun is acceptable. Once established, bulbs are drought tolerant.

Bulbs multiply rapidly by bulbils and should be planted where they may be allowed to roam. If additional plants are required, dig the bulbs after flowering, remove the offsets, and replant them in a suitable location.

Quick Key to Ornithogalum Species

    A. Plant more than 1′ tall
        B. Flowers white with black center, stamens yellow .... *O. arabicum*
      BB. Flowers white or greenish white, center not black, stamens
           not yellow
          C. Blossoms nodding, usually fewer than 12 flowers per stem ....
                                                        O. nutans
        CC. Blossoms erect, usually more than 12 flowers per stem ....
                                                           O. thyrsoides
    AA. Plant less than 1′ tall..................................... *O. umbellatum*

P

Pachysandra (pa-kis-an' dra) Spurge Buxaceae

Although only about 5 species occur, the genus includes one of the most highly cultivated plants in the landscape, Japanese spurge, *P. terminalis*. The spurges' main function in life is as a ground cover, particularly under trees, where they compete well for the limited sun, nutrients and water.

Plants multiply by rhizomes and have alternate leaves, usually grouped in whorls at the end of the stems. Although grown mainly for the foliage, the flowers provide interest as well. They are monoecious (male and female flowers on the same inflorescence), and the long stamens of the male flowers give rise to the generic name. *Pachysandra* comes from *pachys*, thick and *andros*, man; in reference to the thick stamens. Fruit is formed on some plants, however, most forms in cultivation are self-sterile, and little or no fruit occurs.

The spurges are easily propagated by division, or by rooting softwood terminal cuttings in the summer.

Quick Reference to Pachysandra Species

	Height (in.)	Leaf length (in.)	Inflorescence length (in.)
P. procumbens	9–12	3–5	4–5
P. terminalis	9–12	1–3	1–2

-procumbens (pro-kum' benz) Allegheny Spurge 9–12"/12"
Spring Pinkish white Southeastern United States Zones 5–9

Although native from West Virginia, south to Florida and west to Louisiana it is seldom seen in Southern gardens and almost never in the North. Plants are evergreen in the South, although in my garden (zone 8), the leaves look terrible by March and I remove the worst of them. New leaves emerge from the ground

436

on long petioles up to 4″ long. The leaves are mottled purple and are coarsely toothed towards the apex, but entire near the tapered base. Flowers are white but have a pink tinge, particularly if the weather is cool. The flowers are borne at ground level in the axils of the leaves and not terminal as in *P. terminalis*. Leaf litter or other mulch around the plants may need to be removed to find the flowers. It is not as vigorous a ground cover as Japanese spurge but individual clumps are far more handsome. Allegheny spurge is a much overlooked plant and a welcome substitute for *P. terminalis*.

-terminalis (ter-mi-nah′ lis)		Japanese Spurge	9–12″/18″
Late Spring	White	Japan	Zones 4–9

This is certainly one of the most functional plants used in today's landscapes. It is interesting that this visitor from Japan has found conditions in America more to its liking than its American cousin, Allegheny spurge. Because of the rhizomatous nature, plants colonize an area aggressively, thus making a useful and rapid growing ground cover. The dark evergreen leaves are alternate but are grouped in whorls at the top of the stems. They are toothed towards the apex, 1–3″ long and about half as wide. The creamy white flowers are borne at the top of the stems (*terminalis* is derived from the position of the flowers).

A number of diseases such as *Rhizoctonia* root rot, *Fusarium* leaf blight, and leaf blight canker are becoming more prevalent. Euonymus scale also results in significant damage to overgrown clumps. Thinning and grooming the plantings as well as application of fungicides should be practiced regularly.

While it may be overused, a carpet of shining Japanese spurge under mature trees is a beautiful sight. The plantings under the copper beaches at Longwood Gardens are particularly remarkable.

Cultivars:

'Green Carpet' provides a 6–8″ tall carpet. It has darker green leaves and is more compact than the species.
'Silveredge' has thin silver-white margins and is similar to 'Variegata'.
'Variegata' bears irregularly white variegated leaves. Plants are not as vigorous as the species but the leaves are more interesting. 'Variegata' and 'Silveredge' should be located in shade because leaves scorch in full sun. Although minor differences may be seen, the two cultivars are essentially the same.

Quick Key to Pachysandra Species

    A. Leaves 1–3″ long, shiny, flowers terminal .... *P. terminalis*
    AA. Leaves 3–5″ long, dull, flowers borne at base.............. *P. procumbens*

Paeonia (pay-on′ ee-a)   Peony   Ranunculaceae

The peony's great popularity rests upon hardiness, ease of culture, and freedom of bloom in many areas of North America. Add to that the tremendous

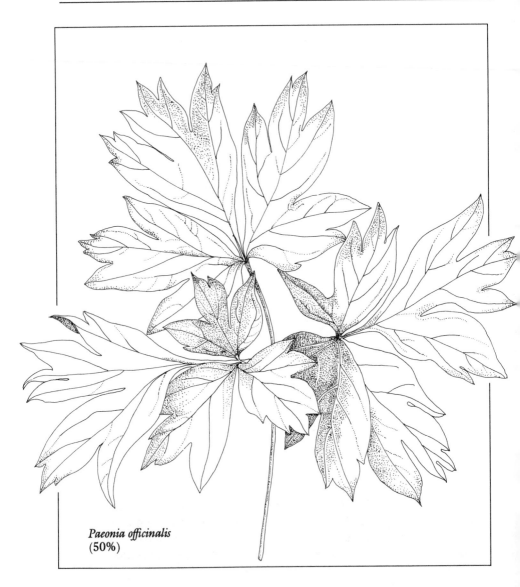

Paeonia officinalis
(50%)

number of flower colors, forms and plant habits and it is not surprising that the peony has attracted the interest of amateur and professional breeders, botanists, taxonomists, and horticulturists, all of whom have become enamoured by the genus.

The common garden peonies are classified into herbaceous species, most of which have arisen from the Chinese peony, *P. lactiflora* and the common peony, *P. officinalis*; and woody species, mainly selections of *P. suffruticosa*. The herbaceous species have received the most attention and are more important garden plants than the tree forms. The classification of the herbaceous species has been tackled by a number of scholars, the most recent being F.J. Stern, who, in 1946 divided the genus into 3 sections, 4 subsections, 16 groups, 33 species, and 12 botanical varieties. All but five of the species and varieties have synonyms, twenty-six have from 1 to 10 synonyms each, seven have from 10 to 20 and one has 34! This not only shows the magnitude of the work of the botanists of the past but also that much confusion exists as to what constitutes a species, sub-species, etc. A more useful horticultural classification based on flowering time divides the genus into three divisions, early-, mid- and late-flowering species and is a useful guide for those wishing to select garden species. The following list of species and their flowering times is based on John C. Wister's book, *The Peonies*, 1962.

Division I. Mostly early May blooming (April in the South)
Very early blooming   *P. wittmanniana, P. w.* var. *macrophylla,*
  P. mlokosewitschii, P. daurica, P. tenuifolia
Later flowering   *P. anomala, P. veitchii*
Latest   *P. coriacea, P. arietina, P. bakeri, P. obovata*

Division II. Mid-May Blooming
  P. officinalis, P. humilis, P. mollis, P. peregrina

Division III. Late-May Blooming
  P. lactiflora

Most of the true species are almost impossible to find in commerce. With the exception of *P. veitchii, P. tenuifolia,* and *P. mlokosewitschii,* and the double forms of *P. officinalis,* most are not terribly good garden plants anyway. The truly good herbaceous peonies are selections of only 2 or 3 species and the gardener need not be confused with classification to enjoy their beauty.

The American Peony Society divides the flowers of herbaceous peonies into four different forms.

Single: Five or more petals are arranged around a center made up of stamens with pollen-bearing anthers.

Japanese: This is really a double form but is characterized by five or more petals around a center made up of stamens with non-pollen bearing anthers (stamenoides). The absence of pollen distinguishes this form from the single flower form. The term "anemone flowered" is used when the stamens in the center have been transformed into narrow petal-like structures called petaloids.

Semi-double: Five or more outer petals are arranged around the center con-sisting of broad petals and stamens with pollen-bearing anthers. There may be a distinct center of stamens or they may be in rings intermixed among the petals, however, the stamens are always clearly visible and prominent.

Double: There are five or more outer petals but the stamens have been com-

439

pletely transformed into petals, making up the bulk of the flower. Often there is no trace of the stamens although in some cultivars they may be present or partially petaloids. In double types, however, stamens are not a prominent part of the flower.

Flowering Times: Peony cultivars are classified not only by flower type but also by relative flowering time. Early-flowering cultivars may flower as early as late March in the South or mid-April further north while the late-flowering types may be in bloom 4–6 weeks later. Those which flower in-between are referred to as mid-season cultivars.

Peonies in the South: Peonies love cold weather; the colder the winter, the better they grow. They go dormant in the fall and require a certain number of chilling hours (hours below 40°F) to break dormancy, grow and flower the next year. Therefore, it is unreasonable to expect peonies to do well in Sarasota, Florida or McAllen, Texas. However, many cultivars do well as far south as zone 8. Many people leave the chilly climates of the Midwest or Northeast to live in the South and are convinced that peonies can not be grown in the Atlanta area. While not all peony cultivars do as well in the South as the North, there is no excuse for transplanted northeners to pine over the absence of their beloved plants. A fair number of cultivars (although only a small fraction of the total available) have been tested at the University of Georgia gardens and a few general statements may be made concerning selection of peony cultivars for southern areas.

1. Select early to mid-season cultivars. The later the flowering time, the warmer the weather and the weaker the stem strength. There is also more chance for disease as the weather becomes warm and humid. Also, with warmer weather, doubles may not fully open.

2. Select single or Japanese flower forms. In general, semi-double or doubles should not be grown. The more petals on the flower, the more rain will be trapped in the flower and disease, especially botrytis, will disfigure the blooms. This still leaves a vast selection of lovely cultivars from which to choose. For those who wish to have semi-doubles or doubles in the southern garden, select only early-flowering cultivars.

Many books specifically dealing with peonies are available (see end of peony section) which go into great detail concerning their cultural requirements. In general, they prefer full sun, well-drained soil and abundant water, particularly when they are vigorously growing in the spring. Plants may be fertilized with a low nitrogen fertilizer such as 8–8–8 but overfertilization can result in reduced flowering. Attention should be paid to planting depth when putting the crowns in the ground. The buds (eyes) on the rootstock should be approximately 2″ below the soil; if they are planted too deep, poor flowering will result. Recent

440

work in Israel by Dr. Abe Halevy suggests that deep planting inhibits flowering due to the absence of light on the crowns. As the soil layer increases, absolutely no light reaches the developing flowering buds and flower initiation does not take place. The relationship of crown depth to flowering is fascinating and additional research is certainly needed.

The American Peony Society has listed many reasons and possible solutions why peonies fail to flower well. They include:

A. *No buds appear*:

1. Plants too young and immature.

Allow them to mature.

2. Planted too deep or too shallow.

Examine and if eyes are more than 3″ below ground, lift and replant.

3. Clumps too large and too old.

Divide the clump if it stops flowering (after 3–10 years), leaving three eyes per division.

4. Too much nitrogen.

Cut down on frequency or concentration of fertilizer

5. Moved and divided too often.

If the clump is flowering well, it should not be moved. Clumps can remain in place well over 10 years.

6. Too much shade.

Move to sunny location.

B. *Buds appear but flowers do not develop*:

1. Buds killed by late frost.

Better luck next year.

2. Buds killed by disease. They usually turn black and die.

Plant earlier cultivars. Spray fungicide as directed for botrytis.

3. Buds attacked by thrips. They open partially, turn brown and fall.

Spray as directed.

4. Buds waterlogged due to excessive rain.

Plant singles or Japanese forms. Bagging buds will help.

5. Plants undernourished.

Fertilize with 8–8–8 and bonemeal.

6. Excessively hot weather.

Plant early-flowering cultivars.

Hybridization and selection of peonies has continued unabated and it is impossible to recommend cultivars. Many hybrids are still available today from the work of Professor A.P. Saunders, who created more hybrid races and varieties than all other breeders, past and present, combined. Growing some of his hybrids is like owning a piece of peony history. Cultivars and hybrids of many other fine breeders such as Auten, Nicholls, Kreckler, Klehm, Franklin, Lemoine, Sass, and Crosse, are also available. Every year new hybrids and selections appear and it is more difficult to keep up with them all. Numerous catalogs glowingly describe hybrids and cultivars and usually provide more than adequate information. The American Peony Society also publishes a list of best cultivars.

Tree Peonies: Tree peonies are not trees at all, but have woody stems which do not die down to the ground in the winter. They should more accurately be called shrub peonies as they seldom attain a height of more than four feet. The most common tree peonies were derived over 1400 years ago from garden forms of the Chinese moutan peony, *P. suffruticosa.* The herbaceous peonies were valued by the Chinese for the medicinal value of their roots while the "improved" or moutan peony was treasured for its ornamental value. By the year 750, lists of over thirty named varieties, including some yellow-flowered types, had been registered in China, although it was not until the late 1700's that any plants found their way to Europe. Until 1846, although hundreds of so-called distinct varieties were imported, they were the same 5 or 6 varieties brought back by the original European explorers. At that time, Robert Fortune, a plant explorer for the Royal Horticultural Society, returned to England with 25 of the finest selections from China, from which today's garden forms have arisen. The yellow tree peony, *P. lutea,* and the maroon tree peony, *P. delavayi,* were not discovered until 1883 and 1884, respectively, and have since been used to create additional hybrids. In America, the first tree peonies were imported from England in the early 1800's and numerous references to the "almost unknown" plant which are ".. adorned by gorgeous blossoms" appeared in the American gardening magazines as late as 1928.

The culture and care of tree peonies need not be shrouded in mystery and once established, are as long lasting as many of the herbaceous types. John C. Wister in *Peonies, the Manual of the American Peony Society,* provides a list of cultural notes. I have interspersed a few of my own comments.

1. Tree peonies are native to mountainous areas and are used to cold and snow in the winter, and heat in the summer. In the Pacific Northwest, adequate summer heat is often lacking and a sufficiently long cold period is not available in the extreme southern states, while some protection may be needed in the Northeast. The southern limit of tree peonies has not been defined and in Atlanta, Georgia, gardeners have had some success while others cannot produce plants with more than one flower per year. I have admired excellent specimens in Betty and Charles Grisham's garden in Huntsville, Alabama (zone 7). Plants are presently being tested at the University of Georgia (zone 8) to provide a few more answers for southern gardeners. Results are encouraging.

2. A slightly basic soil is preferable; good drainage is essential.

3. Plant in the fall. Plant grafted plants 6–12″ below the graft union to encourage formation of roots on scion wood.

4. Plant in partial shade. This is particularly true south of zone 6.

5. Winter protection by covering or wrapping with straw or other material is desirable north of Zone 6.

6. Pruning should be accomplished occasionally and even cutting back to 8–12″ high is beneficial at times to encourage the formation of new shoots.

7. Remove all suckers originating from the rootstock. Production of suckers is greatest the first two years after planting.

Commercial propagation of tree peonies has been accomplished for over 900 years by grafting the desired cultivar on an herbaceous peony root stock and is still practiced today. Research has been conducted on grafting to stocks of *P. suffruticosa* but suckering is too heavy. In all grafted plants, regardless of rootstock, the plants should be set deep enough to encourage the scion to form its own roots. Cuttings of *P. suffruticosa*, if taken in September, root at about a 40% rate, which may be practical for the amateur but not the commercial propagator. Little success has been reported with softwood cuttings taken in April. They may also be propagated by layering, that is, pegging some of the branches in March to root into the ground. At least two years are needed for sufficient root production.

Many fine cultivars of tree peonies are hybrids of *P. suffruticosa* and *P. lutea*. Consult the American Peony Society, a specialist peony producer, or your favorite nurseryman.

Additional Reading:

Books.

Boyd, James (ed.). 1928. *Peonies—The Manual of the American Peony Society.* American Peony Society.

Wister, John C. (ed.). 1962. *The Peonies.* American Horticultural Society.

These two fine reference books cover the two main classes and provide outstanding lists of peonies with proven garden performance.

Manuscripts.

Davis, Rosalie. 1986. Dividing peonies. *Horticulture* 64(11):58–59.

Haw, Stephen. 1986. A problem with peonies. *The Garden* 111(7):326–328.

Associations:

American Peony Society, 250 Interlachen Road, Hopkins, MN. 55343. Publication: *American Peony Society Bulletin.*

Papaver (pa-pah′ ver)   Poppy   Papaveraceae

The poppies are usually represented in American gardens by the Oriental poppy, *P. orientale*. However, about 40 species of poppies are known and most are ornamental. Unfortunately, few are commonly available. One of the most northerly species in the plant kingdom, *P. radicatum* is found on the north coast of Greenland. The most famous member is the annual red poppy, *P. rhoeas*, immortalized by the Canadian poet John McCrae, in the hauntingly beautiful poem "In Flanders Field". This same species was selected and reselected by the Reverend W. Wilks of Shirley, England and is popularly known as the Shirley poppy. Other annuals in this genus include mission poppy, *P. californicum*, tulip poppy, *P. glaucum*, and the infamous opium poppy, *P. somniferum*, although this is often perennial in southerly locales. For garden purposes, all poppies except the Oriental poppies are best treated as annuals, although Iceland poppy and alpine poppy may persist for 2 to 3 years. Many self-sow prolifically and new plants can be counted on year after year.

Poppies are characterized by nodding flower buds, solitary flowers on long flower stalks, milky juice, and lobed or dissected leaves. The seed capsule is hard, oval, and decorative.

Quick Reference to Papaver Species

	Height (in.)	Flower diameter (in.)	Plants go dormant
P. alpinum	8–10	1–2	No
P. nudicaule	12–18	3–6	No
P. orientale	18–36	5–7	Yes
P. somniferum	24–36	3–4	No

-alpinum (al-pine' um)	Alpine Poppy	8–10"/8"
Summer Multicolored	European Alps	Zones 4–7

A dwarf species, it is most suited for the rock garden or front of the border. Plants are not heat tolerant and seldom survive the summer south of zone 7. Regardless of geographic location, well-drained soil is absolutely essential. Plants are tufted (i.e. all leaves emerging from same place) with 2–6" long gray-green leaves. The 1" wide silky flowers are held on bristly-hairy 4–10" long flower stalks. Although not particularly long lived, plants self-sow prolifically.

Cultivars:

var. *burseri* bears white flowers. Some authorities believe *P. burseri* is the correct name for plants grown as *P. alpinum*.

Related Species:

P. kerneri has ½" wide yellow flowers and is closely related to *P. alpinum*.

P. pyrenaicum, Pyrenees poppy, has green rather than gray-green leaves. The plants are 4–6" tall and the 1" wide flowers are yellow to orange.

Seed sown in January will be ready for planting in March. Plants flower the first year from seed.

-nudicaule (new di-kaw' lee)	Iceland Poppy	12–18"/12"
Spring Multicolored	Subarctic regions	Zones 2–7

This northern species is becoming more and more popular in, of all places, the South. Although not perennial, fall plantings produce spectacular drifts of vibrant flowers in the spring. Plants are becoming more visible in public and private gardens every year. Although unable to survive the hot summer in the South, Iceland poppies are perennial in the North, living 2–3 years and flowering from early spring to early summer. Plants are rosetted, stemless, and produce 4–6″ long, gray-green pinnately lobed leaves. The silky flowers are up to 6″ wide and are borne on 12″ high leafless flower stems. Most are seed propagated and mixtures are most common.

Cultivars:

A number of cultivated forms offer specific colors and heights. It seems each new cultivar provides larger and more vibrant flowers than the previous. The majority are propagated from seed and variation inevitably results.

'Champagne Bubbles' has 3″ diameter flowers in mixed colors.

'Coonara Pink' has 2″ wide flowers in pastel pink shades.

'Kelmscott Strain' is 12–18″ tall and mainly consists of pastel colors.

'Monarch Mix' bears flowers up to 2″ wide in many bright colors.

'Popsicle' has 3–4″ wide flowers in an assortment of colors.

'Summer Promise' contains both solid and bicolor 2–3″ diameter flowers on 2′ tall stems.

'Wonderland Mix' is more compact than the type and bears 2–3″ diameter flowers. Bright orange 3″ wide flowers are available as 'Wonderland Orange'. This is the best selection for windy areas and has proven resilient even in the wind swept beds of Auckland Botanical Gardens.

The species also makes a wonderful potted plant for indoor use and more plants may be seen in florists displays and mass market outlets. It is also the only species suitable for cut flowers.

Seed-propagated plants flower the first year. Seeds collected from the garden, however, result in plants dissimilar from the parent plant. In areas where they are perennial, division may be accomplished after 3–5 years.

-orientale (o-ree-en-tah′ lee)		Oriental Poppy	18–36″/24″
Early Summer	Scarlet	Southwest Asia	Zones 2–7

This is certainly the most conspicuous and popular poppy in North America. Few sights are more arresting than the vibrant orange-red flowers of two or three plants massed in the garden. The leaves are pinnately lobed and sharply toothed although they appear sharper and more bristly than they feel. The flowers of the species are 3½–4″ across, scarlet with a black blotch on the base of each petal forming a black eye. The plants, however, have the unfortunate habit of disappearing by mid- to late summer. Plants such as *Mertensia virginica*, Virginia bluebells, which do this can easily be replaced by a few annuals but with large plants such as Oriental poppies, more planning is necessary. Large filler plants such as *Gypsophila*, *Perovskia*, and *Boltonia* will cover much of the space vacated by the poppies and flower later.

In the South (south of zone 7), Oriental poppies perform poorly and are seldom used. The only success I have had is with seed grown plants planted in the fall. Dormant plants ordered from catalogs invariably break dormancy within 2–3 weeks of fall planting and are killed or badly damaged by winter weather. Some mail order firms will ship in the spring and if the plants can be obtained early enough, they do much better in zones 7 and 8 than those fall shipped. Nevertheless, Oriental poppies are cold climate plants and nothing can be done to change that fact.

Cultivars:

Many cultivars are available, some are hybrids with other species, particularly *P. bracteatum*, great scarlet poppy, a species similar to *P. orientale*.

'Barr's White' has pure white flowers and blackish spots at the base of the petals.
'Beauty of Livermore' is one of the finest reds I have seen.
'Brilliant' produces fiery red flowers.
'Carousel' has lovely white flowers with orange margins.
'China Boy' has ruffled orange flowers with a creamy white center.
'Dubloon' flowers earlier than most cultivars and bears orange, fully double blossoms.
'G.I. Joe', included at the request of my eight-year-old son, has deep red flowers and is quite lovely despite the name. It is nice to show him that not all G.I Joes throw grenades and major in hand-to-hand combat.
'Helen Elizabeth' bears salmon-pink flowers without the blotching found in 'Barr's White'.
'Watermelon' is aptly named, producing watermelon-pink flowers.

Oriental poppies are propagated by root cuttings and division. Root cuttings are taken in the spring by dividing the roots into 3–4" lengths, inserting upright in sandy soil, and barely covering. If the root sections are harvested early in the spring or immediately after flowering, the plant may be replaced without damage.

Division may be necessary every 3–5 years and should be done after flowering when dormant. This allows root recovery and growth in the fall so plants flower the next year. Dividing in early spring results in poor flowering that year.

Related Species:

P. bracteatum, great scarlet poppy, grows 2–2½' tall and bears large blood-red flowers. It differs from *P. orientale* in having 2 large leafy bracts at the base of the flowers and lacks the black blotch at their base.

-somniferum (som-ni' fe-rum)		Opium Poppy	2–3'/3'
Late Spring	Multicolored	Greece, Orient	Zones 8–10

446

In northern areas of the country, this species should be treated as an annual but it self-sows prolifically in zones 6–7, and often overwinters with protection in more southerly regions. It is the oldest poppy in cultivation and has been used not only for narcotics, but for the edible seeds, often sold as birdseed under the name of "mawseed". The narcotic properties of the species have long been recognized, in fact, poppy juice was mixed with baby food to make babies sleep. Opium is made from the sap of the green seed capsules and was known by the Greeks and Egyptians several centuries before the birth of Christ.

The plants are tall and the lack of branching further accentuates the height. The gray-green leaves are unequally toothed at the base and clasp the stem. The plants are not particularly attractive but the flowers more than compensate. They are 4–5″ across and range from white through pink, red to purple, although no yellow or blue flowers yet exist. In most flowers, showy black blotches are found at the base of the petals, providing additional beauty. Unfortunately the flowers drop their petals quickly and make poor cut flowers. Two common flower forms are found in gardens today; the carnation-flowered and the peony-flowered strains. The former has fringed petals, the latter does not. The peony-flowered strain is sometimes listed as *P. paeoniaeflorum* and the flowers resemble those of double peonies.

P. somniferum is a short-lived plant but the seed is viable, particularly after being chilled in the winter. Every spring, southern gardens are alive with seedlings of opium poppies, many in different places than the year before. Those allowed to remain flower profusely. Each spring, I take my students to the beautiful garden of Mrs. Laura Ann Segrest in Athens, Georgia. We stand in awe of the symphony of color provided by this magnificent plant best known for its ability to relieve pain rather than its potential for beauty.

Cultivars:

var. *album* has white flowers and whitish seeds.

Quick Key to Papaver Species

    A. Plants less than 12″ tall...................................... *P. alpinum*
  AA. Plants greater than 12″ tall
       B. Stem leaves with broad, clasping base.................. *P. somniferum*
     BB. Stem leaves not clasping
         C. Flowers borne on leafless stems, stem leaves gray-green,
            shallowly pinnately lobed .... *P. nudicaule*
       CC. Flower stems with some leaves, stem leaves green,
            deeply pinnately divided .... *P. orientale*

Additional Reading:

Christopher, Thomas. 1981. Poppies. *Horticulture* 59:24–29.

Cullen, James. 1968. The genus *Papaver* in cultivation. 1. The wild species. *Baileya* 16(3):73–90.

Peltiphyllum (pel-ti-fill′ um) Umbrella Plant Saxifragaceae

(Syn. *Damara*)

The name *peltiphyllum* comes from the Greek *pelta*, shield and *phyllon*, leaf, and refers to the shape and function of the large peltate leaves. There is only one species, *P. peltatum*, definitely not a plant for the small backyard garden.

-peltatum (pel-tay′ tum) Umbrella Plant 3–5′/6′
Spring Pink California, Oregon Zones 4–7

(Syn. *Saxifraga peltata*)

The peltate leaves (the petiole is attached to the leaf inside the margin, usually near the middle) are 6–18″ across, have 6–10 sharply cut lobes and are much paler beneath than above. The leaf petioles arise directly from the rhizome and are cylindrical and hairy. Plants are best suited for shaded stream banks, beside ponds or any watery environment where the roots may be constantly cool and moist. The flowers are small, about ½″ across, pink to white and are borne in numerous terminal corymbs. They appear before the leaves but remain attractive long after the plant has leafed out. Plants do well as far south as zone 7 (occasionally zone 8) if constant moisture is provided.

This species is often confused with *Peltoboykinia tellimoides* (syn. *Boykinia tellimoides*, *Saxifraga tellimoides*), also a large, coarse, water plant. *P. peltatum* is taller and has larger leaves with more lobes. However, the flowers of *P. tellimoides* are white, much larger, and somewhat campanulate. They are held in a raceme while those of *P. peltatum* are borne in a many-flowered corymb. *P. peltatum* makes a better ornamental specimen.

Cultivars:

var. *nana* is a dwarf (12–18″ tall) plant which I have not seen in this country. The size may allow some smaller water gardens the luxury of including this species.

Propagate by division in the summer or fall.

Penstemon (pen-stay′ mon) Bearded Tongue Scrophulariaceae

Of the 250 species, many are native to western North America and Mexico. Although not well-known in American gardens, hybrids have been introduced recently from Europe and their popularity is on the rise. A number of species withstand drought better than most perennials and are excellent for sunny, dry locations. All have opposite leaves, and showy flowers with long corolla tubes which open to five petals. Most species have red, pink, or lavender flowers although *P. confertus* bears sulphur-yellow blooms. Flowers have five stamens, the characteristic upon which the genus name is based, but one of them is sterile (stamenoide) and lacks a well-developed anther.

A number of low-growing species such as *P. caespitosa*, mat penstemon; *P. pinifolius*, pine leaf penstemon, with its needle-like leaves; *P. crandallii*, Crandall's penstemon occur as well as large-flowered species such as *P. davidsonii* and *P. newberryi*. One or two of the eastern plants are creeping into cultivation such as the pink-purple flowered *P. smallii*, one of the finest wild flowers I have grown, *P. laevigatus*, smooth bearded tongue, and *P. australis*, southern penstemon. The lack of consistent winter hardiness and the aversion to wet feet have created problems in cultivating penstemon. Many of the showier species are marginally hardy in the northern states and in the South, significant improvements in soil and drainage are required to provide longevity.

Some of the hardiest garden species are:

P. angustifolius	*P. glaber*
P. barbatus	*P. hirsutus*
P. confertus	*P. laevigatus*
P. diffusus	*P. ovatus*

To be on the safe side, cuttings should be taken in the fall or seed started in winter. Others, such as the showy *P.* × *gloxinoides*, should be well mulched after cuttings have been taken.

Quick Guide to Penstemon Species

	Height (in.)	Flower color
P. barbatus	18–36	Pink, rose
P. campanulatus	18–24	Various
P. × gloxinoides	18–24	Red, scarlet

-barbatus (bar-bah' tus)	Common Bearded Tongue	18–36"/18"
Spring Pink, rose	Southwestern United States, Mexico	Zones 2–8

The tubular flowers are borne in thin spires and are lipped like flowers of *Salvia*. The lower lip has short bristly hairs which extend into the throat, thus providing the common name, bearded tongue. The leaves and stems are glaucous (covered with a whitish substance, epicuticular wax, that rubs off), and the leaves are lance-shaped to linear. The flowers are 1–2" long and usually occur in long narrow, 2–3- flowered racemes which open from the bottom (acropetally) and persist 2 to 3 weeks. Each flower is strongly 2-lipped and varies from light pink to carmine. Plants are quite winter hardy and also tolerate the heat of the South. In the University of Georgia Horticulture Gardens, flowers opened from early May to mid-June. Plants persisted for about three years before division became necessary.

Cultivars:

'Bashful' is a relative newcomer with orange flowers on 12–14" tall plants.
var. *coccineus* grows 15–18" tall with scarlet flowers.

449

'Crystal' is similar to 'Bashful' but bears white flowers.

'Hyacinth Mix' is a popular seed-propagated series which bears mixed colors of red, pink, and scarlet.

'Prairie Dawn' produces pale pink flowers.

'Prairie Fire' bears deep red flowers.

'Rose Elf' is a prolific flowering plant with shell pink flowers.

var. *torreyi* is a scarlet form of the species with little or no beard on the lower lip. It is often sold as 'Torre'.

'Twilight' is a seed-propagated cultivar bearing 2–3" long flowers. Plants are presently available as a mixture of colors only.

Propagation of the named cultivars is by terminal cuttings taken in early to late summer. Some of the named series such as 'Hyacinth Mix' and 'Twilight' can be propagated by seed as can the species and var. *torreyi*.

-*campanulatus* (kam-pahn′ ew-lay-tus)		Harebell Penstemon	18–24"/24"
Summer	Various	Mexico, Guatemala	Zones 4–7

This species is not often seen in American gardens but appears to be the dominant parent of a number of hybrid strains making their way into this country. Hardiness in American gardens is marginal, as the hybrids are not tolerant of winter temperatures below + 20°F or hot summer temperatures of the South. *P. campanulatus* has narrow, lance-shaped, sharply toothed leaves and 3" long tubular flowers. The stamenoide (see introduction above), if one takes the time to look, is bearded and a good identifying characteristic for the species. The flowers are pink, dark purple, or violet and borne in a long, narrow inflorescence in midsummer.

Cultivars:

'Alice Hindley' is a hybrid with *P. barbatus* and bears large (2½–3" long) deep pink tubular flowers with white interiors. Plants are about 2' tall and late flowering. This is a magnificent plant when well grown.

'Evelyn' is about 18" tall with many 1" long flowers of pale pink borne over bushy plants. It is hardier than most of the penstemons, probably having *P. barbatus* in its parentage.

'Garnet' has large, 1½–2" long wine-colored flowers which open in late summer and fall. The thin, lanceolate leaves are bright green but this hybrid is only moderately hardy in the United States, likely having *P. hartwegii* in its parentage.

The hybrids need excellent drainage (incorporate some gravel in the planting hole), and should be mulched in winter and summer.

Hybrids may be propagated from cuttings or division, and the species may also be raised from seed.

-× *gloxinoides* (gloks-in-oi' deez)		Gloxinia Penstemon	18–24"/20"
Summer	Various	Hybrid	Zones 5–7

The specific epithet has no official botanical standing but refers to hybrids between *P. hartwegii* and *P. cobaea*. *P. hartwegii* has drooping scarlet or blood-red flowers and entire leaves while *P. cobaea* has large reddish purple to whitish flowers and sharply toothed leaves. The hybrids have inherited the large flowers from *P. cobaea* and are often referred to as gloxinia penstemons. The flowers are about 2" wide, equally long and borne on tall, open racemes.

Cultivars:

'Firebird' is the best known and has exceptionally deep red flowers.

'Ruby' is similar but the flowers are not as intensely colored.

'Stapleford Gem' ('Sour Grapes') is used in England and is making its way to the United States. The indigo-blue buds swell to form flowers in shades of amethyst and blue. This beautiful plant is likely a hybrid with *P. hirsutus*, hairy penstemon, native to the northeastern states.

None of the hybrids is particularly hardy except on the west coast and all must be well mulched regardless of location. Rooting cuttings prior to the first frost and growing inside under lights ensures survival.

Propagate the hybrids by terminal cuttings taken in late summer.

Quick Key to Penstemon Species

- A. Margins of leaves entire.................................... *P. barbatus*
- AA. Margins of leaves serrated
  - B. Flowers very broad (greater than 1½" across), and long (1½–2")... *P. × gloxinoides*
  - BB. Flowers less than 1" wide, about 1" long .... *P. campanulatus*

Additional Reading:

Chatto, Beth. 1986. Penstemons. *Horticulture* 64(8):10–11.

Associations:

American Penstemon Society, Box 450, Briarcliff Manor, N.Y. 10510. Publication: *American Penstemon Bulletin*.

Perovskia (pe-rof' skee-a)   Perovskia   Lamiaceae

Although approximately seven species occur, only *P. atriplicifolia* is used to any extent. The stems are square in cross section and the flowers are borne in terminal racemes or panicles.

-atriplicifolia (a-tri-plis-i-fo' lee-a)		Russian Sage	4–5'/4'
Summer	Light blue	Afghanistan to Tibet	Zones 3–9

As a garden plant, *Perovskia* provides beauty and fragrance. The plant has pungent foliage, but only when bruised or crushed. The tubular light blue flowers are two-lipped and arranged in whorls along many-branched 12–15" tall panicles. The coarsely toothed gray-green leaves are 1–2½" long and 1" wide. The loose flowers and small foliage provide a feeling of lightness and airiness in the garden. The flowers appear in mid- to late summer and are particularly stunning when combined with a white-flowered species such as *Boltonia asteroides* 'Snowbank'. Flowers persist for up to 15 weeks; lasting from early July to mid-September in my garden. Plants lean toward the light and tend to flop over as they mature.

Full sun and adequate drainage must be provided to survive wet winters. Late frosts will knock plants back badly but in most cases, they recover and grow rapidly. Cut back to 12–18" after the first hard frost in the fall. Leave some of the stem buds as these provide next year's growing points.

Cultivars:
'Blue Mist' flowers earlier and has lighter flowers than the species.
'Blue Spire' has deep violet flowers and deeply cut foliage.

Propagate by offshoots which occasionally arise after 2–3 years or take softwood cuttings in the summer. Take a 3" long shoot, including stem and leaves, dip in root hormone, place in sand, and cover to maintain humidity. Use of plastic to maintain humidity is better than a mist system, as excessive moisture in the rooting bench results in loss of cuttings. Roots appear in 14–21 days.

Related Species:
P. abrotanoides, Caspian perovskia, is more branched, taller, and bears darker blue flowers than *P. atriplicifolia*. The gray-green linear-oblong leaves are 1–2" long and deeply cut. Plants are less compact than Russian sage and it is a inferior garden plant.

P. × 'Mystery of Knightshayes' is a name I am giving to a hybrid seen at Knightshayes Court in England. The flowers were deeper purple and the leaves were larger and less toothed. A beautiful specimen.

P. scabiosifolia is about 4' tall and loaded with small yellow flowers. Although not as common as other species, it is worth trying in a sunny location.

Phlomis (flo' mis)	Phlomis	Lamiaceae

The genus is seldom used in America but plants are offered by a number of nurserymen. Given the proper conditions of soil, sun, and moisture, they can be rather pretty, but I have not seen many good looking plants in my travels except in the northeast United States. These coarse plants look best in flower bud and go downhill from there.

-fruticosa (froo-ti-ko′ sa)		Jerusalem Sage	2–4′/3′
Spring	Yellow	Mediterranean	Zones 4–8

This is one of the best in the genus because of the late summer flowers and gray-green foliage. The 2–4″ long leaves are coarse, wrinkled and white-woolly beneath. The stems have woolly hairs, and are slightly yellowish. The most arresting features (as well as the prettiest) are the flower buds, tightly whorled in the axils of the uppermost leaves. Twenty to thirty tightly closed flower buds occur in tiered whorls, and the flower stems resemble light green candelabras. The sulphur yellow flowers open in late spring in the South and provide a pleasing contrast to the gray-green foliage. Plants flower in the summer in the North, but in winter in southern California.

Full sun is required in the North and partial shade in the South. They are fairly drought resistant and salt tolerant. In the South, leaves remain evergreen in the winter but plants die to the ground north of zone 7.

Propagate by division in the fall or spring, or sow seed. Shoot cuttings, taken in the fall, may also be used. Treat with rooting hormone, place in a loose medium, and cover with clear plastic to maintain humidity. Rooting occurs in 7–14 days.

Related Species:

P. chrysophylla, goldleaf Jerusalem sage, is 2–3′ tall with whorls of golden-yellow flowers. It is not yet available in this country.

P. russeliana (syn. *P. viscosa*), sticky Jerusalum sage, has green heart-shaped leaves, and grows to five feet. The hairy yellow flowers occur in 40 to 50-flowered whorls. It is more ornamental than *P. fruticosa*.

P. samia, Greek Jerusalem sage, has greenish cream-colored flowers which have many dark purple veins or streaks on the lower lips. Plants are 3–4′ tall.

Phlox (floks)	Phlox	Polemoniaceae

Phlox has enough marvelous members that at least one plant should reside in everyone's garden. Although the best known species is *P. paniculata*, garden phlox, many occur which are more disease resistant, lower growing, and easier to cultivate. In fact, the genus is represented by species ranging from 6″ to 3′ in height. The annual phlox, *P. drummondii*, has undergone significant improvements through breeding and is easily grown from seed. The most common perennial phlox is moss phlox, *P. subulata*, whose magnificent mantles of fluorescent pink, white and blue radiate from hills, roadsides, and gardens everywhere in the country. The first specimen of this plant was sent to England by John Bartram in 1745 and was termed a "fine creeping Spring Lychnis". In 1919, the intrepid plant explorer, Reginald Farrer, enthusiastically wrote that "the day that saw the introduction, more than a century since, of *P. subulata*, ought indeed to be kept as a horticultural festival."

453

All species are native to North America and have opposite leaves. In general, low-growing phlox prefer shade whereas taller species do best in full sun. Phlox require well-drained soils to remain in the garden for any length of time yet are often the first plants to show signs of drought. Fall planting is best although early spring planting is almost as safe.

One of the finest breeders of phlox, particularly the low-growing forms, is H. Lincoln Foster, whose Connecticut garden is called Millstream House. Many of our finest cultivars and hybrids bear the 'Millstream' name and attest to his foresight.

Two major pests of phlox result in serious damage. Spider mites attack all species with equal fervor and are particularly damaging in hot, dry weather. Miticides, not insecticides, should be used at the first sign of infestation. If the weather stays particularly warm and dry, continue application every week. Powdery mildew is a fungal disease characterized by white, feltlike growth on the leaves and stems in midsummer. It is particularly offensive on garden phlox, *P. paniculata*. Some cultivars are so susceptible to mildew that they are impossible to grow without application of fungicides. Fungicides should be sprayed around June 15 and applied 10 to 14 days thereafter. *P. maculata*, spotted phlox, has become more popular in recent years because of the relative disdain to mildew.

Most low-growing phlox are propagated by seed or terminal cuttings. Root cuttings may be used with all species and are commonly taken on *P. paniculata* cultivars and other upright species. Two-inch long pieces of larger diameter roots are cut and placed upright, with the base end down, and covered with 1″ of sand or peat-perlite mix. The mix must be kept moist and the environment humid.

Quick Reference to Phlox Species

	Height (in.)	Flower color	Petals notched
P. divaricata	12–15	blue	slightly
P. maculata	24–36	various	slightly
P. nivalis	6–9	various	no
P. paniculata	36–48	mauve	slightly
P. stolonifera	6–12	lavender	no
P. subulata	6–9	various	slightly

-*divaricata* (di-vah-ri-kah′ ta)		Woodland Phlox	12–15″/12″
Spring	Blue	Eastern North America	Zones 3–9

This is one of the most useful and overlooked phlox for today's gardens. The leaves are dark green, oblong, and 1½–2″ long. Plants spread slowly by creeping

Phlox divaricata 'Fuller's White'
(80%)

rhizomes above which 12–15″ tall flower stems ascend in the spring. Shoots which do not bear flowers (sterile) don't ascend, but root at the nodes. The somewhat fragrant 1½″ wide flowers are usually light blue but vary to lighter or darker shades. The ends of the petals are slightly lobed and the flowers are loosely held in panicles. This species makes a wonderful edging plant for partially shaded, moist, well-drained areas.

Cultivars:
'Dirgo Ice' is 8–12″ tall with pale blue flowers.
'Fuller's White' is more dwarf (8–12″) and is so completely covered with clear, white flowers in the spring that it looks like a snowbank. The leaves are slightly smaller than those of the species and the flowers are notched at the end of the petals. It is also more sun tolerant than the species. Although the species is an excellent garden plant, it cannot hold a candle to this cultivar. Flowering starts in early April and persists for 4–5 weeks in my garden.
var. *laphamii* is native to the western United States and bears dark blue flowers and entire petals.
'Louisiana' produces early-flowering purple-blue flowers with a magenta eye.

Related Species:

P. × *arendsii*, Arend's phlox, is the result of crosses between *P. divaricata* and *P. paniculata*, garden phlox, and arose in Arends nursery in Germany in 1912. It is intermediate in height and floriferous.

'Anja' bears reddish purple flowers.
'Hilda' produces mauve blossoms.
'Susanne' has white flowers with a red eye.

For some unfortunate reason, these cultivars are rarely seen in America.

P. bifida, sand phlox, is a low-growing plant with short linear leaves and deeply notched violet-purple to white petals appearing in early spring. It is tough and views poor soils and drought with contempt.

'Colvin's White' is a pure white form bearing deeply cut flowers in spring. The species has been used in creating *P.* × *lilacina* hybrids (see *P. subulata*) and is hardy from zone 4 to zone 8.

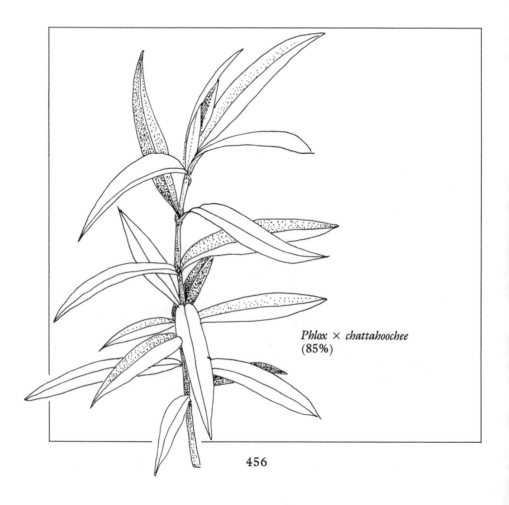

Phlox × *chattahoochee*
(85%)

P. × *chattahoochee*, Chattahoochee phlox, (often mistakenly offered as a cultivar) is a cross between *P. divaricata* var. *laphamii* and the pale purple-flowered downy phlox, *P. pilosa*. The flowers have entire petals with a striking purple eye and the foliage consists of longer, wider, dark green leaves. It is not as long-lived as woodland phlox. Flowering occurs from early April to early June.

P. pilosa tolerates full sun and flowers between *P. divaricata* and *P. paniculata*. Plants grow 1- 1½' tall and are covered with short hairs. Plants perform well in the South.

Woodland phlox may be propagated from seed or by division. The cultivars and hybrids are best multiplied from terminal shoot cuttings, divisions or root cuttings.

-maculata (mak-ew-lah' ta)   Spotted Phlox, Wild Sweet William   24–36"/24"
Early Summer   Mauve-pink   Eastern North America   Zones 3–9

This species is coming into its own now that additional cultivars have entered the market. The mauve-pink flower color did little to inspire excitement and the species labored in relative obscurity. The leaves are 2–4" long, linear to lance-like and arranged up the stem like the steps of a ladder. They are also thick, glossy dark green and slightly pointed. The stems are hairy and usually, but not always, mottled red. The main differences between this species and *P. paniculata* are earlier flowering, darker green leaves, conical panicles, and better mildew resistance.

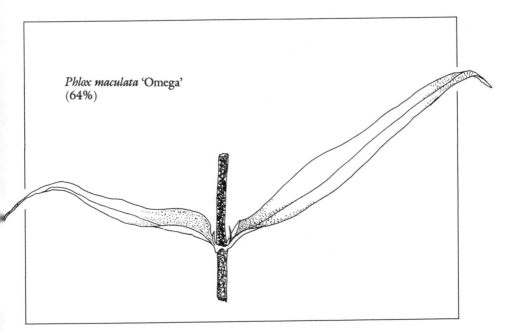

Phlox maculata 'Omega'
(64%)

457

Cultivars:

'Alpha' bears rose-pink flowers with a hint of a darker eye.

'Miss Lingard' brought the species out of obscurity. It is an excellent pure white cultivar which flowers earlier and is much more mildew resistant than the popular summer phlox. The parentage of 'Miss Lingard' is confusing. She has also been attributed to *P. carolina*, Carolina phlox, and may well be a hybrid between the two species.

'Omega' produces white blossoms with a small lilac eye and is more floriferous than 'Miss Lingard'.

'Rosalinde' has dark pink flowers.

Propagate by division of offshoots, from root cuttings, and occasionally from terminal cuttings.

-nivalis (ni-vahl' is)		Trailing Phlox	6–9"/12"
Spring	Various	Southeastern United States	Zones 6–9

Because of the similarity in habit, appearance, and flowering time to the ubiquitous moss phlox, *P. subulata*, *P. nivalis* has been overlooked by breeders and gardeners alike. There are, however, several lovely forms and cultivars available. All make excellent plants for the rock garden or front of the border. The ½" long linear leaves are dark green and carried on creeping stems. The 1" wide flowers are usually entire but may be slightly notched and range from purple to pink or white. Plants differ from moss phlox in that the petals are normally entire (notched in *P. subulata*), and the stamens and style are much shorter (up to one-half inch long in *P. subulata*, less than one-eighth inch long in *P. nivalis*). *Phlox subulata* is much more cold tolerant than *P. nivalis*. Full sun and well-drained soils are necessary for success.

Cultivars:

var. *camia* is a lovely pink form with flowers a little larger than the species.

'Eco Brilliant' and 'Eco Flirtie Eyes' have mauve and white-eyed flowers, respectively. Both were selected by Dr. Don Jacobs at Eco Gardens in Decatur, Georgia.

Propagate by division or cuttings.

-paniculata (pa-nic-ew-lah' ta)		Garden Phlox	3–4'/2'
Summer	Magenta	Eastern North America	Zones 4–8

This species is surely the most magnificent of upright phlox and more cultivars and colors have been advertised in catalogs than all others combined. This has resulted in a most popular plant, which, if placed in the right location, will flower spectacularly. Sites in full sun with good ventilation are necessary for best performance. Plants perform better in the North than in the South as they are not particularly heat tolerant. Under hot summer conditions, plant vigor diminishes and susceptibility to root rot increases. Unfortunately, some cultivars are very susceptible to powdery mildew, regardless of location. To reduce the incidence of disease, thin clumps to four or five strong shoots in the spring, and always apply water to the base of the plant and not the foliage. If overhead watering is necessary, water in the morning to allow the leaves to dry during the day. Watering at night results in rapid mildew infestation; a reason why plants struggle where late afternoon and evening summer thundershowers are common. Mildew is less of a problem in dry seasons and windy locations. Fungi-

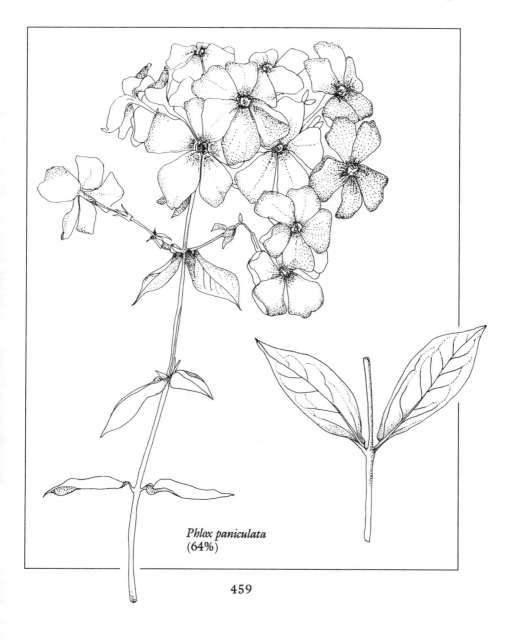

Phlox paniculata
(64%)

cides are available and application should begin in most areas by early June and continue every 10 days to two weeks. If you think this is more trouble than these plants are worth, you may be right. Take advantage of less mildew susceptible species such as *P. maculata*.

The leaves are 2–5" long, and have slender points at the end but are not as thick as those of *P. maculata* or *P. carolina*. The flowers are held in a large, dense pyramidal panicle, up to 8" across; each tubular flower averages one inch across, often in shades of pink or lilac. The stamens and style are often equal to or longer than the corolla tube.

Cultivars:

The species itself is seldom seen in gardens and has been replaced by selections with greater vigor, floriferousness, and attractiveness. Tremendous numbers of cultivars are offered and the best way to choose is to consult one of the many garden catalogs. However, here are a few of my favorites.

Pink:
'Bright Eyes' has pale pink blossoms with a crimson eye.
'Dresden China' produces pastel pink flowers with a deeper rose-pink eye.
'Eva Cullum' has large heads of clear pink flowers with a dark red eye. Plants are 2–2½' tall and do not require staking.
'Pinafore Pink' bears flowers similar to 'Bright Eyes' but occur on dwarf 6–12" tall plants.
'Fairy's Petticoat' has large heads of pale pink with darker eyes.

Purple, Lavender:
'Ann' is a late bloomer with large lavender flower heads.
'Caroline van den Berg' bears flowers of imperial purple.
'Franz Schubert' has lilac blooms with a star-shaped darker eye.
'Progress' has pale violet blossoms with a darker eye.

Salmon, Red:
'Fairest One' has salmon-pink blooms with a dark red eye.
'Othello' sports deep red flowers with a 6–7 week long blooming period.
'Sir John Falstaff' bears large flowers of salmon-pink.
'Starfire' has striking cherry red flowers which immediately catch the eye, even from a distance.

Variegated Leaves:
'Norah Leigh' bears creamy white leaves with a center line of green. The foliage is far more remarkable than the rather common lavender flowers. It makes a wonderful accent for the front or middle of the garden. Afternoon shade is required.

White:
'Blue Ice' bears white flowers with a pinkish blue eye.
'Mt. Fuji' ('Mt. Fujiyama') is the best white by far, bearing dense 12–15″ long
   flower heads. It shines from a distance.
'White Admiral' has clear white large flower heads. Plants bloom 1–2 weeks
   later than 'Mt. Fuji'.

Most garden phlox cultivars are propagated from root cuttings (see *Papaver* for
details). Offshoots, which often arise at a considerable distance from the parent
plant, may be divided in the spring.

| -*stolonifera* (sto-lo-ni′ fe-ra) | Creeping Phlox | 6–12″/12″ |
| Spring   Violet, lavender | Eastern North America | Zones 2–8 |

The species is possibly the most shade tolerant of the phlox and forms a
dense cover under quite shady conditions. Creeping phlox is low growing and,
similar to woodland phlox, produces both flowering and sterile shoots. The
leaves on the sterile shoots are 1–3″ long and narrowed at the base while those
on the flowering shoots are oval, no more than 1″ long, and not as narrow at
the base. The petals are usually unnotched, and the lavender ¾″ wide flowers
are held 2–3 in a cyme. Plants spread by stolons and by rooting at the nodes of
the sterile stems. Although a fine species, it is not as brilliant or as vigorous a
garden performer as other low growing species.

Cultivars:
'Blue Ridge' has blue-lilac flowers.
'Bruce's White' is characterized by white flowers with a yellow eye.
'Pink Ridge' forms 6″ tall mats with dark mauve-pink flowers.
'Sherwood Purple' bears purple-blue, highly fragrant flowers over 6″ tall stems
   and is the most popular cultivar.

Propagate by division any time of year. Terminal cuttings of sterile shoots may
also be used.

Related Species:
   Phlox × *procumbens* is a cross between *P. stolonifera* and *P. subulata*. It com-
bines some of the vigor of *P. subulata* with the larger flowers of *P. stolonifera*.
The plants grow 1′ tall and bear ¾″ wide purple flowers.

'Millstream Variety' is a trailing form with rose-pink flowers spoked with darker
   stripes. Flowering plants are 9–12″ tall.
var. *variegata* is one of the finest varieties I have seen and has dark green leaves
   edged in white with mauve-pink flowers. The foliage is better than the flowers.

-subulata (sub-ew′ lah-ta)		Moss Phlox	6–9″/12″
Early Spring	Various	Eastern North America	Zones 2–9

It is difficult to drive or walk any distance in the spring and not see this species carpeting a bank and providing spring color to an otherwise drab and dreary residential landscape. Plants may be found in blue, white, and purple, but the overwhelming majority in landscapes are pink with a darker eye, thus accounting for one of its common names, mosspink. Plants make few demands, but full sun and well-drained soils result in best performance. The narrow, linear leaves are only about one-half inch long, close together, and quite stiff, almost to the point of being prickly. Three to five flowers are borne in a loose corymb just above the matted foliage. The petals are slightly notched to entire and open flat. The stamens protrude from the flower and the style is up to one-half inch long. Differences between *P. subulata* and *P. nivalis* (the two are often confused) can be found under *P. nivalis*.

Cultivars:

Blue, Purple:
var. *atropurpurea*.
'Blue Hills'
'Cushion Blue'
'Emerald Blue'

Pink:
'Cushion Pink'
'Emerald Pink'

Red:
'Crimson Beauty'
'Scarlet Flame'

White:
var. *alba*.
'Snowflake'
'White Delight'

Propagate by division or layering. To layer, place a section of non-flowering shoot on the ground and cover lightly with soil. Keep the area moist and the stem will root into the soil. Cuttings may also be taken, preferably in late fall for best rooting.

Related Species:

P. × *frondosa* is the result of the inevitable cross between *P. subulata* and *P. nivalis*. Plants are about 6″ tall with rose-red flowers.

'Millstream Daphne' is the best of the lot and bears deep pink flowers.
'Perfection' has pinkish flowers.
'Vivid' has stronger colored red-pink blossoms.

P. × *lilacina*, lilac phlox, resulted from crossing *P. subulata* and *P. bifida*. Bred by Lincoln Foster, these dwarf creeping plants bear star-shaped flowers and are generally assigned astronomical names.

'Mars' has very intense red blooms.
'Millstream Coraleye' has white flowers with a lovely red eye.
'Millstream Jupiter' has intense blue flowers.
'Morning Star' produces flowers of pale pink.
'Venus' bears pink flowers.

Quick Key to Phlox Species
    A. Plants prostrate or matted, usually less than 12″ tall
        B. Leaves narrow-linear, one-eighth of an inch or less wide
            C. Petal lobes distinctly notched, style approx. one-half
                inch long .... *P. subulata*
           CC. Petal lobes usually entire, style one-tenth to one-eighth
                inch long .... *P. nivalis*
        BB. Leaves not narrow-linear, usually at least one-half inch
           wide
            C. Style and stamens much shorter than corolla tube, plant
                not stoloniferous................................... *P. divaricata*
           CC. Style and stamens about as long as corolla tube, plant stoloniferous
                                                P. stolonifera
    AA. Plants erect, usually more than 12″ tall
        B. Inflorescence narrowly cylindrical to cone-shaped, leaves
           thick, stem usually purple spotted........................ *P. maculata*
        BB. Inflorescence broadly pyramidal, leaves thin, leaf margins
           with bristly hairs, stem not purple spotted .... *P. paniculata*

Additional Reading:

Books:

Wherry, E.T. *The Genus Phlox*, Wickersham Printing Co., 1955.

Manuscripts:

Thomas, Christopher. 1986. The phlox that bloom in the spring. *Horticulture* 64(6):44–50.

Physalis (fi-sal-is)   Chinese Lantern   Solanaceae

Of the 80–100 species, only the common Chinese lantern, *P. alkekengi*, is found in American gardens. The name comes from the Greek *physa* meaning bladder and it is mainly grown for its decorative orange fruit which resembles a bladder. It was believed that all members of this genus were edible and of great medicinal value. Sufferers of gout were said to have relieved the disorder by

"..taking eight of these berries at each change of the moon." (Miller, P., *The Gardener's Dictionary*, 1805). It became discredited as a medicinal plant by the end of the eighteenth century and all that can now be said is that if some person "..foolishly be invited to taste of the fruit, they will not surely die; for if not their medical virtues, their innocency has been abundantly proved." (Thornton, R.J., *A Family Herbal*, 1814). The annual *P. ixocarpa*, however, is quite edible. It is native to Mexico and the southern United States, and has wonderful names such as jamberberry, tomatillo, and tomatillo ground cherry.

-alkekengi (al-ke-ken' jee)		Chinese Lantern	18–24"/24"
Summer	White	Japan	Zones 3–9

(Syn. *P. franchetii*)

This species spreads by underground stems and, where it does well, can become a nuisance, creating a definite glut of Chinese lanterns in the neighborhood. The opposite leaves are deltoid-ovate (shaped like a fat arrowhead) and up to 5" long. One inch wide white flowers with yellow stamens are carried singly in the upper leaf axils. The actual fruit is small and cherry-like but is surrounded by the dark orange-red inflated husk, which arises from the mature calyx. Fruit is 2–3" long and up to 6" in circumference. Harvest by late summer because if left on the plant, fruits become skeletonized.

Plant in full sun and provide constant moisture, particularly when the lanterns are developing. Allowing plants to dry out results in weedy looking specimens with small fruit. Fertilize in the spring with side dressing of complete fertilizer but excessive applications may result in luxurious foliar growth with little fruit production.

Cultivars:

'Gigantea' has larger flowers and fruit (up to 8" wide) than the type.
'Pygmaea' grows only 12–15" tall.

Seeds should be chilled for 4–6 weeks at 40°F. Germination is slow and may require 6–8 months. Division in early spring or fall is possible.

Physostegia (fie-so' stee gee-a)   Obedient Plant   Lamiaceae

Twelve species are known; all tall and erect with square stems and lance-like opposite leaves. The only species commonly cultivated is *P. virginiana*, known as obedient plant or false dragonhead.

-virginiana (vir-jin-ee-ah' na)		Obedient Plant	3–4'/3'
Late Summer	Pink	Eastern United States	Zones 2–9

This species has been growing for many years in our cut flower trials at the University of Georgia because of its straight stems, classic spike-like flower heads, and outstanding flowering. Large clumps are formed which spread vigorously in good soil. Plants not supported flop over, especially in rich soils. This is not a plant for the "nice-guy" gardener, as merciless rogueing is needed to keep plants contained. Obedient it is not! The 1″ long flowers are normally pinkish and sessile on 12–18″ tall spikes. *Physostegia virginiana* is a long day plant and begins to flower in August and continues until late September in my garden.

Plants are not fussy as to soil but perform better in acid pH. They are heavy feeders but if too much fertilizer is applied, growth is even more rampant than normal. Plant in well-drained soils in full sun.

Cultivars:

var. *alba* has white flowers and blooms earlier than the species or cultivars; about three weeks earlier than 'Pink Bouquet' in Georgia.

var. *grandiflora* has larger flowers and is taller than the species.

var. *nana* is only 12–18″ tall.

'Pink Bouquet' is a bright pink cultivar which grows 3–4′ tall. Plants are beautiful but not self supporting.

'Summer Snow' has clean white flowers and is a little less invasive than the species.

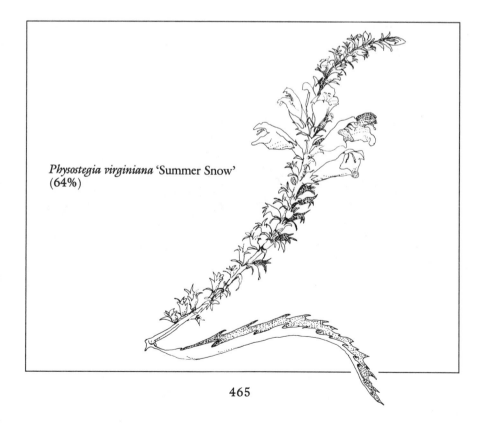

Physostegia virginiana 'Summer Snow'
(64%)

465

'Variegata' is a pleasing variegated form in which the leaves are edged white. It reminds me of *Phlox paniculata* 'Norah Leigh' in that the foliage is more outstanding than the flowers.

'Vivid' is 2–3' tall with vibrant pink flowers. It is the most compact and upright cultivar available.

Additional Reading:

Cantino, Philip D. 1980. The systematics and evolution of the genus *Physostegia* (Labiatae). Ph.D. thesis. Harvard University, 454 p.

Cantino, Philip D. 1982. A monograph of the genus *Physostegia* (Labiatae). Contributions from the Gray herbarium. 211:1–105

Platycodon (pla-tee-ko' don) Balloonflower Campanulaceae

The genus is related to *Campanula*, *Adenophora*, and *Codonopsis* but is characterized by the inflated flower bud which looks about to burst as it matures. The only available species, *P. grandiflorus*, is one of the best plants for a child's garden as kids are truly fascinated by the size of the buds. The flowers are also distinguished by opening at the top rather than on the sides or at the base.

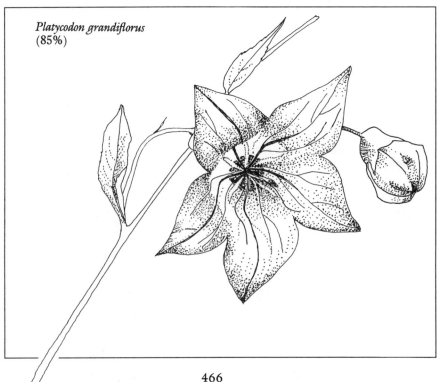

Platycodon grandiflorus
(85%)

-grandiflorus (grand-i-flor' us)		Balloonflower	2 ½–3'/2'
Summer	Blue	China, Japan	Zones 3–8

The leaves, unequally spaced on the upper part of the stem and often whorled at the base, are sharply serrated, ovate and about 1–3" long. The flowers are usually solitary, 2–3" across and bluish purple. When the balloon finally pops, a five-lobed blossom with rich purple veins and yellow-white stamens is revealed. *Platycodon* is one of the latest perennials to emerge in spring so care must be taken not to plant over or dig it out accidentally during spring cleaning. Full sun is necessary in the North but plants appreciate some protection from the afternoon sun in the South. Plants are long lived and ten-year-old plants are not uncommon. They seldom need dividing, and have few insect or disease pests, making this a truly low maintenance species. However, plants of the species, particularly in the South, are too tall and spindly and flop over without support. This is alleviated by proper cultivar selection.

Cultivars:

var. *albus* has white flowers with yellow veins.

'Apoyama' produces violet flowers on 15–18" tall plants.

'Double Blue' bears double, bright blue flowers on 15–24" tall plants. The flowers are fuller than those of var. *plenus*.

'Fuji' series, a seed strain from Japan, with blossoms of pink, white and blue grows 2–3' tall. They are most suitable for cut flowers.

'Komachi' is 12–24" tall with clear blue flowers. The bud swells to about 2" in diameter before opening.

var. *mariesii* is dwarfer (1–2' tall) and more compact with 2" diameter flowers. It should be the variety of choice in most of the country.

var. *plenus*, a double-flowering form, is interesting but not particularly handsome.

'Shell Pink' is a seed propagated selection with 2" wide pink flowers on 18–24" tall stems.

Seed germinates readily with warm temperature and moisture. Some literature states that *Platycodon* does not divide well. I have divided and moved clumps in the spring when shoots were 2–4" tall without damage.

Additional Reading:

Books:

Bailey, L. H. 1953. *The Book of Bellflowers*. Macmillan Co. (See *Campanula*).

Manuscripts:

Dirr, Michael A. 1986. *Platycodon grandiflorus. American Nurseryman* 164(5):202.

Polemonium (po-lee-mo' nee-um)   Jacob's Ladder   Polemoniaceae

Many of the 20–30 species are similar in habit and appearance, and are excellent garden plants. The alternate leaflets are arranged ladder-like along the long leaves. The flowers are usually a shade of blue, but pink, white, and yellow blossoms also occur. Plants range in height from about 3' (*P. foliosissimum*) to about 4" (*P. viscosum*). Many are native to Europe and the western United States and are not particularly long-lived in the eastern half of the country (*P. reptans* is an exception). In general, we have had little success with the genus south of zone 7, particularly *P. caeruleum* and *P. foliosissimum*. They are good plants in cooler climates, requiring full sun to partial shade, and well-drained soil.

Quick Reference to Polemonium Species

	Height (in.)	*Flower color*
P. caeruleum	18–24	Blue
P. carneum	18–24	Pink
P. pulcherrimum	8–12	Blue, yellow throat
P. reptans	8–18	Light blue

-caeruleum (se-ru' lee-um)		Jacob's Ladder	18–24"/18"
Summer	Blue	Europe	Zones 2–7

The leaves bear up to 20 leaflets which supposedly represent the ladder of which Jacob dreamed and the rest of us climbed. The 3–5" long basal leaves form dense tufts and are attached to the base of the stem by 4–6" long petioles. The stem leaves are much smaller and the petiole diminishes until the leaves are sessile at the top of the stem. The leaflets are mostly entire and taper to a long point. The 1" wide, light to deep blue flowers sport yellow stamens and occur in drooping terminal cymes.

Plant in full sun to partial shade in well-drained soils. In general, this species is intolerant of hot, humid conditions and does not do well south of zone 7, although it will produce many evergreen leaves for a few years. Further north and west, it is a much better plant where flowers will be produced for weeks.

Cultivars:

var. *album* has white flowers which are a pleasant contrast with the dark green leaves.

var. *himalayanum* has larger (up to 1½" across), deeper blue flowers than the species. This variety was considered to be a separate species (*P. himalayanum*) and may still be offered as such.

Propagate by seed or division. Sow seed in a humid, 70–75°F environment. Germination occurs in 2–3 weeks. Remove seedlings as soon as first true leaves are visible.

Related Species:

P. boreale, arctic polemonium, grows 9″ tall with ½″ diameter blue-purple flowers and 13–23 leaflets per leaf. This species was extolled for years by L.H. Bailey and admired by the English plantsman Graham Stuart Thomas. Its nomenclature is in great need of study. It may be a hybrid with *P. reptans*, or a variety of *P. caeruleum*. Regardless of the location in the taxonomic cupboard, it should be sought out and tried in North American gardens.

P. foliosissimum, leafy polemonium, is the best of the upright blue species if properly grown. It is stouter, stronger, and has larger flowers than *P. caeruleum*. The flowers have bright yellow stamens and plants are exceptionally vigorous. It is longer lived than *P. caeruleum* and produces little seed. The species does not tolerate heat and high humidity. Unfortunately, although native to western United States, it is seldom offered in this country.

-carneum (kar-nee′ um)	Salmon Polemonium		18–24″/18″
Summer	Pink to Salmon	Western United States	Zones 6–8

The reason I include this species is purely selfish. It is a lovely plant but, unfortunately, not as easy to grow as it is beautiful. Generally, the 3–8″ long leaf consists of 13 to 21 leaflets. The 1½″ long, pink flowers fade to purplish white and are held in lax, few-flowered cymes. Rather fussy about the environment, it does not tolerate heat or full sun and is less cold hardy than other species. Consistent moisture is required but plants decline rapidly if drainage is poor. However, when sited properly, it is a wonderful plant.

-pulcherrimum (pul-cher′ i-mum)	Skunkleaf Polemonium		8–12″/12″
Summer	Blue, yellow throat	Western United States	Zones 3–8

This low-growing species is particularly suited to a dry stone wall in full sun or partial shade. The leaves are 4–6″ long and consist of up to 30 leaflets, although usually fewer than 25 are produced. Small (¼″ long) flowers are held in dense cymes and are usually blue with a yellow throat but vary to violet with white interiors.

Propagate by seed or division.

-reptans (rep′ tanz)	Creeping Polemonium		8–18″/12″
Spring	Light Blue	Eastern North America	Zones 2–8

This is one of the few eastern species and is a wild flower through much of the eastern woodlands and the midwestern plains. They are excellent foliage plants and provide fresh greenery all season. Plants are seldom over one foot high. The common name is a misnomer as the plant has a shallow rhizome and is not stoloniferous. The stems are weak and diffuse, but the plant doesn't creep anywhere. The 7–15 leaflets are about 1″ long and topped by light blue, ½″ long flowers borne in loose drooping clusters (corymbs). If placed in partial shade and kept moist, plants are easy to grow.

Cultivars:

var. *alba* bears white flowers.
'Blue Pearl' grows 8–10″ tall with bright blue flowers.

Quick Key to Polemonium Species

A. Plants usually less than 18″ tall
  B. Flowers have a yellow or white throat................ *P. pulcherrimum*
  BB. Flowers same color throughout .... *P. reptans*
AA. Plants usually more than 18″ tall
  B. Flowers pink... *P. carneum*
  BB. Flowers blue.. *P. caeruleum*

Additional Reading:

Davidson, J. F. 1950. The genus *Polemonium. Univ. California Publ. Bot.* 23:209–282.

Polianthes (po-lee- anth' eez)   Tuberose   Agavaceae

This monotypic genus consists of *P. tuberosa*, the highly fragrant tuberose. The name *Polianthes* may have been derived from *poly*, many and *anthos*, flower, referring to the many-flowered stalks. Others have suggested that it was derived from *polios*, shining white, and *anthos*, flower, referring to the shiny flowers. Only Linnaeus knows for sure. In the early 1900's, North Carolina was one of the major producers of tuberose tubers for export, producing over six million tubers within a 25 mile radius of Magnolia, N.C. Today there is little tuber production in this country, most of it having moved to countries where labor is less expensive.

-tuberosa (tew-ber-o' sa)		Tuberose	3–4'/3'
Late Summer, Fall	White	Mexico	Zones 8–10

Best known for its fragrance and glistening white blossoms, the flowers appear to have been recently waxed. The fragrance is delicious to some and over-bearing to others. Flowers are still used for weddings and only one or two stems is needed to scent a whole room. The plant is derived from a tuberous rootstock, thus the name "tuberose". The leaves are linear, channeled, and spotted with brown on the underside. The 2–2½″ long white, funnel-shaped flowers appear on a 2–3' raceme between August and October.

470

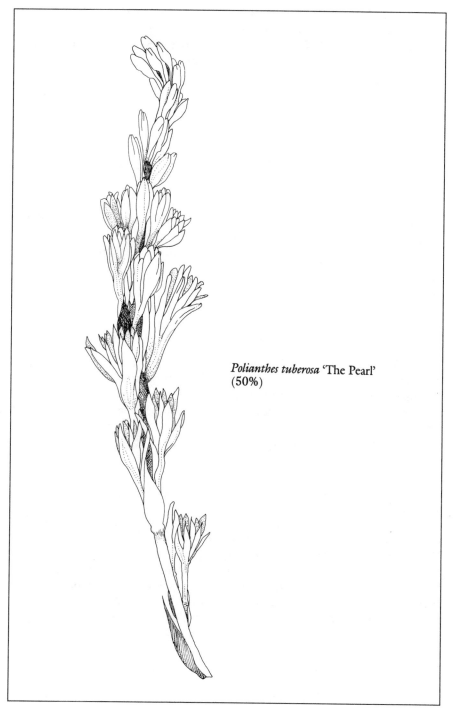

Polianthes tuberosa 'The Pearl'
(50%)

Since tuberose is a heat-loving species, tubers must be started in the house or greenhouse in the spring before soils are warm. Plant in the ground after the threat of frost. After the first frost, lift the tubers and hang them in a cool (45–50°F), dry place. In the Carolinas, Georgia, parts of Tennessee, Florida, the Gulf Coast states and much of California, plants are perennial most winters if mulch is provided. The best mulch is the dead tuberose leaves which carpet the plants after the first hard frost.

Cultivars:

var. *gracilis* has narrower leaves and flowers with longer tubes.

'Mexican Single' is a better cultivar than the species with flowers more closely spaced on the stalk.

'The Pearl', a double-flowered form, has been around for ages and is the best cultivar for the garden. This is one of the unusual instances where doubling the flower petals is a definite improvement. However, it is not as good a cut flower as the single forms because the extra petals decline more rapidly.

Tuberose may be propagated from offshoots removed in the fall when tubers are dug and replanted the following spring.

Polygonatum (po-lig-o-nay' tum)   Solomon's Seal   Liliaceae

Of the approximately 60 species, a number have left the realm of wild flowers and joined the mainstream of garden plants. The botanical name comes from *poly*, many and *gonu*, knee joints, referring to the many jointed rhizome from which the leaves rise. The common name Solomon's seal may have been derived from the circular sunken scars that remain on the rootstock after the leaf stalks die. Gerard, the English plantsman, believed the powdered roots were an excellent remedy for broken bones. He wrote in the late 1590's that roots pulverized and drunk in ale, "soddereth and gleweth together the bones in a very short space . . .". He believed that this property of sealing wounds was why the plant received the name Solomon's seal.

Most species are comprised of long, graceful, unbranched shoots bearing alternate leaves and whitish, pendulous flowers hanging from the leaf nodes. They range in height from the 2–3' tall *P. biflorum*, small Soloman's seal, to the great Solomon's seal, *P. commutatum*, which may grow 7' tall. The main reason for including these plants in the garden is their architectural qualities. The leaf orientation is delightful and the variegated forms are particularly showy. Leaves persist until frost and turn a lovely brownish yellow in the fall. The ⅓" diameter blue-black fruit is interesting if not spectacular and adds to the charm. Placed in the company of red-flowered plants such as azaleas, red colors are redder and bright colors brighter. An indispensible genus for the landscape architect.

Plants tolerate heavy shade and grow well in shady, moist areas. All are readily propagated in the fall by division of the rootstock. It is necessary to leave at

Polygonatum odoratum 'Variegatum'
(62%)

least one bud on the divisions. Seed should be stratified at 40°F for 6 weeks before sowing.

Quick Reference to Polygonatum Species

	Height (ft.)	Flower color	Flowers per axil
P. biflorum	1–3	White	2
P. commutatum	3–7	White	3–8
P. odoratum	1½–2	White	1–2

-biflorum (bi-flo' rum)   Small Solomon's Seal   1–3'/2'
Spring   White-green   Eastern North America   Zones 3–9

This North American species extends as far north as New Brunswick, south to Florida, and west to the Mississippi Valley in shady, cool, woodland areas. The 4–4½" long, alternate leaves are nearly sessile, and have 1–5 main nerves running down the leaves, although only the midrib is prominent toward the leaf tip. The ½ to ¾" flowers are greenish white and occur in pairs beneath the arching stems.

Plants require shade and moisture and are easily propagated by division of the rhizome.

-commutatum (kom-mew-tah' tum)   Great Solomon's Seal   3–7'/4'
Late Spring   White-green   United States to Mexico   Zones 3–7
(Syn. P. giganteum, P. canaliculatum)

A plant which truly needs space, it will gobble up all available acreage as its wings expand. Plants have been known to reach 7' in height (although 5' is more reasonable) and may form colonies equally wide, so it is not a good subject for the average suburban garden. However, there are few plants more outstanding on the edge of a moist woodland where the 3–7" long leaves can be displayed to advantage. Approximately 10 prominent nerves extend the full length of the leaves. The ¾" long yellowish green to whitish green flowers are held in a 3–8-flowered umbel in the leaf axils.

-odoratum (o-do-rah' tum)   Fragrant Solomon's Seal   18–24"/2'
Spring   White-green   Europe, Asia   Zones 3–9
(Syn. P. officinale)

The one-inch long white flowers are constricted at the base and wear a skirt of yellow green. They usually occur in pairs, occasionally singly, dangling from the leaf axils underneath the leaves. On quiet spring evenings, the flowers exude a lovely lily-like fragrance. The stems are somewhat angular and carry 8–12 lance-like leaves along their 18″ length.

Cultivars:

var. *thunbergii* is bigger and stouter in every way than the species. Shoots grow 3′ tall, leaves are 6″ long and flowers are 1–1½″ long.

'Variegatum', with its soft green leaves edged in a broad strip of creamy white, is the best form of this species. The variegation makes the plant jump out, and is a bright addition to dull shade. In the Georgia Horticulture Gardens, flowers appear in mid-April and persist for 2–3 weeks.

There is considerable confusion relative to the proper name of this form. It has always been offered as *P. odoratum* 'Variegatum' but has recently been listed as *P.* × *hybridum* 'Variegatum'. *P.* × *hybridum*, however, has 3–5 flowers per node and a more rounded stem. I can find no evidence in the plants I have observed that *P. odoratum* 'Variegatum' is anything but that.

Related Species:

P. × *hybridum* is a hybrid between *P. multiflorum*, Eurasian Solomon's seal, and *P. biflorum*. (See *P. odoratum* 'Variegatum'). Variety *flore-pleno*, has double, more persistent flowers.

Quick Key to Polygonatum Species

    A. Plant usually less than 3′ tall, 1 or 2 flowers per axil
        B. Major veins 1–5, leaves slightly hairy beneath, usually 2
            flowers per axil with little or no fragrance .... *P. biflorum*
      BB. Major veins more than 5, leaves not hairy underneath, 1–2
            flowers per axil with strong fragrance .... *P. odoratum*
    AA. Plant more than 3′tall, usually 4–5′, 3–8 flowers per axil ....
                                        P. commutatum

Additional Reading:

Ownby, R. P. 1944. The liliaceous genus *Polygonatum* in North America. *Annals of Missouri Botanical Garden* 31:373–413.

Polygonum (po-lig′ o-num)   Smartweed, Knotweed   Polygonaceae

Although most of the approximately 150 species are not ornamental, a few make welcome additions but are generally overlooked. In this country, polygon-ums have been colored with a "weedy" crayon, due to the persistence of such unwelcome guests as *P. aviculare*, the common knotweed of lawns and patios; *P. pensylvanicum*, Pennsylvania smartweed; and the most common of all our weeds, *P. persicaria*, lady's thumb. Unfortunately, these intruders have blinded gardeners and nurserymen to the beauty of some of the cultivated species. Indeed, it is a determined gardener who grows the better species as they are almost impossible to find in catalogs or nurseries. It is difficult to understand why so few nurserymen offer the garden worthy species that abound throughout England and the rest of Europe.

All species have alternate leaves and many have somewhat swollen leaf nodes. Its name has the same roots as that of *Polygonatum* (which see), but *gonu* refers to the jointed stems rather than jointed rhizomes. Several climbing species occur such as the handsome silver fleece-vine, *P. aubertii* and annual black bindweed, *P. convolvulus*, which can be a serious pest. Other species may attain heights of 5–7' and require ample space. *P. amplexicaule*, mountain fleeceflower, is a noble plant; the blood red cultivar 'Atrosanguineum' is even better. *P. cuspidatum*, Mexican bamboo, *P. rude*, and *P. sachalinense,* sacaline, are handsome in a roomy setting where space is not a concern. Otherwise they should be avoided like the plague. On the other hand, the leaves of *P. vaccinifolium* are less than one inch long and plants are less than one foot tall. Long pink flower spikes rise above the spreading plants. Plants known as magic carpet, *P. capitatum*, must be mentioned here although it is an annual in most of the country. Some references list it as cold hardy to zone 6 but it dies in zone 8. However, plants reseed themselves religiously and this low-growing specimen with gorgeous foliage and pretty pink, dense, globular flowers is well worth planting in shady or sunny locations.

Most species are comfortable in semi-shade with constant moisture. While they are not bog plants, dry soil inhibits establishment. Once established, they are persistent. Unfortunately, the more ornamental species are not particularly heat tolerant and perform poorly south of zone 7. However, heat tolerance is improved if consistent moisture is available. All species are easily propagated from division and most may be raised from seed.

Quick Reference to Polygonum Species

	Height (in.)	Flower color
P. affine	6–9	Rose-red
P. bistorta	18–30	Pink
P. milettii	18–24	Crimson

-affine (a-fee' nee)		Himalayan Fleeceflower	6–9"/12"
Summer, Fall	Rose-red	Himalayas	Zone 3–7

Whenever I think of this species, I think of the stairs descending towards the water garden at Wakehurst Place in Ardingly, England. The bank along the stairs and the area leading to the small stream are covered with the small rosy red spikes of *P. affine*. Although far grander plants and displays at Wakehurst may be found, I always look forward to that bank of polygonum when I return.

Plants are most effective as front of the border subjects or ground covers, bearing erect, mostly basal leaves (2½–4" long) which taper to the petiole. The deep green 4" long leaves turn bronze in fall. Numerous deep rose-red flowers are arranged in dense 2–3″ long terminal spikes and turn whitish as they mature. Plants are most effective in cool, moist areas and provide stability and beauty to a troublesome bank, or carpet stones in a rock garden. It is not as invasive as many of the other species and may be controlled with selective pruning. Some shade is tolerated but full sun and moisture are necessary for dense plantings.

Cultivars:

'Darjeeling Red' has deep pink flowers and is a vigorous selection.
'Donald Lowndes' is about 8–10″ tall and carries double salmon-pink flowers. Probably the best selection for American gardens.
'Superbum' is more vigorous than other cultivars and the pink flowers turn crimson as they mature.

The easiest method of propagation is division in the spring or fall. Terminal cuttings (3–4″ long) and seed propagation are also effective. Seeds require stratification (place in moist sand or peat moss at 40°F for 6–8 weeks).

-bistorta (bis-tor′ ta)		Snakeweed	18–30″/30″
Early Summer	Pink	Europe, Asia	Zones 3–8

This clump-forming plant has 4–6″ long, wavy medium green leaves with a striking white midrib. Most leaves arise from the base of the plant and form handsome clumps even when not in flower. The flowers, however, are held well above the foliage and consist of 4–5″ long dense spikes of soft pink. The stamens of the individual flowers protrude resulting in a bottle brush appearance. The flowers are long lasting and used as cut flowers in the florist trade.

Cultivars:

'Superbum' is larger, has bigger flowers and is superior to the species. This cultivar is easier to find than other polygonums mentioned.

Propagate similar to *P. affine*.

-milettii (mill-et′ ee-i)		Millet's Knotweed	18–24″/18″
Summer	Crimson	Western China	Zones 4–7

This species is similar to the previous two, that is, having most of the leaves arise from the base of the plant and narrow, dense spikes of flowers. It flowers later than *P. bistorta* and is not as large. The flowers are a magnificent deep crimson and are held on long flower stalks extending well above the foliage.

Copious moisture and partial shade are necessary for suitable growth.

Quick Key to Polygonum Species
    A. Plants more than 18″ tall
        B. Flower color pink.. *P. bistorta*
        BB. Flower color crimson .... *P. milettii*
    AA. Plant less than 18″ tall.. *P. affine*

477

Additional Reading:

Goode, Jeanne. 1983. Smartweeds. *Horticulture* 61(8):26–29.

Potentilla (po-ten-till′ a)   Cinquefoil   Rosaceae

Most of the 500 species of cinquefoil are herbaceous, although the best known and probably the most useful species in North American gardens is the woody bush cinquefoil, *P. fruticosa*. Cinquefoils prefer cool soils and cool nights to look their best but there are few areas where plants are as pretty as the catalog photo. I am not familiar with any species doing well south of zone 7, although not all species and cultivars have been tested. Many herbaceous species are offered in the trade (more than this genus warrants) and some are seed propagated, resulting in significant variation.

The name comes from *potens*, meaning powerful, in reference to the supposed usefulness of the genus in medicine and magic. In particular, common cinqefoil, *P. reptans*, was considered most effective against ague (chills, fever). The number of leaves a man needed was immaterial as long as "Jupiter is in the ascendant and the Moon applying to him". (Culpepper, 1649). Rudimentary dentists also provided their unsuspecting patients with a root concoction because "the decoction of the roots held in the mouth doth mitigate the paine of the teeth." (Gerard, 1597).

Most cinquefoils have palmate leaves which people may mistake for strawberries and are seldom more than 2′ tall. The 5-petaled flowers may be yellow, red, rose, or white. Many species, useful for the rock garden, form lovely mats of 4–12″ tall foliage.

Quick Reference to Potentilla Species

	Height (in.)	Flower color	Leaves in 3's or 5's.
P. atrosanguinea	18–30	Red	3
P. nepalensis	12–24	Purple	5
P. recta	12–30	Yellow	5
P. tabernaemontani	6–9	Yellow	5
P. tridentata	6–12	White	3

-atrosanguinea (at-ro-sang-guin′ ee-a)   Himalayan Cinquefoil   18–30″/24″
Summer   Red   Himalayas   Zones 5–8

Having seen this in numerous areas, I can confidently state that its main contribution to gardening is as a parent for a number of named hybrids, and not for its own beauty and performance. The silky-hairy leaves are three-parted with toothed margins. The 5–8″ long petioles make the plant look stretched by early summer. The 1″ wide flowers are deep red but plants are not particularly floriferous. Full sun, cool nights and good drainage are prerequisites for good performance.

Related Species:

P. argyrophylla, undersnow cinquefoil, is similar to Himalayan cinquefoil except that the flowers are yellow rather than red.

P. × *menziesii* resulted from crosses between *P. argryophylla* and *P. atrosanguinea*. The silvery-gray foliage is often as decorative as the flowers. Many of today's garden hybrids have been selected from this hybrid. 'Gibson's Scarlet' was highly touted as a tough, brilliantly colored plant but has not lived up to expectations in the United States. The flowers are deep scarlet and plants are more compact than *P. atrosanguinea*. 'Glory of Nancy' ('Gloire de Nancy') is an old hybrid with large, 2″ wide double flowers of red and gold. It also has lovely gray-green leaves and is one of the better hybrids. 'William Rollison' has semi-double vermillion flowers with yellow reverse. Plants grow about 15″ tall. 'Yellow Queen' has bright yellow single flowers over silvery foliage and attains but 12″ in height.

Propagate the species by seed and the hybrids by division.

-nepalensis (ne-pa-len′ sis)		Nepal Cinquefoil	12–24″/20″
Summer	Crimson	Nepal	Zones 5–8

This single-flowered species produces many strawberry-like purple to crimson flowers in early summer and continues to flower sporadically throughout the summer. Although flowering continues for a relatively long time, plants only persist for 2–3 years in most settings. The basal leaves are long stalked, up to 1′ long, and the 2″ long leaflets are coarsely toothed. The 1″ wide flowers are rose-red and held in loose, branching panicles. The plant is compact until the long leafy stems rise to 2′ or more in the summer, at which time severe pruning is necessary.

Cultivars:

'Miss Wilmott' (var. *willmottiae*) is 10–12″ tall and produces carmine flowers with a darker base. It is a better choice than the species.

'Roxana' bears orange-scarlet flowers on 18″ tall stems.

Both cultivars arise fairly true from seed.

Related Species:

P. × *hopwoodiana*, a cross between *P. nepalensis* and *P. recta*, the weedlike sulphur cinquefoil, is about 18″ tall with pink flowers, rosy red at the base and edged white on the margins.

P. thurberi, Thurber cinquefoil, is native to New Mexico and California. It is shorter than *P. nepalensis* and commonly has 7 leaflets rather than 5. The flowers are a rich dark brown to purple and are held in an open inflorescence.

In *P. nepalensis*, the petals are nearly twice as long as the sepals but are about the same size in *P. thurberi*. From the garden viewpoint, there is little difference between them, although *P. thurberi* may be longer lived and more heat tolerent.

P. × tonguei, a cross between *P. anglica* or *P. aurea* and *P. nepalensis*, is offered by many nurserymen. It has lovely copper yellow, single flowers with rosy red centers. Plants are only 3–8" tall and make a pretty ground cover for sunny areas. Cold hardy to zone 5, it has problems with heat south of zone 7.

-recta (rek' ta)		Sulphur Cinquefoil	12–30"/15"
Summer	Yellow	Southern Europe	Zones 3–7

Introduced from Europe, this species can be a troublesome weed, particularly in the limestone areas of the Midwest and Northeast. Plants are tufted and leaves consist of 5–9 toothed, densely-hairy leaflets about 2–4" long. Three-quarter inch diameter yellow flowers are carried on terminal compact corymbs.

Cultivars:

var. *sulphurea* is similar to the species but has sulphur-yellow flowers.
var. *warrenii* has 1" diameter bright yellow flowers in loose terminal clusters. It is not as weedy as the species and flowers for a longer time. This is the best form of the species for the garden.

All are easily seed-propagated under warm (70–75°F), moist conditions. Plants may also be divided after 2–3 years.

-tabernaemontani (ta-ber-nay-mon-tah' nee)		Spring Cinquefoil	6–9"/12"
Spring	Yellow	Western Europe	Zones 4–8

(Syn. *P. verna*)

This mat-producing species has numerous decumbent 2–5" long rooting stems. The long-petioled leaves are 5–7 palmate, wedge-shaped and serrated near the apex. The ½" wide golden yellow flowers are held in 3–5 flowered cymes at the end of 6–8" long ascending stems.

Cultivars:

var. *nana* is only about 4" tall and covered with golden yellow flowers almost the same size as the species.

Related Species:

P. aurea, golden cinquefoil, is also a low growing potentilla with yellow flowers but has fewer stems and smaller flowers. The stems of *P. tabernaemontani* root much like runners and thus the plant becomes a mat whereas those of *P. aurea* ascend, resulting in clumps. Plant offered in the trade as *P. aurea* var. *verna* ('Verna') are similar to var. *nana* described above. It is a useful, colorful ground cover for full sun.

-tridentata (tri-den' ta-tah)   Three-toothed Cinquefoil   6–12"/12"
Summer   White   Northeastern North America   Zones 2–8

The species, native from Greenland to North Georgia, is included because of its tenacious growing habit. It grows on rock outcroppings and fills in areas thought to be unfillable, and is particularly useful for acid soils. The basal leaves consist of 3 leaflets with 3 prominent teeth at the apex (thus the common name). The stem leaves, however, are often entire. The small, ¼" wide white flowers cover the plants in early summer and although many other species are more ornamental, they can be lovely when properly sited and are particularly useful on dry banks and rocky areas.

Propagate by seed or division of the runners.

Quick Key to Potentilla Species

    A. Basal leaves in three's
        B. Flowers white, about ¼" across .... *P. tridentata*
        BB. Flowers red to dark purple, about 1" across .... *P. atrosanguinea*
    AA. Basal leaves 5–7
        B. Flowers rose to purple .... *P. nepalensis*
        BB. Flowers yellow
            C. Stems upright, flowers about 1" across .... *P. recta*
            CC. Stems trailing like runners, flowers less than ½" across ....
                                      P. tabernaemontani

Additional Reading:

Mitchell, Irene. 1984. Cinderella Cinquefoil. *Horticulture* 62(12):22–24.

Primula (prim' eu-la)   Primrose   Primulaceae

Primroses are nature's way of welcoming spring, and their absence from the garden is excusable only if climate does not allow successful culture. Many species are not long lived but their beauty makes them well worth growing, even as an annual. There are over 400 species, many of which are most at home in the moist climates of the British Isles, New Zealand, and the Pacific Coast. However, many primroses are perfectly cold hardy to zone 3 and nearly all are cold hardy to zone 5. A few species do well as far south as zone 8, although it is often assumed, incorrectly in many cases, that they will not survive hot, dry summers. One should never assume anything without testing and within this genus, numerous easy-to-grow species exist. Many perform well regardless of climate, as long as ample soil moisture is available.

The majority of primulas are native to north temperate zones and occur in bogs, meadows, woodsides, and rockeries. They range in size from the tiny 1" tall *P. minima*, least primrose, to tall stately candelabra primroses such as *P. japonica*. The unique *P. vialii*, has violet-blue flowers held in a short, dense spike,

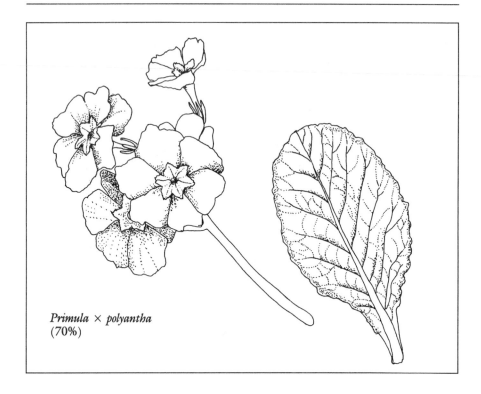

Primula × *polyantha*
(70%)

completely atypical of primrose. Many of the common garden primroses are hybrids of *P. veris*, common cowslip, *P. vulgaris*, English primrose, and *P. juliae*, Julian primrose and are known as polyantha primroses or "polys" for short. Breeders have increased the size of the flowers while making the plants more compact. They are popular as potted plants in Europe and gaining momentum as bedding and potted plants in this country. *P. malacoides*, another pot plant species is used extensively in winter gardens in Australia and New Zealand. Great drifts of white, pink, and burgundy brighten the winter landscape at every corner. The meadowland species of Europe such as *P. veris*, *P. elatior* and *P. vulgaris* are most common in the United States, but species from China (*P. pulverulenta*), Japan (*P. japonica*, *P. sieboldii*), the Himalayas (*P. denticulata*, *P. florindae*), and mountainous regions of Europe (*P. auricula*, *P. allionii*) are also increasing in popularity. All require consistently moist soil and partial shade. Winters seldom result in plant losses, but fluctuations of soil moisture during the hot summer months can be devastating. No primroses enjoy heat, but *P. obconica*, top primrose and *P. sinensis*, are more heat tolerant than most.

The taxonomy of this diverse genus has long occupied the minds of botanists and is presently divided into thirty sections. The most valuable sections horticulturally are Auricula, which contains *P. auricula* and other excellent low-growing species for cool climates and the cool greenhouse; Candelabra, containing a vast array of species with whorls of tiered flowers on long flower stems; Denticulata, the home of the drumstick primrose, *P. denticulata*; and Vernales, where the ever-popular cowslips, oxslips, and polyanthas reside.

Quick Reference to Primula Species

	Height (in.)	Type of inflorescence	Need for moisture
P. auricula	2–8	Umbel	Moderate
P. denticulata	8–10	Globe	Moderate
P. japonica	12–24	Umbels in tiers	Critical
P. × polyantha	8–12	Umbel	Low
P. sieboldii	4–8	Umbel	Moderate
P. vulgaris	6–9	Solitary	Low

-auricula (ow-rik′ ew-la)		Auricula Primrose	2–8″/8″
Spring	Yellow	European Alps	Zones 2–8

Although the flower color of the original species is bright yellow, many color forms are common in cultivation. The 1″ wide flowers are bell-shaped and usually fragrant. The thick leaves are 2–3″ long and equally wide. Two main forms of *P. auricula* occur, those with flowers and stems densely coated with a white mealy substance (farina) and those which are smooth and not powdery. Both types contain flowers of a single color (i.e. no eye) and those with a white or yellow eye. Plants are shallow rooted and should have winter protection to reduce heaving from alternate freezing and thawing. The species is not difficult to grow, but unfortunately, is difficult to locate. Although some of the cultivars are beautiful, there is something wonderful about growing the species that gardeners have been trying to "improve" for over 350 years.

Cultivars:

'Dale's Red' bears brick red flowers with yellow centers and is one of the most popular auriculas.

'Gold of Ophir' has bright yellow flowers.

'Red Dusty Miller' is a farinaceous cultivar with rose-red flowers.

'The Mikado' is dark red and vigorous.

'Yellow Dusty Miller' is farinaceous and bears yellow flowers.

The species and some named cultivars are best propagated from seed. Divisions or 1–2″ long stem cuttings may be taken from established plants after flowering or in the fall. Root in a moist mixture of clean peat and sand. When plants are large enough, they may be placed in the garden.

Related Species:

P. × pubescens, a cross between *P. auricula* and *P. rubra*, bears rose-purple flowers with a white eye. One of the oldest hybrid primrose in cultivation, it is represented by many forms and cultivars.

P. viscosa, sticky primrose, has sticky foliage and ½″ wide rose-red flowers arranged in 10–25 flowered umbels. They are sometimes listed as *P. latifolia*.

'Bewerley White' has creamy white flowers on 6–8″ long flower stems.
'Mrs. J. H. Wilson' bears 1–2″ diameter rose-purple flowers with white eyes.

-denticulata (den-tik-ew-lah′ ta)		Drumstick Primrose	8–10″/12″
Spring	Lilac, White	Himalayas	Zones 4–8

The globular flower heads atop thin stems make this species easy to recognize. The leaves are spatulate (look like spatulas) and sharply toothed. They are 4–6″ long at flowering time, and later expand to a foot after flowering. In North Georgia, my plants were wonderfully green all winter until temperatures of 10°F settled in for several nights. Without snow cover, those temperatures were particularly devastating and plants were badly damaged. Many plants recovered but the flower stems were thin and weak. The use of winter mulch in all climes where snow cover is minimal is highly recommended. Evergreen boughs or loose pine straw should be placed over the plants during the winter. Leaves or other materials that layer and become heavy smother the plants and should be avoided. If plants are grown in a warm greenhouse during the winter and planted in the spring, they may not receive sufficient cold to flower. Fall planting is best because plants receive natural cold treatment in the fall and winter and flowering is improved. Moist, partially shaded areas are necessary for best garden performance.

Cultivars:

var. *alba* is a white-flowered form
var. *cashmeriana* is a large purple-flowered form with yellow powdery farina beneath the foliage.
'Cashmere Ruby' is about 12″ tall and has wine-colored flowers. It looks suspiciously similar to var. *cashmeriana* and is likely the same thing.
'Ronsdorf Strain' is a seed-propagated mixture of white, purple, bluish, or rose flowers held about a foot above the foliage.

All are best propagated by seed. Sow seed in May to June for fall planting or September to October for spring planting. Division is also a useful method of propagation.

-japonica (ja-pon′ i-ka)		Japanese Primrose	12–24″/24″
Late Spring	Various	Japan	Zones 5–7

This and related species have been placed in the division Candelabra due to the many whorls of flowers superimposed on the flower stem. In *P. japonica*, 2–6 whorls of purple flowers occur, each consisting of 8–12 flowers nearly an inch across and held at right angles to the stem on ¾″ long pedicels. To round a corner and see a display of these plants in full bloom is a marvelous sight. The leaves are 6–12" long, 2–4" wide and have irregular sharp dentations on the margins. Conditions for success are critical for all candelabra types. Moist soil or a boggy area which does not dry out in the summer are ideal. Place where there is some water movement as plants languish under stagnant conditions. Roots require cool, moist conditions and the tops should be in a shady area. The nicest diplay I have seen in this country is at Winterthur Gardens, Delaware (zone 6), although lovely plantings occur at Sky Hook in Vermont (zone 4). The grandest planting must be at Longstock Water Gardens in England where hundreds of stately candelabras vie for attention with the gunneras, *Iris laevigata*, hosta, mimulas, ferns and other moisture loving species. A trip in early summer to any of these gardens is worth the effort.

Significant natural hybridization occurs among species and cultivars in the Candelabra group and it is best to locate taxa some distance from each other. Self-sown seedlings develop into lovely, but different colored plants than the parents.

Cultivars:

'Miller's Crimson' has bright red flowers.

'Postford White' is one of the finest cultivars to date. It has large white flowers, each with a yellow eye.

var. *rosea* has pink to rose blooms. 'Miller's Crimson and var. *rosea* come true from seed.

Related Species:

P. × *bullesiana* is a cross between *P. bulleyana* and *P. beesiana*, a species with fragrant rose flowers and yellow eyes. Flowers occur in rich shades of violet, wine, and yellow.

P. bulleyana has flowers of deep reddish orange and has been hybridized with a number of other candelabra species to produce an array of interesting flower shades.

P. heladoxa has large, golden yellow flowers with deeply notched petals. Six 12 to 20-flowered whorls may occur on 24" tall plants. Plants are particularly showy in moist, open places.

P. pulverulenta has deep red flowers with a deeper red or purple eye. The scape is mealy and carries many whorls of flowers. The best cultivar is 'Bartley's Strain', with lovely soft pink flowers. *P. pulverulenta* is an important parent in many hybrid candelabra primroses.

Most candelabra primroses can be raised from seed. Sow seed as soon as ripe or when received. Seeds sown in June or July may be large enough to plant the same year. If sowing is delayed until the fall, plants will not be large enough to transplant until the following spring. *P. japonica* and *P. pulverulenta* are effectively propagated by division but others of the candelabra group may also be carefully divided.

485

- × *polyantha* (pah-lee-anth' a)		Polyantha Primrose	8–12"/9"
Spring	Various	Hybrid	Zone 3–8

This is the most common and popular group of primroses in American gardens. It is a mixture of *P. veris*, the fragrant, deep yellow cowslip primrose, *P. vulgaris*, the sulphur yellow English primrose, and probably *P. juliae*, the bright purple-flowered Julian primrose. The parents are lovely species, and *P. juliae* has also been hybridized to yield such excellent cultivars as 'Wanda', a dark purple red flower, and the interesting 'Garryarde Guinevere', with purple-tinted foliage and shell-pink flowers.

The many years of hybridizing *P.* × *polyantha* have resulted in a glorious array of flower colors, some with large eyes and others clear-faced. The small leaves are dark green and heavily veined. The flowers may be up to 1½" across in single or bicolor shades and arranged in umbels on 4–6" tall stems. The polys belong to the Vernales group and although members do not appreciate dry soils, the requirement for constant moisture is not as critical as for other groups of primrose. Natural fertilizer, such as composted cow manure, applied generously once a year is most helpful. Polys associate well with bleeding hearts, dwarf hostas, forget-me-nots, and hellebores.

The polyantha hybrids have received tremendous attention from plant breeders, particularly those in the greenhouse trade. The florist primrose has long been a staple in the pot plant market in Europe and Japan and is quickly catching up in this country. If a potted primrose is purchased as a gift, enjoy it indoors and then plant when weather permits. Primroses are also the leading bedding plant in the Northwest where conditions are ideal. Slugs and spider mites are the principal pests.

Cultivars:

Many strains and hybrids are available from nurseries, and additional colors and sizes are being developed by American, European, and Japanese breeders every year.

'Barnhaven hybrids' have large vibrant flowers borne on diminutive foliage. One of the finest hybrids developed.

'Pacific Giant' is a seed mixture of large-flowered plants in shades of blue, yellow, red, pink, or white.

'Monarch' strain has 2" diameter flowers of mixed colors but is also available in single colors.

'Giant Bouquet' is similar to 'Monarch' and bears 2–2½" diameter flowers.

Propagate by division or fresh seed.

-*sieboldii* (see-bold' ee-i)		Siebold Primrose	4–8"/8"
Late Spring	Various	Japan	Zones 4–8

Plants are downy everywhere but the flower. The 2–4" long heart-shaped leaves have scalloped margins and petioles often longer than the leaf blades. The

1–1½" wide flowers are held well above the foliage in 6–10 flowered umbels. They are usually purple with a white eye but may be white or rose. It is a wonderfully showy species and needs to be tried more often. In North American gardens, the foliage often goes dormant in late summer.

The species is somewhere between *P. japonica* and *P. × polyantha* in its requirement for moisture. Plants must not be allowed to dry out repeatedly but do not have to be planted in a bog-like setting. They have been used successfully in moist woodland plantings.

Cultivars:

'Akatonbo' has dark rose, lacy flowers.
'Isotaka' bears 8–10 flowered umbels of beautiful white blooms backed in purple-pink hues.
var. *purpurea* bears masses of purple red flowers.
'Snowflake' produces large white flowers.
'Sumina' produces large blooms of wisteria blue.

Propagation by seed but cuttings may be taken similar to *P. auricula*.

-vulgaris (vul-gah- ris)		English Primrose	6–9"/9"
Spring	Yellow	Europe	Zones 5–8

(Syn. *P. acaulis*)

This is one of the easiest primroses to grow, tolerating drier soil conditions and more heat than many others. The leaves are tufted, often wrinkled, and downy beneath resulting in a soft pubescent feel. They are about 2–3" long at flowering time but, like *P. denticulata*, continue to expand and within a month of flowering, double in size. The tubular, 1" wide flowers are sulphur yellow, often with a dark yellow blotch near the eye, and are borne singly. The flowers do not have the "take-your-breath-away" quality of other primroses but a group of a dozen in full spring finery helps provide that elusive, relaxing feel of the English garden.

This species has also been an important parent of the *P. × polyantha* hybrids and so many crosses, self-crosses, and back crosses have occured that the Vernales group is becoming a taxonomic free-for-all.

Cultivars:

var. *rubra* (subsp. *sibthorpii*) has rose-colored flowers. Many garden hybrids have been created using this and other forms of the species.

Propagate by seed or division.

Quick Key to Primula Species

 A. Flowers held in whorled umbels borne in tiers along scape .... *P. japonica*
 AA. Flowers not in tiers, borne in single umbels or solitary

    B. Flowers sessile, in rounded heads .... *P. denticulata*
    BB. Flowers on pedicels
        C. Flowers borne singly, tubular .... *P. vulgaris*
        CC. Flowers 5–20, not tubular
            D. Base of leaves heart shaped or rounded
               E. Leaf margins in wavy lobes, distinct petiole .... *P. sieboldii*
               EE. Leaves not lobed, petiole may be round or flattened..........
                                     P. × vulgaris
            DD. Base of leaves tapers to winged petiole .... *P. auricula*

Additional Reading:

Martin, Tovah. 1985. A primrose palette. *Horticulture* 63(3):45–53.

Richards, John. 1986. Petiolarid primulas in cultivation. *The Plantsman* 7(4):217–232.

Associations:

American Primrose Society, 2568 Jackson Highway, Chenalis, WA., 98532. Publication: *American Primrose Society Quarterly*.

Prunella (pru-nell' a)	Self-heal	Lamiaceae

The genus is still occasionally listed as *Brunella*, from the German *Die Braune*, a disease of the throat called quinsy, which these plants were believed to heal. Of the approximately 12 species, the most common is *P. vulgaris*, the common self-heal which invades lawns. All species have opposite leaves, terminal spikes of whorled flowers and self-sow vigorously. The only one of any use in the garden, and its usefulness is debatable, is *P. × webbiana*, a hybrid of two forms of the large-flowered European self-heal, *P. grandiflora*.

-× *webbiana* (web-ee-ah' na)		Self-heal	9–12"/12"
Summer	Various	Hybrid	Zone 5–8

There is some question as to the origin of this hybrid as well as the cultivars. Plants probably resulted from the crossing of *P. grandiflora* and *P. g.* var. *pyrenaica* (*P. hastaefolia*) and are often simply listed as *P. grandiflora*. The only differences between *P. grandiflora* and *P. × webbiana* are that *P. × webbiana* has shorter blunter leaves, more compact flower spikes, and is shorter. Both have dark purple flowers and similar growth habits.

Consistently moist soil and full sun to partial shade are preferable. Do not plant where they can escape and roam freely throughout the border and do not allow to dry out or plants quickly die. Growth is better in zone 5 than in zone 8.

Cultivars:

'Little Red Riding Hood' has crimson-red spikes and is about six inches tall.
'Loveliness' has pale lavender flowers.
'Pink Loveliness' bears pink flowers.
'White Loveliness' produces large white flowers and is the best of the 'Loveliness' group.

Pulmonaria (pul-mon-air′ ee-a)   Lungwort   Boraginaceae

Of the 12 species, only 4 are particularly attractive for the shade garden. All produce blue or pink flowers in the spring. Flowers often open one color, usually pink, and then turn blue before dropping. This charming habit has given rise to the common name of soldiers and sailors. Flowers open before the foliage emerges or at the same time. The alternate stem leaves are often spotted and provide better identification characteristics than the basal leaves.

In the sixteenth and seventeenth centuries, Jerusalem cowslip, *P. officinalis*,

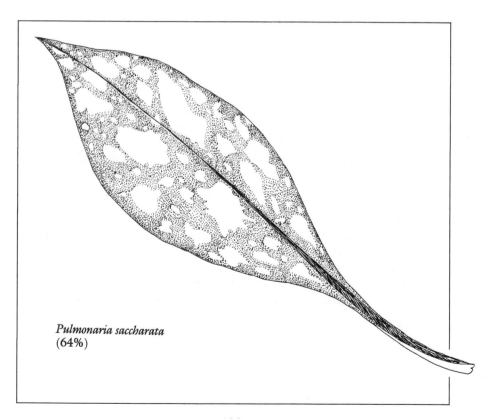

Pulmonaria saccharata
(64%)

489

became an example of the "Doctrine of Signatures", practiced by herbalists of that time. This doctrine, based on a treatise by Theoprastus Bombast von Hohenheim (1493–1541), better known as Paracelsus, suggested that the outward appearance of plants dictated their virtues. Thus, the perforated leaves of common St. John's-wort indicated that it was a useful remedy for cuts and wounds; the convoluted shell of the walnut was specific for troubles of the brain; and the spotted leaf of *Pulmonaria*, which resembled a diseased lung, was an obvious cure for ailments of that organ. The ancient study of herbalism had fallen to some of its lowest depths of irrationality during those times and would never recover.

All the lungworts should be planted in partial shade and provided with adequate moisture. They spread by creeping rootstocks, but are not invasive.

Quick Reference to Pulmonaria Species

	Height (in.)	*Spotted leaves*	*Flower color*
P. angustifolia	9–12	No	Bright blue
P. longifolia	9–12	Yes	Purple blue
P. rubra	12–24	No	Coral-red
P. saccharata	9–18	Yes	Blue

-angustifolia (ang-gus-ti-fo' lee-a)	Blue Lungwort	9–12"/24"
Spring Bright blue	Central Europe	Zones 2–8

Unspotted, bristly, lanceolate leaves emerge with the first flowers. Tight pink buds open into deep blue, drooping, funnel-shaped flowers. It makes an excellent ground cover under shrubs and competes well with many trees for water and nutrients. It performs better in the North than in the South (below zone 6) because the foliage tends to wilt rapidly under the warmer temperatures. Flowering is not affected but the foliage declines more rapidly in the South.

Cultivars:

var. *alba* has handsome white flowers but plants are not particularly easy to locate in the trade.

'Azurea' sports lovely gentian-blue flowers.

'Mawson's Blue' bears bright violet-blue flowers.

'Munstead's Blue' has rich blue flowers and is similar to the previous cultivar.

Propagate by division after flowering.

-longifolia (long-gi-fo' lee-a)	Long-leafed Lungwort	9–12"/24"
Spring Purple-blue	Western Europe	Zones 3–8

The name *longifolia* describes the long, narrow foliage (at least six times as long as wide). The dark green leaves are gray spotted and pointed, becoming narrower and smaller up the stem. Crowded terminal racemes of purple-blue flowers vie for attention in the spring, a little later than other species. It is a good plant for use as a ground cover or in the front of the border and is more adaptable to southern conditions than the other species.

Cultivars:

'Bertram Anderson' has violet-blue flowers and dark green leaves spotted with silvery green.

Propagate by division after flowering.

-rubra (rew' bra)		Red Lungwort	12–24"/30"
Early Spring	Bright Red	Southeastern Europe	Zones 4–7

This species recently appeared in American catalogs and gardens and is unique in a number of ways. Specifically, the flowers open early in the spring, one of the earliest of the lungworts to flower, and the coral-red blooms are a marked departure from the usual blue hues. In fact, this color is rare in plants of Boraginaceae. The light green foliage is evergreen in milder climates and has soft hairs that produce a velvety texture. The oblong leaves narrow abruptly into the stem and are virtually sessile. It is a pretty plant which makes an interesting splash in spring and, if provided with adequate moisture, performs well all year.

Cultivars:

var. *albocorollata* has white flowers that open later than the species.
'Bowle's Red' has deeper red flowers and slightly spotted leaves.
'Redstart' has dark red flowers and is more compact than the species.
'Salmon Glow' has showy salmon flowers.

-saccharata (sa-ka-rah' ta)		Bethlehem Sage	9–18"/24"
Spring	Blue	Italy, France	Zones 3–8

This has become the most popular species of *Pulmonaria* because of the availability of good cultivars and the highly prized spotted foliage. Leaves are more spotted than *P. longifolia* and appear to have had sugar dusted over the green leaves, thus the specific name. Leaves are about three times as long as broad and the white blotches tend to coalesce. The pink flower buds open into funnel-shaped flowers which turn blue with age. It is a useful addition as a foliage accent, even if plants do not flower.

Plants require sufficient moisture if leaves are to remain ornamental throughout the season. The spotted leaves show up well in the garden but few things look worse than wilted, ratty, spotted leaves. Although not as water loving as *Ligularia* or *Primula japonica*, adequate moisture must be provided during the warm days and nights of summer.

Cultivars:

var. *alba* has white flowers and can be raised from seed.

'Boughton Blue' has silvery gray blotches spread randomly throughout the long, narrow leaves. The flowers are clear blue.

'Highdown', a relatively new cultivar, is taller than the species. Dangling rich blue flowers are produced earlier.

'Leopard' bears green foliage marked with silver blotches, and red-purple flowers.

'Margery Fish', named after a noted English horticulturist, is more vigorous than the species and a favorite in Europe.

'Mrs. Moon' is an old favorite with large silver-spotted leaves and pink flowers which turn blue. This may be a hybrid with *P. officinalis*.

'Pink Dawn' has the same striking spotted leaves with sprays of pink flowers.

'Sissinghurst White' has large white flowers and silver-white-spotted leaves. The flowers are most handsome but the foliage is not as striking as the species.

Propagate from division after flowering.

Quick Key to Pulmonaria Species

    A. Leaves usually unspotted, or slightly so
        B. Flowers remain coral to red, do not turn blue . . . . *P. rubra*
        BB. Flowers open pink, turn blue as they age . . . . *P. angustifolia*
    AA. Leaves definitely spotted
        B. Leaves much longer than wide, white spotted . . . . *P. longifolia*
        BB. Leaves ovate, rounded at both ends, white blotched . . . . . . *P. saccharata*

Additional Reading:

Mathew, Brian. 1982. *Pulmonaria* in gardens. *The Plantsman* 4(2):100–111.

Pulsatilla (pul-sa-til′ a)   Pasque Flower   Ranunculaceae

About a dozen species are known, and until recently were included with *Anemone*. Although some taxonomists still retain this marriage, the presence of feathery elongated styles on the fruit has resulted in the separate genus. The fruits, which are as ornamental as the flowers, double the garden value. Flowers are apetalous (no petals) and wrapped in furry, pointed involucral leaves that unfurl as the satiny flowers open. Flower colors include the darkest violet (*P. pratensis*); forget-me-not blue (*P. halleri* 'Budapest'); yellow (*P. sylvestris*); and white (*P. occidentalis*). Blossoms are borne singly in the axils of feathery, tufted foliage. The foliage dies back in mid- to late summer.

The only listing of *Pusatilla* I found in a collection of nursery catalogs was *P. vulgaris*, common pasque flower. While this species is certainly worth growing, so is *P. alpina*, alpine pasque flower, with its much divided foliage, white flowers (yellow in var. *sulphurea*) and huge feathery seed heads. Seldom do we see the considerable charm of *P. nuttalliana*, lion's beard, native of the western United States whose large blossoms appear even before the leaves unfurl. Perhaps the loveliest of dwarf pasque flowers is *P. vernalis*, vernal pasque flower, whose light purple campanulate flowers open even before the snow disappears. A rock garden enthusiast or a local specialty grower can assist in locating some of the difficult to obtain species.

Pulsatilla should be planted in full sun in the North and full sun to partial shade in the South. Many species are excellent rock garden plants and all require excellent drainage. If drainage is poor, plants seldom survive.

-vulgaris (vul-gah'ris)		Pasque Flower	9–12″/12″
Early Spring	Purple	Europe	Zones 5–8

The wine-purple, urn-shaped flowers appear before the foliage has fully emerged. They consist of six pointed sepals which encircle egg yolk yellow stamens. Soon after the flower has closed for the last time, the feathery seed head rises 12–15″ above the foliage. The basal leaves are 4–6″ long, pinnately dissected, and silky-hairy when young.

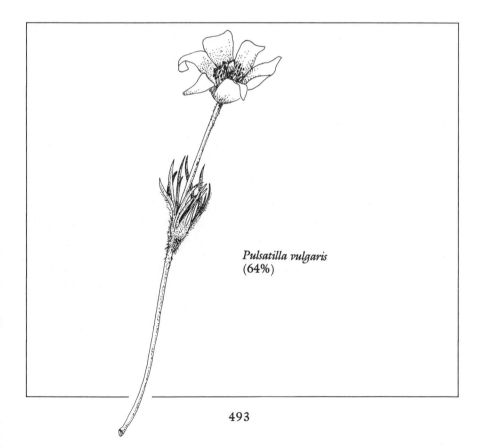

Pulsatilla vulgaris
(64%)

Cultivars:

var. *alba* has pretty, creamy white flowers which offer better contrast to the leaves than the purple flowers of the species. Plants flower in early April in north Georgia and persist two weeks, but the silky flower heads last well into May.

var. *grandis* is the same as the species but is more vigorous, bigger and more suitable for the border.

var. *rubra* has flowers which some call red but are really more of an intense purple.

Propagate by fresh seed because seeds go dormant soon after maturity (See *Actaea*). Plants may be carefully divided after they have been well established but, in general, do not transplant well.

Additional Reading:

Haw, Stephen. 1986. Pasque flowers. *The Garden* 3(4):165–168.

Puschkinia (push-kin' ee-a)   Striped Squill   Liliaceae

This small genus is closely related to *Scilla* and *Chionodoxa* and differs botanically in minor ways. They are less ornamental than those two genera but sufficiently pleasing if planted where they can be admired "up close and personal". Only one species is common in cultivation, *P. scilloides*.

-scilloides (skil-loi' deez)   Striped Squill   4–6"/6"
Early Spring   Pale Blue   Orient   Zones 4–9

This is similar to *Scilla*, thus the specific name *scilloides*, meaning "like *Scilla*". Two to four linear leaves arise in the spring, followed by a leafless flower stalk with 2–6 nodding pale blue, bell-shaped flowers. The petals of each flower have a deep blue stripe running down their center. This stripe plus the paleness of the flowers are good identification features. Plant in hundreds where they may be admired close up, otherwise they are easily overlooked. Not the least of its charms is the pleasant fragrance, which smells like a spice cabinet whose contents were removed so just a faint reminder remains.

Puschkinia tolerates full sun or partial shade. Plant bulbs about 4" deep in mid- to late September. Flowering occurs as early as mid-February in the South and a month or so later in the North. They seldom need division but if flowering is sporadic, the offsets may be removed and replanted.

Cultivars:

var. *compacta* has flowers closer together on the scape, and more flowers than the species. It is not easy to locate.

var. *libanotica* has smaller flowers of purple-blue.

R

Ranunculus (rah-nun' kew-lus)   Buttercup   Ranunculaceae

The genus is somewhat similar to *Anemone* in its diversity; species with tuberous roots (classed as bulb species in the commercial trade) and with fibrous roots are grown. About 250 species occur, but only a few are worthy of inclusion in the garden. The tuberous-rooted species, *R. asiaticus*, was a popular florist plant and cut flower early in this century and is undergoing a renaissance as new cultivars are developed. It can be grown as a garden plant, but tubers must be lifted in the fall in most parts of the country. The small yellow buttercup that children put under their chins to see their skin turn yellow is *R. acris*, tall buttercup, and double forms of this diminutive wild flower have been developed for the garden. One species that has received much attention is an indestructable ground cover. The lesser celandine, *R. ficaria*, has bright yellow flowers and forms tight mats of round, crisp leaves which advance though the neighborhood with abandon. This tuberous-rooted species is about 2–3″ tall but its "pleasant face" so impressed William Wordsworth that it became the subject of his long poem "To the Lesser Celandine" and two more "To the Same Flower". Appreciate it where useful, but keep it out of the small garden.

Several other species should be treated the same way. *R. repens*, creeping buttercup, jogs more than creeps and, as pretty as the flower is (particularly the less invasive double form, 'Flore-pleno'), it can take over an area within a couple of years. Plants may be admired along the Riverwalk in San Antonio where they smother banks with glossy green leaves and double yellow flowers. I like this plant more in my neighbor's garden than in mine.

The flowers of buttercups are usually yellow, but *R. aconitifolius* has white flowers and those of *R. asiaticus* are offered in a rainbow of colors. The leaves are alternate and flowers generally have five petals and sepals in single-flowered species. The petals have a small nectary at their base, a good identification characteristic which serves to separate the genus from *Adonis*, a closely related genus.

Many species such as the European water buttercup, *R. aquatilis*, and the native swamp buttercup, *R. septentrionalis*, thrive in wet places, thus the name *Ranunculus*, derived from rana, a frog.

Quick Reference to Ranunculus Species

	Height (in.)	Flower color	Root type
R. aconitifolius	24–36	White	Fibrous
R. acris	24–36	Yellow	Fibrous
R. asiaticus	12–30	Various	Tuberous
R. montanus	3–6	Yellow	Creeping

-aconitifolius (a-kon-ee-ti-fo′ lee-us)		Aconite Buttercup	24–36″/30″
Spring	White	France	Zones 5–8

The name *aconitifolius* refers to the similarity of the foliage to that of species of *Aconitum*. The glossy green leaves are palmately parted into 3–5 sections. The similarities end there as the flower of this plant is single, about 1″ across, and white. The upper leaves are sessile and flowers are held many to a stem, producing loose sprays in late spring and early summer. The species itself is seldom seen except in botanical gardens and available only from specialty seedsmen. The species and its varieties are best planted in full sun to partial shade and benefit from consistently moist soil. The garden form is the double selection, var. *flore-pleno*.

Cultivars:

var. *flore-pleno*, with double white flowers, introduced to Britain by Huguenot refugees, became known as fair maids of France. It is also known as white bachelors' button being "very suggestive of buttons, but only remotely so of bachelors" (Sutherland, W., *Handbook of Hardy and Herbaceous Plants*, 1871). It is a better garden plant than the species and does not spread as rapidly as other members of this genus.

var. *grandifloris* (var. *platanifolius*) has larger flowers than the species and if the single form is to be grown, this is the variety of choice.

var. *luteo-plenus* is an obscure double, yellow-flowered form seldom seen and even more difficult to locate. The flowers are similar to those of the double common buttercup (*R. acris*) but the plant is not pubescent.

Propagate from seed or division in fall or early spring.

-acris (ah′ kris)		Common Buttercup	24–36″/30″
Spring	Yellow	Europe	Zones 3–7

Although native to Europe, the species has found conditions in Canada, the Atlantic states and as far south as Virginia to its liking, and has naturalized in these areas. The golden yellow flowers are about 1″ across, have spreading sepals and are hairy beneath. The flower buds are also hairy. Leaves are palmately divided into 3–7 sections, five being most common. The plant is much branched and bears many flowers. It is a wonderful weed and, fortunately, two controllable forms occur which are more useful.

Cultivars:

var. *flore-pleno* is sold under names such as *plenus*, *plena*, and *multiplex* but all have the same double yellow button-like flowers. Plants are handsome but if moisture is available and soil is rich, they may spread rather quickly. It is often called the yellow bachelor's button. Plants combine well with lavender flowers.

var. *stevenii* is much less invasive and has single and semi-double flowers. Heights of 3–4′ are not uncommon, however, and plants are more prone to topple than the lower growing forms.

All forms may be propagated by division or seed.

-asiaticus (ah-see-ah′ ti-kus)		Persian Buttercup	12–30″/24″
Spring	Various	Asia, Crete	Zones 8–10

This is a magnificent plant when grown well. In California, I have seen great rows of ranunculus cultivars in pastel shades, each flower fully double and seemingly perfect. I had to remind myself that I was in the rarified growing area of the Salinas Valley and would not have the same success on the East Coast. The history of this species is like a roller coaster. Few flowers have risen so high, to fall so low. In 1665, there were 20 types listed in the catalog of the Royal Gardens of Paris, and in 1775, a nurseryman named James Maddock listed nearly 800 kinds and fifty thousand seedlings were raised annually in his nursery alone. By 1820, the number listed by nurserymen had dropped to 400 and in 1898, Shirley Hibberd wrote in her book *Familiar Garden Flowers*, that the named varieties were reduced to "a few dozen only, or perhaps less than a score". Today it is difficult to find more than mixed colors. One of the main reasons for the decline was the difficulty of cultivation.

Tubers do not tolerate frost and must be lifted after the leaves have turned yellow, and cool spring temperatures are necessary for best quality flowers. They also must have excellent drainage and sucessful gardeners use raised beds. For most gardeners, it is a difficult plant to grow well, although if tubers are planted in early spring and mulched, those plants which do flower are worth the extra effort. Seed-propagated plants should be transplanted early in spring after danger of frost.

The leaves are two- or three-parted and the plant is erect. The flowers are about 3″ across and almost always double. Flower color is variable but tubers may be ordered in separate shades.

Cultivars:

A number of horticultural divisions have resulted from the many years of breeding and selection. The florists' section, called Persian Ranunculi, are variable in form and color and the most highly cultivated members of the genus. The gardeners' section, called Turban Ranunculi, thought to be var. *africanus*, have larger, broader leaves which are less cut than those of the species. The petals are curved inward forming a spherical flower much like a double peony.

'Bloomingdale Strain' was the first hybrid from seed and this low-growing strain has become popular with greenhouse growers as a pot plant. It is more heat tolerant and flowers earlier than previous selections. The large flowers occur in vibrant mixed colors and are enjoyable as an indoor plant or as a garden specimen.

'Color Carnival' is a mixed bag of colorful 18–24″ tall plants, usually available only from seed. The double flowers are camellia-shaped.

var. *superbissimus* is a vigorous tall form with large semi-double flowers. It is sometimes sold as 'Superbissima' and is available in mixed colors from red to white.

'Tecolote Strain' ('Tecolote Giants') are taller than the previous strain and better for cutting. This strain has been in cultivation for a long time and is available in separate shades. New cultivars are being introduced, primarily by Japanese breeders, and ones such as 'Early Dwarf Strain' are exciting and appear easier to grow than many of the previous types.

Tubers can be divided after digging in the fall. Seed of newer hybrid forms may be sown approximately 5 months prior to planting out. Seeds should be sown at 60–62°F but no chilling requirement is needed. Germination occurs over 6–8 weeks.

| *-montanus* (mon-tah′ nus) | | Mountain Buttercup | 3–6″/12″ |
| Late Spring | Yellow | Europe | Zones 5–8 |

(Syn. *R. geranifolius*)

The leaves are 3-parted and the flowers are borne singly. The leaves which emerge from the base are petioled but those on the stems are sessile. The single flowers are yellow and possess the classic buttercup shape and color. The creeping rootstock results in rapid spread in good soils, making it a useful ground cover, but not as invasive as *R. ficaria* or *R. repens*.

Cultivars:

'Molten Gold' is similar to the species but has larger, golden yellow flowers. It does well in well-drained soils and full sun to partial shade.

Propagate from division or seed.

Related Species:

R. yakushimanus is only 2–3″ tall and bears ½″ wide waxy yellow flowers over yellow-veined leaves. It is an undiscovered little ground cover gem.

Quick Key to Ranunculus Species

    A. Flower usually white, single . . . . *R. aconitifolius*
   AA. Flower not usually white, single or double
       B. Plant 3–6″ tall, flower yellow . . . . *R. montanus*
     BB. Plant 9–24″ tall, flowers various
          C. Rootstock tuberous, flowers various, petals reflexed and
              usually double . . . . *R. asiaticus*
        CC. Rootstock not tuberous, flowers yellow, petals curled up
              but not reflexed, double in var. *flore-plena* . . . . *R. acris*

Rheum (ray′ um)   Rhubarb   Polygonaceae

Telling people that rhubarb can be used as an ornamental plant is like telling them to grow goldenrod as a cut flower. In both cases, however, it is simply a matter of selecting the right form and not closing your mind before opening your eyes. The fresh tall panicles of edible rhubarb, *R. rhabarbarum*, add a dimension of height in the spring to my Georgia garden. Although ornamental in the South, where rhubarb is uncommon, I hesitate to recommend it as an ornamental plant except for the potager. In fact, as the petioles are eaten, there is little left of the plant to consider ornamental. However, a number of species are truly ornamental and commercially available in the United States. They taste terrible, but are magnificent garden specimens.

-palmatum (pahl-mah′ tum)	Ornamental Rhubarb	5–7′/6′
Summer Red, White	China	Zone 4–7

This most imposing specimen makes one forget that rhubarb is a vegetable. A constant supply of moisture, well-drained soil, partial shade, copious fertilizer in the spring and plenty of room are prerequisites. The dark green, 2–3′ wide basal leaves are deeply and sharply palmately lobed (thus the species name). Deep red, 2′ long panicles reach to the sky. In combination with red peonies or variegated Solomon's seal, the plant is unforgettable. Unfortunately, plants are not as easy to grow as garden rhubarb and are more sensitive to drought and heat, but if constant moisture is maintained, success is more likely. Fall planting is best. Once established, plants persist for many years.

Cultivars:

'Atrosanguineum' is the best form. Leaves emerge in the spring with a dark purple hue that persists, at least on the reverse, into summer. The flowers are deep cherry-red followed by attractive fruit.

499

'Bowles' Variety' is similar to the previous cultivar but has rose-red flowers.

var. *tanguticum* bears dark purple leaves which are less deeply cut than the species. The flowers appear on erect side shoots rather than terminal as in the previous forms and may be white, pink, or red. Often raised from seed, considerable variation occurs.

Propagation of cultivars is best accomplished by division, being sure that each division has a dormant crown bud. The species and varieties may also be raised from seed.

Related Species:

R. alexandrae is 3–4' tall and bears undivided foliage that resembles overgrown plantain leaves. The pale greenish yellow flowers are borne in a narrow panicle in spring.

Rodgersia (ro-jerz' ee-a)   Rodgersia   Saxifragaceae

Rodgersia contains about five wonderfully ornamental species, native to China and Japan. The genus commemorates the American navy commander, Admiral John Rodgers, who was in charge of the expedition during which *R. podophylla* was discovered. It is ironic that, although discovered by an American, so few are grown in America. However, more American nurseries are now offering *Rodgersia* so perhaps this will change.

They survive in ordinary soil but perform best in rich, moist soils and partial shade. The flowers are borne in large panicles on tall stems and may be white, yellow, or shades of red. All species but *R. tabularis* are apetalous (no petals) and color is provided by the sepals and stamens. Leaves of most species are compound, basal and dark green. Plants spread to 5' and sufficient room is needed to look their best. One or two plants are sufficient to provide unique architectural detail along a stream, lake, or water feature.

Quick Reference to Rodgersia Species

	Height (ft.)	Flower color	Leaf arrangement
R. aesculifolia	3–6	White	Palmate
R. pinnata	3–4	Rose-red	Pinnate
R. tabularis	2–3	White	Lobed

-aesculifolia (ees-skew-li-fo' lee-a)	Fingerleaf Rodgersia	3–6'/6'
Late Spring	White	China	Zones 5–6

The basal leaves are usually composed of seven, 4–10″ long leaflets which are coarsely toothed and narrowed at the base. They are palmately compound and resemble the leaves of the horse-chestnut, *Aesculus*. The 1½–2' long panicle consists of flat clusters of creamy white flowers which open later than the other

500

species. One of the characteristics of this species is the shaggy brown hair which covers the petioles, flower stalks and principal leaf veins. Flowers are not as spectacular as other species but plants are beautiful when sited properly.

Propagate by division or seed. Sow the tiny seeds on the surface and subirrigate so seeds and seedlings are not washed away. Germinate at 70–75°F; after seedlings have emerged, place at 50–60°F.

Related Species:

R. *podophylla*, bronzeleaf rodgersia, is similar to the above species but bears 5 light green leaflets in the spring which turn bronze in the summer. The yellowish white flowers are held in 1' long dense panicles.

-*pinnata* (pi-nah' ta)	Featherleaf Rodgersia	3–4'/4'
Late Spring	Rose-red	China	Zones 5–7

The foliage is often bronzed, particularly in the spring when temperatures are still cool. The leaves are pinnately compound but on some plants the leaflets are so closely attached that the leaves look palmate. It is necessary to closely inspect a number of leaves to be sure. In fact, hybrids between R. *aesculifolia*, R. *pinnata* and others have resulted in the blurring of leaf arrangement among species. Usually, there are five to nine, 6–8" long leaflets, widest in the middle and narrowed at both ends. The rose-red flowers are borne in branched panicles but considerable variation in flower color occurs. The branching habit of the inflorescence results in a dense flower.

Cultivars:

var. *alba* has a long, loose inflorescence composed of creamy white flowers. In some cases the flowers are almost yellow. A beautiful form.

var. *elegans* bears rose-pink flowers.

var. *rosea* has rose flowers.

var. *rubra* has dark red flowers.

var. *superba* has bronze-purple leaves not as coarse as the type and a longer inflorescence of persistent rose-red flowers. This is an excellent garden specimen.

Propagate similarly to R. *aesculifolia*.

-*tabularis* (tab-ew-lah' ris)	Shieldleaf Rodgersia	2–3'/4'
Summer	White	China, Korea	Zones 5–7

(Syn. *Astilboides tabularis*)

Leaves are not compound as in the others but are large, circular and slightly lobed. They are peltate, meaning that the petiole attaches to the middle of the leaf, and may be 3' across. The leaves resemble those of *Peltiphyllum peltatum* while the flowers resemble those of a large *Astilbe*. The inflorescence is made up of long plumes of creamy white flowers which extend well above the foliage.

501

Both sepals and petals are found on the flowers, unlike other species, which are apetalous. Because of the absence of *Rodgersia*-like leaves, this is not as noble as the others mentioned.

Quick Key to Rodgersia Species

    A. Leaves compound, not peltate
        B. Leaves palmately compound, shaggy hair on flower stalk
           and petiole... *R. aesculifolia*
        BB. Leaves pinnately compound, not obviously hairy........... *R. pinnata*
    AA. Leaves simple, peltate....................................... *R. tabularis*

Rudbeckia (rud-bek' ee-a)   Coneflower   Asteraceae

Rudbeckia consists of about 30 North American species of annuals, biennials, and perennials. One of the best known wild flowers, the annual black-eyed Susan, *R. hirta* is included in this genus. In my Georgia garden, *R. hirta* reseeds prolifically every year and flowers for 2–3 months beginning the first week of June. This, of course, is my wife Susan's favorite flower.

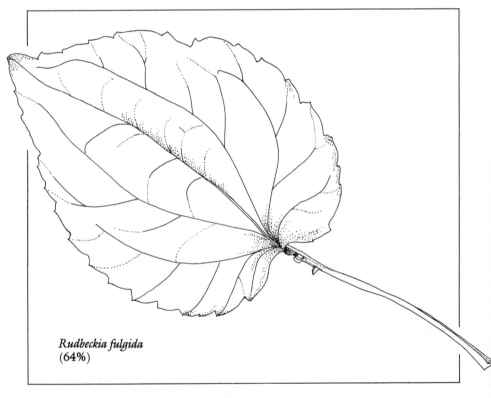

Rudbeckia fulgida
(64%)

Hybridization and selection of *R. hirta* have yielded magnificent cultivars such as 'Marmalade', 'Rustic Colors', and 'Golden Flame' but, regardless of the claims to the contrary, they should be treated as annuals.

Several genera are buried under the name coneflower, including purple cone-flower, *Echinacea*, and *Ratibida* (*Lepachys*), prairie coneflower. Numerous specific morphological differences occur which are the final word in separating some of the genera (such as disc scales being persistent on *Rudbeckia*, deciduous in *Ratibida*). However a few horticultural clues may be useful.

	Coreopsis	*Echinacea*	*Ratibida*	*Rudbeckia*
Leaf arrangement	Opposite	Alternate	Alternate	Alternate
Ray flowers	Yellow	Purple(1)	Yellow	Yellow
Shape of disc	Flattened	Raised	Columnar	Raised(2)

(1) cream colored in *E. pallida*
(2) columnar in *R. laciniata*

In the perennial *Rudbeckia* species, all have yellow to gold ray flowers and brown to black centers. The size and shape of the center (cone) and the height of the plant are distinctive. Of the useful coneflowers, *R. triloba* var. *nana* is about 2' tall while selections of *R. laciniata* may reach 7 feet. The foliage may be entire or deeply cut and is almost always alternate. Growing coneflowers is not at all difficult. They may be grown in full sun to partial shade in ordinary garden soil. Some species, such as *R. laciniata*, thrive in moist soils, while *R. hirta* tolerates dry conditions. Once coneflowers start flowering, color is provided until frost. *R. triloba* var. *nana* starts flowering in my garden in early June, *R. laciniata* in mid-June, and *R. fulgida* and *R. triloba* in late July.

Quick Reference to Rudbeckia Species

	Height (in.)	*Color of disc*
R. fulgida	18–30	Black
R. laciniata	30–72	Greenish
R. nitida	36–48	Greenish
R. triloba	24–36	Black

-fulgida (ful-gi' da)		Orange Coneflower	18–30"/24"
Summer	Yellow	United States	Zones 3–9

This species has entire, slightly hairy foliage. The 3-veined basal leaves are twice as long as broad. The 2–2½" wide flowers consist of up of 12–14 yellow ray flowers surrounding a black to brown disc. Plants are rhizomatous and form large clumps after 2–3 years. Although not invasive, colonies form rapidly in rich loose soil. The species is seldom seen but several varieties and cultivars are popular.

Cultivars:

The varieties and cultivars may be separated by shape and size of foliage. Differences are slight but all are improvements on the species.

var. *compacta* grows 15–18″ tall with smaller flowers.

var. *deamii* has larger basal leaves and is more floriferous than the species. The basal leaves are broadly elliptical (⅜ to ½ as broad as long), while the upper stem leaves are about as large as the basal leaves with small, remotely spaced teeth. Plants grow 24″ tall. Plants are slightly better than the species.

var. *speciosa* (*R. newmanii*, *R. speciosa*) has basal leaves which are entire or shallowly lobed. The stem leaves are coarsely toothed. Plants are about 18″ tall and the flowers are 2½–3″ across and have deep orange ray petals.

var. *sullivantii* is much like var. *deamii* but the stem leaves are successively reduced in size until the uppermost are merely large bracts. 'Goldsturm' is a compact, free-flowering selection of var. *sullivantii* and one of the finest perennials available. The dark green foliage contrasts beautifully with the 2–3″ wide deep yellow flowers. The center consists of a nearly black cone. Full sun and moist soils are necessary for best performance. Plants are magnificent from late July well into September.

All varieties may be propagated by seed, division or terminal cuttings. 'Goldsturm' should only be propagated by division or cuttings. Plants propagated from seed are variable and probably are var. *sullivantii*.

-laciniata (la-sin-ee-ah′ ta)	Cutleaf Coneflower	30″–6′/4′
Summer	Yellow	North America	Zones 3–9

The lower leaves are 3–5 lobed while the upper are less deeply cut into 3 lobes. The stems have short stiff hairs which feel like sandpaper. The 2–3½″ wide blooms are made up of drooping yellow ray flowers surrounding a green cylindrical disc. It is a familiar wild flower at the edge of moist woods from Quebec to Florida and does best in moist soils. Drier soils may be tolerated as long as irrigation is provided during drought. Place in full sun to partial shade. Plants are long-lived and 10 years of good garden performance are not uncommon.

Cultivars:

'Gold Drop' is a superior form for those requiring a smaller plant with large double flowers. It is 2–3′ tall and stems are sufficiently strong to support the heavy golden yellow flowers.

'Golden Glow' propelled this species from an overlooked wild flower to a garden staple. Introduced to the garden trade in 1894 as var. *hortensia*, it has been popular ever since. Plants grow 3–5′ tall and are covered with large, fully double lemon yellow flowers.

Propagate the species from seed, division, or terminal cutting. Cultivars must be propagated vegetatively by division or cuttings.

-nitida (ni-ti' da)		Shining Coneflower	3–4'/3'
Summer	Yellow	Southern United States	Zones 4–10

This species is similar to *R. laciniata* in that the yellow ray flowers droop and the disc is greenish and quite columnar. However, plants are shorter with

Rudbeckia 'Goldsturm'
(64%)

rounded, sparsely toothed, entire leaves. The species is seldom seen in gardens, having been superseded by improved cultivars.

Cultivars:

'Goldquelle' has shaggy double yellow flowers and seldom grows taller than 3'. Flowers open all season if spent blooms are removed.

'Herbstonne' ('Autumn Sun') grows 4–5' tall and is one of the finest coneflowers in cultivation. Dozens of long, drooping sulphur yellow petals surround a green cylindrical disc producing a glorious scene in late August through October. Towering over red dahlias, blue asters and purple coneflowers, it is the king of the sunny fall garden. In the North, the stems usually don't require staking, however, they often tumble in the South.

Propagate the species from seed or division, the cultivars by division only.

-triloba (tri-lo' ba)		Three-lobed Coneflower	24–36"/18"
Summer	Yellow	United States	Zones 3–10

The much branched plants carry many small (1½" across) yellow flowers with purplish black, raised central discs. Flowers appear about the same time as 'Goldstrum' and last nearly as long. The basal leaves are obviously 3-lobed and the stem leaves less so. Plants are seldom listed in perennial catalogs, perhaps because *R. triloba* is technically a biennial (although that does not stop the common foxglove from being listed everywhere). This is unfortunate because it is more persistent than many biennials and, in fact, has been flowering in the same place in my garden for 3 years. Plants perform well in open areas but also tolerate partial shade. Support is necessary to keep plants upright in the South but less so in the North. However, even without support, the attractive flowers turn up to the sun and blanket the ground. This overlooked native plant should be included in more gardens.

Cultivars:

var. *nana* is only 2' tall and is one of the earliest rudbeckias to flower, filling the void between spring- and summer-flowering plants.

Propagate the species by division, seed, or cuttings; var. *nana* is best propagated by division. Plants propagated from seed in the spring flower the first year.

Quick Key to Rudbeckia Species

     A. Disc on mature flower cylindrical, greenish
          B. Leaves deeply 3–5 parted, plant usually 4–6' tall .... *R. laciniata*
          BB. Leaves entire, plant usually 3–4' tall .... *R. nitida*
     AA. Disc on mature flower raised but not cylindrical, brown or
          dark purple
          B. Lower leaves deeply 3-lobed .... *R. triloba*
          BB. Lower leaves not deeply 3-lobed .... *R. fulgida*

Ruta (roo' ta)   Rue   Rutaceae

Many herbs are considered highly decorative and rue surely belongs in that category. A number of plants travel under the common name rue, including rue anemone (*Anemonella thalictroides*), goat's rue (*Galega officinalis*), wall rue (*Asplenium ruta-muraria*), and the various species of *Thalictrum* which make up the meadow rues.

The alternate, pinnately compound leaves of *Ruta* are particularly pungent and dotted with purple glands. The yellow flowers, consisting of four sepals and four petals, are usually borne in corymbs. Plants may be propagated by seed or cuttings.

Of the 40 species, only *R. graveolens* is used to any extent outside the herb garden.

-graveolens (gra-vee' o-lenz)		Rue, Herb of Grace	12–36″/30″
Summer	Pale Yellow	Southern Europe	Zones 4–9

This species was well established in European monastery gardens in the 1100's because its aromatic odor suggested medicinal value. If one could swallow the concoction of leaves and stems without gagging, it was supposed to help one stay young. In fact, the original Greek name was *Rute*, from *ruomai*, to preserve, a reference to the plant's effect on longevity. It is a sub-shrub, meaning that the base of the plant becomes woody but dies back to the ground in the winter. The ¾″ diameter flowers are rather dull yellow. However, the reason for its popularity as an ornamental plant is the lovely glaucous blue, delicately cut foliage, particularly on some cultivars.

Cultivars:

'Blue Beauty', a mounding 18″ tall plant, bears excellent blue-green foliage and is an asset to the front of the border. It is so similar to 'Blue Mound' that I can see no difference.

'Jackman's Blue' is more popular in Europe than here and about 30″ tall. The foliage is glaucous blue and topped by the same pale yellow flowers found in the species. The cultivars help soften some of the screaming reds and yellows in the summer and fall garden.

Propagate the cultivars from terminal cuttings in late summer and early fall.

S

Salvia (sal' vee-a)   Sage   Lamiaceae

One of my fondest memories as a young boy was drinking the nectar from the red salvia flowers that my friend's dad planted in his garden every summer. Plucking out the center of the flower (I had no idea it was called the corolla) and squeezing out the "honey" was a favorite summer pasttime. It is an activity I have not yet outgrown. Those who know *Salvia* only as an annual bedding plant are suprised to learn that this is a vast genus, consisting of over 700 species. *Salvia* is a collectors' dream! To collect them all is impossible but sufficient ornamental species are available that the collector can enjoy this hobby for a lifetime. In this respect, *Salvia* is much like *Campanula*, and *Salvia* zealots have entire gardens in honor of this genus.

In general, members have 4-sided stems and opposite leaves. The tubular two-lipped flowers are produced in terminal and axillary whorls. Blue and red are the predominant flower colors but those with red flowers are almost always annuals or short-lived perennials. Plants range in height from less than 1' (*S. chamaedryoides*) to immense 4' tall hulks such as *S. involucrata*, both native to Mexico.

Many have interesting scented foliage when bruised, and it is always fun to play the game of "What is this smell?" with your friends. *S. rutilans* smells of pineapple, *S. microphylla* (syn. *S. grahamii*) and *S. guaranitica* resemble currants and *S. officinalis*, smells of sage. The scents seem obvious but 9 times out of 10, another person will smell something totally different. My wife, Susan, is convinced that pineapple sage should be changed to carrot cake sage.

Many species are native to Mexico, southwestern United States or Central America and were sent to England in the late 1700's and early 1800's. John Ruskin wrote in *Proserpina* in 1879 that "the exotic sages have no moderation in their hues". . . . and was particularly unhappy with the brilliant blue of *S. patens*, stating that "there's no color that gives me such an idea of violence—a sort of rough, angry scream—as that shade of blue, ungradated". Regardless of Ruskin's hysteria, some of these "exotic" sages are available in various catalogs and nurseries. Many, however, are annuals or half hardy perennials which over-winter only during exceptionally mild winters. A relative hardiness guide to several salvias is provided below. Few of the "hardy" salvias survive north of zone 4 and those designated as "half hardy" overwinter in zones 9 and 10, occasionally zone 8.

Species	Hardy, half hardy, annual, biennial	Flower color
argentea	Biennial	Whitish, yellow
azurea	Hardy	Azure-blue
cacaliifolia	Half hardy	Dark blue
coccinea	Annual	Bright red
elegans	Annual	Bright red
farinacea	Half hardy	Light blue
greggii	Half hardy	Red
guaranitica	Half hardy	Violet-blue
haematodes	Half hardy	Bluish violet
hians	Hardy	Bluish
horminum	Annual	Lilac
involucrata	Half hardy	Pink
jurisicii	Hardy	Deep blue
leucantha	Half hardy	Blue and white
microphylla	Half hardy	Red
officinalis	Perennial	Purple
patens	Half hardy	Gentian-blue
pratensis	Hardy	Blue
sclara	Biennial	Whitish blue
splendens	Annual	Red
superba	Hardy	Purple
uliginosa	Hardy	Sky blue
verticillata	Hardy	Lilac-blue

Looking at the above list, the choice of perennial ornamental sages is lim-ited, but incorporating several tender species such as pineapple sage, *S. rutilans,* usually sold as *S. elegans,* or *S. guaranitica,* with violet-blue flowers and mild currant scent to the leaves, is well worth the effort.

One my favorite sages, particularly for Southern gardeners, is *S. leucantha,* velvet sage. It was introduced to me as a potential cut flower species by Mark Richardson of Goodness Grows, an excellent plantsman at a fine perennial nur-sery in Crawford, Georgia. Plants are half hardy but in a single growing season, this 3–4' tall branching plant produces dozens of magnificent lavender flowers with white corollas which cover the plant from late summer through frost. The leaves are velvety, fragrant and unappetizing to insects or diseases. It appears to be sterile and must be raised from cuttings which root easily throughout the growing season. Need I say more?

Quick Reference to Salvia Species

	Height (in.)	Flower color
S. argentea	24–48	White with yellow
S. azurea	36–48	Azure-blue
S. jurisicii	12–18	Deep lilac
S. pratensis	12–36	Bright blue
S. × superba	18–48	Blue-violet

-argentea (ar-gen-tee′ a)		Silver Sage	24–48″/3′
Summer	Whitish	Southern Europe	Zones 5–9

Grown for the large white-woolly foliage, plants make a wonderful contrast to other green-leaved plants in the garden. The wedge-shaped, wrinkled, and irregularly toothed stem leaves are sessile and about 6–8″ long. The flowers

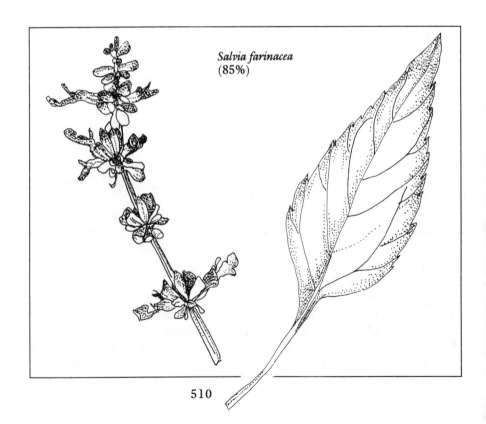

Salvia farinacea
(85%)

appear the second year on seed-propagated plants but are not particularly exceptional. They appear in a slightly branched large panicle, each whorl consisting of 6–10 whitish yellow flowers. The inside part of the flower, the corolla, is about three times longer than the calyx. Having given the details of this flower's structure, I now recommend their removal as soon as possible. This allows the foliage to remain the dominant feature of the plant and insures the plant produces leaves rather than marginally attractive flowers.

In late summer, plants often look the worse for wear, particularly if the summer has been hot and rainy. Hairy-leaved plants such as this and *Stachys* tend to retain moisture, allowing leaf diseases to become established. Although grown as a perennial, it is short lived and responds like a biennial in most areas of the country.

Propagate by seed or self-rooting lateral offshoots which may be detached in the spring and replanted.

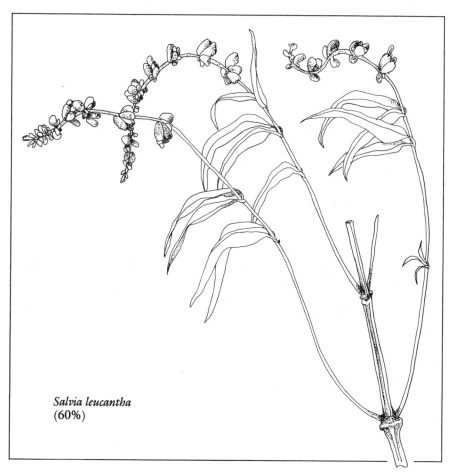

Salvia leucantha
(60%)

| *-azurea* (a-zew' ree-a) | | Azure Sage | 3–4'/4' |
| Fall | Azure-blue | Southeastern United States | Zones 5–9 |

This large plant attains 3–4 feet in height when the long slender spikes of azure-blue flowers appear. The lance-shaped basal foliage is about 3″ long but the leaves become smaller and narrower as they ascend the stem. Flowers are borne in the upper leaf axils in spike-like whorled inflorescences. The pedicels (the individual flower stalks) are short, resulting in flowers densely arranged on the stalk. A native of the Southeast, it is much more tolerant of heat and humidity than many other species. Two or three plants placed about the garden dominant the fall scene. Some of the finest specimens I have encountered are found in the Horticulture Gardens at Massey University in Palmerston North, New Zealand.

Cultivars:

var. *grandiflora* (syn. *S. pitcheri*) has paler green, more hairy leaves and larger, paler blue flowers than the species. It is more available but no better than the type.

Propagate from seed, division, or terminal cuttings.

Related Species:

S. uliginosa, native to southern Brazil and Uruguay, grows 4–5' tall and bears sky blue flowers in late summer and fall. The flowers are densely arranged in 7–20-flowered whorls and occur until frost in the North and through October in the South. Plants need support and winter protection.

| *-jurisicii* (jur-i-sic' ee-eye) | | Jurisici's Sage | 12–18″/12″ |
| Early Summer | Lilac | Yugoslavia | Zones 4–8 |

This species has labored in obscurity for many years but has some excellent attributes. Plants are relatively small and in some cases less than a foot tall, eliminating the problem of staking—a major headache with other species, particularly in zones 6 and south. Thus it may be grown either as a rock garden plant or placed in the front of the border. Stems have long spreading white hairs but the foliage is smooth except around the margins. The branched flower spikes of deep lilac are 8″ long and consist of 3–7 whorls of upside down flowers. This curious habit of inverted flowers combined with the fact that most of the foliage is deeply lobed into pinnate sections (pinnatisect) make this species unique among the garden sages.

Plants tolerate a wide range of soils, accept a lack of rainfall, and, given a sunny location, generally behave.

Propagate from division or seed.

-pratensis (prah-ten' sis)		Meadow Sage	12–36″/36″
Summer	Lavender-blue	Europe	Zones 3–9

(Syn. *S. haematodes*)

The few stem leaves are small and sessile but the 3–6″ basal leaves are ovate to oblong, hairy, with long petioles. The flowering stems rise from the basal leaves and normally bear lavender-blue flowers. Variability in flower color and size is evident in seed grown plants. If spent blooms are removed, another flush usually results. Plants tolerate a wide range of garden soils but the leaves deteriorate if plants dry out often.

Considerable debate rages whether *S. pratensis* is a separate species from *S. haematodes* or if they are minor variations of each other. Seldom are both species offered from the same nursery, although it is possible to find them listed in separate catalogs. Because *S. pratensis* is such a variable species, I decided to list them together although it is probably safe to say that plants listed as *S. haematodes* are more floriferous, form larger panicles and have slightly larger flowers than those sold as *S. pratensis*. Taxonomic foofaraw aside, a number of good selections exist.

Cultivars:

var. *alba* is a white-flowered form.

'Atroviolacea' has dark violet flowers.

'Baumgartenii' is similar to 'Atroviolacea' but bears lighter violet flowers.

'Indigo' ('Indigo Spires') has rich blue flowers on a many-branched plant. This appears to be a cross between *S. pratensis* and *S. farinacea*, mealy-cup sage.

'Lupinoides' produces bluish white flowers.

'Rosea' has rose-purple flowers.

'Rubicundra' bears rose-red blossoms.

var. *tenorii* is probably the best of the plants listed under this species and has lovely deep blue flowers.

'Variegata' produces handsome light blue flowers streaked with white.

The species and varieties may be propagated from cuttings, division or seed but cultivars should be propagated from division or terminal cuttings only. The rootstock is quite woody and care must be taken during division to avoid damage. Cuttings are more reliable than division.

Related Species:

S. patens, gentian sage, bears 1½–2″ long gentian-blue flowers borne sparsely in 2–3-flowered whorls. The 30″ tall plants are half hardy and should be treated as annuals in most of the country. Although the flowers are some of the largest in the genus, the lack of floriferousness makes the plants rather unexciting. 'Cambridge Blue' bears light blue flowers.

-× *superba* (soo-perb' a)		Hybrid Sage	18–48"/36"
Summer	Violet blue	Hybrid	Zones 4–7

(Syn. *S. sylvestris* var. *superba*, *S. nemerosa*)

S. × *superba* appears to be a hybrid of *S. nemerosa*, *S. pratensis*, and *S. villicaulis* and is often offered as *S. nemerosa* in the trade. Given cool nights and good moisture, this is a truly spectacular plant. Numerous dense flower spikes of deep rich violet-blue rise from basal leaves in May and June to make a wonderful show. Unfortunately, I have been disappointed with plants in zone 8: while they survive and flower adequately, they lose their upright habit, flop over, and fade rapidly. They certainly do well, however, north of zone 8. If grown in the South, a low-growing cultivar is much preferred. They are drought tolerant and survive where many plants succumb.

Cultivars:

'Blue Queen' has rich violet flowers on 18–24" tall stems and is heat and drought tolerant.

'East Friesland' ('Ostfriesland') has deep purple flowers and is only 18" tall. It is better than the type where summers are hot as it does not require support.

'Lubecca' is similar to 'East Friesland' but is about 30" tall. Both have violet-blue flowers.

'May Night' ('Mainacht') has deep indigo flowers which are larger than 'Lubecca'. Plants grow approximately 18" high. 'May Night' may be a cultivar of *S.* × *sylvestris*, a hybrid between *S. pratensis* and *S. nemerosa*.

Although seed of *S.* × *superba* may be available, it is best to vegetatively propagate clones. Terminal cuttings or division should be used to multiply or rejuvenate named cultivars.

Quick Key to Salvia Species

     A. Leaves silvery, more or less white woolly...................... *S. argentea*
  AA. Leaves not silvery
       B. Foliage deeply pinnately lobed .... *S. jurisicii*
    BB. Foliage not pinnately lobed
         C. Upper stem leaves petioled............................... *S. azurea*
       CC. Upper stem leaves sessile
           D. Lower stem leaves mostly petioled, leaf blades 2–6" long.........
                                                            S. pratensis
          DD. Lower stem leaves mostly sessile, leaf blades 1–3" long...........
                                                        S. × *superba*

Additional Reading:

Bloom, Alan. 1980. Salvias. *The Garden* 105(7):290–291.

Compton, James. 1985. Some worthwhile Mexican salvias. *The Garden* 110(3):122–124.

Compton, James. 1987. *Salvia guaranitica. The Plantsman* 9(1):38.

Martin, Tovah. 1984. Salvia savvy. *Horticulture* 62(7):12–20.

Sanguinaria (san-gwi-nah' ree-a)   Bloodroot   Papaveraceae

Plants of this monotypic genus are becoming more popular each year, and with good reason. Bloodroot is a good example of the continued blurring of the distinction between wild flowers and garden plants. Although best used in shady woodland settings, it is adaptable to more formal shade gardens as well. The common name is most appropriate, as it has a yellowish red sap which becomes obvious upon division of the rootstock. The sap was used by the Indians as a dye for coloring and war paint. This is a terrific plant for demonstrating that plants can be colorful inside as well as out.

-canadensis (kan-a-den' sis)   Bloodroot, Puckoon   3–6"/8"
Early Spring   White   Eastern North America   Zones 3–9

Walking down a meandering woodland path through a drift of these clean white flowers reaffirms one's faith in this crazy world. The solitary, 3" wide

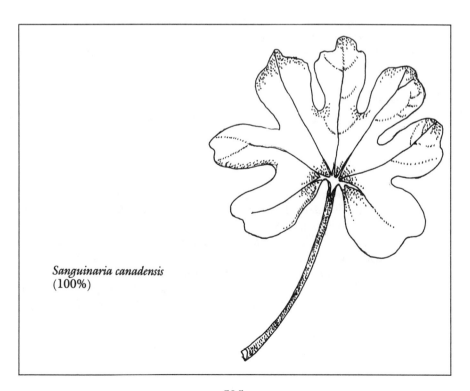

Sanguinaria canadensis
(100%)

515

flowers appear on 6″ long flower stalks before the blue-green leaves have fully matured. The individual flowers, which remain closed on cloudy days, abscise in a few days but additional flowers arise over a 2 week period. The ephemeral bloom of bloodroot was bemoaned even by Thomas Jefferson, who wrote in 1776 that on "April 6, Narcissus and Puckoon open; April 13, Puckoon flowers fallen" (Lawrence, 1987). In north Georgia, the bloodroots are at their peak in mid March through early April. In the North, they may flower as late as early May. The wavy, lobed, kidney-shaped leaves continue to expand once the flowers have finished and are almost as pretty as the flowers. The foliage persists until mid- to late summer before disappearing. Lack of rain results in more rapid disappearance. They combine well with early spring flowers such as *Mertensia virginica* (Virginia bluebells), *Chrysogonum virginianum* (green and gold), and *Aquilegia canadensis* (Canadian columbine).

Cultivars:

var. *major* (*grandiflora*) has larger flowers than the type but is so variable that it is difficult to discern differences.

'Multiplex' is the best cultivar for the garden. The clean white double flowers consist of approximately 50 petals. Flowers persist twice as long as the single-flowered species.

Propagate the species from seed but it is easier to divide the clumps of plants immediately after flowering. 'Multiplex' should be vegetatively propagated by division. Seed must be sown in moist peat moss, warmed to 68°F for 2–4 weeks, cooled 4–6 weeks at 40°F and then slowly raised to 50–55°F.

Additional Reading:

Haywood, Gordon. 1982. Bloodroot lines. *Horticulture* 60(2):50–53.

Sanguisorba (san-gwi-sor′ ba)   Burnet   Rosaceae

This little-known genus contains about 30 species but few nurseries offer them to the public. While it does not offer the splashy color of *Salvia* or *Rudbeckia*, there are, nevertheless, some beautiful species. Plants have handsome pinnate leaves and bottle brush flowers in summer. In some species, separate male and female flowers occur on the same plant, and in others the flowers are perfect (both male and female parts are present in the same flower). All flowers are apetalous and consist of small sepals and long stamens. In general, plants prefer a cool, damp soil but tolerate dry conditions if irrigation is provided.

The name *Sanguisorba* comes from *sanguis*, blood and *sorbere*, soaking up, in reference to its reputed ability to stop bleeding. The young leaves of *S. officinalis* were, and still are, occasionaly used to flavor salads.

Quick Reference to Sanguisorba Species

	Height (ft.)	Flower color
S. canadensis	4–5	White
S. obtusa	3–4	Reddish pink

-canadensis (kan-a-den' sis)		Canadian Burnet	4–5'/4'
Late Spring	White	Eastern North America	Zones 3–8

(Syn. *Poterium canadense*)

The 12" long pinnately compound leaves consist of 8–15, oblong, sharply toothed leaflets. Two to six inch long, rounded spikes of whitish, perfect flowers appear at the end of each stem. The stamens are exserted and give the flowers a bottle brush appearance. The individual flowers are up to 1½" wide and the inflorescence extends 6–8" long. Flowering begins in late spring and lasts well into summer, particularly if flowers are removed as they fade. Planted in combination with the orange spikes of *Kniphofia*, the whites of burnet seem whiter and the oranges of the torch lily brighter.

Plant in full sun in the North, but partial shade and a cooling soil mulch are useful in the South. Plants are vigorous and adequate room for expansion must be provided.

Propagate by seed (similar to *Sanguinaria*) or division in the spring.

-obtusa (ob-tew' sa)		Japanese Burnet	3–4'/3'
Summer	Pink, Red	Japan	Zones 4–8

This is the most ornamental burnet as it combines gray-green leaves with reddish pink flowers. The 18" long pinnate leaves consist of 7–13 leaflets with a gray-green underside. The flowers have long stamens, at least four times as long as the sepals, resulting in an airy, 4" long inflorescence.

Conditions necessary for optimal growth are similar to the previous species, however, because plants are not as leafy or vigorous, they are more appropriate for the border than *S. canadensis*.

Cultivars:

var. *albiflora* is similar but has white flowers.

Propagate by seed or division in the spring similar to *S. canadensis*.

Quick Key to Sanguisorba Species

    A. Flower spikes 2–6" long, flowers white .... *S. canadensis*
    AA. Flower spikes 2–4" long, flowers pink to red.................... *S. obtusa*

Santolina (san-to-leen' a)   Lavender Cotton   Asteraceae

Mainly used as low border or edging plants, their gray-green to bright green color shows off the foliage and flowers of plants associated with them. Of the 8 species, only lavender cotton, *S. chamaecyparissus*, is grown to any extent.

-chamaecyparissus (ka-mie-sip-pa-ris' is)   Lavender Cotton   1–2'/2'
Summer   Yellow   Mediterranean   Zones 6–8

Plants are used as an edging because of the evergreen aromatic gray-green leaves, which in sandy soils and bright light develop a white sheen. The 1½" long alternate leaves are crowded on the stem and white woolly underneath. The flowers are comprised of disc flowers only, resulting in a globular head of marginal attractiveness. Although some people feel the flowers look like "bright yellow lollipops in midsummer," I feel they detract from the foliage and serve no useful function. The shrubby plants become rather woody at the base and require a hard pruning immediately after flowering to keep tidy. The gray leaves combine particularly well with low-growing red-flowering plants such as *Dianthus deltoides*.

Winter hardiness north of zone 6 and summer hardiness south of zone 7 is questionable. The problem in the South is not heat but high humidity and evening rains. Drier climates are more to its liking.

Propagate any time from terminal cuttings. Seed germination is irregular and placing sown seed at 40°F for 2–4 weeks may enhance uniformity.

Related Species:

S. virens, green lavender cotton, has narrow green leaves and solitary yellow flowers on 2' tall stems. Native to the Mediterranean area, plants are winter hardy to zone 6.

Saponaria (sa-po-nah' ree-a)   Soapwort   Caryophyllaceae

A number of common annual and perennial species, suitable for the low border or rockery, are found in the genus. The Midwest roadside weed, bouncing bet, *S. officinalis*, is responsible for the common name. In Gerard's Herball, 1597, the author points out that the leaves "yeelde out of themselves a certain juice when they are bruised, which scoureth almost as well as soap". Actually, the "soap" is rather gooey and is a poor substitute for 'Tide'. The leaves are opposite and entire and the flowers usually have five petals. In general, plants tolerate full sun but require well-drained soil.

Quick Reference to Saponaria Species

	Height (in.)	Habit color	Flower color
S. lutea	3–6	Mat forming	Yellow
S. ocymoides	6–9	Trailing	Pink
S. officinalis	12–30	Upright	Pink

-lutea (lew-tee' a)		Yellow Soapwort	3–6"/6"
Summer	Yellow	Western Alps	Zones 5–8

Although different from the common soapworts and more challenging to grow, this species makes a lovely rock garden plant. The ½" wide leaves are pale green and form a mat which seldom grows taller than 4". Clusters of small yellow flowers with violet stamens rise from the mat in early summer and continue for 3–4 weeks.

It is not as cold tolerant as other soapworts and requires mulch north of zone 5. Unfortunately it is similar to other species in its intolerance to heat and poor drainage.

-ocymoides (o-kim-oi' dees)		Rock Soapwort	6–9"/9"
Early Summer	Pink	European Alps	Zones 2–7

Ease of growth and fresh pink flowers in May and June make the species the most popular garden plant of the genus. The flowers are held in loose sprays (cymes) at the ends of the many branches. It climbs and clambers over rocks and is a particularly valuable trailing plant for walls or raised stonework. The 1" long leaves are flat and olive-green. The lower ones have a short petiole while the uppermost are sessile. Plants should be pruned hard after flowering to force new shoots and restrain growth. Although tolerant of cold temperatures, soapwort is not at all happy in hot summers or in soils that are poorly drained. Although a zone 8 summer rating is often recommended, I would not grow plants south of zone 7 as they tend to die out due to winter rains and summer humidity.

Cultivars:

var. *alba* (*albiflora*) is a difficult to locate white-flowered form of the species. The flowers are pure white and is a good plant where a white trailer is needed.

var. *carnea* has flesh-pink flowers but is otherwise similar to the species.

var. *floribunda* is more floriferous than other varieties. The flowers are soft pink and similar to the species.

var. *rubra compacta* is a non-trailing compact form of the species with crimson flowers. It is a terrific little plant for the front of the border.

var. *splendens* ('Splendens') has large intense rose flowers and is the best garden selection.

var. *splendissima* apparently has larger flowers than var. *splendens* but I have not seen much difference between them.

var. *versicolor* is interesting. The flowers open white, then turn rose. To each his (or her) own. This is likely a cross between the white var. *alba* and var. *splendens*.

Propagate all varieties from seed. Germination is more rapid and uniform if the seed is stratified for 4–6 weeks at 40°F. Plants may be divided and terminal cuttings may also be taken any time of year.

-officinalis (o-fish-i-nah' lis)		Bouncing Bet	12–30"/18"
Summer	Pink	Southern Europe	Zones 2–8

Naturalized in much of the eastern and midwestern parts of the country, it gets little respect and is often considered little more than a pretty weed. Bouncing bet has thrown off the comfort and safety of the garden to become an inhabitant of the open road. She is known as lady-by-the-gate and few old gardens exist where her name is not appropriate.

Plants are more upright than other species although they sprawl when planted in rich soil. The leaves are 2–4" long, about 2" wide, and somewhat elliptical. They are also conspicuously three-nerved and usually dark green. The individual flowers are 1–1½" across, have five notched petals and are held in terminal and axillary cymes. Full sun is necessary, if too much shade is provided, plants become leggy and tall and flowers fade to almost white. Pinching in late spring helps to clean up this coarse and untidy plant as well as force additional flower formation. Plants bloom throughout the summer and spread by underground stolons, thus a few plants can result in a significant colony in a few years. It is interesting that bouncing bet, particularly the double forms, is now being grown commercially as a cut flower for some of the "uptown" modern florists. There is hope that this Rodney Dangerfield of the plant kingdom can be associated with more than the "characteristic odour of American sidewalk ends, where the pavement peters out and the shacks and junked cars begin" (Peattie, D.C., *Flowering Earth*).

Cultivars:

var. *albo-plena* bears white double flowers.

var. *roseo-plena* has double flowers in shades of rose to pink.

var. *rubro-plena* produces red double blooms. They all produce 1–1½" diameter flowers which resemble shaggy carnations.

Stolons are easily divided at any time. Cuttings and seed may also be used. Seed should be stratified as mentioned under the previous species. Not all seed propagated plants of the double varieties will be double, in some cases up to 40% of the offspring may be single.

Quick Key to Saponaria Species
   A. Plants upright, usually taller than 24" .... *S. officinalis*
   AA. Plants trailing or mat forming, usually less than 12" tall
      B. Plants mat forming, flowers yellow........................... *S. lutea*
      BB. Plants trailing, flowers pink .... *S. ocymoides*

Saxifraga (saks-if' rag-a)   Saxifrage   Saxifragaceae

Exceptionally large and enormously diverse, this genus contains more than 300 species and 200 additional natural hybrids and varieties. The name is derived from the Latin *saxum*, rock, and *frangere*, to break, in reference to the fact that the dust-like seeds find their way into minute crevices to germinate. Some species such as *S. granulata*, meadow saxifrage, are well established in song and verse. The double form of this European meadow saxifrage is known as Pretty Maids; and a row of them grew in Mary, Mary, quite Contrary's garden.

The genus consists of small plants, most dwarf and none more than moderate size, best suited for the rock garden. An exception is our native *S. pennsylvanica*, Pennsylvania saxifrage, which grows to 3' tall. Species are predominantly perennial although a few such as *S. sibthorpii*, Sibthorp's saxifrage, are annuals. Many form rosettes of leaves in cushions which may be hard and encrusted, in others moss-like. Most of the species are evergreen, especially the rosette formers, however, a few have alternate, deciduous leaves. The flowers are arranged singly or more often in floriferous panicles and racemes. Flower color is predominantly white but yellow, pink or red are also found. Flowers consist of 5 petals and 10 stamens.

They are mainly alpine plants and in their native habitats, extremely resistant to adverse weather. Hot summer climates are not to their liking and, in general, the further north one gardens, the more chances of success. Few species tolerate full sun and moderate shade is recommended for all locales in the United States. Excellent drainage is essential.

Botanists have classified *Saxifraga* into 15 sections, each clearly distinguished by visible characteristics. However, even within a section, there are numerous morphological differences between species. Although a great number of saxifrages are garden worthy, only a few sections contain species that are of special value to the gardener. The mossy saxifrages (Dactyloides) form cushions of soft-leaved evergreen rosettes. This includes species such as *S. caespitosa*, tufted saxifrage, the magnificent white-flowered *S. trifurcata*, threefork saxifrage, and the popular *S.* × *arendsii* hybrids.

A popular section is the encrusted saxifrages (Euaizoonia). Species in this group have rosettes with stiff, spade-shaped, lime-encrusted leaves which provide a silvery effect. The rosettes die after flowering but underground runners give rise to new ones in the fall. They superficially resemble hens and chicks until their open sprays of summer flowers give them away. This section includes the variable *S. paniculata*, aizoon saxifrage, with many varieties and cultivars.

521

Another section of importance is the Kabschia saxifrages (Porophyllum), characterized by firm dense green cushions of evergreen rosettes. The leaves are small, stiff, and often needle sharp.

The section Robertsoniana contains species which form dense, dark green cushions of evergreen rosettes. It is represented in the garden by the ever-present London pride, *S.* × *urbium*, found in garden centers throughout Europe and now in the United States.

For the southern gardener, the section Diptera contains the useful and popular strawberry geranium, *S. stolonifera*. It is hardy in zones 7–10 but can be enjoyed as a houseplant further north.

Intersectional hybridization has occurred and a number of useful hybrids such as *S.* × *andrewsii*, Andrew's saxifrage, have arisen.

Saxifrages are little used and poorly understood in the United States. Although our climate is not as forgiving as that of England, Germany and the Netherlands, they are plants which, once established, provide years of graceful, maintenance-free beauty.

Propagation is usually by seed, but division, cuttings, and rooted offsets are also used to multiply hybrids and cultivars. The fine seed needs exposure to low temperatures to germinate. Placing the seed flat at 32–40°F for 6 weeks results in more uniform germination. Seedlings are slow to develop and it may take 2–3 years before plants reach flowering size. For best results, seedlings should not be exposed to temperatures greater than 60°F.

The following is but a handful of the saxifrages that may be found through specialist nurseries. The list includes the more available and easy to grow species.

Quick Reference to Saxifraga Species

	Height (in.)	Flowering season	Flower color	Section
S. × arendsii	6–9	Spring	Various	Dactyloides
S. cochlearis	6–12	Spring	White	Euaizoonia
S. cotyledon	18–24	Summer	White	Euaizoonia
S. paniculata	6–24	Summer	Yellow	Euaizoonia
S. trifurcata	6–12	Spring	White	Dactyloides
S. × urbium	9–12	Spring	White	Robertsoniana

- × *arendsii* (ah-rendz' ee-i)	Arend's Saxifrage	6–9"/12"
Spring Various	Hybrid	Zones 5–7

Developed by the Arends nursery in Ronsdorf, Germany (as were many of the hybrid *Astilbe*), the hybrid is a relatively recent addition to the saxifrage family. Plants are mossy-leaved carpet formers and, if proper conditions are provided, will cover a large area in a season. The rosettes remain evergreen and attractive throughout the year. Dozens of thin flower stalks rise over the mossy covering, each bearing a single 5-petaled flower in white, rose, pink or red shades. Semi-shaded conditions and moist soil are preferred. The sunnier the site, the more moisture retentive must be the soil. A problem in growing the mossy saxifrages in warm areas is that they often "melt out", that is, the centers of the plants rot and disappear. This is a particularly severe problem in areas of high humidity. Adding some fine soil or sand to the center of the plant helps reduce the loss.

Cultivars:

'Blood Carpet' is one of the many cultivars in the Carpet series of hybrid saxifrages, most of which are available from seed. It is 4–8″ tall with dark carmine-red flowers. There is little, if any, difference between this and 'Scarlet Carpet'.

'Flower Carpet' is similar to 'Blood Carpet' but the flowers are pinker. It is a reliable, free-flowering cultivar that can be raised from seed.

'Flowers of Sulphur' stands about 4″ tall and has pale sulphur-yellow flowers. It is vigorous with firm tight cushions of foliage.

'Gaiety' is an early-flowering hybrid with deep pink flowers on 4–6″ long scapes. One of the best hybrids with pink flowers.

'Snow Carpet' has masses of relatively large, clear white flowers,and is about 5–7″ tall. It is an old standard cultivar but still one of the best for white flowers.

'Triumph' is one of the best hybrids. The firm lacy green 6–8″ tall cushions are handsome and the dark red flowers are brilliant.

Remove the flower stems after fading. Self-sown plants are interesting but flower colors and habits are not true. Divide pieces of carpet after flowering but prior to the heat of summer.

-cochlearis (kok-lee-ah′ ris)		Snail Saxifrage	6–12″/10″
Spring	White	Alps	Zones 6–8

Numerous small hemispherical rosettes, comprised of many spoon-shaped entire leaves thickly encrusted with lime (leaves exude $CaCO_3$), characterize the species. Rosettes are 1–2″ across, but so closely packed they form small mounds from which 10–12″ tall reddish scapes arise. The ¾″ diameter star-shaped white flowers are held in loose one-sided panicles. Some direct sun is tolerated but partial shade is preferable. Lime should be added regularly for best performance, particularly in areas of acid soils.

Cultivars:

var. *major* has rosettes 1½ times larger than the species. The flowers are a little larger but not significantly so.

var. *minor* has smaller flowers on 4″ long scapes and grows 6″ wide.

Seedlings require 2–3 years to reach flowering size; vegetative propagation is faster and more reliable. Division of the rosettes in early spring or late fall is possible. Propagate in spring by lifting the mother plant and gently tearing down on the outer rosettes. Pieces of root must be removed with the offset which can be immediately planted.

-cotyledon (kot-i-lee′ don)   Jungfrau Saxifrage   18–24″/10″
Summer   White   Pyrenees, Alps to Greenland   Zones 4–7

Masses of flat rosettes are produced, each 5–6″ in diameter. The 3″ long leaves are strap shaped, finely toothed and broader towards the apex. Although the flowering rosettes die after flowering, the central crown sends out new ones resulting in a small colony. The branched scapes rise 18–24″ and bear ¾″ wide white flowers with red veins or red dots on the petals.

This is one of the encrusted saxifrages that is not obviously encrusted with lime. In fact, this species should be grown in lime-free soils in partial or deep shade.

Cultivars:

var. *caterhamensis* is one of the prettiest because of the conspicuous red spotting on the petals. It also is more vigorous than the species.

var. *icelandica* has large rosettes of iron gray leaves with 4′ tall flower stems.

var. *minor* is a dwarf version of the species and smaller in every way, bearing flowers on 6″ tall inflorescences.

Propagation is similar to *S. cochlearis*.

-paniculata (pa-nik-ew-lah′ ta)   Aizoon Saxifrage   6–24″/15″
Summer   Yellowish white   Europe, North America   Zone 2–6

(Syn. *S. aizoon*)

This species occurs in most of the alpine and boreal parts of Europe and Asia, in North America from Greenland and Labrador to Saskatchewan, south to Nova Scotia, New Brunswick, the mountains of Vermont and Lake Superior. With such an extensive range, it is not suprising there are many forms and subspecies. Plants form cushions and mats of small rosettes, 3″ in diameter or less, consisting of spatulate leaves with forward-pointing teeth and silvery encrustations on the margins. The flowers vary tremendously but are borne in a loose 6–18″ tall panicle. The ½″ diameter flowers are yellowish white to white, often spotted purple.

Although tolerant of lime-free situations, lime should be added to the garden site for best performance. Areas of rocky outcrops and partial shade are preferred.

Cultivars:

var. *baldensis* has small rosettes (approximately 2″ across) with reddish flower scapes.

var. *lutea* has pale yellow flowers and is 6–10″ tall in flower.

var. *major* is the largest form of the species and produces 15–18″ high inflorescences. The scapes are reddish and the large leaves (1–2″ long) have a reddish tinge, which deepens in winter.

var. *rosea* has pale pink flowers with yellowish green rosettes.

Propagate similar to *S. cochlearis*.

-trifurcata (tri-fur-cah′ ta)		Threefork Saxifrage	6–12″/36″
Spring	White	Spain, Austria	Zones 5–7

This is one of the prettiest plants in this group. A massive mat in flower, with clouds of clear white flowers flowing through and clambering over rocks, is a magnificent sight. The stems are somewhat woody and the leathery, gray-green leaves are three lobed and divided into numerous triangular sections. The branched, reddish racemes are held 6–12″ above the mossy foliage in spring and flower for 3–4 weeks.

One of the most sun tolerant saxifrages, it can be planted in full sun if sufficient moisture is provided. However, afternoon shade is beneficial.

Propagate by division similar to *S.* × *arendsii*.

Related Species:

S. stolonifera (syn. *S. sarmentosa*), strawberry geranium, colonizes by thread-like runners similar to strawberries. The foliage is silver veined above and reddish beneath. The 1″ wide white flowers have two petals which are 3–4 times longer than the other three. Plants are useful as shade tolerant groundcovers, particularly in the South, and in hanging baskets for patio and deck. Plants are cold hardy to zone 7.

- × *urbium* (ur-bee′ um)		London Pride Saxifrage	9–12″/20″
Spring	White, Pink	Hybrid	Zones 6–7

(Syn *S. umbrosa*)

Although often sold as *S. umbrosa*, that species is seldom found in gardens today. *S.* × *urbium* is a hybrid between *S. spathularis*, a white-flowered species from Portugal and northwest Spain, and *S. umbrosa*, native to the Pyrenees Mountains.

Plants bear loose evergreen rosettes that form dense dark green carpets from which arise the foot-high, wiry, sticky scapes. The ¼″ wide white flowers are starry with a red tinge in the middle. The stamens are longer than the petals and provide an airy look to the sea of bloom. Soil pH is not as critical and plants grow in acid or alkaline soils as long as moisture can be provided. Shady, moist areas are preferred and plants are particularly appealing among ferns.

Cultivars:

'Aureopunctata' has golden variegated leaves and provides a lovely splash of color even when not in bloom. It is more sun tolerant than the other forms of the species.

525

'Chambers Pink Pride' is similar to the type but has soft pink flowers on 9" tall
  scapes. One of my favorites.
'Elliott's Variety' has rose flowers on red 6" tall scapes.
'Ingwersen's Variety' bears bronze foliage and deep red flowers on 4" tall scapes.
var. *primuloides* is a miniature form with smaller leaves and bright pink flowers.
  'Elliott's Variety' and 'Ingwersen's Variety' were selected from this variety.

Easily propagated by division of the mat at any time, but preferably after flowering or in early spring prior to the formation of flower buds.

Quick Key to Saxifrage Species

   A. Cushions or mounds of rosettes, rosettes do not die after
     flowering
     B. More or less dense cushions of variously notched or forked
       leaves, soft-leaved rosettes
       C. Leaves in 3 prongs, similar to stag horns, flowers white ....
                                         S. trifurcata
       CC. Leaves notched, flowers usually rose, pink, purple, or white.........
                                         S. × *arendsii*
     BB. Leaf margins more or less toothed, leaves usually spoon-
       shaped and leathery .... *S.* × *urbium*
   AA. Rosettes made up of stiff tongue or spade-shaped leaves,
     usually lime-encrusted, flowering rosettes die after flowering
     B. Leaves entire or nearly so, spoon-shaped .... *S. cochlearis*
     BB. Leaves distinctly toothed
       C. Flower stem branched from base .... *S. cotyledon*
       CC. Flower stem branched in upper part.................. *S. paniculata*

Additional Reading:

Kohlein, Fritz. 1980. *Saxifrages and Related Genera*. (B.T. Batsford Ltd., London, England.). Translated from German in 1984, this book provides excellent descriptions of the many species and hybrids of the genus.

Scabiosa (skab-ee-o' sa)   Pincushion Flower   Dipsacaceae

The pincushion plant was named for the dark purple flower heads of the
annual *S. atropurpurea* whose tufted appearance was said to resemble a velvet
pincushion. The dark color of that flower also signified death and accounted for
one of its other common names, mournful widow (the dark-purple *Geranium
phaeum* is known as mourning widow, also in reference to the color). Many of
the 60 species are perennial but only 2 or 3 are used to any extent in gardens
today. *S. atropurpurea* and the perennial *S. caucasica* are popular cut flowers and
S. graminifolia and *S. lucida* are more suited to the front of the border. Other
scabiosa-looking species may be found in the genus *Knautia* and *Cephalaria*.

Quick Reference to Scabiosa Species

	Height (in.)	Flower color
S. caucasica	18–24	Bluish
S. graminifolia	10–18	Pink
S. ochroleuca	24–36	Yellow

-caucasica (kaw-ka' si-ca)		Scabious	18–24"/18"
Summer	Bluish	Caucasus Mountains	Zones 3–7

By far the most popular of the perennial scabiosa, this species provides warm blue shades in late summer to complement the yellow daisies flowering at that time. The basal leaves are lanceolate, entire and covered with a whitish bloom giving the leaves a gray-green appearance. The stem leaves are pinnately lobed and opposite. The 3–4" wide inflorescences are flat, and the petals shallowly 3–5 lobed. The petals are pale blue and surround a white to pale yellow center.

Plant in full sun in the North, partial shade in the South, in enriched loamy soil. They should be planted in groups of 3 or more near the front of the garden for best effect. This species does well in cool climates, especially the Northwest, but is not particularly vigorous during hot summers. It is not a recommended plant for the Southeast and even in the Northeast, plants grow rather slowly. Due to the slow growth, plants require division only after 3–4 years.

Cultivars:

var. *alba* is a white-flowered form which comes true from seed but is otherwise similar to the species.

'Blue Perfection' has fringed, lavender-blue flowers and stands 2' tall. It was selected from var. *perfecta* which has large fringed flowers in shades of blue.

'Bressingham White' has 3–4" diameter flowers of clear white on 3' tall stems and has effectively replaced an older white cultivar, 'Miss Wilmott'.

'Compliment' ('Kompliment') is 20–24" tall with dark lavender flowers.

'Fama' has large lavender-blue flowers with a silver center on 18" tall stems. The flower color and plant habit are excellent.

'House Hybrids' ('Issac House Hybrids') are a mixture of blue and white shades. They arose from selections from Issac House in Bristol, England and have been a parent in many of the more recent selections.

'Loddon White' bears large creamy white flowers not too unlike 'Bressingham White'.

var. *perfecta alba* has large cream-white flowers with fringed petals.

'Rumor' has lavender-blue flowers on 18–24" tall stems.

Seed sown in warm conditions (70–75°F) and high humidity should emerge in 2 weeks. Transplant to containers and grow until planting size. Two inch long basal cuttings may be taken in spring, rooted and grown on during the summer, and planted in the garden in the fall. Plants may also be divided every 3–4 years.

527

-graminifolia (grah-mi-ni-fo' lee-a)		Grassleaf Scabious	10–18"/18"
Summer	Pink to Lilac	Southern Europe	Zones 5–8

One of the smaller scabious, plants are best suited to the front of the garden. It has a woody rootstock and entire grasslike leaves which form loose mats of ascending stems. The foliage, silvery white due to a whitish pubescence on the leaves, forms a pleasant backdrop for the 1½–2" wide pale pink flower heads which bloom for about 6 weeks in midsummer. Plants struggle in hot humid summers but are more heat tolerant than the previous species. A sunny well-drained location is best.

Propagation is easiest by division but seed sown in December will provide sufficiently large plants for the garden by May.

-ochroleuca (ok-ro-loo' ka)		Cream Scabious	24–36"/24"
Summer	Cream to Yellow	Southeastern Europe	Zones 5–7

This short-lived species has branched pubescent stems with a whitish pubescence on both sides of the leaves. The bottom leaves are slightly lobed and taper down to form a petiole while the stem leaves are pinnately dissected into linear lobes. The flowers are formed at the end of long scapes resulting in a wiry mass of stems. The 1" wide primrose-yellow flowers are more globular than the previous species. This is an outstanding plant when grown in full sun and well-drained soil.

Cultivars:

var. *webbiana* is a dwarf variant which does not exceed 10" in height. It has wrinkled leaves and flower heads that are creamier white than the species.

Propagate by seed, division, or basal cuttings similar to *S. caucasica*.

Quick Key to Scabiosa Species

    A. Leaves all linear and entire .... *S. graminifolia*
  AA. Leaves not linear, some lobed or cut
      B. Flowers yellowish white................................. *S. ochroleuca*
    BB. Flowers lilac or blue .... *S. caucasica*

Scilla (skil' la)   Squill   Liliaceae

Scilla is a large genus, consisting of 80–100 bulbous species native to Europe, Asia and Africa. A thin covering (tunic) envelops the bulbs, from which arise strap-like leaves and bell-shaped flowers. The garden species are generally less than 12" tall, however, species such as *S. natalensis*, Natal squill, and *S. hyacinthoides*, hyacinth squill, have blue flowers on 18–36" tall racemes. Several species have been taxonomically rearranged. The taller woodland plants, *S. hispanica*, Spanish bluebell, and *S. non-scripta*, English bluebell, are found under

Endymion. A number of differences exist among *Scilla*, *Puschkinia*, and *Chionodoxa*. See *Chionodoxa* for botanical differences.

The garden squills should be planted in the fall in full sun or partial shade in any well-drained soil. Most flower early in the spring starting with *S. tubergeniana*, followed closely by *S. bifolia*, *S. sibirica*, and finally *S. peruviana* in late spring or early summer. Bulbs combine well with other early spring flowerers such as daffodils, chionodoxas, winter aconites, and grape hyacinths. They are inexpensive, long lasting, and should be planted in large drifts, preferably 50 or more. Several late summer- and fall-flowering squills, such as *S. hyacinthoides* and *S. autumnale* either lack hardiness or are not sufficiently showy to be worth the time or expense.

All the squills may be lifted and divided every 4–5 years. Separate the bulbs and bulblets by size, replant the largest, and grow on the smaller sizes in a nursery bed for another year before placing them in their final location. Four to five years are required for squills to reach flowering size from seed. Seeds should be shallowly sown and placed at 60–65°F under humid conditions.

Quick Reference to Scilla Species

	Height (in.)	*Flower* color	*Number of* flowers/stem
S. bifolia	3–6	Mauve	3–12
S. peruviana	6–10	Lilac	20–50
S. sibirica	3–6	Dark blue	1–3
S. tubergeniana	4–6	Pale blue	2–4

-bifolia (bi-fo' lee-a)	Two-leaved Squill	3–6"/3"
Spring Mauve-blue	Southern Europe to Asia Minor	Zones 4–8

This early spring bulb is excellent for naturalizing as it multiplies rapidly by offsets. The deep mauve-blue flowers are almost as rich as those of *S. sibirica*. The foliage usually consists of 2–4 narrow (⅓ to ½" wide), bronze green, channelled leaves about 6" long. Plants bear 6–8 star-like flowers, each about ¾" in diameter on a 4–6" high raceme. They are held on long thin pedicels and dance in the spring breeze.

Cultivars:

var. *alba* has creamy white flowers.

var. *praecox* flowers about a week earlier than the other varieties and is more robust. It has more flowers than the species.

var. *rosea* has blooms of soft shell pink.

var. *rubra* bears rosy salmon flowers.

var. *taurica* has 3–5 leaves and bears deep blue flowers on long pedicels. It is an excellent plant but difficult to locate. In the trade, it is confused with *S. sibirica* var. *taurica* which has lighter blue flowers.

Related Genera:

Scilla biflora has been crossed with *Chionodoxa luciliae* and the resulting progeny are known as × *Chionoscilla* (which see).

-peruviana (pe-roo-vee-ah′ na)		Cuban Lily	6–10″/6″
Late Spring	Lilac	Mediterranean Area	Zones 5–8

The Cuban lily is a misnomer as it has nothing to do with Cuba or Peru but is native to Southern Europe and North African regions around the Mediterranean Sea. The name is thought to have come from the ship, *Peru*, which brought the bulbs to England.

Unlike other species, plants bear 6–9 leaves in a dense basal rosette and a 6–10″ long raceme with up to 50 bright blue, star-like flowers. The leaves are 6–12″ long and 1–1½″ across with dense, bristly hairs on the margins. When the flowers begin to open, they appear to rest on the leaves but as flowering continues, the scape elongates.

Bulbs are quite large and should be planted 4″ deep. Although bulbs are not common in the trade, they should be tried more frequently as they become available. It is the showiest of the squills and does well if placed in raised beds in a warm, sunny location.

Cultivars:

var. *alba* has white flowers.
var. *elegans* bears rosy red flowers.
var. *glabra* has lilac flowers but the leaves are not hairy.

-sibirica (si-bi′ ri-ka)		Siberian Squill	3–6″/4″
Spring	Deep Blue	Eastern Russia, Siberia	Zones 2–8

This most popular species has many attributes. It is exceedingly tough and cold hardy, revelling in arctic chills, and has the most penetrating blue color of any species, heightened even more by the blueness of the anthers. Although only 1–3 nodding flowers appear on the reddish scape, there are often 3–4 scapes on mature bulbs which more than make up for the paucity of flowers per stem. Bulblets are produced readily and self-sown seedlings are abundant. A small planting spreads rapidly.

Three to four strap-like leaves, 6″ long and about ½″ wide, are produced in early spring. The flowers and the foliage appear a little later than snowdrops (*Galanthus*) to continue nature's gift of spring cheer. As with most small bulbs, planting 3 or 4 is disappointing. Plant at least 25 or preferably hundreds. The few dollars paid for 100 bulbs will be enjoyed much longer and with far less indigestion than the same amount paid for dinner at the local Burger Doodle. They may be planted under trees in a woodland or as a spring wake-up in the front of the borders. However, plant them where they are allowed to ramble.

Cultivars:

var *alba* makes a pretty show in the woodland setting with its white flowers against the backdrop of green.

var. *azurea* has flowers of light blue.

'Spring Beauty' (var. *atrocoerulea*) is a popular form of the species and has large flowers in a lovely shade of deep blue with bright blue anthers. It is robust but produces a minimum of seed. This results in the longer lasting flowers but clumps do not multiply as rapidly as the species.

var. *taurica* produces light blue flowers with a dark blue stripe in the center of each segment.

-tubergeniana (tu-ber-gen' ee-ah-na)		Tubergen Squill	4–6"/6"
Early Spring	Pale blue	Iran, Afghanistan	Zones 4–8

Some botanists have changed this species to *S. miczenkoana* (mi-cheng-ko-ah' na) but that is so unpronounceable that I stay with the original name, named after the van Tubergen Nursery in Holland which introduced it into commerce.

Plants are similar to *S. sibirica* var. *taurica* in habit and leaf color but leaves are up to 1" wide and the yellow bulb is about twice as large. They are also the earliest flowering of the squills. The flower spikes appear in early February in the South and about 3 weeks later further north. Flowers break through the ground before the leaves and each spike bears 3–4 light blue flowers with a stripe down the middle of the segments. The flower color is similar to that of the later flowering *Puschkinia*.

Cultivars:

'Zwanenburg' has larger flowers and darker stripes on the petals.

Quick Key to Scilla Species

    A. Flowers in a dense inflorescence having over 20 flowers ...... *S. peruviana*
   AA. Flowers in a lax inflorescence, usually less than 10 flowers
      B. Flowers appearing just before the foliage .... *S. tubergeniana*
    BB. Flowers appearing after foliage has emerged
        C. Usually 2 leaves per bulb, 3–8 flowers per scape, scape solitary......
                                          S. bifolia
      CC. Usually 3–4 leaves per bulb, 1–3 flowers per scape,
         scapes 1–6 .... *S. sibirica*

Sedum (sed' um)   Stonecrop   Crassulaceae

Curiously, few species of this large and diverse genus are seen in American gardens. Although many species are not particularly decorative, there is a wealth of plants usable in the border and rock garden. That *Sedum* is not used more often may be because many of them are rock garden plants and rock gardens

531

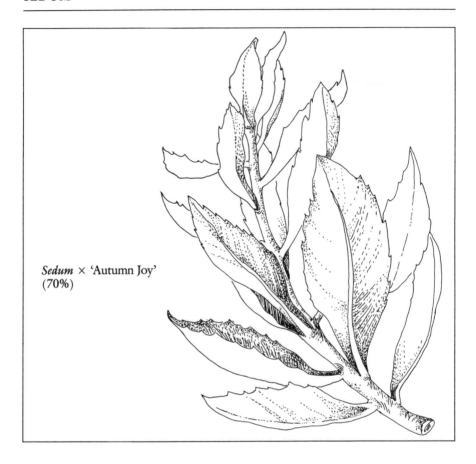

Sedum × 'Autumn Joy'
(70%)

have not been in vogue for many years in America. The other sad truth is that they "all sort of look alike", at least within the rock garden or border species. Finding the correct name for a stonecrop is an adventure in frustration, for even the great plant hunters came back from expeditions with bags of rare plants suitably given their botanical names and "some kind of stonecrop". Several species are native to America such as *S. nevii*, a lovely white-flowered, low-growing rosette former and *S. ternatum*, whose star-like white flowers are effective in the spring garden. As other "wimpy" plants expire and leave barren ground as their tombstone, the sedums continue to provide color and vigor.

The basic botanical definition of *Sedum* is a flowering plant with 5 petals, 5 sepals and 10 stamens. The petals are seldom attached to each other and the sepals are often fleshy and leaf-like. Leaves are also fleshy and usually alternate or whorled. There is, however, so much confusion in taxonomic circles as to what does or does not constitute a species of *Sedum* that the number has risen from 29 during Linnaeus's time, 88 in 1828, 228 in 1885, 470 by the botanist

Berger in 1930, but only 350 by Froderstrom in the same year, and 340 species listed by Jacobson in 1960. Since then, approximately 160 new names have been published in *Index Kewensis* placing the number between 500 and 650. Do not lament if unsure of the botanical name of a stonecrop in the garden, you are in good company.

In general, plants prefer well-drained soils and full sun. In the South, a number of rock garden species are at their finest during the cool fall, winter, and spring months and barely hang on during the summer. Partial shade is beneficial below zone 6. All tolerate drought and require little maintenance.

The majority of stonecrops are easily propagated by 1–3" long terminal cuttings taken in spring through summer. They generally root within 2 weeks. Too much water in the propagation phase results in root rot and severe decline. Seed may also be sown and plants reach flowering size in 2 years. For many rock garden species, division is easy and the method of choice.

Quick Reference to Sedum Species

	Height (in.)	*Flower color*	*Flowering time*
S. *acre*	2–3	Yellow	Late Spring
S. *aizoon*	12–15	Yellow	Summer
S. × 'Autumn Joy'	12–24	Pink	Late Summer
S. *kamtschaticum*	4–9	Yellow	Summer
S. *spurium*	2–6	Rose	Late Summer
S. *ternatum*	2–6	White	Late Spring

-acre (a' ker)	Goldmoss Stonecrop	2–3"/18"
Spring Yellow	Europe, North Africa, West Asia	Zones 3–8

The small stature and minute leaves of this common mat-former make it excellent for planting between stepping stones, on walls and ledges, or as a filler in areas where few plants grow. The stems are decumbent (grow along the ground with their tips sticking up). Each light green, pointed, ¼" long leaf overlaps the one above it like shingles on a roof so that the stems appear scaly. The golden yellow ½" wide flowers are produced in terminal cymes. Flowering commences in late spring and continues well into summer. In North Georgia (zone 8), it is at its best in late May, in upper New York (zone 5), mid-June.

Vigorous growers, plants obediently fill in any miserable area in the garden. However, if provided full sun, reasonable soil, and a little moisture, the flowers can be most showy. Perhaps because the flowers were so brilliant, plants received the common name "Welcome-home-husband-though-never-so-drunk." Thin every 2–4 years to keep them in check, otherwise little maintenance is required.

Cultivars:

'Aureum' is a lovely plant with young leaves and shoot tips edged with a golden tint in the spring. Unfortunately, the tint is lost in the summer. The flowers are lighter yellow than the species.

'Elegans' is similar to 'Aureum' but the leaves and shoot tips are silvery. It does not lose the tint as rapidly but is not as showy as 'Aureum'. Neither of these cultivars is as vigorous as the species.

var. *majus* is larger than the species and has paler green leaves with flowers up to ¾" across. The stems are not as densely packed as the species and are more prone to breakage in winter.

var. *minus* is the opposite of var. *majus* and seldom grows over 1" tall. All parts are smaller than the species, making a compact, neat carpet.

Division may be accomplished any time of year, and even pieces of plant accidently broken will root where they fall. Seed should be covered lightly and watered gently or from the bottom so it is not washed away. Provide consistent moisture and place the seed flat at 70–75°F. Two years are necessary to reach flowering size.

Related Species:

S. reflexum, stone orpine, has bright yellow flowers over a loose mat of creeping, rooting stems. The linear, bluish green leaves are rounded in cross-section (terete) and densely arranged on the stems. Plants flower in midsummer and grow 6–10" tall.

-aizoon (aye' zoon)		Aizoon Stonecrop	12–15"/18"
Summer	Yellow	Siberia, China, Japan	Zones 4–9

The leaves are alternate and sessile, scattered along the unbranched stem and bent somewhat backwards (reflexed). The flat leaves are about 2" long and ½" wide, the margins sharply and irregularly toothed. The terminal yellow flowers are held on a short scape and literally sit on top of the plant. The individual flowers are about ½" across and the flat inflorescence (cyme) is 3–4" wide. Unlike the previous species, plants die to the ground in late fall.

Although not the most ornamental sedum, the flowers are showy for a few weeks in midsummer. It is tall enough to compete with *S. spectabile* cultivars (eg. 'Meteor') but too tall to be used for the carpeting effect provided by *S. acre*.

Cultivars:

var. *aurantiacum* is showier than the species due to its red stems, dark green leaves, deep orange to yellow flowers and red fruit. Plants grow 10–18" tall.

'Euphorboides' is more compact than the species and has larger (up to 4" across) deep yellow flower heads.

Propagate by division after flowering.

Related Species:

There is confusion as to the status of *S. maximowiczii*. Some authors consider it synonymous with *S. aizoon*, others feel that the red, taller stems, and broader leaves make it a subspecies of *S. aizoon*, while others consider it a separate species. Regardless, plants with a *maximowiczii* label are more showy in leaf and flower than *S. aizoon* and more useful for the garden.

- × 'Autumn Joy'	Autumn Joy Sedum		12–24"/24"
Late Summer, Fall	Pink	China	Zones 3–10

This is one of the finest garden plants available today. The 2–3" long fleshy leaves are sessile, sharply and irregularly toothed. My children like to gently part the upper and lower base of a leaf and blow it up like a balloon. To do this, one must have great patience and a plant tough enough to survive the rigors of being unclothed by hordes of little children.

The upper leaves are smaller with more rounded bases than the lower leaves and all have a prominent midrib. Green shoots are always just below the soil surface and by early March, mounds of light green foliage freshen the garden. By midsummer, the flower buds have initiated and start to appear. Plants require full sun, otherwise stems are weak and the heavy flowers cause the stems to topple. Because my plants are in partial shade, I cut them back to 12" in late June. Flowers are smaller and more numerous but plants are more attractive than if they are spread-eagled across the ground. Alternatively, the plants may be supported and larger flowers will result. I also grow 'Autumn Joy' through a large clump of *Iris pseudacorus* which provides natural support. Support in shaded gardens is especially useful in the South where plants often grow over 2' tall. North of zone 7, cutting back the plants is not necessary unless they are over fertilized. The flower buds appear whitish, slowly turn shell pink, and age to a deep bronze-red. Many flowers are formed in the flat-topped 6" diameter corymbs. They bloom well into the fall and dry on the stem. To some gardeners, these dried flowers are picturesque and provide lovely decoration to the winter garden. To me, however, they simply look like dead flowers and I remove them after they turn brown.

Authorities list the plant as a cultivar of *S. spectabile*, *S. telephium* or *S. purpureum* (a synonym of *S. telephium*) but it was raised by Arends nursery in 1955 from a cross between *S. telephium* and *S. spectabile*. It is commonly listed as a cultivar of *S. spectabile* but that species has opposite, scattered leaves and 'Autumn Joy' has alternate leaves.

Divide in early spring or fall. Terminal cuttings root in 7–10 days.

Related Species:

S. maximum, great stonecrop, is 2' tall with succulent leaves and flat flower heads of greenish yellow stars. The best form is 'Atropurpureum' which sports dark purple foliage and whitish star-shaped flowers with dark red centers.

S. spectabile, showy stonecrop, is up to 2' tall and bears 3" long opposite leaves. Cultivars are similar to, but not as compact as *S.* × 'Autumn Joy'.

'Carmen' is the best cultivar and bears many carmine-pink flowers on 18–24" stems.

'Meteor' is indistinguishable from 'Autumn Joy'. According to Evans (see references), plants are not as compact and flowering is not as long lasting. I can see no difference.

S. × 'Sunset Cloud' is similar to 'Vera Jameson' but bears wine-colored flowers.

Sedum × 'Autumn Joy'
(64%)

S. telephium, orpine, with alternate leaves and carrot-like roots differs from *S. spectabile* by having short stamens that barely exceed the petals. Plants are 12–18″ tall and bear large terminal and lateral red-purple flower heads (cymes). The best known cultivar is 'Munstead Red' with dark red flowers.

S. × 'Vera Jameson' is short (9–12″ tall) and bears blue-green leaves and 2–4″ wide flower heads of ½″ wide pink flowers. It is a hybrid between *S. maximum* 'Atropurpureum' × (*S. cauticola* × *S.* 'Ruby Glow'). An excellent selection for the sunny garden.

-kamtschaticum (kamt-sha' ti-cum)	Kamschatka Stonecrop	4–9″/15″
Summer Yellow	Kamschatka, Korea, Japan	Zones 3–8

The normally unbranched pale green stems give rise to flat, terminal inflorescences of 6–10 yellow flowers. The leaves are alternate, about 1½″ long and ½″ wide, and sharply toothed above the middle but entire near the base. The flowers are showy, about ½″ across, but seldom is the plant a mat of yellow as in *S. acre*.

Plants spread well if provided good drainage and full sun, and although too tall and open for a ground cover, are excellent for hillsides and banks. A tangled mass of stems occurs in the summer, and after flowering, which occurs sporadically throughout the year, small rosettes appear at the base of the plant and are next year's leaves. Most of the rest of the plant dies away by late fall.

Cultivars:

var. *floriferum* is, as the name suggests, more floriferous than the species. It produces numerous flowering shoots along the whole length of the stem. The flowers are smaller and paler yellow, but overall, plants put on a better show than the type. It is sometimes listed as a separate species (*S. floriferum*).

'Takahira Dake' is more compact and erect than the species with reddish stems and more flowering branches. The flowers are similar to the type.

'Variegatum' has a broad white band on the leaf margins and deeper orange flowers than the species. It is not as vigorous as the species and remains more compact. The leaves readily revert to green and any such growth that originates from the rootstalk should be removed.

Related Species:

S. ellacombianum is sometimes classified as a variety of *S. kamtschaticum* but the stems are not branched, the leaves are opposite and have scalloped rather than toothed margins. It is shorter (4–6″) and more compact.

S. middendorffianum, Middendorf stonecrop, has unbranched stems and narrower leaves (about 1/10″ wide). The leaves also have a sunken median groove making them somewhat V-shaped. The flowers of all three species are similar.

537

-spurium (spur' ee-um)		Two Row Stonecrop	2–6"/18"
Summer	White to Rose	Caucasus	Zones 3–8

One of the tougher and showier stonecrops for a ground cover or rock garden. Many shoots arise from branches which root at the nodes, making a vigorous and rapidly spreading plant. However, it is straggly, coarse, and invasive. Ronald Evans, (*Handbook of Cultivated Sedums*), in describing *S. spurium*, states that "no plant should be called completely useless, however, and from its vegetative aspect, it could be recommended for quickly covering a heap of rubble." In spite of Mr. Evans's opinion, plants have become popular because of the showy flowers. The flowering stems are about 4" long and give rise to terminal four-branched inflorescences consisting of many ¾" diameter flowers. The anthers are orange-red, the petals rosy red and flowers persist for 3–4 weeks. A large planting of *S. spurium* can be a brilliant blaze of color. The opposite leaves are bright green with a reddish margin and the leaves near the end of the stems turn redder in the fall and remain evergreen. Plants are not as vigorous in the South as in the North and as with most sedums, look terrible in midsummer. Although native to moist alpine meadows, it is not tolerant of wet feet and should be grown where drainage is excellent.

Cultivars:

'Bronze Carpet' has a distinct bronzing of the leaves and is similar to 'Dragon's Blood'. The leaves are less permanently bronzed than 'Dragon's Blood' and some reversion to green stems occurs.

'Coccineum' is similar to the species but has scarlet flowers.

'Dragon's Blood' is the most popular cultivar with foliage strongly and permanently suffused with purplish bronze. During the spring and summer, plants are covered with dark red starry flowers. It is not as vigorous as the species. In the South, plants often melt out in the summer.

'Red Carpet' has red flowers over bronze foliage and grows 3–4" tall. Similar to 'Bronze Carpet'.

'Variegatum' has green leaves surrounded by creamy pink margins. Some leaves are entirely pinkish red but reversion to green shoots is not uncommon.

All forms of this species may be divided any time during the season.

Related Species:

S. × 'Ruby Glow' (*S. cauticola* × *S.* 'Autumn Joy') is about 12" tall and bears irridescent dark ruby flowers. It is an excellent front-of-the-border plant and is particularly colorful in late summer and fall.

S. spathulifolium is native to the West Coast and bears ¾" wide yellow flowers and short trailing stems of blue-green spatulate leaves. 'Cape Blanco' has silvery leaves with a purplish red margin. It does poorly in hot, humid summers.

-ternatum (ter-na' tum)	Whorled Stonecrop	2–6"/18"
Late Spring	White	Eastern United States	Zones 4–8

The common name comes from the arrangement of leaves in whorls of three. The rounded pale green stems root from the nodes. After flowering, stems die in the fall but offshoots remain, resulting in evergreen plants. The ¾" long, roundish leaves are borne in rosettes crowded at the ends while the lower stem is barren. The pure white star-like flowers are effective for 2 to 4 weeks in April and May. Plants tolerate shady moist conditions better than most other species. For rocky slopes, few species are better. Unfortunately, *Botrytis* infections can be serious and plants are lost in wet winters in areas of little or no snow.

Cultivars:

'Minus' is similar but smaller in all parts with a mature height of 2–3", and bears leaves only at the end of the stems. The flower is smaller but otherwise similar to the type.

Reproduce plants vegetatively from stems which root and break away from the mother plant. These remain small during the winter and begin to grow the next spring. Plants may also be divided in early spring or fall.

Quick Key to Sedum Species

    A. Plants creeping (growing along the ground) or decumbent
       (lying on ground with ends ascending)
       B. Flowers yellow.. *S. acre*
      BB. Flowers white or rose
          C. Flowers white.. *S. ternatum*
         CC. Flowers rose .... *S. spurium*
    AA. Plants upright
       B. Flowers yellow
          C. Height 12–15", leaves broadest at or below middle,
             teeth begin below middle of leaf, many flowers (16–200) ....
                                                                    S. aizoon
         CC. Height 4–9", leaves broadest above middle, teeth begin
             above middle of leaf, few flowers (8–65).......... *S. kamtschaticum*
      BB. Flowers pink....................................... *S.* × 'Autumn Joy'

Additional Reading:

Books:

Evans, Ronald L. 1984. *Handbook of Cultivated Sedums*. Science Reviews Ltd., Middlesex, England. This excellent well-written text covers most of the species found in gardens today. The best book on *Sedum* I have found.

Manuscripts:

Bloom, Alan. 1978. Herbaceous sedums. *The Garden* 103(9):372–373.

Foster, Catherine Osgood. 1982. Sedums reconsidered. *Horticulture* 60(6):38–49.

Hansen, Karel and Nynke Groendijk-Wilders. 1986. An account of some sedums cultivated in Europe. *The Plantsman* 8(1):1–20.

Sempervivum (sem-per-veev' um)   Hens and Chicks, Houseleek   Crassulaceae

If there was but a single plant my grandparents remembered, it would be hens and chicks. Used everywhere from small side gardens to plantings on grave sites, few gardens were complete without *Sempervivum*. One of the reasons for its popularity was the ease of growth and adaptability to any and all conditions. The name comes from the latin *semper*, always, and *vivo*, live, and live forever it does. Hens and chicks belong to the same family as *Sedum* but differ in the floral parts; in multiples of 6 or more while those of *Sedum* are in fives. All of the appproximately 25 species appear similar and all are known as hens and chicks.

All species have thick, fleshy, alternate leaves and flowers which rise from the rosettes in coarse cymes. The flowers are often rosy red but may be white, green, yellow, or purple. Young plants are formed around the base of the plant and after flowering, the flowering rosettes—"hens"—often die leaving the "chicks" to carry on for another year. Removing the offsets and planting elsewhere is the easiest method of propagation. Seed may also be obtained but three years are necessary before plants flower.

Several species are offered by specialists including the cobwebbed houseleek, *S. arachnoideum*, which weaves gray threads from leaf to leaf and forms dense webbing, particularly in full sun. Rose-red flowers appear in midsummer on stout flower stems. *S. soboliferum* produces dense mats of small green rosettes. The many offsets are attached to the mother plant by thin weak stolons and detach easily. Due to the ease with which offsets were formed and allowed to leave home, this species was the original hens and chicks. Pale yellow flowers are formed. The common houseleek seen in the most nurseries, gardens, and catalogs is *S. tectorum*.

-tectorum (tek-to' rum)	Common Houseleek	8–12"/9"
Summer *Purple-red	Pyrenees, Alps, Apennines	Zones 3–8

The 3–4" diameter rosettes consist of 50–60 leaves, often tinged purple on the margins. The plant is stoloniferous and the new offsets are densely crowded around the parent. The leaves are flat on the face, rounded on the back and often reddened at the base. The hairy 12" long flower stem is clothed with hairy

lance-like leaves. The flowers are 12-parted, purple red, and about 1″ across. The offsets are strong and produced on thick stolons. It is evergreen in all parts of the country. In the South, drainage is more critical than in the North.

Cultivars:

var. *calcareum* has smooth leaves with brown-purple tips.
var. *cupreum* has larger rosettes which are rosy in cool seasons.

Related Species:

S. *tectorum* has hybridized with many species, in nature as well as in gardens, producing numerous named forms and hybrids. S. × *pomellii*, Pomel's houseleek, and S. × *thompsonii*, Thompson's houseleek, are hybrids between S. *arachnoideum* and S. *tectorum* while S. × *schottii*, Schott's houseleek, is the union of S. *montanum* and S. *tectorum*.

Sidalcia (see-dal′ see-a)	Checker-mallow	Malvaceae

Sidalcea is related closely to the genus *Sida*, a little-known group of plants native to North America, and to *Alcea*, the hollyhock. It bears mallow-like flowers but is not as tall as hollyhock. In recent years, improvements have occurred in flower and habit. About 8 species, all native to western North America, are known. Most have rose to pink flowers but one species, S. *candida*, has small white flowers with bluish anthers. Most of the improvements in the genus have occurred with S. *malvaeflora*, checkerbloom.

-malvaeflora (mal-vay-flo′ ra)	Checkerbloom	2–5′/3′
Summer	Rose, pink, purple	California	Zones 5–7

The 2″ wide lilac flowers are borne in terminal racemes. The basal leaves are rounded and lobed while the stem leaves are deeply cut into 5–7 smooth segments. *Sidalcia* thrives in cool, dry climates and performs poorly in the heat and humidity of the midwestern and eastern states. Misery was its middle name in my Georgia garden. Plant in full sun to partial shade in well-drained soil. Seldom is the species seen in cultivation as it is too variable and tall to be of ornamental value. Improvements in flower color and plant habit resulted from crosses between S. *candida*, white checker-mallow, and S. *malvaeflora*.

Cultivars:

'Brilliant' is 2–2½′ tall and carries carmine-red flowers.
'Elsie Heugh' is offered by most nurserymen and bears lovely pale pink, fringed flowers on a 2–3′ tall plant.
'Loveliness' is a recent introduction and is characterized by the shell pink flowers and compact habit. Plants stand 2½′ tall and seldom need support.

541

'Mr. Lindbergh' has rosy red flowers and grows 2' tall.

'Mrs. Alderson' is 3–4' tall and bears spikes of large rose-pink flowers. This was the parent from which the dwarf cultivars, 'Oberon' and 'Puck' arose .

'Oberon' has deep rose-pink flowers and is 2–2½' tall.

'Puck' is the dwarfest of the cultivars, attaining a height of 2', and bears clear pink flowers. This cultivar and the previous are worth trying where others grow too tall, particularly in the South. These excellent cultivars were bred by Bloom's Nursery in England.

'Rose Queen' has rose-pink flowers on 3–4' tall stems. One of the oldest cultivars, it is becoming more difficult to find.

'Stark's Hybrids' is a seed-propagated mix bearing pale pink to deep rose flowers that range in height from 2–3'.

'Sussex Beauty' grows 3–4' tall and has bright, satiny pink flowers.

'William Smith' has salmon-rose flowers and grows to 3' tall.

Propagate by lifting the clump in the fall, using vigorous sections from the outside of the plant and discarding the center. Divide every 3–4 years. The species and a number of named forms (eg. 'Stark's Hybrids') may be raised from seed in April and planted in the fall.

Silene (si-lee' nee) Campion Caryophyllaceae

Of the approximately 300 species, a few have found their way into widespread cultivation, particularly those suitable for the front of the garden or for the rock garden. The leaves are entire and the flowers are borne solitary or on 1-sided spikes. The calyx (the group of sepals) is often inflated giving the flowers a bladder-like appearance. *Silene* is closely related to *Lychnis*, *Melandrium*, and *Viscaria* and the genera are often used interchangeably. Differences between *Silene* and *Lychnis* were discussed under *Lychnis* and are based on the number of styles. The differences among *Silene*, *Viscaria*, and *Melandrium* are less obvious, as seen in the following table.

	Number of styles	Number of cells in seed capsule	Number of stamens	Number of species
Lychnis	5	1	10	10
Melandrium	3	1	10	60
Silene	3	3	10	300
Viscaria	5	5	10	4

The only species of *Melandrium* in gardens is our native *M. virginicum*, fire pink, still often listed as *Silene virginica*, *M. elizabethae* (*Silene elizabethae*), a fine rock garden plant, and *M. wherryi* (*Silene wherryi*), a 6" tall plant with many small pink flowers. *Viscaria vulgaris*, catchfly, is an interesting plant whose common name comes from the fact that flies stick to its sticky stem.

A number of striking species are grown for the rock garden such as *S. acaulis*, moss campion, *S. hookeri*, Hooker's campion, and *S. maritima*, robin white breast, but these can be difficult and disappointing for many gardeners. Two species of *Silene* which are useful and much less demanding for the front of border or in the rock garden are *S. polypetala*, fringed campion, and *S. schafta*, schafta campion.

-polypetala (pah-lee' pet-a-la)		Fringed Campion	4–6"/18"
Late Spring	Pink	Southeastern United States	Zones 6–8

This wild flower is on the endangered species list for the State of Georgia. However, collections reside happily in botanical gardens in the Southeast and tissue culture techniques have increased numbers substantially. The evergreen foliage is dark green and contrasts well with the light lavender-pink, fringed petals which emerge in late spring. The flowers are 1¼" in diameter and produced for 3–4 weeks. If placed in full sun, the foliage yellows and becomes sparse, therefore, partial to heavy shade is recommended. Plants require well-drained moist soil. If planted in the front of the border, be sure soil is porous enough to reduce water retention around the crown.

Division may be accomplished in spring or fall. Seed may also be used but plants will not flower without a cold period. Tissue culture techniques have been fine tuned by Dr. Michael Dirr and Mildred Pinnell at the University of Georgia and this work should soon allow an increased supply of this fine plant.

Related Species:

Dr. Jim Ault, while working at the University of Georgia, crossed *S. virginica* (*Melandrium virginicum*) and *S. polypetala*. The resulting hybrid has beautiful deep pink, fringed petals and appears to have exciting garden potential. Plants are presently being tested in the Horticulture Gardens.

-schafta (shaf' ta)		Schafta Campion	3–6"/12"
Summer	Magenta-pink	Caucasus	Zones 4–8

Many unbranched stems ascend laterally from a woody rootstock to form tufted mats of light green foliage. One or two pinwheel-shaped flowers (¾" diameter) are produced at the end of each stem during mid summer to late summer and continue for 3–4 weeks. The 1" long calyx is not inflated and is light green with 10 veins. The magenta-pink petals are notched. Full sun and coarse, gritty soil are preferable. Plants are valuable not only because of their colorful blooms but also because of late flowering.

Cultivars:

'Splendens' has rose-colored flowers on 8–10" tall plants.

Propagate by seed, division, or terminal cutting.

Sisyrinchium (si-see-ring' kee-um) Blue-eyed Grass Iridaceae

Although many of the 60–75 species are native to North America, few have found their way into our gardens. The common name came from *S. angustifolium*, with grass-like leaves and starry blue flowers, native from Southern Canada into much of the eastern United States. *S. bellum* is similar but has a yellow throat. One of the finest species is *S. douglasii*, western grass-widow which bears large satiny purple, nodding flowers among rush-like foliage. Some of the blue-eyed grasses, however, bear yellow flowers, such as the 4–6" tall *S. brachypus*, or white flowers (*S. filifolium*). The most ornamental is *S. striatum*, Argentine blue-eyed grass.

-striatum (streye-a' tum)		Argentine Blue-eyed Grass	12–24"/18"
Early Summer	Cream	Argentina, Chile	Zones 4–8

This lovely plant bears 9–12 creamy yellow flowers on an upright spike, similar to a gladiolus. The ¾–1" wide flowers are darker in the center and striped with purple on their backsides (thus the name *striatum*). The foliage is wider than most species (up to 1" across) and can be mistaken for *Iris* when not in flower. Plants have creeping rootstocks and form large clumps but are not at all invasive. After flowering, plants become messy and should be fertilized to reduce the number of leaves which naturally turn yellow, or cut back to 6" of the ground. Full sun and well-drained moist soils are ideal. It is not as floriferous in the South as further north but worth trying regardless of locale.

Cultivars:

'Variegatum' is particularly attractive with creamy white margins on the gray foliage providing additional interest after flowering. This is my favorite blue-eyed grass for the garden.

Propagate by division or seed. Plants should be divided at least every 2–3 years. The small seeds should be barely covered and placed at 70–75°F and high humidity. Germination is erratic but seedlings should emerge within 3–4 weeks.

Smilacina (smy-lass-ee' na) False Solomon's-seal Liliaceae

Approximately 25 species of this native wild flower are known and all are found in moist shady areas. It is similar to Solomon's seal, *Polygonatum biflorum*, with alternate leaves on arching stems, berries in the fall, and golden fall color. Plants of both genera may be found side by side at the edge of humus-rich woods. There, the similarities end. Many small flowers are borne in dense terminal inflorescences in *Smilacina* whereas those of *Polygonatum* are rather inconspicuous and bell shaped, borne in the leaf axils beneath the arching stems. Fruit is red in *Smilacina* and blue-black in *Polygonatum*. Plants of false Solomon's seal are best used for naturalizing in a wild flower garden or near wood's edge.

-racemosa (ra-say-mo' sa)		False Solomon's-seal	2–3'/4'
Spring	Cream	North America	Zones 3–7

This wild flower is native from Quebec, south to Tennessee, east to Virginia and west to Arizona. One of my favorite plantings, however, is at Wakehurst Place, Ardingly, England, where huge, shining panicles drew me like a moth to light. When plants are well grown, panicles are visible 50 yards away. The arching stems bear 10–15 slender-pointed lanceolate leaves, each about 5–9" long. The rootstock is long and thick and over the years produces an ever-widening clump. Hundreds of flowers are borne in a somewhat pyramidal panicle at the end of each stem. The individual flowers are small (⅙" wide), fragrant, and composed of 6 spreading, equal segments. After flowering, numerous red berries with small purple spots develop. They are a favorite food for many small animals and seldom persist.

Plants thrive in shaded, moist areas such as the edge of a wooded area or near a pond or stream. The soil should be lime free, rich in humus and deep enough to allow easy penetration of the rootstock. They should not be disturbed for at least 3 years to allow establishment of the spreading root system. It is not tolerant of hot weather and does much better in cool climates. Although plants grow and survive south of zone 7, they are not particularly ornamental unless copious amounts of water are supplied.

Cultivars:

var. *cylindrica* has shorter leaves and is smaller than the type. The panicle is more cylindrical than pyramidal but there are few obvious differences between this variety and the species. The native range extends south to Georgia, and it is slightly more heat tolerant.

Seed must be stratified and germination can take up to a year. Careful division of mature plants in the spring or fall is the most common method of propagation.

Related Species:

S. stellata, starry Solomon's-seal, is also known as star-flowered lily-of-the-valley because of the similarity of the leaves to those of *Convallaria*. It is 1–2' tall, has light green linear leaves and starry white flowers in an open raceme. Although the flowers are a little larger, the inflorescence is much smaller than *S. racemosa* and not as ornamental.

Solidago (so-li-day' go)	Goldenrod	Asteraceae

Considered a nuisance weed by some, or a handsome wild flower by others, the genus has been all but ignored as a garden flower in the United States. Perhaps because goldenrods have been unfairly accused of causing hay fever (ragweed is the bad guy), or because they are common roadside fixtures, few find their way into cultivation. This is not the case in Europe where garden hybrids have been developed and used for late summer flowering. Hybridization of some of their finest cultivars has relied heavily on our native goldenrod, *S. canadensis*, as one of the parents. Once again, the Europeans have introduced new and attractive garden forms from plants that are common in our own back yard.

Solidago virgaurea, European goldenrod, was highly valued for healing wounds, either externally or internally applied. However, even in England, where everything seems to grow so well, our native *S. canadensis* was not particularly popular. William Robinson wrote in 1883 that these "North American Composites in borders exterminate valuable plants, and give a coarse, ragged aspect to the garden". Of course, they still do. However, today's compact and colorful hybrids would make even Mr. Robinson sit up and look twice. The taller hybrids resulted from *S. canadensis* and *S. virgaurea* while the shorter ones originated from × *Solidaster luteus* (a intergeneric cross descended from *S. missouriensis* and *Aster ptarmicoides*) and *S. brachystachys*, a 6–9″ miniature goldenrod. Only the the smaller forms can be recommended as they do not dominate the garden or require support. Except for a few cultivars, I still do not find them outstandingly attractive. I prefer the taller goldenrods by the roadside rather than in my garden. All do best in humusy soils and full sun.

Cultivars:
'Baby Gold' stands 2–2½' tall with large racemes of bright yellow flowers.
'Cloth of Gold' is a dwarf but vigorous grower with dense, deep yellow flowers and grows 18–24″ tall.
'Golden Baby' grows 2' tall with golden yellow plumes.
'Golden Gates' has bright lemon-yellow flowers atop 2' tall compact plants.
'Goldenmosa' has yellow-green foliage and bears yellow flowers in early August on 2½' tall stems.
'Golden Thumb' ('Tom Thumb','Queenie') grows about 1' tall with yellow flowers and yellowish green foliage. My choice as the most ornamental and useful cultivar.
'Golden Wings' is 5–6' tall, too tall for most gardens. Although a lovely deep yellow, it is too close in habit to *S. canadensis* to be of value.
'Lemore' is 2½–3' tall with large inflorescences of primrose-yellow flowers. The flowers fade to white as they mature. Not as good a garden selection as 'Golden Thumb'.
'Peter Pan' ('Goldstrahl') has canary-yellow flowers and stands 2–3' tall. Plants associate well with red flowers of *Lobelia cardinalis* and *Crocosmia* hybrids. Flowering continues through early September and October.

Related Species
Although the hybrids are best for gardens, those who would like to incorporate wild flowers in a meadow or in a sunny area might consider other useful North American species.

S. caesia, wreath goldenrod, has distinctive wavy, yellow flower spikes and bluish purple, wiry stems. Flowers form along the whole length of the arching stems, not just at the top. Plants grow 2–3' tall and flower in late August and September. This is one of the more unusual goldenrods.

S. odora, sweet goldenrod, is an excellent plant for the fragrant garden. The narrow leaves smell like anise when crushed. It stands 3–4' tall and bears yellow flowers on small, spreading, one-sided panicles. Hardy from zone 3 to 9.

S. rugosa, rough stemmed goldenrod, is 4–5' tall and has conspicuous hairy stems. The arching stems form a large panicle of golden yellow flowers in late September and October. Not as stoloniferous as some other native goldenrods, it can be used without fear of invasion. Plants look particularly good in combination with fruit of *Callicarpa americana*, our native beautyberry.

S. sempervirens, seaside goldenrod, is 4–6' tall and flowers on one side only, forming a dense one-sided raceme in September and October. A useful plant for saline and sandy areas, the roots also retard sand erosion.

Divide or use stem cuttings for the hybrids while the species may be raised from seed. The seeds germinate readily if placed under warm, humid conditions.

Additional Reading:
Bubel, Nancy. 1985. Goldenrods for the Garden? *Horticulture* 63(5):20–23.

Sparaxis (spa-raks' is)   Wandflower   Iridaceae

This colorful bulbous genus is winter hardy only in the warmest parts of the country but may be grown for late spring color and handled in the same manner as *Gladiolus* and *Ixia*. Of the four species, the most colorful is *S. tricolor*.

-tricolor (tri' ko-lor)	Wandflower	9–12"/12"
Spring Orange-red	South Africa	Zones 9–10

The lance-shaped leaves emerge early in the spring and give rise to short spikes bearing 3 to 6 flowers of intense orange-red with yellow throats. The 1½–2" diameter flowers have 6 equal and flared segments but due to the great variability in the species, flowers range from pure white to yellow or red. However, the yellow throat is consistent in all flowers. Bulbs should be planted as soon as the threat of frost has passed and lifted and separated in the fall. They are best placed in containers in the fall in a cold frame and planted out, pot and all, in the spring. Fortunately, the corms are inexpensive and mistakes in culture are affordable. This species is too lovely not to try at least once. I grew it in Georgia but corms lasted only one or two years. Plants do well in California where the warm days, cool nights, and dry summers resemble its native habitat.

Although single colors have been named, wandflower is generally available only as a mix of colors.

Spigelia (spy-geel' ee-a)   Spigelia   Loganiaceae

Thirty species are native from the southeastern United States to South America. Plants bear opposite, entire leaves and tubular upright flowers. They are wonderful plants for gardens and along paths in shaded, moist areas.

-*marilandica* (mar-i-land-i' ca)   Indian Pink, Pinkroot   1–2'/2'
Early Summer   Red   Southeastern United States   Zones 6–9

In early summer, plants produce 2″ long, 1″ wide sharply lobed, tubular red flowers with yellow throats. Flowers are upright and borne above the 4–7 pairs of 4″ long ovate sessile dark green leaves. Place in the front of the garden or in wild flower areas in partial shade and moist soils. En masse, they are a striking, beautiful addition to any garden.

Stachys (sta' kis)   Betony   Lamiaceae

Over 300 species occur but only a handful are used as ornamental plants. Leaves are opposite and flowers are generally blue to purple, although some species bear white, yellow, or red flowers. The flowers are not particularly showy and in one case, plant breeders produced a non-flowering garden cultivar.

Most species do well in well-drained garden soils in partial shade to full sun.

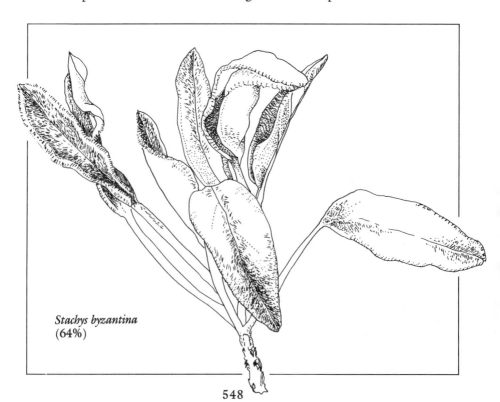

Stachys byzantina
(64%)

Quick Reference to Stachys Species

	Height (in)	Foliage color	Flower color
S. byzantina	12–15	Gray	Purple
S. macrantha	12–24	Green	Purple
S. officinalis	18–24	Green	Red-purple

-byzantina (bi-zan-teen' a)		Lamb's-ears	12–15"/12"
Spring	Purple	Caucasus to Iran	Zones 4–8

(Syn. *S. lanata*, *S. olympica*)

Mats of velvety, white woolly leaves have made this a much used species for edging and design work. The foliage provides an excellent demonstration of the term tomentose—a covering of dense matted, short, woolly hairs. Plants look best in spring when the foliage is fresh but tend to decline by mid-August, particularly in humid, wet summers. The hairy foliage traps moisture and dew, and if summers are hot, particularly at night, significant leaf disease occurs, resulting in dead patches. In my garden, it looks fresh in the spring but usually melts out in the summer. Plants recover in the fall and foliage remains evergreen in milder parts of the country. The purple flowers are held in whorls on a 4–6" densely hairy spike. The corolla tube is less than ½" long and barely protrudes from the calyx. In most perennials, the onset of flowering is anticipated, but in this case the flowers detract from the foliage. Not only do they take the eye from the handsome foliage to the mundane flower, but look worse once they have faded. Flowers should be removed as they develop.

Moist but well-drained soils are ideal. Subirrigation is better than overhead watering and all irrigation should be accomplished in the morning to allow foliage to dry out.

Cultivars:

'Primrose Heron' is a recently introduced cultivar with primrose-yellow foliage in the spring that reverts to gray-green as summer progresses. The flowers are similar to the species.

'Sheila McQueen' is about 1' tall and is more compact than the type. The leaves are slightly larger and less woolly.

'Silver Carpet' is the best cultivar for low maintenance gardening. No flowers are produced and carpets of silvery foliage spread rapidly.

Cultivars are propagated by division and the species may be raised from seed. Germination is erratic but is not difficult at warm temperatures (70–72°F) and humid conditions.

-macrantha (ma-kranth′ a)		Big Betony	12–24″/12″
Late Spring	Purple	Caucasus	Zones 2–8

(Syn. *S. grandiflora, Betonica macrantha*)

While the flowers of the previous species are not particularly revered, a flowering mass of this species makes a magnificent sight. The broadly ovate, dark green leaves are wrinkled and roughly hairy (scabrous). All leaves have scalloped edges but the uppermost leaves are much smaller than those toward the base. Plants spread rapidly to form mats in rich moist soils. The violet flowers are held in 2–3 distinct whorls of 10–20 flowers each about 8″ above the foliage. The corolla tube is about 1″ long and 3–4 times longer than the calyx.

Full sun and well-drained soils are preferable in the North but partial shade is necessary in the South. More flowers are produced in cooler areas of the country but if moisture is applied consistently, plants tolerate heat. In my garden, plants perform well in the spring but few flowers are produced.

Cultivars:

var. *robusta* is the most common form, grows 24″ tall and bears spikes of 4–5 whorls of rosy pink flowers. This is one of the best forms for the garden.

var. *rosea* is similar to the species but produces rose-red flowers.

var. *superba* has loose spikes of deep purple violet. There is little difference between this and var. *violacea*.

var. *violacea* has deep violet flowers.

Although the varieties come true from seed, division is the fastest and best means of propagation.

-officinalis (o-fi-shi-nah′ lis)		Wood Betony	18–24″/24″
Late Spring	Violet	Europe	Zones 4–8

(Syn. *S. betonica*)

Few differences exist between this and the previous species. The 4–5″ long, ovate lower leaves have long petioles and scalloped margins while the upper leaves are lanceolate and sessile. The violet to pink flowers are about ½″ long and twice as long as the calyx. Cultural requirements are similar to *S. macrantha* but it will not tolerate as much shade.

Cultivars:

var. *alba* has creamy white flowers.

var. *rosea* bears rose-colored flowers.

Propagate similar to the previous species.

Quick Key to Stachys Species

    A. Leaves densely whitish woolly, corolla short and barely
        exserted from the calyx.................................... *S. byzantina*
   AA. Leaves green, corolla much longer than calyx
       B. Upper stem leaves ovate, corolla 3–4 times longer than calyx ....
             S. macrantha
      BB. Upper stem leaves lanceolate, corolla twice as long as calyx.............
             S. officinalis

Stokesia (stoks' ee-a)   Stokes' Aster   Asteraceae

The only species, *S. laevis*, occurs from South Carolina to Florida and Louisiana. This wild flower has undergone a series of breeding "operations" resulting in larger and more colorful flowers than the species. It has adapted itself so well to formal gardens that it is seldom thought of as a wild flower anymore.

-laevis (lay' vis)   Stokes' Aster   12–24"/18"
Summer   Blue   Southeastern United States   Zones 5–9

(Syn. *S. cyanea*)

The dark evergreen entire leaves, which often have a pronounced white midrib, are 6–8" long, alternate and provide pleasant greenery in the winter when not covered by snow. Leaves at the base have a long petiole but become sessile toward the top of the plant. Two to four flowers are borne on a single stalk but open one or two at a time. Many flower stalks are present and flowering continues for about 4 weeks. The individual flowers are 2–3" across and consist of two series of ray flowers. The outer are much larger than the inner set and have 4–5 deeply cut lobes. Plants are best placed at the front of the border in filtered sunlight and well-drained soil as they do not tolerate wet feet in the winter. If planted in zone 5, a winter mulch should be applied.

Cultivars:

'Alba' has white flowers and although not as floriferous as the blue cultivars, the flowers contrast well against the foliage.
'Blue Danube' produces lavender-blue flowers up to 5" in diameter. The most popular of the named forms.
'Blue Star' has a little less lavender in the flowers and is almost a spode-blue.
'Silver Moon' bears creamy white flowers. They are larger than those of 'Alba' and equally handsome.
'Wyoming' bears many flowers of rich deep blue.

Propagate by divisions in the spring. The species may be raised from seed. Germination is irregular; seeds should be placed at 40°F for 6 weeks prior to sowing at 70°F.

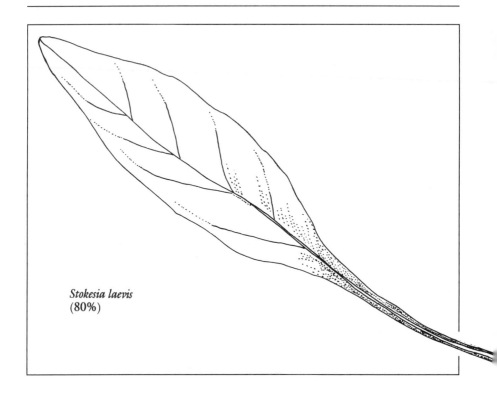

Stokesia laevis
(80%)

Stylophorum (sty-lah' for-um)   Celandine Poppy   Papaveraceae

This genus consists of three species but only the native species, S. *diphyllum*, is common in American gardens.

-diphyllum (di-fil' lum)   Celandine Poppy   12–18"/12"
Spring   Yellow   Eastern North America   Zones 4–9

This species is native to woodsides from Pennsylvania to Tennessee, and from Wisconsin to Missouri. Cut stems exude a yellow sap once used by American Indians for dye. The lower stem is bare of foliage but 3–4 light green leaves occur about two thirds up the stem. The leaves are 10–15" long and deeply cut into 5–7 lobed divisions. The 1½–2" diameter bright yellow flowers consist of four petals and many stamens. Three to five flowers open in each terminal inflorescence. A beautiful plant for the shaded, moist wild flower garden, it is equally at home in the shady perennial garden. If left undisturbed, the plants will colonize large areas. Foliage often disappears by late June in normal garden conditions, however, if grown in consistently moist soils, foliage persists into fall. People are inevitably drawn towards the plants regardless of other plants in

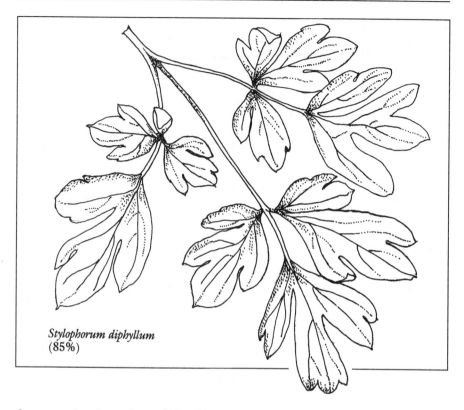

Stylophorum diphyllum
(85%)

flower at the time. One of the finest wild flowers for bright, effective spring color.

Seed is not difficult to germinate if sown in moist medium at 68–72°F. Plants should be left undisturbed but may be divided successfully if care is taken not to damage the long, thick roots. Divide in early spring or fall.

Symphytum (sim′ fi-tum)   Comfrey   Boraginaceae

It is debatable if any of the 25 species of this herb belong in the flower garden. *S. officinale* was used in Europe in monastery gardens in the twelfth century and is still found in herbal gardens. It was used as a poultice to help the healing of broken bones and became known as boneset. A number of species were introduced as forage and make excellent plants for the production of compost. Some gardeners grow *S. officinale* or *S. asperum*, a 5–6′ tall species, in a shaded wild flower area.

Most species are upright and 2–4′ tall although *S. grandiflorum*, a rapidly spreading ground cover with yellow-white flowers, and *S. rubrum*, a red-flowered form, are less than 18″. Some of the clearest and prettiest blue flowers in the plant kingdom occur in this genus. The flowers are often held in scorpioid cymes, similar to those of forget-me-nots and Virginia bluebells. All species are most suitable for moist areas in sun or dappled shade.

Divide the fleshy roots in the spring and replant immediately.

Quick Reference to Symphytum Species

	Height (in.)	Flower color
S. caucasicum	18–24	Blue
S. grandiflorum	12–15	Yellow
S. rubrum	15–18	Red
S. × uplandicum	36–48	Blue

-caucasicum (kaw-ka′ si-cum)		Caucasian Comfrey	18–24″/24″
Spring	Blue	Caucasus	Zones 3–8

The softly hairy foliage consists of 8″ long basal leaves and 6″ long upper leaves. The base of the leaves runs along the stem for a short distance (decurrent). The drooping, ¾″ long, bell-shaped flowers open pink, then turn azure blue with maturity. The corolla (petals) is 2–3 times longer than the calyx (sepals) and flowers are borne in terminal, paired, scorpioid cymes. Partial shade and moist soils are necessary for best performance. The coarse-textured plants are excellent subjects for the wild flower area but may also be useful in the border or as specimen plants in the garden.

-grandiflorum (grand-i-flo′ rum)		Large Flowered Comfrey	12–15″/18″
Spring	Yellow	Caucasus	Zones 3–8

Rhizomes give rise to many unbranched stems resulting in rapidly spreading colonies. The stem is roughly hairy (scabrous) and bears shiny, ovate leaves of different sizes. Those on flowering stems are only about 1½″ long while those on non-flowering (sterile) stems are up to 7″. The sterile stems lie on the ground with the ends pointing up (decumbent) and are characteristic of the species. Tubular, creamy yellow, ¾″ long flowers are produced in terminal, few-flowered cymes for about 3–4 weeks. A vigorous grower that competes well against weeds, it is shade and drought tolerant. Although tolerant of dry conditions, growth is superior in moist soils.

Cultivars:

'Variegatum' is an outstanding cultivar bearing creamy white margins around the light green leaves. The plant is much brighter than the species, particularly when planted in shady corner of the garden.

- × rubrum (rew′ brum)		Red Flowered Comfrey	15–18″/18″
Early Summer	Red	Hybrid	Zone 3–8

This may be used as a ground cover because of its tendency to spread, although not as rapidly as one of its parents, *S. grandiflorum*. The foliage is dark green and not as hairy as many of the other species. Dark red, tubular flowers bequeathed by *S. officinale* 'Coccineum' occur in terminal cymes. The drooping red flowers, however, do not contrast well with the hairy dark leaves. Full sun may be provided in the North but partial shade is best in the South. Provide even moisture in times of dry weather.

-× uplandicum (up-land' i-kum)		Russian Comfrey	36–48"/36"
Late Spring	Blue	Hybrid	Zones 4–8

(Syn. *S. peregrinum*)

This upright plant is the result of a cross between *S. asperum*, a 5' tall bristly plant, and *S. officinale*. The stems are highly branched and bear 8–10" long basal leaves and 2–3" long upper leaves. The basal leaves are decurrent (see *S. caucasicum*), and all foliage is softly hairy. The 1" long, tubular flowers appear in various shades of purple and blue in forked cymes in the upper axils of the plant.

Cultivars:

'Variegatum' has leaves with broad creamy white margins and lilac blue flowers.

Quick Reference to Symphytum Species

    A. Flowers purple, blue, or lilac
        B. Plants usually less than 2', flowers bell-shaped, calyx not
            divided to middle .... *S. caucasicum*
      BB. Plants usually taller than 2', flowers tubular, calyx divided
            to the middle .... *S.* × *uplandicum*
  AA. Flowers white, yellow, or red
      B. Flowers creamy yellow to white........................ *S. grandiflorum*
      BB. Flowers red .... *S.* × *rubrum*

T

Tellima (te′ li-ma)   Fringe-cup   Saxifragaceae

The genus has been reduced to a single species, *T. grandiflora*, native to western North America. *T. odorata* is considered a synonym of *T. grandiflora* and the pink-flowered *T. parviflora* has been placed in the genus *Lithophragma*.

Tellima is often confused with *Tiarella* and *Mitella* and, in fact, is an anagram of *Mitella*. *Tellima* differs from both genera in having an inflated calyx (similar, but not as obvious as that found in *Silene*). The fruit of all three is a capsule, but in *Tellima*, the capsule has 2 beak-like projections, whereas *Mitella* and *Tiarella* have none. All have similar shade and moisture requirements. However, if we put the confusion behind us and concentrate on garden performance, *Tiarella* is more rewarding than the other two.

-grandiflora (grand-i-flo′ ra)   Alaska Fringe-cup   1–2′/2′
Spring   Creamy white   Alaska to California   Zones 4–7

The 3–4″ long lobed leaves are heart-shaped, slightly toothed and evergreen. The ½″ long flowers are greenish to creamy white and as many as 30 may occur on a single scape. As the flowers mature, they change to rose-red. The sepals are united into an inflated calyx tube and the petals are pinnately cut into long, thread-like segments resulting in a "fringed cup".

Plants should be grown in ample shade and moist soil rich in organic matter. Incorporate plenty of peat or other water-holding material to maintain moisture around the roots. After blooming, the flowers become messy and should be removed unless seeds are to be collected.

Cultivars:

var. *purpurea* (syn. *rubra*) is about 1–1½′ tall with redder foliage and yellow flowers.

Teucrium (tewk' ree-um)   Germander   Lamiaceae

Members of this genus of herbs were used medicinally for hundreds of years. The name was derived from King Teucer, the first king of Troy, who used germander to relieve stomach pain and gout. The plants, somewhat woody at the base and technically subshrubs, are usually grown for their attractive, opposite leaves rather than the small purplish mint-like flowers. Of the 100 or so species, only a handful are particularly decorative and even fewer are available. One of the taller species is *T. canadense*, wild germander, which is native to southern Canada and the United States. Three feet tall in moist soil, it bears purple- to cream-colored flowers in a loose unbranched spike. A species commanding a loyal following in England is *T. scorodonia* 'Crispum', crispy wood germander. The wavy, crested green leaves are tinged purple in winter and decorative, particularly in the cooler months. It is winter hardy to zone 6 with mulch. Another crinkled leaf species is *T. massilense*, scented germander, whose gray-green foliage is accentuated by rose-colored flowers on 18″ tall plants. The foliage is highly aromatic. The most common germander is wall germander, *T. chamaedrys*. All species are aromatic and neighborhood cats will reward your plant selection with their never-ending presence.

-chamaedrys (ka-mie' drees)   Wall Germander   10–12″/12″
Summer   Purple   Europe   Zones 4–9

This small evergreen subshrub is popular because of the compact habit and shiny green leaves. It tolerates a particularly cruel form of abuse called "edge hedging" where it is sheared into formidable evergreen globs. When allowed to grow naturally, plants are far more decorative. The scalloped, ovate leaves are about 1″ long and borne on branched ascending stems. Two to six rosy purple flowers are produced in a single whorl in late summer and continue for approximately 3–4 weeks. Individual flowers are ½–¾″ long and the long, lower lip is usually spotted white and red.

When planted as a hedge, invariably some plants will be less vigorous than others, perhaps because of more shade or poorer soil. Doubtless a cat will love a portion of it to death, or a particularly cold winter will kill a few plants. The result is a spotty planting which pleases no one.

Plants should be grown in full sun (although tolerant of partial shade) and not be allowed to dry out.

Cultivars:

'Prostratum' is 6–10″ tall with rose-pink flowers in summer.

Propagate by seed or by 1–2″ terminal cuttings in May and root in a peat-perlite mixture. Excessive moisture in the rooting bench should be avoided. Rooting takes place in 3–4 weeks and plants may be grown in pots and placed in the garden in the fall or subsequent spring. Divisions may be taken in the spring.

557

Thalictrum (tha-lik' trum)   Meadow-rue   Ranunculaceae

The meadow-rues consist of numerous excellent species for the garden and although grown as ornamental plants for hundreds of years, they are still underused. In Europe, leaves of *Thalictrum* were used as a cure for the plague and jaundice, but few recoveries were recorded. The Romans also believed that to lay a newborn baby on a pillow stuffed with thalictrum flowers was to ensure riches throughout life.

Many species have fern-like foliage and great puffs of airy flowers. The apetalous flowers are ornamental because of the colored sepals and stamens. In some cases, male and female flowers occur on separate plants, such as the dainty early meadow-rue, *T. dioicum*, but others are bisexual. In general, they should be planted in partial shade with adequate moisture. Many are tall and most suited for the middle or back of the border, however, *T. alpinum*, alpine meadow-rue, and *T. kiusianum*, Kyushu meadow-rue, grow less than 12" tall.

Quick Reference to Thalictrum Species

	Height *(ft.)*	*Flower* *color*	*Leaflet* *color*
T. aquilegifolium	2–3	Lilac	Blue-green
T. delavayi	2–4	Lilac	Green
T. minus	1–2	Yellow	Green
T. speciosissimum	3–5	Yelow	Blue-green

-aquilegifolium (a-kwi-leeg' i-fo-lee-um)   Columbine Meadow-rue   2–3'/3'
Late Spring   Lilac   Europe, Northern Asia   Zones 5–8

This is one of the prettiest and showiest of the meadow-rues. The lovely blue-tinted leaves are similar to columbine, thus the specific name. There are many leaflets, each about 1½" wide and 3–5 lobed. The flowers are ornamental because of the conspicuous ½" long lilac stamens. The sepals are greenish or white and abscise rapidly. The lilac flowers are held in a 6–8" wide many-flowered corymbose panicle, and look like a big purple powder puff. This is the earliest meadow-rue to flower and opens as early as April 25 in my Georgia garden. Unfortunately, flowers persist only for about 2 weeks. However, the drooping, somewhat inflated fruits (achenes) are interesting with their 3 small wings and persist throughout the growing season.

This is the best meadow-rue for the South. The leaves, flowers, and seeds are ornamental and the plant is heat tolerant. It should be planted in a rich moist soil in partial shade. Direct sun results in less vigorous plants and later flowering.

Cultivars:

'Album' has white flowers atop a 3–4' tall plant. The white flowers contrast well with the blue-green foliage. The plant is otherwise similar to the species.

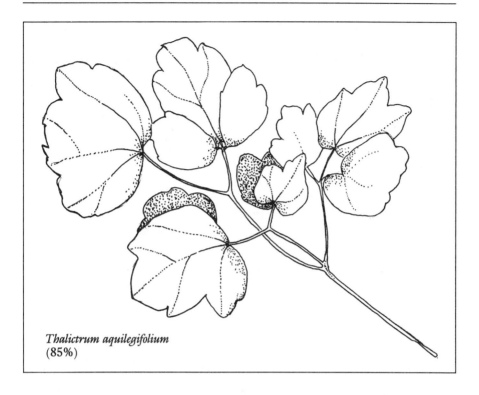

Thalictrum aquilegifolium
(85%)

var. *atropurpureum* (syn. *purpureum*) has dark purple stems and stamens. The variety listed as *purpureum* is likely the same, however, the stems are not as highly colored as var. *atropurpureum*. Apparently there is also a dwarf (2') form of the variety.

'Dwarf Purple' stands about 2½' tall, has lilac flowers and is otherwise similar to the species.

'Roseum' bears handsome light pink to pale rose flowers.

'Thundercloud' has deep purple flowers and larger flower heads than the type.

'White Cloud' is the best of the white-flowered forms with larger, whiter flowers than 'Album'.

Seed germinates readily and is the best method of propagation for the species and varieties. Cultivars may be divided in early spring or early fall. Divisions are slow to recover and must be handled carefully. Although divisions may be used to increase stock, division of the clump is not necessary for at least five years.

-delavayi (de-la-vay' ee)		Yunnan Meadow-rue	24–48"/36"
Summer	Lilac	Western China	Zones 4–7

From the point of view of garden performance and show, it is a lovely plant. The foliage is divided in 3–5 sections, each with three, ½" wide leaflets. The foliage is much more fern-like and graceful than that of *T. aquilegifolium*. Lilac sepals and creamy yellow stamens characterize flowers held in an airy, open, pyramidal panicle. The flowers are excellent for cutting but if the plants are grown too close together, the flowering stems get terribly tangled and are almost impossible to extract intact. Although often listed summer hardy to zone 8, performance has been disappointing in my garden. Plants survive, but are not particularly effective south of zone 7. Regardless of geographic location, plants require support to keep the slender stems erect when in flower. Similar to other meadow-rues, rich, moist soil and partial shade are beneficial.

Cultivars:

'Album' has white sepals but is not as vigorous as the type.

'Hewitt's Double' has double lilac flowers which last longer than flowers of the type. The stamens are petal-like (petaloid) resulting in the fuller flowers. An excellent garden plant.

Propagate the species from seed or division and the cultivars from division. 'Hewitt's Double' is commercially propagated by tissue culture.

Related Species:

T. dipterocarpum differs so little that, from the gardener's viewpoint, it is the same. Most plants sold under *T. dipterocarpum* are probably *T. delavayi*. The fruits are keys to separating the two species. The fruit of *T. delavayi* has 1 or 2 inconspicuous wings whereas those of *T. dipterocarpum* has three distinct wings. For gardeners with curiosity and patience, a 10X magnification lens is useful. Garden culture and performance are similar.

T. rochebrunianum grows 3–5' tall and bears pale purple flowers similar to *T. delavayi*. The common name is lavender mist and it is often sold under that name. The stems are thicker than *T. delavayi* and plants are self supporting.

-minus (my' nus)		Lesser Meadow-rue	12–24"/24"
Summer	Yellow	Europe, Asia	Zones 3–7

(Syn. *T. adiantifolium*)

This species is particularly variable and consists of many races (a group of plants from the same species but with slightly different properties; a race comes true from seed) to which over 200 different specific names have been given. Names such as *T. babingtonii*, *T. foetidus*, *T. kochii*, *T. majus*, and most commonly *T. adiantifolium* have been applied to this species.

In general, the leaflets are three lobed and look like those of the maidenhair fern, *Adiantum pedatum*. The ½" wide flowers are borne in loose panicles with spreading branches. The greenish sepals abscise rapidly and the yellow color of the flower is the result of the slender stamens. The roots are stoloniferous but plants are not invasive. The plant is best grown for the elegant foliage and not the rather inconspicuous flowers.

Cultivars:

var. *adiantifolium* is the best form. Because of the variability within the species, the foliage can range from minute to the size of a half dollar. Plants of this description will at least have maidenhair-like foliage.

Propagate good forms vegetatively by division. Seed-propagated plants will vary.

-speciosissimum (spee-cee-o-sis' i-mum)   Dusty Meadow-rue   3–5'/4'
Summer   Yellow   Southern Europe   Zones 5–8

(Syn. *T. glaucum*, *T. flavum* var. *glaucum*)

The beauty of the species is in the blue-green foliage as well as the bright yellow panicles. Good sized clumps form within 2–3 years as a result of the stoloniferous roots. The 1½" wide leaflets and leaves are useful in floral decorations and plants are worth growing for the foliage alone. The flowers, consisting of pale yellow sepals and bright yellow, slender protruding stamens, are held in an upright compact 2–4" wide pyramidal panicle and have a faint but pleasant odor. Plants are often sold under the name of *T. glaucum* because of the foliage.

The species is more heat tolerant than others and worth growing in the South. Plant in rich, moist soil in partial shade.

Divide the plant when needed or raise from seed.

Related Species:

T. flavum, yellow meadow-rue, bears yellow flowers but the foliage does not have the glaucous characteristic found in *T. speciosissimum*.

Quick Key to Thalictrum Species

   A. Plants less than 12" tall, flowers yellow .... *T. minus*
  AA. Plants taller than 12", flowers yellow or lilac
     B. Flowers lilac
       C. Foliage blue-green, flowers held in a tight many-
         flowered fluffy panicle............................ *T. aquilegifolium*
      CC. Foliage green, flowers in a loose, airy pyramidal panicle............
                                         T. delavayi
     BB. Flowers yellow....................................... *T. speciosissimum*

Thermopsis (ther-mop' sis)   False Lupine   Fabaceae

The genus is well named, coming from *thermos*, lupin, and *opsis*, like. The flowers in all but one or two of the 20 species are yellow and similar in shape to the lupine. The compound leaves consist of 3 palmately arranged leaflets and 2 smaller leaf-like stipules. Occasionally they may be confused with the closely

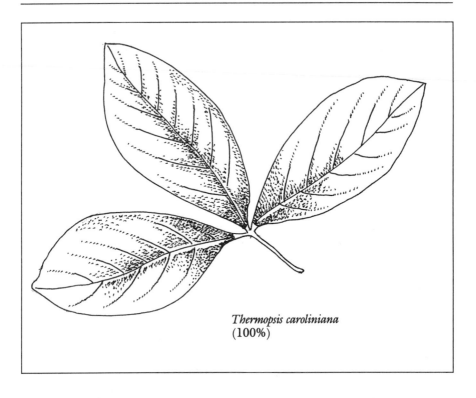

Thermopsis caroliniana
(100%)

related *Baptisia*, however, the foliage of most *Baptisia* species is blue-green and the seed pods are inflated. In *Thermopsis*, the foliage is green and the seed pods flat. A number of species are native to the United States and may be used to provide lupin-like flowers where lupins do not perform well.

Quick Reference to Thermopsis Species

	Height (in.)	Flower color
T. caroliniana	30–48	Yellow
T. lupinoides	9–12	Yellow
T. montana	12–24	Yellow

-caroliniana (ka-ro-lin-ee ay' na)	Southern Lupine	30–48"/48"
Spring	Yellow	Eastern United States	Zones 3–9

This is surely one of the most overlooked garden plants. The blue-green leaves are divided into 3 obovate leaflets, each 2–3" long and finely hairy beneath. The bright yellow, pea-like flowers emerge in late March in the South, 2–3 weeks later in the North, and remain colorful for 3–4 weeks. They are held in compact, erect 6–12″ long racemes. On a three-year-old clump at the University of Georgia, over 30 flower stems were produced.

Plant in partial shade in the South, full sun in the North. The flower stalks are a little longer under shade and plants may require support. The foliage should be cut back about a month after flowering as it declines rapidly, particularly in dry situations.

Cultivars:

'Album' is a more compact (2½′ tall) and more uncommon cultivar with creamy white flowers.

Seed propagation is the best means of increasing numbers and fresh seed germinates well. Older seed requires a scarification treatment for uniform germination. Treatment with sulphuric acid is effective but should only be undertaken by trained personnel (i.e. someone with experience in a seed laboratory). Division is more difficult as plantlets do not transplant well and require significant time to recover.

Related Species:

T. montana, mountain thermopsis, is the western cousin of *T. caroliniana*. It is 12–24″ tall, has a shorter (up to 8″ long), less dense raceme, and bears linear-lanceolate leaflets compared with obovate leaflets of *T. caroliniana*. Some authors claim it is invasive in rich soils but I have not noticed a problem. Hardy in zones 3–7.

-lupinoides (loo-peen-oi′ deez)	Lanceleaf Thermopsis	9–12″/18″
Spring	Yellow	Alaska, Siberia	Zones 2–7

(Syn. *T. lanceolata*)

Small stature and sessile, silky hairy leaves differentiate this species from the previous. Plants form 1–2′ wide clumps but are not at all invasive. The bright yellow flowers appear whorled and are held in a terminal upright raceme well above the foliage. The strongly recurved pods are unique and provide one of the identifying characteristics of the species.

Place in full sun or partial shade, particularly if planted south of zone 6. Native to northern locales, it is not as tolerant of heat as the previous species. This is a good, if not spectacular, plant in the right climate.

Propagate by seed or by division. Although division is possible, months are necessary for the plants to recover.

Quick Key to Thermopsis Species

    A. Plants less than 18″ tall, pods recurved .... *T. lupinoides*
  AA. Plants greater than 18″ tall, pods straight
        B. Leaflets ovate to obovate, raceme dense .... *T. caroliniana*
     BB. Leaflets linear to linear-lanceolate, racemes loose .... *T. montana*

Tiarella (tee-a-rel' a) Foamflower Saxifragaceae

Approximately 6 species occur; 5 are native to North America and 1 to Asia. Foamflower is an ideal evergreen, white-flowering ground cover for the shaded garden and can be spectacular in mass plantings. They are excellent low maintenance plants and should be more widely planted.

Quick Reference to Tiarella Species

	Height (in.)	*Leave shape*	*Stoloniferous (Y or N)*
T. *cordifolia*	6–12	Simple	Yes
T. *trifoliata*	9–20	Trifoliate	No

-cordifolia (kor-di-fo' lee-a) Allegheny Foamflower 6–12"/24"
Spring White Eastern North America Zones 3–8

Each 3–4" wide, heart-shaped leaf consists of 3 to 5 lobes. The evergreen foliage has burgundy variegation along the veins most noticeable in the spring and fall and often turns completely bronze during the winter. Foliage is similar to *Heuchera americana*, American alumroot, in this respect although significant

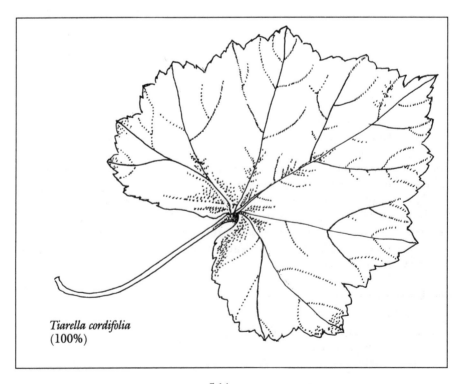

Tiarella cordifolia
(100%)

differences in flowers occur. Delicate pink-tinged flower buds gracefully evolve into starry creamy white flowers on 3–4" long racemes. The ¼" wide flowers consist of sepals about ½ as long as the petals, 10 stamens with brown anthers, and remain in flower for about 6 weeks. Plants are stoloniferous and rapidly form large masses.

Plants are effective with other shade and moisture tolerant species such as trilliums, woodland phlox, false Solomon's-seal, or Christmas fern.

Tiarella requires moisture retentive, highly organic soils in medium to heavy shade. Dry soils or exposure to full sun results in anemic, scrawny plants which never fill out. Soils may be enriched with organic matter such as well-rotted oak leaves.

Cultivars:

var. *albiflora* has whiter flowers than the species because of the white rather than brown anthers.

var. *purpurea* has handsome leaves that remain bronze for a longer period of time. The flowers are pale pink to rose.

Propagate from seed or division. Seed should be shallowly sown in early spring in a protected area such as a cold frame. Transplant seedlings to 3–4" containers in 6–8 weeks.

Related Species:

var. *collina* (*T. wherryi*), Wherry's foamflower, differs in subtle ways. The plant is taller and, unlike the stoloniferous *T. cordifolia*, is a clump-forming species. Upon close inspection, one notices that the anthers are yellowish orange rather than brown as in *T. cordifolia*. It is equally attractive and ornamental. Plants have performed well in zone 8. Propagate by spring division.

-trifoliata (tri-fo' lee-ah-ta)		Three Leaved Foamflower	9–20"/24"
Spring	White	Western North America	Zones 4–7

This species is almost unknown in gardens in the United States, although native to the Pacific Coast. Instead of simple lobed leaves, the foliage consists of three leaflets (trifoliate). The middle one has three lobes and the laterals two. The leaflets provide a more delicate appearance than the previous species, but the lovely bronze tint found in other species is not present in *T. trifoliata*. The flowers are minute, consisting of thread-like petals held in long, narrow panicles. Plants are less tolerant of heat and humidity than previous species and less suitable to gardens east of the Rockies. Seed is the best means of propagation. Propagate similar to *T. wherryi*.

Quick Key to Tiarella Species

    A. Leaves simple
        B. Plants stoloniferous, form mats, anthers brown .... *T. cordifolia*

BB. Plants not stoloniferous, form clumps, anthers yellowish orange........
T. *cordifolia* var. *collina*
AA. Leaves trifoliate... *T. trifoliata*

Tigridia (ti-gri' dee-a) Tiger Flower Iridaceae

All 30 species of this colorful genus are native to South and Central America. Only the showiest species, *T. pavonia*, however, is commonly offered for sale. Bulbs are consistently winter hardy south of zone 8, but must be treated similar to gladioli in the rest of the country. Plants are a fascinating addition to any bulb collection and should be tried at least once. Plants are 20–24″ tall with a fan of basal leaves and 2–3 stem leaves. Flowers are 4–6″ wide and their riot of color and shape is almost indescribable. They are red, orange, yellow, or white and variously blotched with red or yellow in the center. The flower, which opens in early July in the South and as late as early September in the North, consists of 3 large outer segments and 3 smaller inner segments surrounding the speckled cup-like center. The flowers persist but a day (another common name is one-day lily), but the succession of bloom lasts for 2–4 weeks.

Plant 3–4″ deep in rich well-drained soils in full sun. The best cultural method is to treat as annuals, replacing the bulbs each year. Although the foliage returns each year in zones 7 and 8, few flowers appear. Digging bulbs every fall and separating the bulbils is possible, but their relatively low cost justifies spring replacement.

Cultivars:

Generally they are only available as a mixture of colors but a few varieties may be obtained from specialists.

var. *alba immaculata* bears white flowers with centers free of spots. A number of cultivars are available without the spots in the center and all bear the "immaculata" name. This is such an exotic looking flower, growing an un-spotted form is like raising a spotless leopard.

Tovara (to-vah' ra) Tovara Polygonaceae

Named for the Spanish physician, Simon Tovar, plants are used as tall ground covers or edging. The genus consists of 2 species with inconspicuous flowers and is sometimes listed under *Polygonum*.

-virginianum (vir-jin-ee-aye' num) Virginia Tovara 2–4'/6'
Summer Brownish green Eastern North America Zones 4–7

(Syn. *Polygonum virginianum*)

The pure green-leaved species is seldom seen but the green and white varie-gated form, 'Variegata', is handsome. The elliptical 4–10″ long leaves are slow to emerge in the spring but clothe the plants in dense green and white by early summer. Plants should be protected from the wind as leaves are damaged easily. In rich, moist soils and partial shade, tovara spreads rapidly and can become a nuisance if planted close to non-aggressive species.

Cultivars:

'Painter's Palette' is similar to 'Variegata' but has a V-shaped reddish-pink blotch in the center of each leaf. The new leaves are creamy white and touched with light green and pink. A superior cultivar.

Propagate by division in spring or fall.

Tradescantia (tra-des-kant' ee-a)   Spiderwort   Commelinaceae

Approximately 100 species of tender and hardy plants are named after John Tradescant, the English horticulturist and botanist. He received a plant from a friend in Virginia which was subsequently named *Tradescantia virginiana* by Linneaus. The genus commemorates both father and son, Tradescant the Younger, who travelled to Virginia in 1637 and brought back to England such staples as Virginia creeper and Michaelmas daisies. Tradescant the Elder became gardener to Charles I in 1629 and was followed by his son after his death in 1638. Some of the better known species of *Tradescantia* are known as wandering jew, and are indoor plants only, or occasionally used in the South as an annual creeping ground cover.

Several ornamental species native to the United States occur. *T. hirsuticaulis* is a compact species (18–24" tall) with dark purple flowers somewhat hidden in the light green, strap-like foliage. *T. ohiensis*, has 3' tall stems which bear light blue flowers about 1" across. Although these species are occasionally seen in gardens, only *T.* × *andersoniana*, usually offered under the old name of *T. virginiana* is commonly available.

-× *andersoniana* (an-der-son-ee-aye' na)	Spiderwort	1–2'/3'
Summer	Variable	Hybrid	Zones 4–9

(Syn. *T. virginiana*)

Most of the garden cultivars of spiderwort resulted from hybridization among *T. ohiensis*, *T. subaspera*, and *T. virginiana*. The dense, dull green, linear foliage is 18" long and declines after flowering. Many flower buds are formed in terminal umbels and although each flower opens for one day, flowering continues for 8 weeks. The flower parts occur in threes; 3 sepals, 3 petals, and 6 stamens form the 1–3" diameter flower. They usually occur in blue to purple hues but pink, white, and red-flowered cultivars are available.

Plant in full sun in any well-drained garden soil. Plants grow well, but produce fewer flowers, in partial shade. Divide to rejuvenate the clump every 2 to

3 years. When the foliage declines, cut back to 8–12″. New foliage reappears in the fall.

Cultivars:

Blue and purple flowers:

'Bluestone' bears mid blue flowers.

var. *caerulea plena* has double dark blue flowers.

'Isis' has Oxford-blue 3″ diameter flowers. This is one of the best of the blue cultivars.

'J.C. Weguelin' is an excellent, vigorous cultivar with 2½″ wide China-blue flowers.

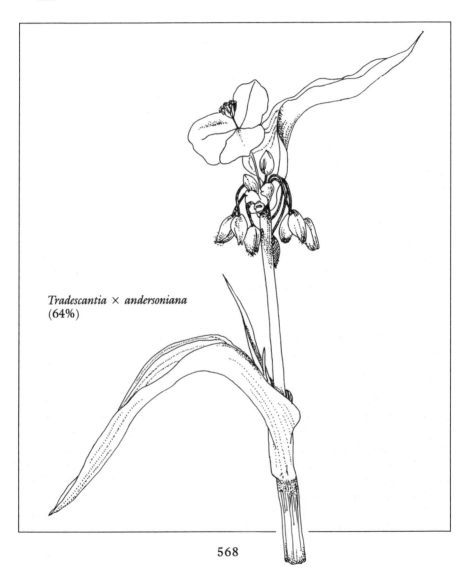

Tradescantia × *andersoniana* (64%)

'Leonora' has violet-blue flowers on 18″ tall plants.
'Pauline' bears lilac flowers about 2–2½″ wide.
'Purple Dome' stands about 2′ tall and is laden with flowers of rich purple.
'Valor' is 18–24″ tall and bears crimson-purple flowers.
'Zwanenburg Blue' bears 3″ wide, deep blue flowers.

Carmine and red flowers:
'Carmine Glow' has deep carmine flowers
'Pauline' offers flowers described as orchid-pink.
'Purewell Giant' bears flowers between deep rose and purple.
'Red Cloud' has rosy red blooms on 2′ tall plants. One of the best cultivars available.

White flowers:
'Innocence' has large creamy white flowers.
'Iris Pritchard' bears pure white flowers suffused with violet.
'Osprey' has large blue feathery stamens which contrast well with the large white flowers.
'Snowcap' is probably the purest white form with 2½–3″ wide flowers.

Propagate all cultivars by division in spring or fall.

Additional Reading:

Miller, Heather. 1983. *Tradescantia. Horticulture* 61 (6):20–21.

Tricyrtis (tri-ser′ tis)   Toad-lily   Liliaceae

The toad-lilies have a particular personality difficult to explain. Gardeners often grow them because they are unusual rather than showy. The flowers never fail to elicit conversation and their curious beauty should be admired close up. When pointing out a toad-lily, I can almost guarantee that you will be asked the origin of the common name. A name like toad-lily doesn't easily slip through the conversation unnoticed. The name probably came from their spotted flowers; however, with the discovery of *T. imeldae*, (named after the former first lady of the Phillipines), on Mindanao in the Phillipines, a more descriptive account was provided. The area where this species was found is occupied by the Tasaday tribe, who rub the juice from the flowers and leaves on their hands before setting out to collect frogs; apparently it is considered attractive to frogs and makes them less slippery. Perhaps they should be called frog-lilies.

Several species form compact clumps, although some are stoloniferous and form large patches. They grow up to 3′ tall with arching stems. The flowers are terminal or, more often, occur in the axils of the leaves. They open in the fall when few other plants are in flower and continue for at least 6 weeks. Flowers of most species are shades of purple but those of *T. macrantha* are primrose yellow. A well-grown clump of *Tricyrtis* has few equals in the fall garden.

569

Quick Reference to Tricyrtis Species

	Height (in.)	Roots stoloniferous	Base of leaves clasping the stems
T. formosana	1–2'	Yes	No
T. hirta	2–3'	No	Yes

-formosana (for-mo' sah-na)   Formosa Toad-lily   1–2'/2'
Late Summer   Lilac   Taiwan   Zones 4–9

(Syn. *T. stolonifera*)

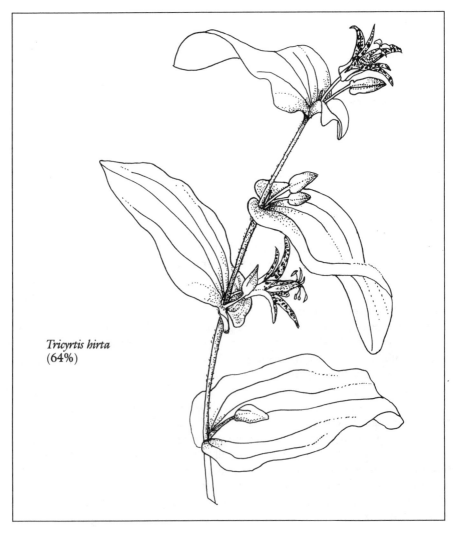

Tricyrtis hirta
(64%)

This species is not as well known as the next but is becoming more popular. Often listed as *T. stolonifera*, recent studies have shown that *T. formosana* and *T. stolonifera* are the same. The base of the leaves of the species narrows to a tubular sheath rather than being wrapped around the stem as in *T. hirta*. However, most plants grown as *T. formosana* have a semi-clasping leaf base indicating some degree of hybridization with *T. hirta*. The leaves are 4–5" long and about 1" wide with widely spaced internodes. The leaves are hairy on the undersides, particularly along the veins. The flowers are held in terminal cymes and open over a long period. Although borne in the terminals first, flowers subsequently appear in the upper 4 to 6 leaf axils. They are funnel shaped, about an inch long and ½" wide. The background color is white to slightly pinkish and the interior is prominently spotted red with a small yellow eye in the center. The filaments and styles are spotted crimson. Overall, it is a most interesting flower. In north Georgia (zone 8), flowers open the second week of September and persist until frost. The roots are stoloniferous and if grown in moist, semi-shady conditions, a large colony develops in 3–5 years. It is not, however, invasive. This is the best garden species because of the flower size, color, and longevity.

Cultivars:

var. *amethystina* has bluish purple flowers with a white throat spotted with red. It opens earlier than the species, flowering in the South from late July until frost. Recently introduced by John Elsley of Wayside Gardens, it is not yet common in cultivation. Plants do not seem to be as cold tolerant and are listed to zone 6, however, with additional testing in northern states, the variety may prove as cold hardy as the species.

var. *stolonifera* is similar to the species but grows to 3½' tall. It bears paler flowers with fewer spots on the petals.

Division is the propagation method of choice, accomplished in early spring. Seed may also be sown in a cold frame in the fall or early spring. Plants require about 5 months to reach transplantable size.

-hirta (hir' ta)		Common Toad-lily		2–3'/2'
Late Summer	Lilac		Japan	Zones 4–8

The common species has 2–3' long gracefully arching stems. The stems carry many closely-set, clasping, soft-hairy pointed leaves about 3–6" long and 1–2" wide. In each leaf axil, one to three 1" diameter flowers, which typically have a whitish or pale purple background covered with darker purple spots and blotches, are carried on short stalks (pedicels). Flowers also occur at the end of the stems. Flowering begins in mid-September in the South, a week or two later in the North, but are not as persistent as *T. formosana*. In our gardens, flowering was completed by mid-October whereas the flowers of *T. formosana* continued for an additional 3 weeks. The roots are not stoloniferous and large clumps do not form, however, there has been some hybridization between this and *T. formosana*. Moist, fertile soil in partial shade is ideal.

Cultivars:

var. *alba* has pure white flowers with pink stamens.

var. *masamunei* has leaves without hairs but otherwise is similar to the species. It is seldom seen in gardens.

'Miyazaki' appears to be a hybrid between *T. hirta* and *T. formosana* with graceful arching stems and lovely axillary flowers which open in early fall. Also introduced by Wayside Gardens.

Divide in the early spring while plants are still dormant. Seed propagation is similar to *T. formosana*. Seeds collected from garden plants may not be true if other species are grown nearby.

Additional Reading:

Mathew, Brian. 1985. A review of the genus *Tricyrtis*. *The Plantsman* 6 (4):193–224.

Quick Key to Tricyrtis Species

    A. Flowers mainly in axils, plants not stoloniferous, lower leaf
        bases clasping stem .... *T. hirta*
    AA. Flowers mainly terminal, plants stoloniferous, lower leaf bases
        not clasping stem .... *T. formosana*

Trillium (tril-lee′ um)   Trillium   Liliaceae

Trilliums, especially *T. grandiflorum*, are the epitome of the American wild flower. They are cherished in woodlands and most species should remain there and not in the border. Although the thirty species of trilliums are spectacular to wildflower enthusiasts, few are useful as garden plants.

The species are divided by the presence or absence of a flower stalk (pedicel). Those without such a structure are interesting to the plantsman, but not exceptional to the gardener. Two species of this group are *T. sessile*, with purplish flowers sitting atop a whorl of dark green leaves, and *T. cuneatum*, toad trillium, with similar brownish red flowers and mottled foliage. Barrie Crawford (*For the Love of Wildflowers*) states that it is a plant "that seems hard to love" whose "brown flowers are totally unappealing". I must agree. The flowers of the yellow trillium, *T. luteum*, are more ornamental but also squat on a leafy throne. This does not say that the above group does not have many admirers, and to the trillium lover, there is no such thing as a bad trillium.

Species whose flowers are held by pedicels are generally showier than those whose flowers are sessile. However, the flowers of some species in this group are held beneath the foliage and as my colleague Dr. Michael Dirr states, "only toads could love or see them". Some garden worthy species include the foul-smelling purple trillium, *T. erectum*, and the lovely *T. stylosum* (*T. catesbaei*), nodding wake-robin, whose nodding pink or white flared flowers are hidden beneath the large green leaves. The most ornamental is great white trillium or wake-robin, *T. grandiflorum*, and although other species are interesting plants for the wild flower garden, this defines the genus. When provided with rich soil, moisture and shade, it is truly spectacular.

-grandiflorum (grand-i-flor′ um)		Great White Trillium	18–24″/2′
Spring	White, pink	Eastern North America	Zones 4–9

Every time I read about the species, I find another common name listed. It is known as wake-robin, showy trillium, snow trillium, wood lily, great white trillium, and trinity flower. Plants occur as far northeast as Quebec, west to Minnesota, southwest to Missouri and south to Florida. The sessile leaves are often wavy and may be up to 6″ long, although 3–4″ is more common. The flowers consist of 3 large flaring petals with wavy edges subtended by 3 smaller greenish sepals. The 2–3″ wide flower usually opens white then fades to a soft pink. About 6–8 weeks after flowering, round berries are produced. Foliage persists only to late summer, particularly if plants are allowed to dry out regularly.

Rhizomes should be planted approximately 4″ deep in highly organic, moist, well-drained soils in partial to heavy shade. Soils should be neutral to slightly acidic. The addition of well-rotted compost such as aged manure or rotted leaves results in more rapid growth and larger plants. Interplant with other species of trilliums or with hepaticas, wild gingers, bloodroot or native ferns. If plants are stressed due to poor soil or lack of shade, they will rapidly perish.

This is the most ornamental trillium and the most abused flower of the woods. More plants have been dug from the woods, the majority dying, than all other wild flowers combined. This may have made some sense at one time when few nurseries propagated wild flowers but today this species is offered by many mail order and local nurseries for a reasonable price. Unfortunately a few disreputable nurseries still dig from the wild. Nature takes years to build up a colony but man requires only five minutes and a shovel to destroy it.

Cultivars:

var. *roseum* is a beautiful pink-flowered form which is absolutely magnificent. I remember first seeing it in the garden of Mrs. Gertrude Wister in Swarthmore, PA., one of the finest shade gardens anywhere, here or abroad. Colonies of pink trilliums shone like rosy beacons from the beds of green throughout the garden. Some authorities feel this form is simply a variation of natural flower color and should not be treated as a separate variety.

'Flore-pleno', a double form, is beloved or disliked with equal fervor. Some find the flowers unobtrusive and charming while others feel the doubleness reduces the natural charm of the plant and replaces it with artificiality. A handsome plant.

Propagation by seed is a long process, generally taking up to 8–12 months for germination and 2 to 3 years to produce a flowering plant. The seeds should be inspected as the berries ripen (about 5–6 weeks after flowers open). Seeds are mature when they are a dark or russet color and should be sown immediately. Sow in a moist medium and allow the seed flat to overwinter in a protected area. Germination occurs the next spring. If seeds are purchased they will be dormant and much slower to germinate. Eight years for germination have been reported. Removing the soil around the base of the plant and cutting a V-shaped groove along the length of the rhizome causes the production of bulblets which may be removed one year later. The wound should be dusted with fungicide prior to replanting.

Additional Reading:

Phillips, Harry R. 1985. *Growing and Propagating Wild Flowers*. The University of North Carolina Press, Chapel Hill, NC. 331 pp. This excellent text deals with many aspects of American wild flowers and is a must for all gardeners interested in use and propagation of native plants. The section on *Trillium* is particularly informative.

Trollius (tro'lee-us)   Globeflower   Ranunculaceae

About 20 species are native to Europe, Asia, and North America and all are suited to moist, heavy soils. They are not tolerant of heat or drought and perform poorly south of zone 6. However, where cool, moist soils exist, *Trollius* is not difficult to grow in sun or partial shade. If this condition is fulfilled, plants may succeed as far south as zone 7. The dark green foliage is palmately divided or lobed and often declines by mid- to late summer. The foliage of most species should be pruned at that time. The orange to yellow solitary flowers consist of showy sepals. The small petals are found in the midst of the stamens and their size relative to the stamens is a useful identification characteristic.

Propagate by division in late fall or early spring. A year is often necessary for plants to recover and flowering is reduced the first year after division. Fresh, ripe seed obtained from flowering plants requires approximately 3 weeks to germinate although germination will probably be less than 40%. Purchased or old seeds require over a year to germinate, if they germinate at all, and 5% germination is not uncommon.

Quick Reference to Trollius Species

	Height (in.)	Flower color	Sepals spreading or rolled in
T. × *cultorum*	24–36	Orange, yellow	Rolled In
T. *europaeus*	20–24	Yellow	Rolled In
T. *ledebourii*	24–36	Orange	Spreading
T. *pumilus*	9–12	Yellow	Spreading

- × *cultorum* (kul-tor' um)   Hybrid Globeflower   2–3'/3'
Late Spring   Orange to Yellow   Hybrid origin   Zones 3–6

Plants grown under this name are hybrids among *T. europaeus*, *T. asiaticus*, and *T. chinensis*. All cultivars have showy globular, buttercup-yellow flowers consisting of layers of incurved petal-like sepals which eventually open to expose the many stamens. The leaves consist of 5–6 deeply cut lobes and are also ornamental. Cut back foliage in mid- to late summer.

Cultivars:

'Alabaster' is one of the more unusual globeflowers with cream-tinged flowers rather than the common yellow or orange. It is not as vigorous (2' tall) and flowers tend to lose their globe shape early.

'Canary Bird' bears tight, globe-shaped, light yellow flowers with a tinge of green.

'Commander-in-Chief' has deep orange, 2" wide flowers.

'Earliest of All' is one of the earliest of this group and flowers in early May. The flowers are pale orange-yellow.

'Etna' is vigorous, growing 3' tall with dark orange flowers.

'Fire Globe' ('Feuertroll') bears some of the deepest orange flowers.

'Goldquelle' is one of the most popular cultivars and produces 2½" wide pure yellow flowers. The many blossoms are long lasting and useful for cut flowers.

'May Gold' stands about 2' tall with 2½" diameter lemon-yellow flowers in early spring. This is one of the earliest cultivars to flower.

'Orange Princess' is an excellent choice for cut flowers. It has 2½–3" wide, deep orange flowers and grows only 2' tall.

'Pritchard's Giant' commonly reaches 3' in height. The medium yellow flowers are long lasting and retain their globe shape. This is also an excellent cut flower cultivar.

'Salamander' is similar to 'Fire Globe' with 2½" wide fiery orange flowers.

-*europaeus* (u-ro' pay-us)   Common Globeflower   20–24"/24"
Early Spring   Yellow   Northern Europe   Zones 4–7

The 1–2" diameter lemon-yellow globular flowers are usually borne singly or occasionally in 2's. Ten to fifteen sepals enclose the many stamens and the 5 small spatulate petals. The leaves are 5-parted and the leaflets are lobed and toothed. The lower leaves are petioled while those higher on the stem are sessile. This is a common garden plant in Europe and being planted more in the United States. Plants are more tolerant of dry soil than most others, although performance is still mediocre if soils dry out.

Cultivars:

'Superbus' is similar to the species but flowers more prolifically. It is more difficult to find the species in commerce than this cultivar.

-ledebourii (led-e-boor′ ee-eye)   Ledebour Globeflower   2–3′/2½′
Spring   Orange   Siberia   Zones 3–6

Plants are vigorous and heights of 3′ are not uncommon in well-grown specimens where soils are consistently moist. The leaves are deeply cut to the base and the leaflets lobed and toothed. The deep orange, cup-shaped flowers consist of 5 spreading sepals which readily display the many stamens and narrow, upright petals. The petals are more visible than those in the previous species and are about the same length as the stamens. It flowers approximately one week later than *T. europaeus*. These are magnificent plants for the shaded bog garden or other suitably moist area.

-pumilus (pew′ mi-lus)   Dwarf Globeflower   9–12″/12″
Spring   Yellow   Himalayas   Zones 4–6

This species is particularly suited to the rock garden or the front of the moist border. The stems are almost leafless and the 1–2″ wide basal leaves are 5-parted. Each leaflet is 3-lobed. The 1″ wide flowers consist of 5–6 notched stamens and 10–12 narrow petals about the same size as the stamens. Rich, moist well-drained soils snd afternoon shade are ideal. A lovely plant for small niches in the garden.

Related Species:

T. laxus, is native from New Hampshire to British Columbia, and easier to establish in the shady, moist garden than many of the foreigners. Plants are approximately 12″ tall and bear solitary 1–2″ diameter greenish yellow flowers (white to cream in var. *albiflorus*). Excellent plantings may be found in The Garden in the Woods in Framingham, Massachusetts.

Quick Key to Trollius Species

    A. Flowers globe shaped, at least when they emerge
        B. Petals usually exceeding stamens, flowers yellow to orange . . . .
                                  T. × *cultorum*
        BB. Petals equal to or a little shorter than stamens, flowers orange . . . .
                                    T. europaeus
  AA. Flowers spreading
        B. Petals much exceeding stamens, plant 2–3′ tall . . . . *T. ledebourii*
        BB. Petals about the same length or shorter than stamens, plant
            9–12″ tall . . . . *T. pumilus*

Tulipa (tew′ li-pa)   Tulip   Liliaceae

No plant heralds spring like the tulip. Although gardeners are deluged with advertisements in newspapers and garden centers for hybrid tulips each fall, it is well worth remembering that over 100 species are known and many are excellent garden plants. Tulips range in height from the 6″ tall Duc von Toc type to the stately 3′ tall stems of the Darwins, and flower from late March to late May. The garden tulip was introduced to Europe in 1572 by Ogier Ghiselin de Busbecq, Ambassador of the Holy Roman Empire to Suleiman the Magnificent of Turkey. At that time, great numbers of tulips existed in Turkey and in 1715, a list of 1,323 varieties appeared in a paper by Sheik Mohammed Lalizare in the reign of Ahmed III. In 1948, *The Classified List of Tulip Names*, published by a joint committee of the Tulip Nomenclature Committee in England and the General Dutch Bulb-Growers' Society included well over 4300 names. There are many more today.

All hybrid tulips and most species should be treated as biennials or short-lived perennials in this country. While this is not a particularly popular opinion, it is nevertheless true. Most tulips perform poorly the third year, worse the next year, and seldom "strut their stuff" by the fifth year. Unfortunately, this is difficult for many gardeners to understand. Most of my friends consider a bulb a perennial, which once planted, should return year after year. In their zeal for tulip perenniality, they tell me that their tulips look as good the third year as the first. I know that the quality of the tulip has not gone up, rather their standards have gone down. In the South, it is even more difficult to find tulips performing well for 2 or more years. Sufficient cold is not available to force the flower stalk to its potential height, high night temperatures reduce stored food in the bulb, and warm summer soils promote pests and diseases.

The depth of planting should be three times the diameter of the bulb, except in heavy clay soils, where shallow planting is more beneficial. In general, the depth of planting for most cultivars in average soils is about 5″. Plant in full sun in mid-September in zones 2–4, as late as early November in zones 7–8. Tulips should not be lined up like tin soldiers all in a row. Plant in bunches of at least 30, no more than 6″ apart, preferably bulb to bulb. If bulbs are left in the garden, the flowers must be removed before seed develops and leaves should be allowed to yellow prior to removal. Since the leaves provide food to the bulb, it makes little sense to tie the leaves up in elastic bands or string to "get them out of the way". To propagate, bulbs should be removed, cleaned and graded by size. The largest bulbs may be replanted and bulblets placed in a propagation bed where they grow and mature. Three years are required to produce a mature bulb from a small bulblet.

The most recent reorganization of the genus provides 23 different classes of tulips, many of minor importance in this country and some almost impossible to find. The following is a summary of the classification used for garden tulips and a few corresponding cultivars. There are literally thousands of cultivars; those mentioned are typical of their classification.

Classification	Comments	Cultivars
Duc van Tol	Very early, rarely exceeding 6″	—

Classification	Comments	Cultivars
Single	Early. Derived from *T. ges-neriana* and *T. suaveolens*, 12–14″ tall, usually fragrant, flower in April and early May.	'Bellona', 'Diana', 'Princess Irene', 'General de Wet'
Double Early	10–12″ tall, flower late April	'Electra' 'Peach Blossom'
Mendel	Derived from Duc von Tol and Darwin tulips. Less than 18″ tall, bloom in mid-May.	'Apricot Beauty', 'Olga', 'Pink Trophy'
Triumph	Derived from single early and Darwin tulips. About 2′ tall, bloom in mid-May	'First Lady', 'Merry Widow', 'Pink Glow'
Darwin	Short, rounded petals, flower almost rectangular in outline. Up to 3′ tall, flower mid- to late May.	'Aristocrat', 'Golden Age', 'Mamsa', 'Pink Supreme'
Darwin Hybrids	Derived from Darwins and *T. fosteriana*. Grow less than 2′ tall, have largest flowers of all classes, bloom late April to mid-May.	'Apeldoorn', 'Big Chief', 'Golden Parade', 'Orange Sun', 'Parade'
Lily-Flowered	Derived from *T. retroflexa* and cottage tulips. Flowers have pointed, reflex petals. About 2′ tall, May flowering.	'Aladdin', 'Red Shine', 'West Point', 'White Triumphator'
Cottage	Have egg-shaped blooms, grow 20 to 30″ tall. Late, single tulips.	'Halcro', 'Maureen', 'Mrs. J. Scheepers'
Rembrandt	Darwin tulips with streaks on petals	'American Flag', 'Union Jack'
Parrot	Have feather-like petals, usually in colorings of red, orange, blue, and green. Flower with Darwins.	'Black Parrot', 'Blue Parrot', 'Fantasy', 'Flaming Parrot'
Double Late	Bear peony-like flowers in May. Grow 16–24″ tall.	'Eros', 'Gold Medal', 'Orange Triumph'

Classification	Comments	Cultivars
	Blooms are up to 4″ across and long lasting.	
Fosteriana	Derived mainly from *T. fosteriana*, hybrids have broad gray-green leaves and bear 4″ wide flowers on 12″ tall stems in March/April.	'Candela', 'Canopus', 'Red Emperor', 'White Emperor'
Greigii hybrids	Leaves heavily mottled and striped with purple. Bears large flowers, with black base on 9″ stems in April/May. Useful for foliage effect alone.	'Plaisir', 'Prima Donna', 'Oriental Splendor', 'Red Riding Hood'
Kaufmanniana	Known as the water-lily tulip, hybrids one of the earliest to bloom. Short (4–8″) stems useful for rockery or exposed positions.	'Gaiety', 'Heart's Delight', 'Stressa', 'Tartini'
Bouquet	Multi-flowered tulips, each 2′ tall stem bears 3–5 flowers. Derived mainly from *T. praestans*.	'Georgette', 'Orange Bouquet', 'Toronto'

Other Species

T. acuminata	Known as the horned tulip, has narrow pointed petals, May flowering	'Fireflame'
T. clusiana	Known as Lady tulip, 9–12″ long. White flowers striped with red, April flowering.	'Candycane'
T. praestans	Multi-flowered, 12–18″ tall. Flowers in shades of red open in late April to early May.	'Fusilier', 'Tubergen's Var.', 'Zwanenburg'
T. tarda	Flowers in March, 6–9″ tall. Bears up to 5 white flowers with yellow eye per stem. Rock garden.	—

V

Vancouveria (vang-koo-ve′ ree-a)   Vancouveria   Berberidaceae

Three species of ground-hugging plants are native to woodlands of the northwest United States. They are similar to *Epimedium* but have 6 stamens and petals rather than 4. If cool, moist conditions can be provided, they are useful ground covers for areas with light shade.

-hexandra (heks-an′ dra)   American Barrenwort   10–12″/12″
Early Summer   White   Washington to California   Zones 5–7

Each 2–3″ long leaf is 2 or 3 times ternately (in threes) compound resulting in carpets of fern-like foliage that die to the ground in the fall. The white, ½″ long flowers have reflexed sepals and petals and are held in 10–20-flowered panicles at the end of a leafless flower stem.

Plants spread by slender, underground rhizomes in cool, moist, acidic, organic soils. They are difficult to establish in areas of hot, dry summers. Although the flowers are showier, it is not as tough as *Epimedium*.

Related Spcies:

V. chrysantha, golden vancouveria, has ½″ long yellow flowers held in a few flowered panicle on 12″ tall plants. Native to southern Oregon and northern California.

V. planipetala, redwood ivy, has white flowers sometimes tinged lavender. This species and the previous are evergreen, prefer a pH around 5.0, and are more difficult to establish than *V. hexandra*.

Propagate by dividing the rhizome in spring or fall.

Veratrum (vay-rah′ trum)   False Hellebore   Liliaceae

This genus contains 18 species, although only *V. viride* is grown in the United States. Plants are not commonly offered by nurseries, thus *Veratrum* is not well known by the gardening public. The leaves, seeds and roots are poison-ous (all contain veratrine) and this unfortunate character flaw has also limited popularity. The leaves are particularly showy in the spring and are followed by tall panicles in the summer. The most common species, *V. viride*, Indian poke, has yellowish green flowers, but *V. album*, white false hellebore, and *V. califor-nicum*, California false hellebore, have whitish green flowers. *V. nigrum*, black false hellebore, produces dark purple flowers but is seldom available. The botan-ical name comes from *vere atrum*, truly black, in reference to the color of the roots.

-viride (vi' ri-dee)		Indian Poke	2–6'/2'
Summer	Yellow-green	North America	Zones 3–7

Native from New Brunswick to Georgia, and west to Oregon and Alaska, this wild flower is most impressive. The pleated, light green leaves are reminis-cent of hosta foliage as they emerge to form large arching mounds. The oval lower leaves are about 12″ long and clasp the stem with a long narrow sheath while the upper stem leaves become progressively smaller. The 18–24″ long flower stalks of broad, yellow-green flowers are reminiscent of a tall, green ver-bascum.

Plants are best in the spring as the fresh foliage emerges. Although the pan-icles are relatively large, I have trouble getting excited about green flowers. Moist soils are necessary; if allowed to dry out, the edges of the leaves turn brown. Protection from afternoon sun is helpful to maintain freshness of the foliage. *Veratrum* does not perform particularly well under the stress of high heat and humidity and is more suited for zones 4–6 than zones 7 and 8. In the spring, slug pellets or other deterrents keep the foliage tidy. Leaves of *Veratrum* and *Hosta* are gourmet treats for slugs.

Seedlings require a year before they can be transplanted and reach flowering size in 3 years. Seeds must be subjected to a warm-cold-warm stratification pe-riod. Sow seed in the fall and allow it to remain under snow cover or mulch until spring. See seed treatment for *Actaea*. Division in the fall or early spring is a more effective and faster means of propagation.

Verbascum (ver-bas' cum)   Mullein   Scrophulariaceae

When mullein is mentioned, most people think of the large, hairy roadside weed with small yellow flowers, *V. thapsus*. Few realize that this genus contains wonderful, more civilized garden brethren. *Verbascum* contains about 300 spe-cies, many are biennial and hybridize readily. Species range in height from the the 6″ high *V. dumulosum*, a vivid yellow-flowering plant that cascades over rocks and soil to the 6–8' tall Olympic mullein, *V. olympicum*, whose branched yellow racemes look down upon the rest of the garden members. *V. bombyci-ferum* is a spectacular biennial species with rosettes of 12–18″ long downy silvery-white leaves. With foliage like that, the rather ordinary yellow flowers

Verbascum chaixii
(64%)

are irrelevant. Hybridization has resulted in named selections, and availability of useful *Verbascum* hybrids is slowly increasing.

A few perennial species occur, all more or less tomentose (hairy), with soft alternate leaves. Flowers are generally yellow but occasionally purple- or white-flowered species occur.

Quick Reference to Verbascum Species

	Height (in.)	Flower color	Leaves gray-green
V. chaixii	2–3	Yellow	Yes
V. olympicum	3–5	Yellow	Yes
V. phoeniceum	2–4	Purple	No

-chaixii (shay' zee-eye)		Nettle-leaved Mullein	2–3'/3'
Late Spring	Yellow	Southern Europe	Zones 5–8

The stalked 3–6″ long basal foliage is wedge shaped at the base with round-toothed (crenate) margins. The upper leaves are sessile with rounded bases. Leaves are green or slightly whitish green and hairy. The ¾″ diameter yellow flowers are held in tall racemes, each blossom bearing purple, woolly stamens. The inflorescences are unbranched the first 2 years but are many-branched as plants mature.

Some authorities refer to this species as biennial, but it is perennial (although short lived) in most gardens. Well-drained soils in full sun are necessary for optimum performance. Spider mites find all verbascums particularly appealing and plants should be treated with miticides during the summer.

Cultivars:

var. *album* has white flowers but is otherwise similar to the species. The rose to purple stamens on the white backdrop of the petals give the flowers an attractive wine-pink hue. Flowers open about June 1 in zone 8 and bloom for approximately 4 weeks.

Seed germinates quickly under warm, moist conditions. Root cuttings may also be used for propagation. Take 3″ long root cuttings in late winter or early spring and insert them upright in equal parts of moist sand and peat. Place them at 60–70°F and transplant when 3 to 4 leaves have developed.

Related Species:

V. nigrum, dark mullein, has purple stamens, long pedicels and yellow flowers. The flowers, however, are only about ½″ across and the inflorescence is unbranched. It is one of the parents (with *V. spinosum*, spiny mullein) of 'Golden Bush', an upright 2–3' tall, yellow-flowered mullein which sends up multitudes of stems and flowers for 4–6 weeks.

-olympicum (o-lim' pi-cum)		Olympic Mullein	3–5'/4'
Summer	Yellow	Greece	Zones 6–8

This imposing, long-lived perennial requires good drainage, full sun and lots of space. Part of its appeal is the entire, white, woolly 6–8" long leaves that are attractive even when the plant is not in flower. They are arranged in basal rosettes up to 3' across. The 1" diameter flowers are bright yellow with white-bearded stamens and held in branched 2–3' tall panicles. Plants remain in flower for 6–8 weeks and if spent inflorescences are removed, they can reflower in the fall.

The more I see this species, the more I appreciate it. It is too tall and gangly to be called beautiful but is more than just interesting. Plants are constantly changing throughout the season and if provided with basic needs of moisture and sun, they will return for years and years. Fertilizer should be applied sparingly; plants grown in rich soils and treated too kindly reach heights of 7–8 feet.

Propagate by seed or root cuttings similar to *V. chaixii.*

-phoeniceum (foy-nee' see-um)		Purple Mullein	2–4'/2'
Spring	Purple, White	Southern Europe, Northern Asia	Zones 6–8

Dark green 18" diameter rosettes of crinkled, shallowly lobed foliage give rise to 8–10 unbranched racemes, each bearing 1" diameter rose-pink to purple flowers. Flowers are borne about 1 month earlier than those of *V. chaixii.* The leaves are smooth above and pubescent beneath. Plants can be quite variable and seedlings may yield flowers of purple, red , rose or white. Full sun and well-drained soils are best but plants tolerate afternoon shade, particularly in zone 8. If overfertilized, it can grow to four feet.

This is a fair garden plant for the South but terribly susceptible to spider mites. Although tolerant of drought, it has never been outstanding in my garden for the 5 years I have grown it. Flowers are fleeting, blooming for about two weeks, and then disappearing into anonymity.

Seed propagation of *V. phoeniceum* is easy under moist, warm (70–75°F) conditions. Flower color will vary.

Related Species:
V. × hybridum resulted from crosses between various vigorous species such as *V. olympicum* and *V. phoeniceum*. Many sterile-flowered forms with slightly tomentose foliage have resulted. Flowers occur in late spring to early summer and cutting back the spent flowers induces secondary inflorescences. Unfortunately, due to the biennial nature of the parents, they are short lived and only survive 2–4 years.

'Cotswold Gem' is 3–4' tall and bears racemes of rosy flowers with purple centers. A number of other 'Cotswold' cultivars have appeared including 'Cotswold Beauty', dull yellow with lilac stamens, and 'Cotswold Queen' which produces terra-cotta flowers with maroon stamens.

'Domino' is a popular plant in the United States and produces 1–1½" diameter rose-pink flowers on 3–3½' long stalks.

'Gainsborough' has pale sulphur-yellow flowers and gray-green leaves. It is about 3–4' tall but can reach 5' in rich soils.

'Hartleyi' sends up many shoots of large canary yellow flowers suffused with plum. A magnificent plant.

'Mt. Blanc' has foliage similar to 'Gainsborough' but bears white flowers.

'Silver Candelabra' bears 6' tall spikes of bright yellow flowers with silver woolly foliage.

Propagate hybrids by root cuttings similar to *V. chaixii*.

Quick Key to Verbascum Species

   A. Flowers not yellow.. *V. phoeniceum*
  AA. Flowers yellow
      B. Anthers purple, woolly leaves with rounded lobes, plant 2–
        3' tall .... *V. chaixii*
     BB. Anthers not purple, woolly leaves entire, plant 3–5' tall.. *V. olympicum*

Additional Reading:

Davis, Rosalie, H. 1986. Stalking the cultivated *Verbascum. Horticulture* 54(11): 22–25.

Verbena (ver-been' a)   Verbena   Verbenaceae

Verbena consists of approximately 200 species and 6 or 7 are in cultivation. The most common is the annual bedding plant, *V.* × *hybrida*, the result of hybridization of *V. peruviana, V. incisa, V. phlogifolia* and *V. platensis*. Demand for the annual is high and additional species are being incorporated into this stew every year. The perennial species are generally rose-purple, persistent bloomers, and hardy south of zone 6. Unfortunately, the annual hybrids so dominate the market that the perennial species are not commonly offered.

Plants generally have opposite, dentate foliage and terminal flowers. They perform best in well-drained soils in full sun.

Quick Reference to Verbena Species

	Height (in.)	Flower color	Upright or spreading
V. bonariensis	36–48	Violet	Upright
V. canadensis	8–18	Red, Pink	Spreading
V. rigida	12–24	Violet	Upright
V. tenuisecta	8–12	Purple	Spreading

-bonariensis (bo-nah-ree-en' sis)   Brazilian Verbena   3–4'/3'
Summer   Rose-violet   South America   Zones 7–9

    This is one of the taller verbenas and particularly effective in the middle of the border. It was named for the city of Buenos Aires, where first discovered. It has since become naturalized in the United States from South Carolina to Texas. The 4" long elliptical leaves are sessile and clasp the stem. They are sharply serrated above the middle and entire towards the base. The wiry stems are roughly hairy and conspicuously 4-angled. The flowers consist of 5 petals and a corolla tube nearly twice as long as the calyx. The individual flowers measure only about ¼" across but the entire panicle is 2" wide.

Verbena tenuisecta
(64%)

It is an excellent plant for southern gardens but needs to be massed in groups. If grown in rich soil or overfertilized, it can easily reach 4' and require severe pruning. Cutting back the plant results in a many-branched specimen which takes on a shrub-like habit. Once in flower, it remains in bloom until frost. A drawback, however, is the susceptibility to powdery mildew, which should be treated with appropriate chemicals beginning in June. Personally, I prefer not to spray for mildew and although the white spots are unsightly, the disease does not appear to reduce vigor.

Propagate from root cuttings in the spring similarly to *Anemone* × *hybrida*. Seed sown in moist media should be placed at 40°F for 3–4 weeks, after which time the tray may be moved to 60–70°F temperatures. Germination is erratic and seedlings appear over a 3–5 week period. Two to three inch long terminal cuttings of new spring growth may also be rooted and transplanted 3–5 weeks later.

-canadensis (kan-a-den' sis)		Clump Verbena	8–18"/36"
Summer	Red, Pink	North America	Zones 6–10

This species is usually treated as a annual in most of the country but is native from Virginia to Florida and west to Colorado and Mexico. The many-branched pubescent stems lie on the ground with the ends ascending (decumbent), and rooting occurs where the lower stems touch the soil. The deeply lobed ovate leaves are 1–3" long and about 1" wide with a triangular to wedge-shaped base. The rose-red to pink corolla tube is about twice as long as the calyx but each flower is only about ½" wide. Up to 20 flowers may be present on each of the spikes.

This species has an excellent clumping habit and may be cut back severely if the stems lose leaves or become too long. A sunny place in the border with excellent drainage is necessary. If drainage is poor, plant vigor declines rapidly and no amount of corrective surgery will improve its demeanor. Like other members of the genus, susceptibility to mildew and spider mites is a problem.

Cultivars:

'Gene Cline', named after plantsman Gene Cline of Canton, Georgia, is about 6–9" tall and bears deep rose flowers. An excellent ground cover for sunny, well-drained areas.

'Lavender' bears lavender flowers with a trace of white and 'Rosea' has bright rose-red blooms. Both grow 8–12" tall.

Seed and cutting propagation are similar to *V. bonariensis*.

Related Species:

V. peruviana, Peruvian verbena, hugs the ground and bears bright scarlet flowers. The leaves are not as incised or deeply cut as *V. canadensis*, nor are plants as tall or as winter hardy (zone 7–10).

-rigida (ri′ gi-da)		Rigid Verbena	12–24″/18″
Summer	Purple	Brazil, Argentina	Zones 8–10

(Syn. *V. venosa*)

This South American species has become naturalized from North Carolina to Florida, and Southern gardeners are taking advantage of the heat and drought tolerance and persistent flowering, continuing through mid-October in my garden. Tuberous roots are formed, which if mulched heavily in the fall, survive as far north as zone 7. The 4-angled stems, similar to those of *V. bonariensis*, bear oblong, rigid, sessile leaves. Each 2–4″ long leaf is roughly pubescent and has wide spreading teeth. The intense purple flowers are about ½″ wide and consist of a ½″ long corolla tube 2–3 times longer than the calyx.

In general, this plant looks like a miniature *V. bonariensis* with similar cultural and propagation requirements. An excellent front of the border species, it requires no pruning to maintain vigor or habit.

Cultivars:

'Flame' stands only 6″ tall and produces an abundance of scarlet flowers. It is more vigorous than the species and spreads more rapidly. It is likely a hybrid between *V. rigida* and a low-growing species such as *V. canadensis*.

Propagate similar to *V. bonariensis*.

-tenuisecta (ten-you-i-sec′ ta)		Moss Verbena	8–12″/spreader
Spring	Lavender	Southern South America	Zones 8–10

(Syn. *V. erinoides*)

Here is a plant which should be as common in the South as bedstraw in the North. Naturalized from Georgia to Louisiana and south to Florida, it flourishes by roadsides and in fields. Many decumbent stems bear triangular leaves about 1–1½″ long which are divided into linear segments. The spikes are terminal, solitary and composed of 5–15 small (½″ wide) lavender flowers. The flowers are about ½″ long and compactly arranged when they first open but elongate to 1″ or more as the flowers mature.

I first obtained terminal cuttings from south Georgia. Plants rooted in less than 2 weeks and 8 cuttings carpeted 20–30 square feet in the first 6 weeks. It has overwintered in zone 8 two years out of 4 and I take cuttings in the fall and overwinter them. Given sufficient protection, it may be considered hardy in zone 8. If plants become leggy, they may be sheared with a lawnmower to 2″ tall and they return as fresh as ever. If sheared too close to the ground, however, it will take a long time to fill in. For gardeners further north, it makes an excellent annual. Although not as colorful as the annual hybrids, plants require far less maintenance and provide better garden performance.

Cultivars:

'Alba' is similar to the species but bears white flowers. Not quite as vigorous but still a rapid grower.

Propagation is easy from 2–3" long terminal cuttings taken any time in the season. Rooting occurs in 5–8 days if cuttings are placed in a moist, warm area.

Quick Key to Verbena Species

A. Plant upright, flowers borne in panicles or cymes
   B. Plant 1–2' tall, corolla tube 2–3 times longer than calyx...... *V. rigida*
   BB. Plant 3–5' tall, corolla tube 1½ –2 times longer than calyx.............
   V. bonariensis
AA. Plant spreading, flowers borne in spikes
   B. Flowers lavender, purple, foliage cut into linear divisions..............
   V. tenuisecta
   BB. Flowers red, rose, foliage not cut into linear divisions .... *V. canadensis*

Veronica (ve-ron' i-ca)   Speedwell   Scrophulariaceae

There are about 250 species including a dozen herbaceous members suitable for the garden. The name *Veronica* is thought to have arisen because markings on the flowers of some species resemble the markings on the sacred handkerchief of St. Veronica. One species, *V. officinalis*, was substituted for tea in Europe until the nineteenth century.

Most species have opposite leaves, and flowers are usually held in racemes. In general, *Veronica* has blue flowers but *V. peduncularis* is a wonderful 8–12" tall species with white flowers tinged with rose. Species vary from the prostrate *V. repens*, creeping speedwell, to the 4' tall *V. longifolia*, long leaf speedwell. Identification among species is difficult and the length of the pedicel (individual flower stalk) in relation to the length of the sepals is a useful identification characteristic.

Full sun and well-drained soils are their only demands, otherwise they are relatively easy to grow. Significant variablility occurs in some species, particularly *V. teucrium*, Hungarian speedwell, and nursery catalogs may list the same cultivar under 2 or 3 different species.

Taxonomists don't agree on the placement of *V. virginica*, Culver's root. I have listed it as *Veronicastrum virginicum* and its description may be found there.

Quick Reference to Veronica Species

	Height (in.)	Flower color	Inflorescence terminal or axillary
V. alpina	4–8	Blue	Terminal
V. gentianoides	6–20	Pale Blue	Terminal

	Height (in.)	Flower color	Inflorescence terminal or axillary
V. incana	12–18	Blue	Terminal
V. longifolia	24–48	Lilac	Terminal
V. pectinata	3–6	Deep Blue	Axillary
V. prostrata	3–8	Blue	Axillary
V. spicata	10–36	Blue	Terminal
V. teucrium	6–20	Deep Blue	Axillary

-alpina (al-pine′ a)		Alpine Speedwell	4–8″/12″
Spring	Blue	Europe, Asia	Zones 3–8

This small, undemanding plant bears shiny green entire leaves about 1–1½″ long. The upper leaves are larger than the lower and all are elliptical to oblong. Plants spread by a creeping rootstock but are not rampant. The flowers are up to ¼″ across and held in a dense spike-like raceme. Each raceme persists for at least one week.

This plant performs as well in the heat of zone 8 as in the cool of zone 3. The flowers are borne in the spring and continue off and on again in September and October in the South. Plants are evergreen in the South but die back in the North. It is an excellent plant for the front of the border or for the rock garden.

Cultivars:

'Alba' is a white-flowered form which has essentially replaced the species in cultivation. It is vigorous and free flowering.

'Goodness Grows' is a long flowering hybrid which likely arose from *V. alpina* 'Alba' and *V. spicata* at Goodness Grows Nursery in Crawford, Georgia. It has the low-growing habit (10–12″) of the former and the long blue racemes of the latter.

Propagate by division in the spring or fall. Seed germinates quickly when sown in moist media and placed in warm humid conditions.

-gentianoides (gen-tee-a-noi′ deez)		Gentian Speedwell	6–20″/18″
Spring	Pale Blue	Caucasus	Zones 4–8

For reasons I do not comprehend, this species is seldom seen in American gardens. Flowering stems with small bract-like leaves rise above rosettes consisting of many entire 1–3″ long leaves. The ½″ wide, pale blue to almost white flowers are held in loose 10″ long racemes. It differs from most upright garden species in that the pedicel (the connecting stem between the flower and the raceme) is much longer than the sepals. Usually the pedicel is about the same size or shorter. When not in flower, the creeping rootstock forms dense mats of glossy foliage.

This useful plant suits the front to mid-border and is highly recommended for the rock garden because of its mat-forming tendencies. Full sun and well-drained soil should be provided. It is more tolerant of moist soils than other species and should not be allowed to dry out.

Cultivars:

'Variegata' has white-margined foliage but flowers are similar to the species. Splashes of white appear on the basal leaves and are not particularly obvious. The variegation is best on the small stem leaves where each margin is dressed in pure white.

Propagate similar to *V. alpina*.

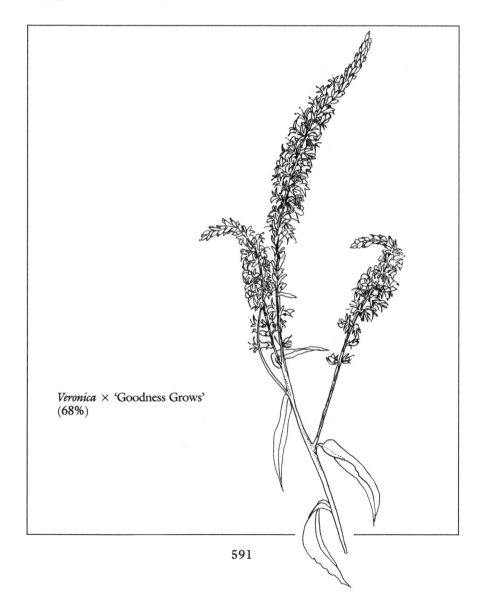

Veronica × 'Goodness Grows'
(68%)

-incana (in-kah' na)   Woolly Speedwell   12–18"/18"
Summer   Blue   Russia   Zones 3–7

This is one of the few veronicas grown for the foliage as well as the flowers. The 1–3" long toothed leaves are white-tomentose, resulting in an overall silvery-gray appearance. The lower leaves are matted and oblong while the uppermost are lanceolate; all are narrowed at the base. Small blue flowers (¼" across) are borne on short pedicels in 3–6" long terminal racemes and persist for about 4 weeks.

This popular edging plant provides good foliage contrast. Plants perform poorly in high heat and high rainfall areas because the hairy leaves trap moisture, resulting in foliar disease. Provide full sun to partial shade in well-drained soils. Plants particularly dislike wet, cold soils.

Cultivars:

var. *candidissima* has 6" long leaves that are not as tomentose as the species. Otherwise, plants are similar.
var *glauca* bears more silvery foliage and deeper blue flowers than the species.
'Rosea' has a pink tinge to the flowers.
'Saraband' is about 18" tall with compact gray-green leaves and dense racemes of violet-blue flowers. This is a hybrid with one of the forms of *V. spicata*.
'Wendy' is also a hybrid with *V. spicata* and bears grayish foliage and lavender-blue flowers. It grows 2' tall.

Divide the plants in spring or take 2" long terminal cuttings from the sterile basal branches during the summer. Sow the fine seed in a well-drained medium and barely cover. If seed is covered too deeply, germination is poor. After germination, reduce the temperature to approximately 60°F.

-longifolia (long-gi-fo' lee-a)   Long-leaf Veronica   24–48"/24"
Summer   Lilac   Europe, Asia   Zones 4–8

Heights of 2½' are average but 3½ to 4' tall plants occur in rich soils and warm climates. The stem is hairless or nearly so and the 2½–3" long leaves are sharply toothed and pointed. Leaves are oblong to lanceolate with slightly hairy undersides. The lower leaves are opposite but the uppermost are often arranged in whorls. The ¼" wide flowers are arranged in dense 12" long racemes. Flowering persists for 6–8 weeks.

This tall lanky plant is most effective in groups of three or more. If placed in too much shade or fed too generously, staking is required. This is more of a problem in the South than in the North. The species is native to moist areas and does poorly if soil is allowed to dry out.

Cultivars:

var. *alba* is 1½' tall and bears white flowers.
'Blue Giant' is 3–3½' tall with lavender-blue flowers.

'Foerster's Blue' stands 1–2' tall and produces deep blue flowers for 8 weeks in the summer.

var. *glauca* has deep purple flowers and blue-green foliage.

'Icicle' is one of the finest white-flowered veronicas and is probably a hybrid with *V. longiflora* var. *subsessilis* and *V. spicata*. It grows 18–24″ tall and flowers from June to September.

'Romilley Purple' bears deep violet-blue flowers on 2' tall stems. Although popular in Europe, it is difficult to find in this country.

var. *rosea* is greatly branched and has rose-pink flowers.

var. *subsessilis* is one of the best, most popular forms. It is 2–3' tall, much more branched and compact with longer inflorescences and larger flowers than the type. Flowering occurs about 2 weeks later than the species.

Propagate by division in the spring or sow seed similar to *V. incana*.

Related Species:

V. exaltata is closely related and considered a synonym by many taxonomists. It blooms in mid- to late-summer and bears light blue ¼″ diameter flowers in dense terminal racemes. Plants grow 3–4' tall but little or no staking is required.

V. spuria, bastard speedwell, is similar to *V. longifolia* but is distinguished by the triangular leaf base (cuneate) and the loose arrangement of flowers on the raceme. Leaves are occasionally arranged in whorls. Variety *elegans* produces more stems and has downy leaves.

-pectinata (pek-ti-nah′ ta)	Comb Speedwell	3–6″/spreading
Spring	Deep Blue	Asia Minor	Zones 2–7

This prostrate species is particularly useful for edging or for dry areas in the rock garden. The base of the plant is woody and the foliage forms a dense evergreen mat. The sessile, oval leaves are ½ to ¾″ long and covered with long white hairs. They are bluntly toothed and somewhat resemble the teeth of a comb, thus earning the plant's common name. It spreads by rooting at the nodes of the prostrate stems. The axils of the ascending stems bear 3–5″ long, many-flowered, elongated racemes consisting of ¼″ diameter blue flowers with white centers.

Native to dry, shady areas, plants are more tolerant of drier conditions than other species. Good drainage and full sun to partial shade are ideal.

Cultivars:

var. *rosea* has numerous racemes of rose-pink flowers. The racemes are a little shorter (2–4″ long) than the type but otherwise few differences are obvious.

Related Species

V. austriaca has foliage similar to *V. pectinata* but is much taller (18–24″) with deep blue flowers. It is attractive but difficult to locate in the United States.

Propagate by division in early spring or treat seed similar to *V. incana*.

593

-prostrata (pros-trah' ta)		Harebell Speedwell	3–8"/spreading
Summer	Blue	Europe, Northern Asia	Zones 5–8

(Syn. *V. rupestris*, *V. teucrium* var. *prostrata*)

Plants produce both sterile and flowering stems. The sterile stems remain prostrate and form mats of grayish green, slightly hairy foliage. The ascending flowering stems grow to 8" tall. Ovate to linear leaves are toothed, wedge-shaped at the base and ½ to 1" long. Short dense racemes of pale to deep blue, ⅓" diameter flowers are formed in the axils of the ascending stems.

This is a fine plant for front of the garden, rockeries or edging. Flowers cover the foliage in the summer and provide brief (2–3 weeks) but brilliant spots of color throughout the garden. If the mats of foliage become too vigorous, they may be pruned to desirable proportions. Provide full sun and well-drained soil.

Cultivars:

'Blue Sheen' has small racemes of wisteria-blue flowers on 2–3" tall plants.

'Heavenly Blue' has gained immense popularity. It bears sapphire-blue flowers and creeps along at a height of about 2–4".

'Loddon Blue' has rich deep blue flowers and is about 4" tall.

'Mrs. Holt' has bright pink flowers in the summer and grows about 6" tall. It is not as vigorous as the type.

'Spode Blue' bears light blue flowers.

Propagate by division or by seed similar to *V. incana*.

-spicata (spee-kah' ta)		Spiked Speedwell	10–36"/24"
Summer	Blue	Europe, Northern Asia	Zones 3–8

One of the most popular veronicas in American gardens, it is also the parent of many hybrid cultivars. The 2" long glossy leaves are lanceolate and toothed except at the base and tip. The blue flowers are only about ¼" in diameter but have long purple stamens. They are held in dense 1–3' long spike-like racemes.

Flower color ranges from deep blue to white with an occasional light pink. Flowers are produced for 4–7 weeks and provide excellent color for the front and middle of the garden. Plants require sunny well-drained conditions. In the South, winter drainage is particularly important because plants succumb to many root rot organisms which proliferate in wet, cool soils.

Cultivars:

var. *alba* is similar to the species but with white flowers.

'Barcarolle' was raised at Bloom's Nursery in Diss, England and is one of a number of hybrids between *V. incana* and *V. spicata*. It has rose-pink flowers, stands 12–15" tall and has leaves which are somewhat gray-green, due to the influence of *V. incana*.

'Blue Fox' has bright lavender-blue flowers on 15–20" tall stems.

'Blue Peter' grows 24″ tall and produces dark blue flowers on 12″ spikes.

'Blue Spires' has glossy green leaves and many deep blue flower spikes on 12–18″ tall plants. Plants flower for about 4 weeks in late June and July in the Georgia Horticulture Gardens.

'Heidekind' is 8–10″ tall with compact rose-pink spikes in late spring. It is not as cold hardy as the species and does poorly north of zone 5.

'Minuet' has a similar parentage to 'Barcarolle' and grows 12–18″ tall. The foliage is grayer than that of 'Barcarolle'.

var. *nana* is similar to the species but only about 8″ tall.

'Red Fox' has deep rosy red flowers and glossy leaves. It stands about 15″ tall, is free flowering and blooms for over 5 weeks.

var. *rosea* has pinker flowers than the above cultivar.

'Snow White' has branching spikes of white flowers on 18″ tall stems.

Propagation of the species and varieties from seed is similar to *V. incana*. Terminal cuttings and divisions are the best means to propagate cultivars.

Related Species:

V. pinnata is 1–3′ tall with numerous finely divided 2½″ long leaves. The flowers are dark blue on branched racemes. 'Blue Eyes' has lighter blue flowers than the species and is only about 10″ tall.

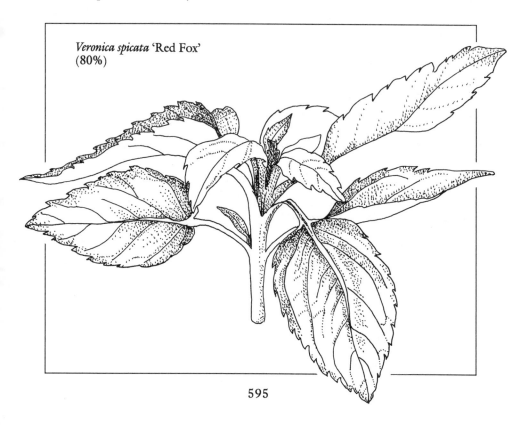

Veronica spicata 'Red Fox'
(80%)

× 'Sunny Border Blue' is 18–24″ tall with violet-blue flowers in mid summer to fall. Introduced into the trade in 1946 by Robert Bennerup of Sunny Border Nurseries, Kensington, Connecticut.

-teucrium (tewk′ ree-um)	Hungarian Speedwell	6–20″/spreading
Spring Blue	Southern Europe	Zones 3–8

(Syn. *V. latifolia*)

This is such a variable species that some botanists divide it into 5 sub-groups. For our purposes, it is a low-growing, prostrate plant with ascending sterile and flowering stems. The 1½″ long leaves are ovate to oblong and more or less toothed or sometimes slightly lobed. They resemble the leaves of germander, *Teucrium*, thus its specific epithet. The ½″ wide flowers arise in elongated axillary racemes from the upper 2–3 nodes and when in flower, plants are a sea of blue. In zone 8, flowers open in early May and persist for about 4 weeks. In Philadelphia (zone 6), flowering begins about 2 weeks later.

In warm climates, cut back hard after flowering. It does best in full sun but will also tolerate some afternoon shade.

Cultivars:

'Blue Fountain' is more erect and one of the tallest selections of this species. It has dense bright blue racemes on 20–24″ tall plants.

'Crater Lake Blue' is an outstanding 12–15″ selection with short racemes of intense blue flowers. It is one of the best cultivars for filling in a sunny area in the front of the garden.

'Royal Blue' bears deep blue flowers on 12–18″ tall bushy plants.

'Shirley Blue' is only about 8″ tall with short, dense racemes of mid to dark blue flowers.

'Trehane' has yellow-green foliage from which arise short racemes of deep blue flowers. The plants are 6–8″ tall.

'True Blue' is an excellent 12″ tall, free-flowering cultivar with deep blue flowers.

Propagate by division as well as by terminal cuttings of sterile branches. Seed may be treated similar to *V. incana*.

Related Species:

V. repens, creeping speedwell, is a prostrate species that loves to scramble over rocks or walls in full sun and well-drained conditions. The light blue to almost white flowers are held in terminal racemes and appear in late summer.

Quick Key to Veronica Species

    A. Inflorescence axillary
       B. Calyx (sepals) with 5 lobes
          C. Non-flowering stems ascending . . . . *V. teucrium*

CC. Non-flowering stems prostrate........................ *V. prostrata*
BB. Calyx with 4 lobes .... *V. pectinata*
AA. Inflorescence terminal
  B. Plants 4–8″ tall .... *V. alpina*
  BB. Plants greater than 8″ tall
    C. Leaves white woolly .... *V. incana*
    CC. Leaves not white woolly, but may be hairy
      D. Pedicels much longer than the sepals............. *V. gentianoides*
      DD. Pedicels same size as or shorter than sepals
        E. Entire length of leaf sharply serrated, leaves often whorled ....
           V. longifolia
      EE. Leaves not toothed at base or tip, leaves opposite,
        not whorled .... *V. spicata*

Additional Reading:

DeWolf, Gordon P. Jr. 1956. Notes on cultivated Schrophulariaceae. 4. *Veronica*. *Baileya* 4:143–159.

Ruffier-Lanche, R. 1958. Notes on some veronicas. *Baileya* 6: 55–57.

Veronicastrum (ve-ro-ni-kas' trum)   Culver's Root   Scrophulariaceae

The only cultivated species in the genus is *V. virginicum* which has been tossed back and forth between this genus and *Veronica*, obviously indicative of the close taxonomic relationship.

-virginicum (vir-jin' i-cum)   Culver's Root   4–6′/4′
Late Summer   Whitish   Eastern United States   Zones 3–8

The lanceolate leaves are arranged in whorls of 3–6 around the unbranched stems. Each pointed leaf is 2–4″ long, sharply toothed, smooth above and somewhat pubescent below. The pinkish white to pale blue ¼″ long flowers are arranged in dense, terminal, erect 6–9″ long racemes. After initial flowering, lateral racemes take over resulting in a 4–6 week flowering period.

This is an imposing plant if grown in full sun, watered well and fertilized 2–3 times a year. If placed in partial shade, plants need support and are rather unattractive.

Cultivars:

var. *alba* has pure white flowers more persistent than those of the species or the pale pink-flowered var. *rosea*. This is an exceptional garden plant.

Propagate by seed similar to *Veronica incana*, but germination requires 4–6 weeks. Terminal cuttings (remove flowers) and divisions are also used.

597

Vinca (ving- ka)   Vinca, Myrtle, Periwinkle   Apocynaceae

Of the 12 species, 2 are popular ground covers. In some parts of the country, small oceans of periwinkle may be found around every corner. All species have opposite leaves and solitary flowers borne in the leaf axils. The annual bedding plant, Madagascar periwinkle, formally called *Vinca rosea*, is correctly known as *Catharanthus roseus*.

-major (may' jor)		Large Periwinkle	12–18"/24"
Spring	Blue	Europe	Zones 7–9

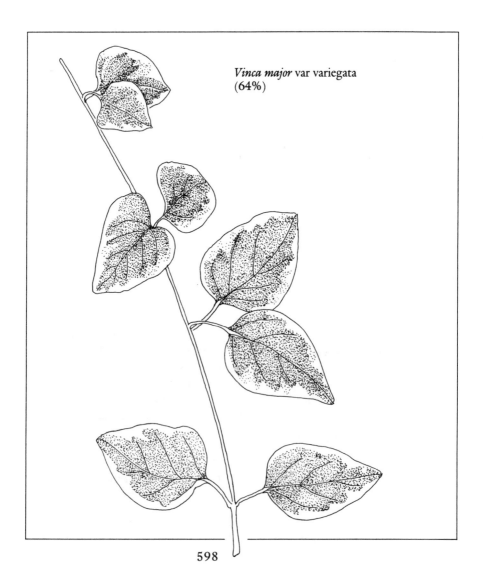

Vinca major var variegata
(64%)

Due to the lack of winter hardiness, *V. major* is seldom used as an outdoor ground cover north of zone 6, and even there, some protection is necessary. The non-flowering stems are prostrate while the ascending flowering stems bear 2–3″ long glossy, ovate, evergreen leaves with small hairs on the margins (ciliate). The blue, funnel-shaped flowers are 1–2″ in diameter with sepals almost as long as the corolla tube. They are borne in abundance in early spring and sporadically throughout the summer.

Non-flowering stems root at the tips where they touch the ground. If provided with moist soils in partial shade, plants fill in vigorously. It is also an excellent plant for trailing over banks, or cascading from window boxes or planters.

Cultivars:

var *alba* has white flowers.

var. *pubescens* (*hirsuta*) bears more pubescent leaves than the species and red-purple flowers with narrow petals.

var. *reticulata* has foliage netted with yellow lines.

var. *variegata* is popular in hanging baskets and window boxes and has creamy white blotches on the leaves. Flowers are blue and plants are sometimes known as 'Elegantissima'.

Propagate by terminal cuttings of non-flowering stems in late spring or divide throughout the season.

-minor (mine' or)		Common Periwinkle	6–12″/spreading
Spring	Blue	Europe	Zones 4–9

That this species is so widely used in the United States testifies to its toughness and ability to tolerate a wide range of climatic conditions. Such a lovely plant has a rather gruesome history. In the Middle Ages, it adorned the heads of criminals on their way to execution and was called *Fiore di morte* in Italy because it was placed on the bodies of dead infants. However, not everyone shared such gloom and plants soon became known as Joy of the Ground, a name occasionally used today.

V. minor produces non-flowering stems which root at all nodes, with elliptical 1½″ long evergreen leaves with smooth, entire margins. The tubular bluish purple flowers are ¾–1″ across and the sepals are about ⅓ as long as the corolla tube. Flowers open in the spring and, similar to *V. major*, appear sporadically all season.

Plants are vigorous and prefer shade and moist areas. An excellent species for erosion control on banks.

Cultivars:

var. *alba* has white flowers which make a nice contrast with the dark green foliage.

var. *alboplena* bears white double flowers.

var. *atropurpurea* produces dark purple flowers.

'Bowles Variety' (var. *bowlesii*) bears light blue 1–1¼″ diameter flowers and is less vigorous than the species. This is also known as 'La Graveana' ('La Grave').

'Multiplex' has double, plum-purple flowers.

'Jekyll's White' has single pure white flowers and is more floriferous than var. *alba*.

'Sterling Silver' bears dark blue flowers and foliage with white margins.

'Variegata' produces yellow variegated leaves and pale blue flowers.

Propagate by division throughout the season. Terminal cuttings of non-flowering stems may also be used.

Viola (vie′ o-la)   Violet   Violaceae

Over 300 species of violets are distributed in the north and south temperate zones. For garden purposes, violets may be divided into two large groups. The first is the true violets such as *V. cornuta*, tufted violet, and *V. odorata*, sweet violet which are treated as perennials and flower in late fall and early spring.

The second group consists of true pansies such as *V. tricolor*, heartsease, *V. lutea* and *V. altaica*. Hybridization of these species and others has given rise to the myriad of modern garden pansies, collectively known as *V. × wittrockiana*. Although perennial in most of the country, they are available as bedding plants and generally used as annuals for early spring flowering.

Two kinds of flowers are produced by most true violets. In the spring, the large, showy, infertile flowers consisting of five sepals, petals and stamens open. The lower petal bears a spur, similar to *Aquilegia*. In the summer, flowers with rudimentary or no petals are formed at the base of the plant. These never open but self-pollinate within the closed calyx and are known as cleistogamous flowers. Seed capsules are formed which spew out small seeds to great distances. Many of the non-stoloniferous species appear like magic because of this quarterback-like property. The dried, open seed capsules can easily be seen if the leaves are pushed aside in late summer and fall. The foliage of most cultivated violets is evergreen.

Garden species of violets are low growing and suitable for the front of the border or for a wild flower garden. Most tolerate full sun but prefer shaded, moist conditions. A number of native wild flowers such as *V. papilionacea* (syn. *V. sororia*), confederate violet, *V. pedata*, bird's-foot violet, and *V. canadensis*, Canada violet, are ornamental but little selection or hybridization has been undertaken to introduce them as garden subjects. Their potential for improvement is great.

Species hybridize readily making identification difficult. In fact, L.H. Bailey stated in *The Standard Cyclopedia of Horticulture* (Vol III, 1943) that there were more natural hybrids than there were species. Taxonomic differences among species are subtle and for those inclined to use a 10X hand lens, one of the best structures to study is the shape of the style. It is one of the few morphological factors that distinguish violet species. See the section on additional reading at the end of the genus.

Quick Reference to Viola Species

	Height (in.)	Stems (yes or no)	Stoloniferous (yes or no)	Color of seeds
V. cornuta	4–12	Yes	No	Black
V. cucullata	3–6	No	No	Black
V. labradorica	1–4	Yes	No	Brown
V. odorata	2–8	No	Yes	Cream
V. pedata	2–6	No	No	Copper
V. pubescens	8–12	Yes	No	Brown
V. rotundifolia	3–6	No	No	White

-cornuta (kor-new′ ta)		Horned Violet, Tufted Violet	4–12″/12″
Spring	Violet	Pyrenees	Zones 6–9

The stems are more or less prostrate at the base before ascending and the whole plant appears tufted, thus accounting for its common name. A vigorous grower, it is often used as a ground cover and an accent plant. The evergreen leaves are ovate, 1–2″ long, less than 1″ wide and have an extended pointed tip (acuminate). The nodes of the stem bear opposite leafy stipules about the same length as the petiole. The 1–1½″ diameter flowers are borne on 2–4″ long peduncles which arise from the leaf axils. The petals are spread apart, resulting in star-like flowers on some varieties. They are slightly fragrant with a long slender spur, thus accounting for the other common name.

Flowers occur in spring and, if the plant is cut back in the summer, flower again in the fall. In the South, plants are heat tolerant and although some stress-related damage may occur during July and August, they do not perish like annual pansies.

Cultivars:

var. *alba* has clean, pure white flowers.

'Arkwright Beauty' is listed as a cultivar of *V. cornuta* but looks suspiciously like a garden pansy. It bears crimson flowers with a black blotch at the center. The flowers are 1½″ across but not as floriferous as var. *lilacina*.

'Blue Perfection' is 6–8″ tall and produces sky blue flowers in early spring and again in the fall.

'Chantreyland' is similar to the above cultivar but has apricot flowers.

'Jersey Gem' has broad petals of rich blue purple.

var. *lilacina* is one of my favorite violas as it bears abundant pale lilac-blue flowers with spreading petals. It is heat tolerant and performs well year after year.

601

'Lord Nelson' is one of the most durable selections of the species and produces small (¾" across) violet flowers with a tiny yellow eye.

'Scottish Yellow' has pure yellow 1–1½" wide flowers.

'White Perfection' has clean white flowers on 6–8" tall plants.

Propagate by division in the fall or early spring. Terminal cuttings, approximately 2" long, taken in spring or summer will root in 10–15 days if placed under moist, warm conditions. Seed germinates quickly if lightly covered and placed at about 62°F under high humidity. After germination, move the seedlings to 55–60°F location.

Related Species:

V. × *williamsii* is a group of plants which resulted from crossing *V. cornuta* with the garden pansy, *V.* × *wittrockiana*. Referred to as violettas, they are compact white-flowering plants.

-cucullata (kuk-eh-lah´ ta)	Marsh Blue Violet	3–6"/12"
Spring	Violet	Eastern North America	Zones 4–9

(Syn. *V. obliqua*)

The leaves and flower stems arise from the rootstock, resulting in a stemless species. The pale green foliage is broadly ovate to heart shaped, 3–4" wide, and held on 3–5" long petioles. The margins are somewhat wavy and the whole leaf is essentially hairless. The stipules are lanceolate and entire. Each ½–1" diameter flower has purple veins on the lower petal while the lateral ones have dense beard-like hairs. Scaly rhizomes result in large clumps but plants are not stoloniferous.

Plants are particularly effective in moist shady places. The foliage is produced throughout the year resulting in an effective ground cover. It self sows everywhere, however, and can soon become a nuisance.

Cultivars:

'Freckles' produces a unique flower with a light blue background liberally sprinkled with purple flecks. It grows about 6" tall.

'Priceana' is usually listed under this species but is probably a cultivar or hybrid of *V. papilionacea*. It is a magnificent selection with white flowers, a large purple center and a small yellow eye. Often referred to as the confederate violet.

'Red Giant' has rose-red flowers.

'Royal Robe' bears deep blue flowers on 4–6" tall flower stems.

'White Czar' has lovely white flowers with a yellow center and dark netted markings in the throat. Plants grow vigorously and tolerate more sun than the species. It possibly is a hybrid with *V. odorata* 'Czar'.

Divide the rhizome every 2–3 years or sow seed similar to *V. cornuta*.

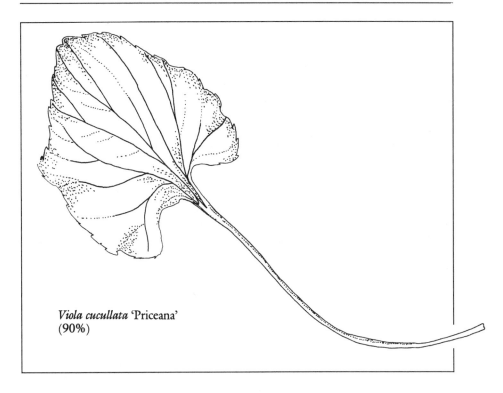

Viola cucullata 'Priceana'
(90%)

-labradorica (lab-ra-do' ri-ka)	Labrador Violet	1–4"/12"
Spring Violet	Northern United States, Greenland	Zones 3–8

One of the shortest garden violets, the species makes an excellent filler for the front of the border or for the rock garden. Although native to northeastern states, parts of Canada, and as far north as Greenland, it is not cultivated to any great extent in the United States. The 1" wide, broadly ovate foliage is shallowly toothed and arises from a short stem. The stipules are lanceolate with sparse teeth on the margins. The mauve, ¾" wide flowers, suffused with dark purple, appear in early spring and sporadically the rest of the season.

Although native to northern areas, it does well in the South. Spreading by slender creeping rhizomes, plants fill in areas rapidly. Provide shade and moisture and sit back and enjoy.

Cultivars:

var. *purpurea* has leaves suffused with purple and appear dark green, particularly in the spring and fall. New spring and fall growth is dark purple which lightens somewhat during the summer. Flowers are similar to the type.

Divide every 2–3 years if it starts to ramble too aggressively. Seed may be treated similar to *V. cornuta*.

-odorata (o-do-rah′ ta) Sweet Violet 2–8″/15″
Spring Violet Europe, Asia Zones 6–9

Whenever this species is planted in a garden, centuries of history are planted with it. Plants have been cultivated as long as there have been gardens, and are mentioned frequently in Greek and Latin classics. The flower market in Athens, Greece handled violets as early as 400 B.C. and the sweet violet became the symbol of Athens. As F. E. Dillistone writes (*Violet Culture for Pleasure and Profit,* 1933), violets were "as proud a device of the Ionic Athenians as the rose of England or the lilies of France". It was also adopted as the symbol and pass-word of Napolean's supporters after he was exiled to Elba; he always presented sweet violets to Josephine on their wedding anniversary. The medicinal and chemical uses are also well documented but the fragrance distinguishes it from others. The substance that provides the fragrance is ionine, which is soporific, meaning that the nose perceives the odor but for a short time. Thus the scent of violets is sweet, but not long-lasting. This property spawned huge acreages of violets for the perfume industry, particularly in France and also in England, in this century. The use of violets for perfume continued into the 1940s and

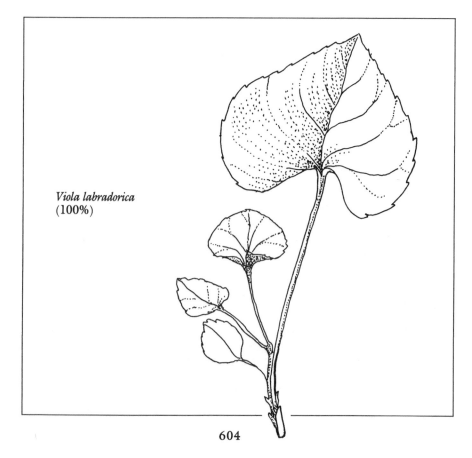

Viola labradorica
(100%)

1950s until chemists found a way to manufacture ionine synthetically. Little natural "fragrance of violet" is found in today's perfumes. Sweet violets, however, are still sold as cut flowers in Europe but are only useful for local markets due to the transitory nature of the fragrance.

The tufted foliage is broadly ovate to kidney-shaped and arises from the rootstock. Each finely pubescent leaf is 2–3″ wide and has blunt shallow serrations on the margin. The ¾″ long flowers are usually violet, but rose and white forms also exist. Flowers occur in the fall and appear throughout the winter in mild climates and into the spring. Prostrate runners root at the tips and allow it to spread rapidly. Flowering occurs the second year from rooting. Large-flowered double types arose in the late 1800s and became known as Neapolitan or Parma violets. They are fragrant but their ancestry is rather obscure, perhaps being derived from *V. alba* rather than *V. odorata*.

Plants grow best in the cool times of the year (this is true for all violets), but are not winter hardy north of zone 6 without protection. Full sun is tolerated as long as adequate soil moisture is provided, otherwise partial shade is necessary. Every gardener should have one or two plants if for no other reason than to occassionally feel like Josephine. I would not have a garden without them.

Cultivars:

'Czar' was one of the earliest selections and bears single, deep violet flowers on narrow stems. 'White Czar' may also belong here. See *V. cornuta*.

'Duchesse de Parme' bears double lavender-violet flowers, 'Lady Hume Campbell' has double lavender flowers, and 'Marie Louise' produces deep double violet-mauve flowers. These cultivars carry flowers on long stems which are suitable for cutting. These are but three of the group of plants referred to as Parma violets, an important cut flower crop in Europe in recent years. They are not particularly easy to find in this country.

'Queen Charlotte' has dark blue flowers on 6–8″ tall stems.

'Rosina' has rose-pink flowers with a dark center.

'White Queen' has small white flowers on 6″ tall plants.

Division of the plantlets resulting from the stoloniferous runners is practiced in the fall. Seed of the species and varieties should be handled similar to *V. cornuta*.

Additional Reading:

Coombs, Roy E. 1979. Parma violets. *The Plantsman* 1(3):167–176.

Coombs, Roy E. 1982. The Parma Violet 'Marie Louise'. *The Plantsman* 4(2):112–115.

-pedata (pe-dah′ ta)		Bird's-foot Violet	2–6″/12″
Spring	Violet	Eastern North America	Zones 4–9

One of our prettiest native flowers, *V. pedata* is easy to identify because the leaves look like a bird's foot. This particular bird has feet palmately divided into

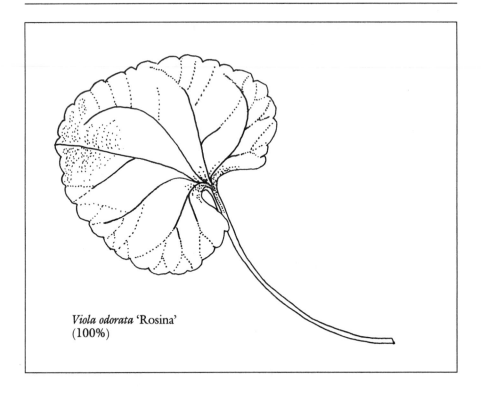

Viola odorata 'Rosina'
(100%)

3–5 narrow segments. Plants are stemless and flowers are ¾–1½" across, borne on 2–6" long peduncles. The upper two petals are dark violet while the lower three are pale lilac with dark veins. Five orange stamens are clustered in the center.

It is not the easiest violet to cultivate and demands especially good drainage and partial shade. Planting in soil over a layer of coarse gravel helps establishment. The rhizome must be kept free of standing water or rot will develop.

There are enough commercial sources of this violet available that no one need remove them from the wild. Transplanting from the wild is likely to be unsuccessful.

Cultivars:

var. *alba* has white flowers that contrast well with the palmate foliage.

var. *concolor* is a southern variant of the species and bears larger (1½") violet flowers with a white spot at the base of the lower petal. It is particularly suited to southern gardens.

Seed must be refrigerated for 5–6 weeks at 35–40°F to insure germination. If seed is sown directly in the garden, seedlings will appear the following spring. Leaf-bud cuttings (a leaf blade, petiole, with a piece of rhizome attached) may be placed in sand in late fall and winter. Rooting will occur in 4–7 weeks. Division of the rhizome may also be accomplished in late fall and winter.

-pubescens (pew' bes-cens)	Downy Yellow Violet	8–12"/12"
Spring Yellow	Eastern North America	Zones 3–7

The stem and triangular to kidney-shaped foliage is softly pubescent to the touch, thus the common name. The round, toothed leaves are 3–4" across and usually occur on short petioles at the top of the stem. The lower stem is often bare of leaves for 2–3" and the upper is often branched. The large stipules (about ½" wide) are lanceolate and entire. The bright yellow ½" wide flowers are borne in the leaf axils and consist of lower petals veined with purple, providing a nice contrast to the yellow.

Plants are native to dry, rich, shaded areas and should be placed in a well-drained shady area in the garden. It is not as heat tolerant as many violets and performs better in zones 4–6 than in zone 8.

Propagate from seed similar to *V. cornuta*. If seedlings fail to germinate within 6 weeks, place in the refrigerator for 4–6 weeks and treat like *V. pedata*. Divide the short rhizome in late fall or early spring.

Realated Species:

V. nuttallii, Nuttall violet, also has downy foliage (but only underneath) and yellow flowers. The leaves are present at the base of the plant (lacking in *V. pubescens*) and narrower. Native to the North American prairie states.

-rotundifolia (ro-tund-i-fo' lee-a)	Roundleaf Violet	3–6"/9"
Spring Yellow	Maine to North Georgia	Zones 3–7

This native species has oval to circular 2–4" wide foliage directly from the rootstock. Plants produce sprawling purplish stems after flowering which result in a matlike habit. The lower 3 petals of the 2" wide yellow flowers are brown veined. Flowers are borne on 2–4" long stalks in early spring. Plants perform particularly well in cool climates but simply open up and look sad where summers are hot.

Propagate by seed similar to *V. cornuta* or by division in spring or fall.

Quick Key to Viola Species

    A. Plants stemless, leaves and flowers arising directly from
        rhizome
        B. Leaves palmately divided.................................... *V. pedata*
      BB. Leaves not palmately divided
          C. Plant stoloniferous....................................... *V. odorata*
        CC. Plant not stoloniferous, grows in clumps
            D. Plant less than 8" tall, foliage round, dark green,
                flowers yellow .... *V. rotundifolia*

DD. Plant more than 8″ tall, foliage broadly ovate or
kidney-shaped, pale green, flowers violet .... *V. cucullata*
AA. Plants with stems
B. Flowers 1″ or more across, violet, stipules deeply toothed ... *V. cornuta*
BB. Flowers less than 1″ across, yellow or violet, stipules not
deeply toothed
C. Flowers yellow, foliage very pubescent .... *V. pubescens*
CC. Flowers violet, foliage not obviously pubescent ...... *V. labradorica*

Additional Reading:

Books:

Baird, Viola Brainerd. 1942. *Wild Violets of North America*. Berkeley and Los Angeles, University of California Press. A beautifully illustrated and well-documented text.

Chittenden, Fred J. (ed.) 1974. *The Royal Horticulture Society Dictionary of Gardening*, 2nd ed. vol.IV: 2237. This reference provides more information on the shape of the style of different species.

Manuscripts:

Coombs, Roy E. 1981. Cultivated violets, are they really unscented? *The Plantsman* 3(1):60–62.

W

Waldsteinia (wald-stein' ee-a)   Barren-strawberry   Rosaceae

Approximately 5 species of this strawberry-like genus occur and 2 are occasionally seen in American gardens. Both bear trifoliate leaves, yellow flowers, and small inedible fruits. *Waldsteinia* is more ornamental than, but not as vigorous as another insidious relative known as mock strawberry, *Duchesnea indica*. *Waldsteinia* differs by having short surface runners, smaller fruit and 2–5 pistils (*Duchesnea* has 15 or more). *Waldsteinia* is a favored guest; *Duchesnea* an uninvited party crasher.

-fragarioides (fra-gah-ree-oi' deez)   Barren-strawberry   4–6"/24"
Spring   Yellow   Eastern United States   Zones 4–7

The trifoliate glossy, evergreen leaves are slightly hairy and the broad, wedge-shaped toothed leaflets are 1–2" long. The yellow flowers, about ½" across, are carried in 3–8 flowered racemes on 4" long scapes.

Full sun is preferable but partial shade is tolerated. Plants form a pretty mat particularly useful for edging or filling in areas along a path. Unfortunately, the flowers do not emerge through the mat but push out the sides so the planting is never covered with blooms. Performance is poor in hot, wet climates and although native as far south as North Georgia, it does not thrive under cultivated conditions in zone 8.

Propagate by division in spring or fall or sow seed in warm, moist conditions. It germinates erratically. After germination, place the plants at 60–65°F.

Related Species:

W. ternata, Siberian barren-strawberry, is native to Siberia and is a better ground cover than *W. fragarioides*. The leaves occur in rosettes and are borne on short petioles resulting in more compact plants. Cool climates are also necessary for best growth. A winner in the Pacific Northwest.

Z

Zantedeschia (zan-te-desh' ee-a)   Calla Lily   Araceae

Approximately 8 species are native to South Africa and used more as cut flowers than garden plants. The flowers consist of the large ornamental spathe enclosing the erect spadix. All must be dug and stored through the winter (similar to a gladiolus) in all but the warmest areas of the country. The flowers are used by florists in arrangements, particularly the white calla, *Z. aethiopica*, and unfortunately have been associated with funerals, making some people hesitant to use them as garden plants. Placed in containers or in the garden, they provide a classical air to the patio, porch, or garden.

In the garden, they prefer partial shade but tolerate full sun. The flower stems are longer on plants grown in the shade. Callas are also excellent water plants and may be planted in a bog or beside a pond or pool. If planted below the water's freezing line, plants may be overwintered *in situ*.

Quick Reference to Zantedeschia Species

	Height (in.)	Flower color	Leaf shape
Z. aethiopica	24–30	White	Arrow
Z. albo-maculata	24–30	Greenish white	Arrow
Z. rehmannii	9–15	Pink	Lanceolate

-*aethiopica* (aye-thee-o' pi-ka)   White Calla   24–30"/24"
Summer   White   South Africa   Zones 9–10

In my garden travels around the world, I cannot help but associate certain plants with certain countries. Calla lilies are to New Zealand as tulips are to Holland. Naturalized throughout the country in paddocks and low-lying moist areas, they share space with thousands of sheep and brighten up dark and dismal

610

winter days. To see hundreds of white callas in drifts around a pond is indeed a magnificent sight. The plants are stemless; all parts arise from the broad root-stock. The dark green leaves are twice as long as broad, and carried on long petioles. The pure white spathe flares outward and is 6–10″ long. The spadix is prominent but only about ⅓ the length of the spathe. Breeding has resulted in dwarf 18″ to 2′ tall compact forms as well as those with cream and green tints in the spathe.

Cultivars:

var *childsiana* ('Child's Perfection') is dwarfer, more compact and more floriferous than the type. They are particularly useful as potted plants for the green-house industry.

'Crowborough' was developed in Crowborough, England and is more winter hardy and sun tolerant than the species. Otherwise, few differences exist.

'Little Gem' is 12–18″ tall and suitable for patio containers or indoors. It is more fragrant than the type.

Propagate by cormels that readily form after the first year's growth. Lift the plants and separate from the main corm. Seed collected from plants may be sown in pots in the fall and will germinate within 1–3 months. Grow in pots until sufficiently established for placement in the final location.

-albo-maculata (al-bo-mak-ew-lah′ ta)	Spotted Calla	24–30″/24″
Summer Creamy white	South Africa	Zones 8–10

The leaf blades are 12–18″ long, 3–4″ wide and spotted with white. The creamy white spathe is trumpet-shaped (not flaring as in the previous species), 4–5″ long, and has a purple blotch at the base.

The main value is increased cold tolerance over other species which permits overwintering in zone 8 with protection. It has been used extensively in hybrid-ization to take advantage of cold hardiness genes.

Related Species:

Z. elliotiana, Elliot's calla, has silvery white spots on the foliage and produces 4–5″ long bright yellow spathes in summer. Spathes do not have a purple blotch on the back. Plants are not as hardy as either of the above species.

Propagation is similar to *Z. aethiopica*.

-rehmannii (ray-mahn′ ee-aye)	Pink Calla	9–15″/20″
Summer Pink, Rose	South Africa	Zones 9–10

This dwarfer species has 7–15″ long lanceolate leaves covered with small greenish or white spots. The 4″ long spathe is trumpet-shaped and varies from pink to rose to white with a pink tint. Size makes it particularly suitable for pot culture.

Propagate similar to *Z. aethiopica*.

Related Species:

Many hybrids are available which are commercially used as cut flowers or pot plants. Some of the finest cultivars are emerging from nurseries in New Zealand. These plants sport red, pink, yellow, gold and green spathes mostly with spotted leaves. Many of the hybrids have the purple blotch in the bottom of the spathe associated with *Z. albo-maculata*. Cultivars include 'Black Magic', yellow with a prominent black blotch in the spathe; 'Majestic Red', rose-red flowers and 'Pink Perfection', light pink spathe. These and many others are being developed by Topline Nurseries in New Zealand. All have been overwintered in zone 8.

Quick Key to Zantedeschia Species

A. Leaves lanceolate, flowers pink or rose .... *Z. rehmannii*
AA. Leaves arrow shaped, flowers usually white or yellow
    B. Spathe white, flared at top, leaves not spotted white ...... *Z. aethiopica*
    BB. Spathe creamy white, not flared, leaves spotted white ....
                                      Z. albo-maculata

Additional Reading:

Traub, H.P. 1948. The genus *Zantedeschia*. *Plant Life* 4: 8–32.

Zauschneria (zowsh-ner' ee-a)   False Fuchsia   Onagraceae

Four species of this little-known genus occur, all are small sub-shrubs native to the western United States. Only *Z. californica* is found in gardens.

-californica (ka-li-forn' i-ca)   California False Fuchsia   1–2'/18"
Late Summer   Scarlet   California   Zones 7–10

The linear to lanceolate, sessile, pubescent foliage varies from green to gray-green. The lower leaves are opposite while those toward the top are alternate. The 1–1½" long bright scarlet flowers are held in racemes and are fuchsia-like. Plants are tetraploid (having twice the number of chromosomes) resulting in increased vigor.

The showy flowers and low-growing habit make plants suitable for the front of the border or the rock garden. It tolerates either full sun or partial shade but good drainage is essential, particularly in the Southeast, where winter rains are common. One of the drawbacks is the hairy, messy seeds which detract from the plants in the fall. Removal of the spent flowers reduces the problem. Plants have been grown successfully in zone 7 with suitable protection.

Cultivars:

'Dublin' is smaller than the species, growing only 12–18" tall.

Propagate by seed in a moist, warm (70–75°F) environment. Seed emerges within 3 weeks. Terminal cuttings may also be used in early summer. Cut 2–3" long terminals and place in sand or a peat-vermiculite mix. Maintain moisture and warmth until roots appear (usually within 2–3 weeks).

Zephyranthes (ze-fi-ranth' eez)　　　Zephyr Lily　　　Amaryllidaceae

The zephyr lily takes its name from *zephyros*, west wind, a reference to the New World (being in the west), from where the genus arrived in Europe. Thus it also became known as the Flower of the West Wind. Individual species also have common names. Flowers of *Z. grandiflora*, rose-pink zephyr lily, open after the rain and are known as rain lilies. The most common member of the genus native to the southern states is the atamasco lily, *Z. atamasco*.

All have narrow leaves and funnel-shaped flowers borne singly on a hollow scape. In general, they prefer moist conditions in full sun or partial shade and are rather tender, usually being winter hardy only to zone 8, zone 7 with protection. However, they make excellent potted plants for the deck or patio and 10–12 bulbs of *Z. grandiflora*, in a 6–8" container makes a glorious display. If the bulbs are stored over winter, place in moist sand or peat moss in a cool (50°F) area. If pot grown, simply keep the soil moist, not wet, and store in the same area.

Most of the approximately 35 species are spring and summer flowering, however, *Z. candida* and *Z. rosea* flower in late summer and fall. There are few obvious differences among species based on botanical characteristics, and the easiest way to separate them is by flower color and season of bloom.

Quick Reference to Zephyranthes Species

	Height (in.)	Flower color	Bloom season
Z. atamasco	18–36	White	Spring
Z. candida	9–15	White	Fall
Z. grandiflora	9–15	Rose	Summer
Z. rosea	9–15	Rose	Fall

-atamasco (a-ta-mas' ko)　　　Atamasco Lily　　　18–36"/18"
Spring　　　White　　　Southeastern United States　　　Zones 7–10

The earliest flowering and most robust zephyr lily, it produces 4–6 bright green, channelled evergreen leaves about 18" long and ¼" wide. The pure white fragrant flowers emerge as pointed, pink striped buds and open flat and star-like. The perianth may be up to 4" long. Flowers open in April and May and continue for 4–6 weeks.

This species is native to damp, acid, meadowlands and dry conditions result in small, fleeting flowers. If planted in protected areas and provided with mulch, bulbs may overwinter as far north as New York. If bulbs are removed in the fall, dig before the first hard frost and store in peat moss in an area which does not freeze. Replant in the spring after the last frost.

Propagate by removal of the small bulblets in the fall or by seed. Seeds sown in a warm (70–75°F), moist area germinate within four weeks. Flowering occurs the second or third year.

Related Species:

Z. × *ajax* is a hybrid between *Z. candida* and *Z. citrina,* a lemon-colored crocus-like species. The leaf shape is similar to *Z. candida* and the pale primrose-yellow flowers resemble *Z. citrina.* It is hardy to zone 8.

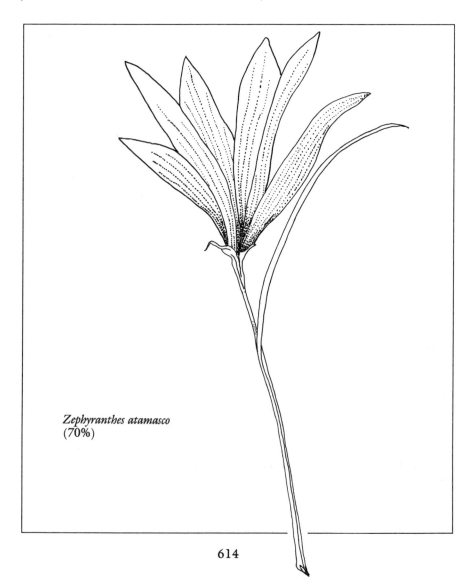

Zephyranthes atamasco
(70%)

Z. candida is known as La Plata lily because of the abundance of the silvery flowers around an unnamed river in Argentina. The presence of such beauty led the discoverer, Diaz de Solis, to name it Rio de La Plata (River of Silver). Plants produce grassy leaves and silvery white crocus-like flowers with rich orange stamens which open in late May.

Z. treatiae is native to Florida and blooms 2–4 weeks earlier than atamasco lily. The dull gray-green foliage is less than 1/10″ wide and red flower buds open to blossoms of pure white. Hardy in zones 9 and 10.

Zephyranthes candida
(60%)

615

-grandiflora (grand-i-flo′ ra)		Rose-pink Zephyr Lily	9–15″/18″
Summer	Rose	Guatamala	Zones 9–10

(Syn. *Z. carinata*)

The foliage is 10–15″ long, narrowly strap-shaped and spreads out over the ground. The rose-red flowers are 3–4″ long and emerge from a maroon-red flower bud atop a 7″ tall scape.

My great uncle Peter in Mansonville, Quebec, Canada beams over his pots of lilies that flower like magic on his porch after every summer rain. The same excitement and enthusiasm comes from Mark Krause, one of the outstanding horticulturists at Disney World in Orlando, Florida. It is little wonder that this is the most popular species of zephyr lily. Bulbs look wonderful in containers and bring rave reviews from guests.

Propagate similar to *Z. atamasco*.

Related Species:

Z. rosea, Cuban zephyr lily, has flowers of similar color to *Z. grandiflora* but less than half the size and appear 3–4 weeks later. Leaves are about 8″ long and ¼″ wide. It is also a good container plant but not as long-lived in the ground as *Z. grandiflora*.

Additional Reading:

Herklots, G.A.C. 1980. Windflowers, Part I: *Zephryanthes. The Plantsman* 2:8–19.

Herklots, G.A.C. 1981. Windflowers, Part II: *Zephyranthes* subgenus *Cooperia. The Plantsman* 3:108–112.

Bibliography of
Reference Books

Manuscipts appear with appropriate genus

Aden, Paul. 1988. *The Hosta Book*. Timber Press Inc., Portland, OR.

Bailey Hortorium. 1976. *Hortus Third, a Consise Dictionary of Plants Cultivated in the United States and Canada*. Macmillan Publishing Co., New York, NY.

Bailey, L.H. 1943. *The Standard Cyclopedia of Horticulture*, 3 volumes. MacMillan Publishing Co., New York, NY.

Bailey, L.H. 1951. *Manual of Cultivated Plants*. MacMillan Publishing Co., New York, NY.

Bailey, L.H. 1953. *The Garden of Bellflowers*. MacMillan Publishing Co., New York, NY.

Baird, Viola B. 1942. *Wild Violets of North America*. University of California Press, Berkeley and Los Angeles.

Beckett, Kenneth A. 1981. *Growing Hardy Perennials*. Croom Helm Ltd., London, England.

Bloom, Adrian. 1981. *Adrian Bloom's Guide to Garden Plants*. Book 3. *Perennials*, part 1. Jarrold and Sons Ltd., Norwich, England.

Bloom, Adrian. 1981. *Adrian Bloom's Guide to Garden Plants*, Book 4. *Perennials*, part 2. Jarrold and Sons Ltd., Norwich, England.

Bloom, Alan. 1965. *Hardy Plants of Distinction*. W.H.and L. Collingridge Ltd., London, England.

Bloom, Alan. 1968. *Alan Bloom's Selected Garden Plants*. Jarrold and Sons Ltd., Norwich, England.

Bloom, Alan. 1975. *Making the Best of Alpines*. Jarrold and Sons Ltd., Norwich, England.

Boyd, James. 1928. *Peonies. The Manual of the American Peony Society*. J. Horace McFarland Co., Harrisburg, PA.

Brown, Emily. 1986. *Landscaping with Perennials*. Timber Press, Portland, OR.

Cassidy, G.E. and S. Linnegar. 1982. *Growing Irises*. Croom Helm Ltd., London, England.

Chatto, Beth. 1978. *The Dry Garden*. J. M. Dent and Sons Ltd., London, England.

Chatto, Beth. 1982. *The Damp Garden*. J. M. Dent and Sons Ltd., London, England.

Coats, Alice M. 1956. *Flowers and Their Histories*. Adam and Charles Black, London, England.

Chittenden, Fred J. (ed.) 1974. *The Royal Horticultural Society Dictionary of Gardening*. 4 volumes and supplement. Clarendon Press, Oxford, England.

Coombes, Allen J. 1985. *Dictionary of Plant Names*. Timber Press, Portland, OR.

Crawford, Barrie F. 1985. *For the Love of Wildflowers*. Buckeye Press, Columbus, GA.

Damp, Philip. 1981. *Growing Dahlias*. Croom Helm Ltd., London, England.

Dillstone, F.E. 1933. *Violet Culture for Pleasure and Profit*. London, England.

Doerflinger, Frederic. 1973. *The Bulb Book*. Charles and Davis Ltd., Devon, England.

Duncan, Wilbur H. and Leonard E. Foote. 1975. *Wildflowers of the Southeastern United States*. University of Georgia Press, Athens, GA.

Dykes, W. R. 1912. *Irises in Present-Day-Gardening Series*. Ballantyne, Hanson and Co., Edinburgh, Scotland

Evans, Ronald L. 1984. *Handbook of Cultivated Sedums*. Science Reviews, Middlesex, England.

Fish, Margery. 1970. *Ground Cover Plants*. David and Charles, Newton Abbot, Devon, England

Fisher, John. 1982. *The Origins of Garden Plants*. Constable and Company Ltd., London, England.

Foster, H. Lincoln. 1968. *Rock Gardening*. Houghton Mifflin Co., Boston, MA.

Fox, Derek. 1985. *Lilies*. A Wisley handbook. Cassell Ltd., London, England.

Fox, Derek. 1985. *Growing lilies*. Croom Helm Ltrd., London. Good descriptions and botanical treatments of most species.

Genders, Roy. 1960. *Bulbs all the Year Round*. Latimer Trend and Co., Whitstable, England.

Genders, Roy. 1973. *Bulbs, A Complete Handbook*. Robert Hale and Co., London, England.

Gerard, John. 1636. *Gerard's Herball. The Essence Thereof Distilled by Marcus Woodward*. Cresent Books. New York, NY.

Giles, F.A., R. McIntosh Keith and D.C. Saupe. 1980. *Herbaceous Perennials*. Reston Publishing Co., Reston, VI.

Grigsen, G. 1974. *A Dictionary of English Plant Names*. Allen Lane, London, UK.

Harper, Pamela and Fred McGourty. 1985. *Perennials. How to Select, Grow and Enjoy*. HP Books Inc. Tuscon, AZ.

Hay, Roy and Patrick Synge. 1975. *The Color Dictionary of Flowers and Plants for Home and Garden*. Crown Publishers Inc., New York, NY.

Hebb, Robert S. 1975. *Low Maintenance Perennials*. Arnold Arboretum of Harvard University. Jamaica Plain, MA.

Hudak, Joseph. 1976. *Gardening with Perennials*. Timber Press, Portland, OR.

Kelsey, H.R. and W.A. Dayton. 1942. *Standardized Plant Names*, 2nd ed. J. Horace McFarland Co., Harrisburg, PA.

Kohlein, Fritz. 1984. *Saxifrages and Related Genera*. B.T. Batsford Ltd., London, England

Lacy, Allen. 1988. *The American Gardener*. Farrar Straus Giroux, New York, NY.

Lawrence, Elizabeth. 1986. *The Little Bulbs*. Duke University Press, Durham, NC.

Lawrence, Elizabeth. 1987. *Gardening for Love*. The Market Bulletins. Duke University Press, Durham, NC.

Lloyd, Christopher. 1984. *The Adventurous Gardener*. Random House Inc., New York.

Lynch, R. Irwin. 1904. *The Book of the Iris*. John Lane Publishing, London, England.

MacNeil, Ester and Alan MacNeil. 1946. *Garden Lilies*. Oxford University Press, New York.

Mathew, Brian. 1973. *Dwarf Bulbs*. Arco Publishing Co., New York.

Mathew, Brian. 1978. *The Large Bulbs*. B.T. Batsford Ltd., London, England.

Mathew, Brian. 1987. *Flowering Bulbs for the Garden*. A Kew Gardening Guide. Collingridge Books, Middlesex, England.

Morse, Harriet K. 1962. *Gardening in the Shade*. Charles Scribner's and Sons, New York, NY. (also available through Timber Press, Portland, OR.)

Nehrling, Arlo and Irene Nehrling. 1964. *The Picture Book of Perennials*. Hearthside Press Inc., New York.

Patterson, Allen. 1981. *Plants for Shade*. J.M. Dent and Sons Ltd., London, England.

Perry, Frances. 1958. *Complete Guide to Hardy Perennials*. Charles T. Branford Co., Boston, MA.

Phillips, Harry R. 1985. *Growing and Propagating Wild Flowers*. University of North Carolina Press, Chapel Hill, NC.

Pinnell, M.M., A. M. Armitage and D. Seaborn. 1985. *Germination Needs of Common Perennial Seed*. University of Georgia Research Bulletin 331. Athens, GA.

Reader's Digest Staff. 1978. *Reader's Digest Encyclopaedia of Garden Plants and Flowers*. 2nd ed. Reader's Digest Assoc., London, England.

Snyder, Leon C. 1983. *Flowers for Northern Gardens*. University of Minnesota Press, Minneapolis MN.

Still, Steven. 1987. *Manual of Herbaceous Ornamental Plants*, 3rd ed. Stipes Publishing Co., Champaign IL.

Symons-Jeune, B.H.B. 1953. *Phlox*. Collins Press, London, England.

Synge, Patrick, M. 1980. *Lilies. A Revision of Elwes' Monograph of the Genus Lilium and its Supplements*. B.T. Batsford Ltd., London, England.

Thomas, Graham Stuart. 1970. *Plants for Ground-Cover*. J. M. Dent and Sons Ltd., London, England.

Thomas, Graham Stuart. 1982. *Perennial Garden Plants*. J. M. Dent and Sons Ltd., London, England.

Thomas, Graham Stuart. 1984. *The Art of Planting*. J. M. Dent and Sons Ltd., London, Enland.

Titmarsh, Alan. 1983. *The Rock Gardener's Handbook*. Croom Helm Ltd., London, England.

Usher, George. 1947. *A Dictionary of Plants Used by Man*. Hafner Press, New York, NY.

Van Pelt Wilson, Helen. 1976. *Successful Gardening with Perennials*. Doubleday and Company Inc., Garden City, NY.

Weathers, John. 1911. *The Bulb Book*. E.P. Dutton and Company, New York, NY.

Wherry, Edgar T. 1955. *The Genus Phlox*. Morris Arboretum Monograph III. Wickersham Publishing Co., Lancaster, PA.

Wilder, Louise Beebe. 1936. *Adventures with Hardy Bulbs*. MacMillan Publishing Co., New York, NY.

Wister, John (ed.). 1962. *The Peonies*. American Horticultural Society, Washington D.C.

Wyman, Donald. 1977. *Wyman's Gardening Encyclopedia*. MacMillan Publishing Co., New York, NY.

Yeo, Peter. 1985. *Hardy Geraniums*. Timber Press, Portland, OR.

Zakary, M. 1982. *Plants of the Bible*. Cambridge University Press, Cambridge, England.

Glossary of Terms

a-: prefix meaning not or without. eg. apetalous, without petals.

acuminate: usually referring to a leaf blade whose sides are somewhat concave and taper to a point.

alternate: arrangement of leaves where one leaf occurs at each node.

apex: the tip or terminal end

aromatic: obviously scented, at least if broken or crushed.

ascending: gradually curving upward.

basal: pertaining to leaves which arise from the base of the plant.

bearded: having long hairs.

biennial: of two seasons' growth, flowers and fruit are produced the second season from seed germination. Plants die after fruiting.

biternate: twice divided into threes. eg. leaves of *Aquilegia*, whose primary divisions are again divided into three.

bract: a much reduced leaf, usually scale-like and associated with flowering. eg. flowers of *Eryngium* are subtended by bracts.

bulb: a fleshy underground stem with a short central axis surrounded by fleshy scale-like leaves. eg. *Lilium*

bulbil: small bulb arising around the parent bulb

bulblet: small bulb arising in the leaf axils.

calyx: the sepals as a group, directly below petals.

campanulate: bell-shaped, as flowers of *Campanula*.

cespitose: growing in tufts or dense clumps.

clasping: leaf without petiole, with the base partly surrounding the stem.

clustered: leaves tightly arranged, but not opposite or alternate. Also in reference to flowers.

composite: a member of the *Asteraceae*.

compound leaf: a leaf with two or more leaflets. *Palmately compound* when three or more leaflets arise from the same point, *pinnately compound* when the leaflets are arranged along a common axis, *ternately compound* when the leaflets are in 3's.

cordate: heart-shaped.

621

corm: solid bulb-like underground stem, not differentiated into scales. eg. *Crocus*.

cormel: small corm arising from parent corm.

corolla: the petals as a group.

corona: an extrusion of tissue that stands between the corolla and the stamens, or on the corolla. eg. the cup of *Narcissus*.

corymb: More or less flat-topped indeterminate inflorescence, the outer flowers open first.

crenate: rounded teeth on margin.

crown: the central growing point beneath or near the surface of the ground.

cyme: more or less flat-topped determinate inflorescence, the outer flowers open last.

decumbent: reclining or lying on the ground, but with ends ascending.

decurrent: extending down the stem, as the leaf of *Verbascum*.

deltoid: triangular.

dentate: having teeth perpendicular to the margin, do not point forward.

determinate: refers to an inflorescence whose center flower opens first and axis prolongation is thereby arrested.

dibble: to make a hole in soil, to be filled with seed, cutting or plantlet.

dioecious: male and female flowers on separate plants.

disk flower: tubular flower at the center of composites. eg. *Aster*.

diurnal: flowers open only during the day.

downy: having soft hairs.

emarginate: with a shallow notch at the apex.

ensiform: sword-shaped.

exserted: projecting beyond, as in stamens beyond a corolla.

farinaceous: having a powdery or mealy coating, as in some species of *Primula*.

filament: the stalk of the stamen.

flaccid: limp.

flexuous: having a zigzag or wavy form, refers to stems.

foliage: leaves.

gland: a general term for oil-secreting organs, sometimes a projection at the base of a structure.

glaucous: covered with a waxy bloom or whitish substance that rubs off easily.

globose: round or spherical shape.

glossy: shining, lustrous.

habit: the general outline or shape of a plant.

hairy: pubescent with long hairs.

hastate: in the shape of an arrowhead; the basal lobes are pointed and nearly at right angles.

head: a short dense inflorescence; the inflorescence in *Asteraceae* consisting of ray and disc flowers.

622

herbaceous: having no persistent woody tissue above the ground.
hispid: having stiff or bristly hairs.
hybrid: plant resulting from a cross between two or more species or genera.

imperfect flower: one which lacks either stamens or pistils.
incised: sharp incisions, between toothed and lobed.
incomplete flower: one which lacks either calyx, corolla, stamens or pistils.
indeterminate: inflorescence whose center flowers open last, the growth and elongation of the main axis is not arrested with the opening of the first flowers.
involucre: one or more whorls of small leaves or bracts close beneath a flower or flower cluster.

lateral: borne at or on the side, as in the flower bud borne in a leaf axil.
linear: long and very narrow, as in leaves.
lobe: usually a division of leaf, calyx, or petals cut to about the middle.

mealy: a granular appearance.
midrib: the main vein of a leaf or leaflet.

native: inherent or original to an area.
node: a joint on a stem from which leaves arise.

oblong: longer than broad, the sides nearly parallel.
obovate: broadest above the middle.
opposite: two at a node, as arrangement of leaves.
ovate: egg-shaped in outline, broadest below the middle.

paired: occurring in two's.
palmate: fan-like from a common point.
panicle: an indeterminate inflorescence whose primary axis bears branches of pediceled flowers.
parallel: running side to side from base to tip, as in the veins of monocot leaves.
parted: cut deeply but not quite to base.
pedicel: the stalk of a flower or fruit.
peduncle: the stalk of a flower cluster or of a single flower when the flower is solitary.
peltate: the petiole attached inside the margin, the leaves are typically shield-shaped, as in *Peltiphyllum peltatum*.
perfect flower: having both functional stamens and pistils.
perfoliate: the leaf blade surrounding the stem, as in *Baptisia perfoliata*.
perianth: the calyx and corolla together. Often used when calyx and corolla are indistinguishable.
petaloid: structure not a petal but resembles a petal.
petiole: leaf stalk.
plumose: feather-like.
procumbent: lying flat but stems not rooting at the nodes or tips.

prostrate: lying flat on the ground.
pubescent: covered with short, soft hairs.
punctate: with translucent or covered dots, depressions, or pits.

raceme: a simple indeterminate inflorescence with pedicelled flowers.
racemose: having flowers in racemes.
rachis: the axis bearing leaflets or the primary flowers of an inflorescence.
reflexed: bent abruptly backward or downward.
revolute: rolled toward the back, as in a revolute margin.
rosette: a crown of leaves, at or close to the surface of the ground.
rotate: wheel-shaped with inconspicuous corolla tube, usually refers to flowers.

sarmentose: having long, flexuous runners or stolons.
scape: a leafless peduncle arising from a basal rosette. Occasionally bract-like
    leaves may be present.
sessile: without a petiole or stalk.
simple: a leaf not compounded into leaflets, an unbranched inflorescence.
spike: an unbranched indeterminate inflorescence with sessile flowers.
spikelet: a secondary spike.
stalk: a supporting structure for a leaf, flower, or fruit.
stellate: star-like.
sterile: barren, not able to produce seed.
stolon: a horizontal stem at or below surface of the ground that roots at the tip
    and gives rise to a new plant.
stoloniferous: bearing slender stems just on or under the ground which root at
    the tips.

tepal: a segment of perianth not differentiated into calyx and corolla. eg. tulips.
terminal: at the end.
ternate: in threes.
tomentose: densely woolly, hairs soft and matted.
trailing: prostrate but not rooting.
trifoliate: three-leaved. eg. *Trillium*.
tuber: a short, thickened organ, usually an underground stem.

umbel: an indeterminate inflorescence usually flat-topped with pedicels arising
    from a single point, like an umbrella.
umbellate: having umbels.
undulate: wavy, as a leaf margin.

verticillate: arranged in whorls.
viscid: sticky.

whorl: three or more leaves or flowers at one node, in a circle.
woolly: having long, soft and more or less matted hairs.

Index to Scientific Names

Index to
Common Names